U.S. STANDARD ATMOSPHERE, 1976

Special Recognition

Early in the "space race" of the 1950's, Norman Sissenwine recognized the urgent need for more complete data on the properties of the high atmosphere. He set in motion, in 1953, the U. S. Committee on Extension to the Standard Atmosphere (COESA), which led to the publication of the 1958 "U.S. Extension to the ICAO Standard Atmosphere," "U.S. Standard Atmosphere, 1962" and "U.S. Standard Atmosphere Supplements, 1966." Norman Sissenwine served as a co-chairman of COESA from its founding in 1953 until July 1973, originally with the late Dr. Harry Wexler (USWB) and subsequently with Dr. Sidney Teweles (NOAA), and with Maurice Dubin (NASA). During these 20 years he also acted as the COESA Working Group Executive Secretary, becoming the driving force in standard and reference atmosphere research in the United States. Former and current COESA members join in expressing thanks and appreciation to Norman Sissenwine for 20 years of sustained effort, accomplishment, and leadership in COESA affairs.

The members also express their gratitude to Dr. Sidney Teweles, COESA Co-Chairman during 1962-1974. His contributions were made directly through leadership in the work of the Committee and indirectly through his outstanding research on stratospheric problems. His work on the enigmatic winter "sudden warmings" increased our awareness of the large variability associated with this phenomenon, a factor now receiving greater attention in standard atmosphere depictions.

U.S. STANDARD
ATMOSPHERE, 1976

NATIONAL OCEANIC AND AMOSPHERIC ADMINISTRATION
NATIONAL AERONAUTICS AND SPACE ADMINISTRATION
UNITED STATES AIR FORCE

Washington, D.C.
October 1976

NOAA—S/T 76-1562

For sale by the Superintendent of Documents, U.S. Government Printing Office
Washington, D.C. 20402 - Price $6.20

Stock No. 003-017-00323-0

Abstract

The *U.S. Standard Atmosphere, 1976,* which is a revision of the *U.S. Standard Atmosphere, 1962,* was generated under the impetus of increased knowledge of the upper atmosphere obtained over the past solar cycle. Above 50 km, this Standard is based on extensive new rocket data and theory for the mesosphere and lower thermosphere, and on the vast resources of satellite data for the thermosphere acquired over more than one complete solar cycle. This Standard is identical with the ICAO Standard (1964) up to 32 km and the ISO Standard (1973) to 50 km. Part 1 gives the basis for computation of the main tables of atmospheric properties, including values of physical constants, conversion factors, and definitions of derived properties. Part 2 describes the model and data used up to 85 km, in the first section; and the model and data used above 85 km, in the second section. The theoretical basis of the high-altitude model is given in an appendix. Part 3 contains information on minor constituents in the troposphere, stratosphere, and mesosphere. The main tables of atmospheric properties to 1000 km are given in Part 4. The international system of metric units is used.

Contents

FIGURES

ix

TABLES

Symbols

a a coefficient, used in specifying the elliptical segment of the temperature-height profile, $T(Z)$

a_i a set of species-dependent coefficients which, along with values of b_i are used in defining the set of height-dependent functions D_i

A a coefficient used in specifying the elliptical segment of $T(Z)$

b a dimensionless subscript designating a set of integers

b_i a set of species-dependent exponents, which, along with values of a_i, are used to define the set of height-dependent functions D_i

C_s the height-dependent speed of sound

D_i the set of height-dependent, species-dependent, molecular-diffusion coefficients, for O, O_2, Ar, He, and H

$f(Z)$ the hydrostatic term in the height-dependent expression for n_i

F_i the set of sea-level, fractional-volume concentrations, for each of the several atmospheric gas species

F_i' the set of fractional-volume concentrations of the several atmospheric gas species adjusted for 86-km height to account for the dissociation of O_2

g the height-dependent, 45-degree-latitude, acceleration of gravity

g_0' the adopted constant, involved in the definition of the standard geopotential meter, and in the relationship between geopotential height and geometric height

H geopotential height used as the argument for all tables up to 84.852 km' (86.000 km)

H_P the height-dependent, local, pressure scale height of the mixture of gases comprising the atmosphere

H_ρ the height-dependent, local, density scale height of the mixture of gases comprising the atmosphere

i a subscript designating the ith member of a set of gas species

k the Boltzmann constant

k_t the height-dependent coefficient of thermal conductivity

K the height-dependent, eddy-diffusion (or turbulent-diffusion) coefficient

L the height-dependent, mean free path

$L_{M,b}$ a set of gradients of T_M with respect to H

$L_{K,b}$ a set of gradients of T with respect to Z

M the height-dependent, mean molecular weight of the mixture of gases constituting the atmosphere

M_i the set of molecular weights of the several atmospheric gas species

N the height-dependent, total, number density of the mixture of neutral atmospheric gas particles

n_i the set of height-dependent, number densities of the several atmospheric gas species

N_A the Avogadro constant

0 a subscript designating the sea-level value of the associated variable

P the height-dependent, total atmospheric pressure

P_i the partial pressure of the ith gas specie

q_i one set of six adopted sets of species-dependent, constants, i.e., set q_i, set Q_i, set u_i, set U_i, set w_i, and set W_i, all used in an empirical species-dependent expression for the flux term $v_i/(D_i + K)$

Q_i see q_i

r_0 the adopted, effective earth's radius, 6356.766 km, used for computing $g(Z)$ for 45-degree north latitude, and used for relating H and Z at that latitude

R^* the universal gas constant

S	the Sutherland constant, used in computing μ
t	the height-dependent Celsius temperature
T	the height-dependent, Kelvin kinetic temperature, defined as a function of Z for all heights above 86 km and derived from T_M for heights below 86 km
T_c	a derived coefficient used in specifying an elliptical segment of $T(Z)$
T_M	the height-dependent, molecular-scale temperature, defined as a function of H for all heights from sea-level to 86 km
T_∞	the exospheric temperature
u_i	see q_i
U_i	see q_i
v_i	the flow velocity of the ith gas species
v_m	the height-dependent mole volume
V	the height-dependent mean particle speed
w_i	see q_i
W_i	see q_i
Z	geometric height used as the argument of all tables at heights above 86 km
Z_c	the height coordinate of the center of the ellipse defining a portion of $T(Z)$
α_i	the set of species-dependent, thermal-diffusion coefficients
β	a constant used for computing μ
γ	a constant taken to represent the ratio of specific heat at constant pressure to the specific heat at constant volume, and used in defining C_s
Γ	the ratio g_0/g_0'
ε	a factor relating F_i to F_i'
η	the height-dependent kinematic viscosity
λ	a coefficient used in specifying the exponential expression defining a portion of $T(Z)$
μ	the height-dependent coefficient of dynamic viscosity
v	the height-dependent mean collision frequency
ξ	a function of Z used in the exponential expression defining a portion of $T(Z)$
ρ	the height-dependent mass density of air
σ	the effective mean collision diameter used in defining L and v
τ	a height-dependent coefficient representing the reduced height of the atomic hydrogen relative to a particular reference height and used in the computation of $n(H)$
ϕ	the vertical flux of atomic hydrogen
Φ_G	the potential energy per unit mass of gravitational attraction
Φ_C	the potential energy per unit mass associated with centrifugal force

Foreword

The *U.S. Standard Atmosphere, 1976,* with tables and graphs extending to 1000 km, was adopted by the United States Committee on Extension to the Standard Atmosphere (COESA) in February 1975. This edition is the same as COESA's *"U.S. Standard Atmosphere, 1962"* below 50 km, but replaces the 1962 Standard Atmosphere at higher altitudes.

That portion of the 1962 and 1976 U.S. Standard Atmospheres up to 32 km is identical with the International Civil Aviation Organization (ICAO) "Manual of the ICAO Standard Atmosphere," as revised in 1964 (International Civil Aviation Organization 1964). The definition of the lowest 50 km was recommended as the standard for international adoption by the International Standards Organization (ISO) cognizant committee, ISO/TC 20/SC 6, and appeared as Draft International Standard ISO/DIS 2533. It was approved by the ISO Member Bodies in September 1973 as the *ISO Standard Atmosphere* (ISO 1973). Addendum I to ISO/DIS 2533, characteristics of the atmosphere from 50 to 80 km, has been included in the tables as the Interim Standard Atmosphere. The numerical data in Addendum I also are identical with the data in this Standard. COESA has recommended that the ICAO also extend its standard atmosphere to 50 km, by accepting for its own standard the definition of the 32- to 59-km region of the 1962 and 1976 U.S. Standard Atmosphere in order to insure a single, accepted international standard to the altitude of 50 km. The ICAO has not acted on this recommendation at the time of this publication.

COESA is a group of organizations established in 1953 to take action required to provide the then newborn missile industry with a realistic description of the atmosphere extending beyond altitudes of conventional aircraft operations. Sponsors of this effort are the National Aeronautics and Space Administration (NASA), National Oceanic and Atmospheric Administration (NOAA), and the United States Air Force (USAF). Air Force K. C. Task responsibility was assigned to the Air Force Cambridge Research Laboratories (AFCRL). Today, 29 participating organizations, representing government, industry, research institutions, and universities, support this effort. These organizations are listed below with names of the scientists and engineers who are members of the COESA Working Group:

Aerospace Corporation
  James A. Pearson
  Hugh R. Rugge
Air Force Cambridge Research Laboratories,
  AFSC, USAF

  K. S. W. Champion
  A. E. Cole, Executive Secretary of
    Working Group
  J. F. Forbes
  A. J. Kantor
  T. J. Keneshea
  N. Sissenwine
  S. P. Zimmerman
Air Force Systems Command, USAF
  W. A. Finley
Air Weather Service, USAF
  H. S. Appleman
  G. S. Boughton
  T. E. Stanton (ETAC)
Applied Physics Laboratory, Johns Hopkins
    University
Army Ballistic Research Laboratory
Army Electronics Command, USA
    (Atomspheric Sciences Laboratory)
  D. P. Avara
  N. Byers
Army Missile Command, USA
  O. M. Essenwanger
Battelle Memorial Institute
The Boeing Company
  R. R. Green
Defense Nuclear Agency
Environmental Protection Agency
  H. J. Viebrock
Federal Aviation Agency, DOT
Goddard Space Flight Center, NASA
  A. J. Krueger
  R. A. Minzner
  G. P. Newton
  C. A. Reber
  J. S. Theon
Langley Research Center, NASA
  R. A. Hord
  G. M. Keating
Lockheed Missiles and Space Company
  A. D. Anderson
Marshall Space Flight Center, NASA
  L. DeVries
  O. E. Smith
  R. E. Smith
McDonnell Douglas Astronautics Co.
  O. K. Moe
National Bureau of Standards, Department of
    Commerce
  D. P. Johnson
National Center for Atmospheric Research
  H. D. Axelrod
  I. H. Blifford, Jr.
  R. D. Cadle
National Oceanic and Atmospheric

Administration
J. O. Ellis (Env. Data Service)
A. R. Hull (Env. Data Service)
R. S. Quiroz (National Weather Service)
T. Shimazaki (Env. Res. Labs.)
T. E. Van Zandt (Env. Res. Labs.)
Naval Research Laboratory, USN
P. Mange
National Aeronautics and Space Agency,
Headquarters
M. Dubin
Pennsylvania State University
J. Nisbet
Smithsonian Astrophysical Observatory and
Harvard College Observatory
L. Jacchia, Chairman of Working Group
J. Slowey
The RAND Corporation
E. S. Batten
G. F. Schilling
University of Michigan, High Altitude
Engineering Laboratory
F. L. Bartman
L. M. Jones
University of Minnesota
A. O. Nier
University of Texas at Dallas
B. A. Tinsley

The 1962 predecessor of this *U. S. Standard Atmosphere, 1976* attempted to depict idealized middle-latitude year-round mean conditions for the range of solar activity that occurs between sunspot minimum and sunspot maximum, but subsequent observations have shown mean conditions of solar activity to be considerably lower. The World Meteorological Organization's (WMO) definition of a standard atmosphere has been accepted by COESA and is as follows:

"... A hypothetical vertical distribution of atmospheric temperature, pressure and density which, by international agreement, is roughly representative of year-round, midlatitude conditions. Typical usages are as a basis for pressure altimeter calibrations, aircraft performance calculations, aircraft and rocket design, ballistic tables, and meterological diagrams. The air is assumed to obey the perfect gas law and hydrostatic equation which, taken together, relate temperature, pressure and density with geopotential. Only one standard atmosphere should be specified at a particular time and this standard atmosphere must not be subjected to amendment except at intervals of many years."

Because of the COESA interest in standard and reference atmospheres to much higher altitudes

than that currently being considered by the WMO, the Working Group agreed to add to the above definition the following statement:

"This atmosphere shall also be considered to rotate with the earth, and be an average over the diurnal cycle, semi-annual variation, and the range of conditions from active to quiet geomagnetic, and active to quiet sunspot conditions. Above the turbopause (about 110 km) generalized forms of the hydrostatic equations apply."

The much greater inventory of experimental data assembled since 1962, over parts of the solar cycle not available for the 1962 Standard Atmosphere, is the basis for this revision. Recently compiled statistics revealed that densities are about 10% lower in the 70- to 80-km region and 10% higher in the 90-km region than in the 1962 Standard. An exospheric isothermal temperature of 1000 K, now considered representative of the mean for solar activity, is 500 K cooler than the 1500 K in the *U.S. Standard Atmosphere, 1962.* Progress in upper atmospheric science over the decade of the 1960's has been extensive, and the results of this progress have demonstrated the need for this revision.

In view of these developments the COESA Working Group, which had been dormant following completion of the *U.S. Standard Atmosphere Supplements, 1966,* was reactivated. A meeting was held in September 1971 and recommendations for a revision were made. Three task groups were established to review the structure of (1) the mesosphere, (2) the transition layer between mesosphere and thermosphere, and (3) the thermosphere. A fourth task group, which included the conveners of the above three, was established to merge the work of the first three task groups. A fifth task group was made responsible for gathering supplemental information on the minor constituents of the atmosphere. The members of these task groups are:

Task Group I (50 to 100 km)
A. E. Cole, Convener	AFCRL
N. J. Byers	USAEC
L. M. Jones	U. of Michigan
A. J. Kantor	AFCRL
O. E. Smith	MSFC
T. E. Stanton	AWS (ETAC)
J. Theon	GSFC
R. Quiroz	NOAA

Task Group II (80 to 200 km)
R. A. Minzner, Convener	GSFC
C. Reber, Co-convener	GSFC
K. S. W. Champion	AFCRL

F. G. Huang	Computer Science Corp.
O. K. Moe	McDonnell Douglas
A. O. Nier	U. of Minn.
G. Swenson	MSFC
S. P. Zimerman	AFCRL

Task Group III (140 to 1000 km)

L. Jacchia, Convener	Smithsonian and Harvard
J. Forbes	AFCRL
G. A. Keating	LRC
P. Mange	NRL
G. P. Newton	GSFC
J. Nisbet	Penn State U.
R. Smith	MSFC
B. A. Tinsley	U. of Texas
T. E. Van Zandt	NOAA

Task Group IV (Unification of 50 to 1000 km)

K. S. W. Champion, Convener	AFCRL
E. S. Baten	RAND
A. E. Cole	AFCRL
L. DeVries	MSFC
O. M. Essenwanger	USAMC
R. Hord	LRC
L. Jacchia	Smithsonian and Harvard
R. A. Minzner	GSFC

Task Group V (minor constituents up to mesopause including particulates)

R. D. Cadie, Convener	NCAR
H. D. Axelrod	NCAR
I. H. Blifford	NCAR
K. S. W. Champion	AFCRL
L. DeVries	MSFC
W. Hering	AFCRL
A. Kreuger	GSFC
T. Keneshea	AFCRL
T. Shimazaki	NOAA
N. Sissenwine	AFCRL
D. Snider	AWS
H. Viebrock	EPA
R. C. Whitten	ARC

Although density is the primary atmospheric property measured or deduced for very high altitudes, it is necessary to define the revision of the standard atmosphere in terms of temperature in order to retain continuity between higher and lower altitudes. In 1962 this was accomplished by defining a molecular-scale temperature involving the assumption of constant molecular weight at all altitudes. Kinetic temperature was derived from the molecular-scale temperature by computing the vertical profile of mean molecular weight, assuming diffusive equilibrium above the mesopause. For this revision sufficient scientific data and physical theories are available to estimate kinetic temperatures at various levels and to fit these with an analytical expression of temperature versus height which is continuous from the mesopause through the thermosphere. The temperature-height profile for lower altitudes, made up of linear segments, joins smoothly with this analytical temperature-height profile at the mesopause.

Part 1 of this revision provides the basis for computing tables presented in Part 4. Part 2 describes the model and data of the new standard (a) below 86 km and (b) above 86 km, and includes background information on the atmospheric variability. Part 3 provides information on minor constituents. The tables in Part 4 are presented in metric units, in accordance with the trend toward abandonment of the English system of units. Conversion factors to English units and tabulations (in metric units) with altitudes in English units, are provided.

From information provided by the COESA Working Group, this publication was prepared by the scientific editors from each of the sponsoring organizations: A. J. Kantor, AFCRL; R. A. Minzner, NASA; and R. S. Quiroz, NOAA. Contributions were made by other personnel from these and other organizations: D. D. Grantham (AFCRL), W. Winkler (NOAA), J. O. Ellis (NOAA) for review and technical editing; E. Koehler (NOAA), I. Brainerd (GPO), C. Shahin (NOAA), H. Hoener (NOAA), E. Crone (NOAA), E. Liddel (NOAA) for copy and printing preparation, and T. Carpenter (NOAA) and F. G. Huang (CSC) for computer programing of the main tables.

The Co-chairmen wish to thank the many Working Group scientists and engineers who contributed unselfishly of their time and energies to bring this new representation of the atmosphere into being. Our special thanks and that of all the COESA organizations go to the individuals who contributed sections of this report.

MAURICE DUBIN ARNOLD R. HULL K. S. W. CHAMPION
NASA NOAA (DoC) USAF (DoD)
Co-chairmen, U.S. Committee on Extension to the Standard Atmosphere

PART 1
Defining Constants and Equations

1.0 INTRODUCTION

The U.S. Standard Atmosphere, 1976 is an idealized, steady-state representation of the earth's atmosphere from the surface to 1000 km, as it is assumed to exist in a period of moderate solar activity. For heights from the surface to 51 geopotential kilometers (km'), the tables of this standard are identical with those of the U.S. Standard Atmosphere, 1962 (COESA 1962) and are based on traditional definitions. These definitions, especially for heights below 20 km', do not necessarily represent an average of the vast amount of atmospheric data available today from observations within that height region. For heights from 51 km' to 84.852 km' (i.e., 51.413 to 86 geometric kilometers), the tables are based upon the averages of present-day atmospheric data as represented by the traditional type of defining parameters. These include the linearly segmented temperature-height profile, and the assumption of hydrostatic equilibrium, in which the air is treated as a homogeneous mixture of the several constituent gases.

At greater heights, however, where dissociation and diffusion processes produce significant departures from homogeneity, the definitions governing the Standard are more sophisticated than those used at lower altitudes. In this high-altitude regime, the hydrostatic equation, as applied to a mixed atmosphere, gives way to the more general equation for the vertical component of the flux for individual gas species (Colegrove et al. 1965; Keneshea and Zimmerman 1970), which accounts for the relative change of composition with height. This flux equation simplifies to the hydrostatic equation for the special case when the atmospheric gases remain well mixed, as is the situation below 86 km.

The temperature-height profile between 86 and 1000 km is not expressed as a series of linear functions, as at lower altitudes. Rather, it is defined in terms of four successive functions chosen not only to provide a reasonable approximation to observations, but also to yield a continuous first derivative with respect to height over the entire height regime.

Observational data of various kinds provide the basis for independently determining various segments of this temperature-height profile. The observed temperatures at heights between 110 and 120 km were particularly important in imposing limits on the selection of the temperature-height function for that region, while the observed densities at 150 km and above strongly influenced the selection of both the temperature and the extent of the low-temperature isothermal layer immediately above 86 km.

In spite of the various independent data sets upon which the several temperature-height segments are based, it is desirable, for purposes of mathematical reproducibility of the tables of this Standard, to express the temperature in a series of consecutive height functions from the surface to 1000 km, with the expression for each successive function depending upon the end-point value of the preceding function, as well as upon certain terms and coefficients peculiar to the related height interval. This total temperature-height profile applied to the fundamental continuity models (i.e., the hydrostatic equation and the equation of motion), along with all the ancillary required constants, coefficients, and functions, defines the U.S. Standard Atmosphere, 1976. The specification of this definition without any justification in terms of observed data is the purpose of Section 1.

1.1 INTERNATIONAL SYSTEM OF UNITS

The 1976 U. S. Standard Atmosphere is defined in terms of the International System (SI) of Units (Mechtley 1973). A list of the symbols, names, and the related quantities of the applicable basic and derived SI units, as well as of the non-standard metric units and the English unit employed in this Standard is presented in table 1.

1.2 BASIC ASSUMPTIONS AND FORMULAS

1.2.1 ADOPTED CONSTANTS.—For purposes of computation it is necessary to establish numerical values for various constants appropriate to the earth's atmosphere. The adopted constants are grouped into three categories. Category I includes those constants which are common to many branches of the physical and chemical sciences, and are here considered to be fundamental constants. Some of these may be multi-valued as in the case of M_i representing the molecular weight of the ith gas species. Category I includes three single-valued and one multi-valued constant. Category II includes those constants which, in addition to the

1

TABLE 1.—Units Applicable to the U.S. Standard Atmosphere 1976

	Symbol	Name	Quantity
Basic SI			
	m	meter	length
	kg	kilogram	mass
	s	second	time
	K	kelvin	thermodynamic temperature
	mol	mole	the amount of a substance
Derived SI			
	N	newton	force (kg·m/s^2)
	Pa	pascal	pressure (N/m^2)
	J	joule	work, energy or quantity of heat (N·m)
	W	watt	rate of energy (or heat) transfer (J/s)
Non-Standard			
	mb	millibar	pressure 100 (N/m^2)
	torr at 0°C	torr	pressure 133.322 (N/m^2)
	°C	Celsius degree	temperature kelvin minus 273.15
English			
	ft	foot	length 0.3048 m*

* exact definition

category I constants and a suitable set of equations, are sufficient to define that portion of the 1976 Standard Atmosphere below 86 km. This category includes nine single-valued and three multi-valued constants. Category III includes all the remaining constants which, along with category-I and category-II constants and the related equations plus an expansion of that set are necessary to define that portion of the 1976 Standard Atmosphere above 86 km. This category includes 7 single-valued and 11 multi-valued constants.

The constants, with appropriate dimensions and symbols, are listed according to categories in three successive sections of table 2.

The definition as well as the authority for the value of each constant is discussed separately from the tabular listing. The multi-valued constants, with one exception, have only their general symbol and dimensions listed in table 2, while the multiple values of these constants, i.e., one value for each of several gas species, or one value for each of several height levels, are listed in tables 4 through 7.

Discussion of the Adopted Values of the Primary Constants:

Category I Constants

k The Boltzmann constant, $k = 1.380622 \times$

TABLE 2.—Adopted constants

A. Category I Constants

Symbol	Value
k	1.380622×10^{-23} N·m/K
M_i	the set of the first 10 values (kg/kmol) listed in table 3
N_A	6.022169×10^{26} kmol^{-1}
R^*	8.31432×10^{-3} N·m/(kmol·K)

B. Category II Constants

Symbol	Value
F_i	the set of the 10 values (dimensionless) listed in table 3
g_0	9.80665 m/s^2
g_0'	9.80665 m^2/(s^2·m')
H_b	the set of eight values (km') listed in table 4
$L_{M,b}$	the set of seven values (K/km') listed in table 4
P_0	1.013250×10^5 N/m^2 (or Pa)
r_0	6.356766×10^3 km
T_0	288.15 K
S	110 K
β	1.458×10^{-6} kg/(s·m·K$^{1/2}$)
γ	1.40 (dimensionless)
σ	3.65×10^{-1} m

C. Category III Constants

Symbol	Value
a_i	the set of 5 values (m^{-1}·s^{-1}) listed in table 6
b_i	the set of 5 values (dimensionless) listed in table 6
K_7	1.2×10^2 m^2/s
K_0	0.0 m^2/s
$L_{K,b}$	the set of 2 values (K/km) listed in table 5
$n(O)_7$	8.6×10^{16} m^{-3}
$n(H)_{11}$	8.0×10^{10} m^{-3}
q_i	the set of 4 values (km^{-3}) listed in table 7
Q_i	the set of 4 values (km^{-3}) listed in table 7
T_9	240.0 K
T_∞	1000.0 K
u_i	the set of 4 values (km) listed in table 7
U_i	the set of 4 values (km) listed in table 7
w_i	the set of 4 values (km^{-3}) listed in table 7
W_i	the set of 4 values (km^{-3}) listed in table 7
Z_b	the set of 6 values (km) listed in table 5
α_i	the set of 6 values (dimensionless) listed in table 6
ϕ	7.2×10^{11} m^{-2}·s^{-1}

10^{-23} N·m/K, is theoretically equal to the ratio R^*/N_A, and has a value, consistent with the carbon-12 scale, as cited by Mechtly (1973).

M_i The set of values of molecular weights M_i listed in table 3 is based upon the carbon-12 isotope scale for which C^{12} = 12. This scale was adopted in 1961 at the Montreal meeting of the International Union of Pure and Applied Chemistry.

N_A The Avogadro constant, $N_A = 6.022169 \times 10^{26}$ kmol^{-1}, is consistent with the carbon-12 scale and is the value cited by Mechtly (1973).

$R*$ The gas constant, $R* = 8.31432 \times 10^3$ N·m/(kmol·K), is consistent with the carbon-12 scale, and is the value used in the 1962 Standard. This value is not exactly consistent with the cited values of k and N_A.

Category II Constants

F_i The set of values of fractional-volume concentrations F_i listed in table 3 is assumed to represent the relative concentrations of the several gas species comprising dry air at sea level. These values are identical to those given in the 1962 Standard (COESA 1962), and except for minor modifications which are based upon CO_2 measurements by Keeling (1960), these values are the same as those given by Glueckauf (1951), and are based upon the earlier work of Paneth (1939).

g_0 The quantity g_0 ($= 9.80665$ m/s^2) represents the sea-level value of the acceleration of gravity adopted for this Standard. This value is the one originally adopted by the International Committee on Weights and Measures in 1901 for 45° latitude, and even though it has since been shown to be too high by about five parts in ten thousand (List 1968), this value has persisted in meteorology and in some standard atmospheres as the value associated with 45° latitude, even though it applies more precisely to a latitude of 45° 32′ 33″.

g_0' The dimensional constant g_0' selected to relate the standard geopotential meter to geometric height is numerically equal to g_0, but with appropriately different dimensions. This constant implicitly defines one standard geopotential meter as the vertical increment through which one must lift one kilogram to increase its potential energy by 9.80665 joules. The geometric length of this vertical increment varies inversely with the height-dependent value of g.

H_b Each of the members of the set of geopotential-height values H_b listed in table 4 represents the base of one of eight successive atmospheric layers. The pairs of values of H_b and L_{Mb} are based partly on tradition and partly on present-day observations. The first five of these pairs are identical to those of the

TABLE 3.—Molecular weights and assumed fractional-volume composition of sea-level dry air

Gas species	Molecular weight M_i (kg/kmol)	Fractional volume F_i (dimensionless)
N$_2$	28.0134	0.78084
O$_2$	31.9988	.209476
Ar	39.948	.00934
CO$_2$	44.00995	.000314
Ne	20.183	.00001818
He	4.0026	.00000524
Kr	83.80	.00000114
Xe	131.30	.000000087
CH$_4$	16.04303	.000002
H$_2$	2.01594	.0000005

TABLE 4.—The defined reference levels and gradients of the linearly segmented temperature-height profile from the surface to 86 geometric kilometers

Sub-script b	Geopotential height H_b (km′)	Molecular-scale temperature gradient $L_{M,b}$ (K/km′)	Form of function relating T to H
0	0	−6.5	Linear
1	11	0.0	Linear
2	20	+1.0	Linear
3	32	+2.8	Linear
4	47	0.0	Linear
5	51	2.8	Linear
6	71	−2.0	Linear
7	84.8520		

Note: These values plus T_0, the defined sea-level value of T, equal to $T_{M,0}$ completely specify the geopotential-height profile of T_M from the surface to 86 geometric kilometers.

first five layers of the 1962 Standard, while the remaining two values of both H_b and $L_{M,b}$ have been newly selected to provide a reasonable fit to the presently available atmospheric data. The first two values of the related sets have their origin in one of the earliest aeronautical standard atmospheres (Toussaint 1919), and were approximated in the first U.S. Standard Atmosphere (Diehl 1925).

$L_{M,b}$ Each member of the set of seven gradients $L_{M,b} = dT_M/dH$ [i.e., of molecular scale temperature T_M (Minzner and Ripley 1956) with respect to geopotential H] listed in table 4 represents the fixed value appropriate throughout its related layer, H_b to H_{b+1}.

P_0 The standard sea-level atmospheric pressure P_0 equal to 1.013250×10^5 Pa (or N/m^2) was adopted in 1947 in

Resolution 164 of the International Meteorological Organization, and corresponds to the pressure exerted by a column of mercury 0.760 m high, having a density of 1.35951×10^4 kg/m³ and subject to an acceleration due to gravity of 9.80665 m/s². This equivalency definition was adopted by the International Commission on Weights and Measures in 1948.

r_0 The effective earth's radius for purposes of calculating geopotential at any latitude is readily obtained from equations given by Harrison (1968). The value of r_0 ($= 6356.766$ km) used in this Standard corresponds to the latitude for which $g = 9.80665$ m/s².

T_0 The standard sea-level temperature T_0 is 288.15 K. This value is based upon two international agreements. The first of these is Resolution 192 of the International Commission for Air Navigation which in 1924 adopted 15°C as the sea-level temperature of The International Standard Atmosphere. This value has been retained unchanged in all known standard atmospheres since that date. The second agreement is that of the 1954 Tenth General Conference on Weights and Measures which set the fixed point of the Kelvin temperature scale at the triple-point temperature 273.16 K, which is 0.01 K above the ice-point temperature at standard sea-level pressure.

S The Sutherland constant, S = 110 K, (Hilsenrath et al. 1955) is a constant in the empirical expression for dynamic viscosity.

β The quantity, $\beta = 1.458 \times 10^6$ kg/(s·m·K$^{1/2}$), (Hilsenrath et al. 1955) is a constant in the expression for dynamic viscosity.

γ The ratio of specific heat of air at constant pressure to the specific heat of air at constant volume is a dimensionless quantity with an adopted value $\gamma = 1.400$. This is the value adopted by the Aerological Commission of the International Meteorological Organization, in Toronto in 1948.

σ The mean effective collision diameter σ ($= 3.65 \times 10^{-10}$ m) of molecules is a quantity which varies with gas species and temperature. The adopted value is assumed to apply in a dry, sea-level atmosphere. Above 85 km the validity

of the adopted value decreases with increasing altitude (Hirschfelder et al. 1965; Chapman and Cowling 1960) due to the change in atmospheric composition. For this reason the number of significant figures in tabulations of quantities involving σ is reduced from that used for other tabulated quantities at heights above 86 km.

Category III Constants

a_i The quantity a_i represents a set of five values of species-dependent coefficients listed in table 6. Each of these values is used in a particular function for designating the height-dependent, molecular-diffusion coefficient D_i for the related gas species. (See b_i.)

TABLE 5.—The reference levels and function designations for each of the four segments of the temperature-height profile between 86 and 1000 km, with gradients specified for two linear segments, and with an intermediate reference height for the adopted atomic-hydrogen number-density value

Subscript b	Geometric height Z_b (km)	Kinetic-temperature gradient $L_{K,b}$ (K/km)	Form of function relating T to Z
7	86	0.0	linear
8	91		elliptical
9	110	12.0	linear
10	120		exponential
11	500		
12	1000		

Note: These specifications, along with a defined value of temperature at 110 km, and the temperature at 86 km (84.8520 km) given in table 4, plus the requirement of a continuous first derivative, dT/dZ, above 86 km, define the temperature-height profile between 86 and 120 km. The definitive form of the exponential function eq (31) is required to complete the specification of the temperature-height profile from 120 to 1000 km. (See Appendix B for the derivation of the elliptical segment given by eq (27)).

b_i The quantity b_i represents a set of five values of species-dependent exponents listed in table 6. Each of these values is used, along with the corresponding value of a_i, in eq (8) for designating the height-dependent, molecular-diffusion coefficient for the related gas species. The particular values of a_i and b_i adopted for this Standard have been selected to yield a height variation of D_i assumed to be realistic.

K_7 The quantity $K_7 = 1.2 \times 10^2$ m²/s is the adopted value of the eddy-diffusion coefficient K, at $Z_7 = 86$ km and in the height interval from 86 up to 91 km. Beginning at 91 km and extending up to 115 km, the value of K is defined by eq (7b). At 115 km the value of K equals K_{10}.

K_{10} The quantity $K_{10} = 0.0$ m^2/s is the adopted value of the eddy-diffusion coefficient K at $Z_{10} = 120$ and throughout the height interval from 115 km to 1000 km.

$L_{K,b}$ The two-valued set of gradients $L_{K,b} = dT/dZ$ listed in table 5 was specifically selected for this Standard to represent available observations. Each of these two values of $L_{K,b}$ is associated with the entire extent of a corresponding layer whose base is Z_b and whose top is Z_{b+1}.

$n(O)_7$ The quantity, $n(O)_7$ ($= 8.6 \times 10^{16}$ m^{-3}), is the number density of atomic oxygen assumed for this Standard to exist at $Z_7 = 86$ km. This value of atomic oxygen number density, along with other defined constants, leads to number densities of N$_2$, O$_2$, Ar, and He at 86 km. (See Appendix A.)

$n(H)_{11}$ The quantity, $n(H)_{11}$ ($= 8.0 \times 10^{10}$ m^{-3}), is the assumed number density of atomic hydrogen at height $Z_{11} = 500$ km, and is used as the reference value in computing the height profile of atomic hydrogen between 150 and 1000 km.

q_i The quantity q_i represents the first set of six species-dependent sets of coeffi-

cients or terms (i.e., sets of q_i, Q_i, u_i, U_i, w_i, and W_i), the corresponding members of all six of which are simultaneously used in an empirical expression [eq(37)] for the vertical transport term $v_i/(D_i + K)$ in the vertical flux equation for the particular gas species. The species-dependent values of all six sets have been selected for this Standard to adjust number-density profiles of the related gas species to particular boundary conditions at 150 and 450 km, as well as at 97 km in the case of atomic oxygen. These boundary conditions all represent observed or assumed average conditions. These six sets of values are listed in table 7.

Q_i The quantity Q_i represents the second set of the six sets of constants described along with q_i above.

T_9 The quantity T_9 ($= 240.0$ K) represents the kinetic temperature at $Z_9 = 110$ km. This temperature has been adopted along with the gradient $L_{K.9}$ ($= 12$ K/km) to generate a linear segment of $T(Z)$ for this Standard between 110 and 120 km. This segment of $T(Z)$ represents a mean of observed temperature-height data for the corresponding height region.

T_∞ The quantity, T_∞ ($= 1000$ K) represents the exospheric temperature, i.e., the asymptote which the exponential function representing $T(Z)$ above 120 km closely approaches at heights above about 500 km, where the mean free path exceeds the scale height. The value of T_∞ adopted for this Standard is assumed to represent mean solar conditions

u_i The quantity u_i represents the third set of the six sets of constants described along with q_i above.

U_i The quantity U_i represents the fourth set of the six sets of constants described along with q_i above.

TABLE 6.—A set of species-dependent, thermal-diffusion coefficients and two other sets of species-dependent constants required in specifying the height-dependent function of the molecular-diffusion coefficient for the several species listed

Gas	α_i (dimensionless)	a_i (m$^{-1} \cdot$ s^{-1})	b_i (dimensionless)
N$_2$	0.00	....	....
O	0.00	6.986 x 10^{20}	0.750
O$_2$	0.00	4.863 x 10^{20}	0.750
Ar	0.00	4.487 x 10^{20}	0.870
He	−0.40	1.700 x 10^{21}	0.691
H	−0.25	3.305 x 10^{21}	0.500

TABLE 7.—Values of six sets of species-dependent coefficients applicable to the empirical expression representing the flux term $v_i/(D_i + K)$ in the equation for number density of the four species listed

Gas	Q_i (km^{-3})	q_i (km^{-3})	U_i (km)	u_i (km)	W_i (km^{-3})	w_i (km^{-3})
O	−5.809644 × 10^{-4}	−3.416248 × 10^{-3*}	56.90311	97.0	2.706240 × 10^{-5}	5.008765 × 10^{-4}
O$_2$	1.366212 × 10^{-4}	0	86.000	......	8.333333 × 10^{-5}	....
Ar	9.434079 × 10^{-5}	0	86.000	......	8.333333 × 10^{-5}	....
He	−2.457369 × 10^{-4}	0	86.000	......	6.666667 × 10^{-4}	....

* This value of q_i applies only for $86 \leq Z \leq 97$ km. For $Z > 97$ km, $q_i = 0.0$ km^{-3}.

w_i The quantity w_i represents the fifth set of the six sets of constants described along with q_i above.

W_i The quantity W_i represents the sixth set of the six sets of constants described along with q_i above.

Z_b The quantity Z_b represents a set of six values of Z for b equal to 7 through 12. The values Z_7, Z_8, Z_9, and Z_{10} correspond successively to the base of successive layers characterized by successive segments of the adopted temperature-height function for this Standard. The fifth value, Z_{11}, is the reference height for the atomic hydrogen calculation, while the sixth value, Z_{12}, represents the top of the region for which the tabular values of the Standard are given. These six values of Z_b, along with the designation of the type of temperature-height function associated with the first four of these values, plus the related value of $L_{K,b}$, for the two segments having a linear temperature-height function, are listed in table 5.

α_i The quantity α_i represents a set of six adopted species-dependent, thermal-diffusion coefficients listed in Table 6.

ϕ The quantity ϕ $(= 7.2 \times 10^{11}$ m$^{-2} \cdot$ s$^{-1})$ for the vertical flux is chosen as a compromise between the classical Jeans escape flux for $T_\infty = 1000$ K, with corrections to take into account deviations from a Maxwellian velocity distribution at the critical level (Brinkman 1971), and the effects of charge exchange with H$^+$ and O$^+$ in the plasmasphere (Tinsley 1973).

1.2.2 EQUILIBRIUM ASSUMPTIONS.—The air is assumed to be dry, and at heights sufficiently below 86 km, the atmosphere is assumed to be homogeneously mixed with a relative-volume composition leading to a constant mean molecular weight M. The air is treated as if it were a perfect gas, and the total pressure P, temperature T, and total density ρ at any point in the atmosphere are related by the equation of state, i.e., the perfect gas law, one form of which is

$$P = \frac{\rho \cdot R^* \cdot T}{M} \qquad (1)$$

where R^* is the universal gas constant. An alternate form of the equation of state, in terms of the total number density N and the Avogadro constant N_A is

$$P = \frac{N \cdot R^* \cdot T}{N_A}. \qquad (2)$$

This form represents the summation of P_i, the partial pressures of the individual gas species, where P_i is related to n_i the number density of the ith gas species in the following expression:

$$P_i = n_i \cdot k \cdot T \qquad (3)$$

where k is the Boltzmann constant.

Within the height region of complete mixing, the atmosphere is assumed to be in hydrostatic equilibrium, and to be horizontally stratified so that dP, the differential of pressure, is related to dZ, the differential of geometric height, by the relationship

$$dP = - g \cdot \rho \cdot dZ \qquad (4)$$

where g is the height-dependent acceleration of gravity. The elimination of ρ between eq (1) and (4) yields another form of the hydrostatic equation, which serves as the basis for the low-altitude pressure calculation:

$$d\ln P = \frac{dP}{P} = \frac{- g \cdot M}{R^* \cdot T} \cdot dZ. \qquad (5)$$

Above 86 km the hydrostatic equilibrium of the atmosphere gradually breaks down as diffusion and vertical transport of individual gas species lead to the need for a dynamically oriented model including diffusive separation. Under these conditions it is convenient to express the height variations in the atmospheric number density in terms of the vertical component of the flux of the molecules of individual gas species (Colgrove et al. 1965). In terms of the ith gas species, this expression is

$$n_i \cdot v_i + D_i \cdot \left(\frac{dn_i}{dZ} + \frac{n_i \cdot (1 + \alpha_i)}{T} \cdot \frac{dT}{dZ} + \frac{g \cdot n_i \cdot M_i}{R^* \cdot T} \right)$$
$$+ K \cdot \left(\frac{dn_i}{dZ} + \frac{n_i}{T} \cdot \frac{dT}{dZ} + \frac{g \cdot n_i \cdot M}{R^* \cdot T} \right) = 0 \qquad (6)$$

where

v_i =   the vertical transport velocity of the ith species,

D_i =   the height-dependent, molecular-diffusion coefficient of the ith species diffusing through N_2,

α_i =   the thermal-diffusion coefficient of the ith species.

M_i =   the molecular weight of the ith species,

M =   the molecular weight of the gas through which the ith species is diffusing, and

K =   the height-dependent, eddy-diffusion coefficient.

The function K is defined differently in each of three height regions:

1. For $86 \leq Z < 95$ km,

$$K = K_7 = 1.2 \times 10^2 \text{ m}^2/\text{s} \qquad (7a)$$

2. For $95 \leq Z < 115$ km

$$K = K_7 \cdot \exp\left[1 - \frac{400}{400 - (Z - 95)^2}\right] \qquad (7b)$$

3. For $115 \leq Z < 1000$

$$K = K_{10} = 0.0 \text{ m}^2/\text{s}. \qquad (7c)$$

The function D_i is defined by

$$D_i = \frac{a_i}{\Sigma n_i} \cdot \left(\frac{T}{273.15}\right)^{b_i} \qquad (8)$$

where a_i and b_i are the species-dependent constants defined in table 6, while T and Σn_i are both altitude-dependent quantities which are specified in detail below. The values of D_i, determined from these altitude-dependent quantities and the defined constants a_i and b_i, are plotted in figure 1 as a function of altitude, for each of four species, O, O_2, Ar, and He. The value of D_i for atomic hydrogen, for heights just below 150 km, is also shown in figure 1. This same figure contains a graph of K as a function of altitude. It is apparent that, for heights sufficiently below 90 km, values of D_i are negligible compared with K, while above 115 km, the reverse is true. In addition, it is known that the flux velocity v_i for the various species becomes negligibly small at altitudes sufficiently below 90 km.

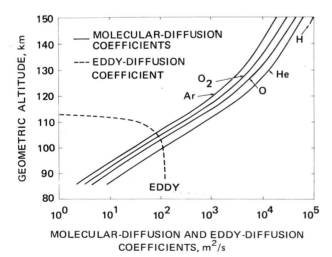

Figure 1. Molecular-diffusion and eddy-diffusion coefficients as a function of geometric altitude.

The information regarding the relative magnitudes of v_i, D_i, and K permits us to consider the application of eq (6) in each of several regimes.

One of these regimes is for heights sufficiently below 90 km, such that v_i and D_i are both extremely small compared with K. Under these conditions, eq (6) reduces to the following form of the hydrostatic equation:

$$\frac{dn_i}{n_i} + \frac{dT}{T} = \frac{-g \cdot M}{R^* \cdot T} \cdot dZ. \qquad (9)$$

Since the left-hand side of this equation is seen through eq (3) to be equal to dP_i/P_i, eq (9) is seen to be the single-gas equivalent to eq (5). Consequently, while eq (6) was designed to describe the assumed equilibrium conditions of individual gases above 86 km, it is apparent that eq (6) also describes such conditions below that altitude, where the partial pressure of each gas comprising the total pressure varies in accordance with the mean molecular weight of the mixture, as well as in accordance with the temperature and the acceleration of gravity. Nevertheless, eq (5), expressing total pressure, represents a convenient step in the development of equations for computing total pressure versus geometric height, when suitable functions are introduced to account for the altitude variation in T, M, and g.

It has been customary in standard-atmosphere calculations, to effectively eliminate the variable portion of the acceleration of gravity from eq (5) by the transformation of the independent variable Z to geopotential altitude H, thereby simplifying both the integration of eq (5) and the resulting expression for computing pressure. The relationship between geometric and geopotential altitude depends upon the concept of gravity.

1.2.3 GRAVITY AND GEOPOTENTIAL ALTITUDE— Viewed in the ordinary manner, from a frame of reference fixed in the earth, the atmosphere is subject to the force of gravity. The force of gravity is the resultant (vector sum) of two forces: (a) the gravitational attraction in accordance with Newton's universal law of gravitation, and (b) the centrifugal force, which results from the choice of an earthbound, rotating frame of reference.

The gravity field, being a conservative field, can be derived conveniently from the gravity potential energy per unit mass, that is, from the geopotential Φ. This is given by

$$\Phi = \Phi_G + \Phi_C \qquad (10)$$

where Φ_G is the potential energy, per unit mass, of gravitational attraction, and Φ_C is the potential energy, per unit mass, associated with the centrifugal force. The gravity, per unit mass, is

$$\mathbf{g} = \nabla\Phi \qquad (11)$$

where $\nabla\Phi$ is the gradient (ascendant) of the geopotential. The acceleration due to gravity is denoted by g and is defined as the magnitude of $\mathbf{g}$; that is,

$$\mathbf{g} = |\mathbf{g}| = |\nabla\Phi|. \qquad (12)$$

When moving along an external normal from any point on the surface Φ_1 to a point on the surface Φ_2 infinitely close to the first surface, so that $\Phi_2 = \Phi_1 + d\Phi$, the incremental work performed by shifting a unit mass from the first surface to the second will be

$$d\Phi = g \cdot dZ. \qquad (13)$$

Hence,

$$\Phi = \int_0^Z g \cdot dZ. \qquad (14)$$

The unit of measurement of geopotential is the standard geopotential meter (m') which represents the work done by lifting a unit mass 1 geometric meter, through a region in which the acceleration of gravity is uniformly 9.80665 m/s².

The geopotential of any point with respect to mean sea level (assumed zero potential), expressed in geopotential meters, is called geopotential altitude. Therefore, geopotential altitude H is given by

$$H = \frac{\Phi}{g_0'} = \frac{1}{g_0'} \cdot \int_0^Z g \cdot dZ \qquad (15)$$

and is expressed in geopotential meters (m') when the unit geopotential g_0' is set equal to 9.80665 m²/(s²·m').

With geopotential altitude defined as in eq (15), the differential of eq (15) may be expressed as

$$g_0' \cdot dH = g \cdot dZ. \qquad (16)$$

This expression is used in eq (5) to reduce the number of variables prior to its integration, thereby leading to an expression for computing pressure as a function of geopotential height.

The inverse-square law of gravitation provides an expression for g as a function of altitude with sufficient accuracy for most model-atmosphere computations:

$$g = g_0 \cdot \left(\frac{r_0}{r_0 + Z}\right)^2 \qquad (17)$$

where r_0 is the effective radius of the earth at a specific latitude as given by Lambert's equations (List 1968.). Such a value of r_0 takes into account the centrifugal acceleration at the particular latitude. For this Standard, the value of r_0 is taken as 6,356,766 m, and is consistent with the adopted value of $g_0 = 9.80665$ m/s² for the sea-level value

of the acceleration of gravity. The variation of g as a function of geometric altitude is depicted in figure 2.

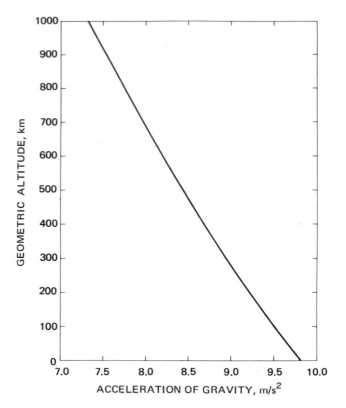

Figure 2. Acceleration of gravity as a function of geometric altitude

Integration of eq (15), after substitution of eq (17) for g, yields

$$H = \frac{g_0}{g_0'} \cdot \left(\frac{r_0 \cdot Z}{r_0 + Z}\right) = \Gamma \cdot \left(\frac{r_0 \cdot Z}{r_0 + Z}\right) \qquad (18)$$

or

$$Z = \frac{r_0 \cdot H}{\Gamma \cdot r_0 - H} \qquad (19)$$

where $\Gamma = g_0/g_0' = 1$ m'/m.

Differences between geopotential altitudes obtained from eq (18) for various values of Z, and those computed from the more complex relationship used in developing the U.S. Standard Atmosphere, 1962, are small. For example, values of H computed from eq (18) are approximately 0.2, 0.4, and 33.3 m greater at 90, 120, and 700 km, respectively, than those obtained from the relationship used in the 1962 Standard.

The transformation from Z to H in eq (5) makes it necessary for the altitude variation of T as well as any variation in M between the surface and 86 km also to be defined in terms of H. It is convenient therefore to determine the sea-level value of M as well as the extent of any height dependence of this quantity between the surface and 80 km. Then, for this low-altitude regime, the two variables T and M are combined with the constant M_0 into a single variable T_M, which is then defined as a function of H.

1.2.4 MEAN MOLECULAR WEIGHT.—The mean molecular weight M of a mixture of gases is by definition

$$M = \frac{\Sigma(n_i \cdot M_i)}{\Sigma n_i} \qquad (20)$$

where n_i and M_i are the number density and defined molecular weight, respectively, of the ith gas species. In that part of the atmosphere between the surface and about 80 km altitude, mixing is dominant, and the effect of diffusion and photochemical processes upon M is negligible. In this region the fractional composition of each species is assumed to remain constant at the defined value F_i, and M remains constant at its sea-level value M_0. For these conditions n_i is equal to the product of F_i times the total number density N, so that eq (20) may be rewritten as

$$M = M_0 = \frac{\Sigma[F_i \cdot N(Z) \cdot M_i]}{\Sigma[F_i \cdot N(Z)]} = \frac{\Sigma(F_i \cdot M_i)}{\Sigma F_i}. \qquad (21)$$

The right-hand element of this equation results from the process of factoring $N(Z)$ out of each term of both the numerator and the denominator of the preceding fraction, so that, in spite of the altitude dependence of N, M is seen analytically to equal M_0 over the entire altitude region of complete mixing.

When the defined values of F_i and M_i (from table 3) are introduced into eq (21), M_0 is found to be 28.9644 kg/kmol. At 86 km (84.852 km'), however, the defined value of atomic-oxygen number density $(8.6 \times 10^{16}$ m$^{-3})$ is seen, in Appendix A, to lead to a value of $M = 28.9522$ kg/kmol, about 0.04 percent less than M_0. To produce a smooth transition from this value of M to M_0, the altitude profile of M has been arbitrarily defined at intervals of 0.5 km' for altitudes between 79.006 and 84.852 km', in terms of the ratio M/M_0 as given in table 8. These ratio values have been interpolated from those initially selected for intervals of 0.5 geometric kilometers between 80 and 86 km to satisfy the boundary conditions of $M = M_0 = 28.9644$ at 80 km, and $M = 28.9522$ at 86 km, and to satisfy a condition of smoothly decreasing first differences in M within the height interval 80 to 86 km.

These arbitrarily assigned values of M/M_0 may be used for correcting a number of parameters of this Standard if the tabulations are to correctly fit the model in the fifth and perhaps in the fourth significant figures within this height region. This after-the-fact correction is required because these values of M/M_0 were not included in the program used for computing the tables of this Standard be-

low 86 km, and hence, the tabulations of some of the properties may show a discontinuity of up to 0.04 percent between 85.5 and 86 km. This situation exists particularly for four properties in addition to molecular weight, i.e., kinetic temperature, total number density, mean free path, and collision frequency. For these five parameters the discrepancy in the tables between 80 and 86 km can be readily remedied by a simple multiplication or division: tabulated values of M, T, and L must be multiplied by the corresponding values of M/M_0 from table 8; tabulated values of N and v must be divided by the corresponding values of M/M_0.

Three other properties, dynamic viscosity, kinematic viscosity, and thermal conductivity, which are tabulated only for heights below 86 km, have similar discrepancies for heights immediately below 86 km. These values are not so simply corrected, however, because of the empirical nature of their respective defining functions. Rather, these quantities must be recalculated in terms of a suitably corrected set of values of T, if the precisely correct values are desired for geometric altitudes between 80 and 86 km.

TABLE 8.—Molecular-weight ratio geopotential and geometric altitudes in meters

H	Z	M/M_0	Z	H	M/M_0
79000	79994.1	1.000000	80000	79005.7	1.000000
79500	80506.9	0.999996	80500	79493.3	0.999996
80000	81019.6	0.999988	81000	79980.8	0.999989
80500	81532.5	0.999969	81500	80468.2	0.999971
81000	82045.4	0.999938	82000	80955.7	0.999941
81500	82558.6	0.999904	82500	81443.0	0.999909
82000	83071.5	0.999864	83000	81930.2	0.999870
82500	83584.8	0.999822	83500	82417.3	0.999829
83000	84098.0	0.999778	84000	82904.4	0.999786
83500	84611.4	0.999731	84500	83391.4	0.999741
84000	85124.8	0.999681	85000	83878.4	0.999694
84500	85638.4	0.999679	85500	84365.2	0.999641
			86000	84852.0	0.999579

1.2.5 MOLECULAR-SCALE TEMPERATURE VS. GEOPOTENTIAL ALTITUDE 0.0 to 84.8520 KM—The molecular-scale temperature T_M (Minzner et al. 1958) at a point is defined as the product of the kinetic temperature T times the ratio M_0/M, where M is the mean molecular weight of air at that point, and M_0 $(=28.9644$ kg/kmol) is the sea-level value of M discussed above. Analytically,

$$T_M = T \cdot \frac{M_0}{M}. \qquad (22)$$

When T is expressed in the Kelvin scale, T_M is also expressed in the Kelvin scale.

The principle virtue of the parameter T_M is that it combines the variable portion of M with the variable T into a single new variable, in a manner somewhat similar to the combining of the variable portion of g with Z to form the new variable H. When both of these transformations are introduced into (5), and when T_M is expressed as a linear function of H, the resulting differential equation has an exact integral. Under these conditions, the computation of P versus H becomes a simple process not requiring numerical integration. Traditionally, standard atmospheres have defined temperature as a linear function of height to eliminate the need for numerical integration in the computation of pressure versus height. This Standard follows the tradition to heights up to 86 km, and the function T_M versus H is expressed as a series of seven successive linear equations. The general form of these linear equations is

$$T_M = T_{M,b} + L_{M,b} \cdot (H - H_b) \qquad (23)$$

with the value of subscript b ranging from 0 to 6 in accordance with each of seven successive layers. The value of $T_{M,b}$ for the first layer ($b = 0$) is 288.15 K, identical to T_0, the sea-level value of T, since at this level $M = M_0$. With this value of $T_{M,b}$ defined, and the set of six values of H_b and the six corresponding values of $L_{M,b}$ defined in table 4, the function T_M of H is completely defined from the surface to 84.8520 km' (86 km). A graph of this function is compared with the similar function of the 1962 Standard in figure 3. From the surface to the 51-km' altitude, this profile is identical to that of the 1962 Standard. The profile from 51 to

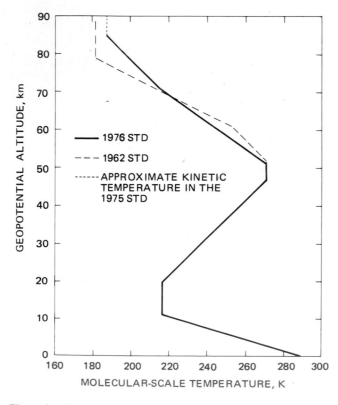

Figure 3. Molecular-scale temperature as a function of geopotential altitude.

84.8520 km' was selected by Task Group I, and abbreviated tables of thermodynamic properties of the atmosphere based upon this profile were published by Kantor and Cole (1973).

1.2.6 KINETIC TEMPERATURE VERSUS GEOMETRIC ALTITUDE, 0.0 TO 1000 km—Between the surface and 86-km altitude, kinetic temperature is based upon the defined values of T_M. In the lowest 80 kilometers of this region, where M is constant at M_0, T is equal to T_M in accordance with (22). Between 80 and 86 km, however, the ratio M/M_0 is assumed to decrease from 1.000000 to 0.9995788, as indicated in table 8, such that the values of T correspondingly decrease from those of T_M. Thus, at $Z_7 = 86$ km, a form of eq (22) shows that T_7 has a value 186.8673 K, i.e., 0.0787 K smaller than that of T_M at that height.

At heights above 86 km, values of T_M are no longer defined, and geopotential is no longer the primary argument. Instead, the temperature-altitude profile is defined in terms of four successive functions, each of which is specified in such a way that the first derivative of T with respect to Z is continuous over the entire altitude region, 86 to 1000 km. These four functions begin successively at the first four base heights, Z_b listed in table 5, and are designed to represent the following conditions:

    A.   An isothermal layer from 86 to 91 km;

    B.   A layer in which $T(Z)$ has the form of an ellipse from 91 to 110 km;

    C.   A constant, positive-gradient layer from 110 to 120 km; and

    D.   A layer in which T increases exponentially toward an asymptote, as Z increases from 120 to 1000 km.

86 to 91 km

For the layer from $Z_7 = 86$ km to $Z_8 = 91$ km, the temperature-altitude function is defined to be isothermally linear with respect to geometric altitude, so that the gradient of T with respect to Z is zero (see table 5). Thus, the standard form of the linear function, which is

$$T = T_b + L_{K,b} \cdot (Z - Z_b) \qquad (24)$$

degenerates to

$$T = T_7 = 186.8673 \text{ K} \qquad (25)$$

and by definition

$$\frac{dT}{dZ} = 0.0 \text{ K/km.} \qquad (26)$$

The value of T_7 is derived from one version of eq (22) in which T_M is replaced by T_{M7}, a value determined in 1.2.5 above, and in which M/M_0 is replaced by M_7/M_0 with a value of 0.9995788 in accordance with values of M_0 and M_7 discussed in 1.0.0 below. Since T is defined to be constant for the entire layer, Z_7 to Z_8, the temperature at Z_8 is T_8 $= T_7 = 186.8673$ K, and the gradient dT/dZ at Z_8 is $L_{K,8} = 0.0$ K/km, the same as for $L_{K,7}$.

91 to 110 km

For the layer $Z_8 = 91$ km to $Z_9 = 110$ km, the temperature-altitude function is defined to be a segment of an ellipse expressed by

$$T = T_c + A \cdot \left[1 - \left(\frac{Z - Z_8}{a} \right)^2 \right]^{1/2} \quad (27)$$

where
$T_c = 263.1905$ K, $A = -76.3232$ K, $a = -19.9429$ km, and Z is limited to values from 91 to 110 km.

Eq (27) is derived in Appendix B from the basic equation for an ellipse, to meet the values of T_8 and $L_{K,8}$ derived above, as well as the defined values $T_9 = 240.0$ K, and $L_{K,9} = 12.0$ K/km, for $Z_9 = 110$ km.

The expression for dT/dZ related to eq (27) is

$$\frac{dT}{dZ} = \frac{-A}{a} \cdot \left(\frac{Z - Z_8}{a} \right) \cdot \left[1 - \left(\frac{Z - Z_8}{a} \right)^2 \right]^{-1/2} . \quad (28)$$

110 to 120 km

For the layer $Z_9 = 110$ km to $Z_{10} = 120$ km, $T(Z)$ has the form of (24), where subscript b is 9, such that T_b and $L_{K,b}$ are, respectively, the defined quantities T_9 and $L_{K,9}$, while Z is limited to the range 110 to 120 km. Thus,

$$T = T_9 + L_{K,9} (Z - Z_9) \quad (29)$$

and

$$\frac{dT}{dZ} = L_{K,9} = 12.0 \text{ K/km}. \quad (30)$$

Since dT/dZ is constant over the entire layer, $L_{K,10}$, the value of dT/dZ at Z_{10}, is identical to $L_{K,9}$, i.e., 12.0 K/km, while the value of T_{10} at Z_{10} is found from eq (29) to be 360.0 K.

120 to 1000 km

For the layer $Z_{10} = 120$ to $Z_{12} = 1000$ km, $T(Z)$ is defined to have the exponential form (Walker 1965)

$$T = T_\infty - (T_\infty - T_{10}) \cdot \exp(-\lambda \xi) \quad (31)$$

such that

$$\frac{dT}{dZ} = \lambda \cdot (T_\infty - T_{10}) \cdot \left(\frac{r_0 + Z_{10}}{r_0 + Z} \right)^2 \cdot \exp(-\lambda \cdot \xi)$$
$$(32)$$

where

$\lambda = L_{K,9}/(T_\infty - T_{10}) = 0.01875$, and
$\xi = \xi(Z) = (Z - Z_{10}) \cdot (r_0 + Z_{10})/(r_0 + Z)$.

In the above expressions, T_∞ equals the defined value 1000 K. A graph of T versus Z from 0.0 to 1000 km altitude is given in figure 4. The upper portion of this profile was selected by Task Group III to be consistent with satellite drag data (Jacchia

1971), while the mid-portion, particularly between 86 and 200 km and the overlap to 450 km was selected by Task Group II (Minzner et al. 1974) to be consistent with observed temperature and satellite observations of composition data (Hedin et al. 1972).

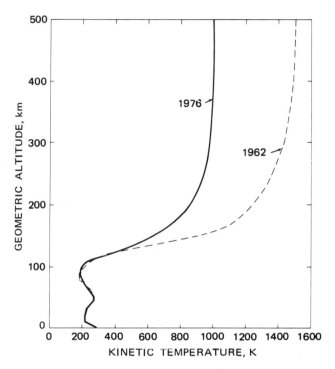

Figure 4. Kinetic temperature as a function of geometric altitude

1.3 COMPUTATIONAL EQUATIONS

The tables of this Standard have been computed in two height regions, 0 to 84.852 km' (86 km), and 86 to 1000 km, because the computations for each region are based on compatible but different sets of initial conditions. These two different sets of initial conditions lead to two different computational procedures. Consequently, the following discussion of computational equations, which is presented according to a series of atmospheric parameters, does not necessarily follow in the order in which the calculation is actually performed for each altitude region. The equations used for computing the various properties of the atmosphere for altitudes below 86 km are, with certain noted exceptions, equivalent to those used in the 1962 standard, and the various equations involving T_M came from expressions used in the ARDC Model Atmosphere, 1956 (Minzner and Ripley 1956).

1.3.1 PRESSURE.—Three different equations are used for computing pressure P in various height regimes of this Standard. One of these equations applies to heights above 86 km, while the other two apply to the height regime from the surface up to 86 km, within which the argument of the computation is geopotential. Consequently, expressions for computing pressure as a function of geopotential altitude stem from the integration of eq (5) after replacing $g \cdot dZ$ by it equivalent $g_0' \, dH$ from eq (16), and after replacing the ratio M/T by its equivalent, M_0/T_M in accordance with eq (22). Two forms result from this integration, one for the case when $L_{M,b}$ for a particular layer is not equal to zero, and the other when the value $L_{M,b}$ is zero. The first of these two expressions is

$$P = P_b \cdot \left[\frac{T_{M,b}}{T_{M,b} + L_{M,b} \cdot (H - H_b)} \right]^{\left[\frac{g_0' \cdot M_0}{R^* \cdot L_{M,b}} \right]}$$

(33a)

and the latter is

$$P = P_b \cdot \exp \left[\frac{-g_0' \cdot M_0 \, (H - H_b)}{R^* \cdot T_{M,b}} \right]. \quad (33b)$$

In these equations g_0', M_0, and R^* are each defined single-valued constants, while $L_{M,b}$ and H_b are each defined multi-valued constants in accordance with the value of b as indicated in table 4. The quantity $T_{M,b}$ is a multi-valued constant dependent on $L_{M,b}$ and H_b. The reference-level value for P_b for $b = 0$ is the defined sea-level value, $P_0 = 101325.0$ N/m² (1013.250 mb). Values of P_b for $b = 1$ through $b = 6$ are obtained from the application of the appropriate member of the pair eq (33a) and (33b) for the case when $H = H_{b+1}$.

These two equations yield the pressure for any desired geopotential altitude from sea level to H_7, where H_7 is the geopotential altitude corresponding to the geometric altitude $Z_7 = 86$ km. Pressures for H from 0 to -5 km' may also be computed from eq (33a) when subscript b is zero.

For Z equal to 86 km and above, the value of pressure is computed as a function of geometric altitude Z, and involves the altitude profile of kinetic temperature T rather than that of T_M, in an expression in which the total pressure P is equal to the sum of the partial pressures for the individual species as expressed by eq (3). Thus, for $Z = 86$ to 1000 km,

$$P = \Sigma P_i = \Sigma n_i \cdot k \cdot T = \frac{\Sigma n_i \cdot R^* \cdot T}{N_A}. \quad (33c)$$

In this expression
- k = the Boltzmann constant, defined in table 2a,
- T = $T(Z)$ defined in eq (25), (27), (29), and (31) for successive layers, and
- Σn_i = the sum of the number densities of the individual gas species comprising the atmosphere at altitude Z above 86 km, as described below.

Neither n_i, the number densities of individual species, nor Σn_i, the sum of the individual number densities, is known directly. Consequently, pressures above 86 km cannot be computed without first determining n_i for each of the significant gas species.

1.3.2 NUMBER DENSITY OF INDIVIDUAL SPECIES.—The values of n_i, the number densities of individual species, have not been presented in the detailed tables of this Standard for low altitudes where it is assumed that complete mixing keeps F_i, the fractional concentrations of the individual species, at the sea-level value. For altitudes below 80 km, the altitude profile of number density for any particular major species i is equal to F_i times the altitude profile of the total number density N, a quantity which is tabulated in this Standard, in accordance with eq (41) below. Thus, for $Z < 80$ km,

$$n_i = F_i \cdot N \quad (34)$$

where values of F_i for the various species are defined in table 3. For altitudes between 80 and 86 km, the value of n_i determined by eq (34) and the tabulated values of N will need to be increased by the factor M_0/M to be rigorously correct in accordance with the discussion in 1.2.4. At altitudes above 86 km, however, the model assumes the existence of various processes which lead to particular differing height variations in the number-density values of several individual species, N_2, O, O_2, Ar, He, and H, each governed by eq (6). Ideally, the set of equations eq (6), each member of which is associated with a particular species, should be solved simultaneously, since the number densities of all the species are coupled through the expressions for molecular diffusion which are included in eq (6). Such a solution would require an inordinate amount of computation, however, and a simpler approach was desired. This was achieved with negligible loss of validity by some simplifying approximations, and by calculating the number densities of individual species one at a time in the order $n(N_2)$, n (O), $n(O_2)$, $n(Ar)$, $n(He)$, and $n(H)$. For all species except hydrogen (which is discussed in the section on atomic hydrogen) we divide eq (6) by n_i, and integrate directly to obtain the following set of simultaneous equations, one for each gas species:

$$n_i = n_{i,7} \cdot \frac{T_7}{T} \cdot \exp \left\{ -\int_{Z_7}^{Z} \left[f(Z) + \left(\frac{v_i}{D_i + K} \right) \right] dZ \right\}. \quad (35)$$

In this set of equations
- $n_{i,7}$ = the set of species-dependent, number-density values for $Z = Z_7 = 86$ km, one member for each of the five designated species, as derived in Appendix A and listed in table 9,
- T_7 = 186.8673 K, the value of T at Z_7, as specified in eq (25),
- T = $T(Z)$ defined in eq (25), (27), (29) and (31) for the appropriate altitude regions.

$f(Z)$ = the function written as eq (36) below, and

$\dfrac{v_i}{D_i + K}$ = the set of empirical functions written as eq (37) below:

For $f(Z)$ we have

$$f(Z) = \frac{g}{R^* \cdot T} \cdot \left(\frac{D_i}{D_i + K} \right)$$
$$\cdot \left[M_i + \frac{M \cdot K}{D_i} + \frac{\alpha_i \cdot R^*}{g} \cdot \frac{dT}{dZ} \right] \quad (36)$$

TABLE 9.—Number densities of various species at 86-km altitude

Species	Number density (m^{-3})
N_2	1.129794×10^{20}
O	$8.6 \quad\;\; \times 10^{16}$
O_2	3.030898×10^{19}
Ar	1.351400×10^{18}
He	$7.5817 \quad \times 10^{10}$

where

D_i = $D_i(Z)$ as defined by eq (8) for the ith species,

K = $K(Z)$ as defined by eq (7a), (7b), and (7c),

M_i = the molecular weight of the ith species as defined in table 3,

α_i = the thermal diffusion coefficient for the ith species as defined in table 4,

dT/dZ = one of eq (26), (28), (30), or (32), as appropriate to the altitude region, and

M = $M(Z)$ with special considerations mentioned below.

For $[v_i/(D_i + K)]$ we have the following set of empirical expressions.

$$\frac{v_i}{D_i + K} = Q_i \cdot (Z - U_i)^2 \cdot$$
$$\exp \left[-W_i \cdot (Z - U_i)^3 \right] + q_i \cdot (u_i - Z)^2$$
$$\cdot \exp \left[-w_i \cdot (u_i - Z)^3 \right]. \quad (37)$$

This set of equations, while representing a function of both D_i and K, involves a series of six other coefficients which, for each of four species, have been empirically selected to adjust the number-density profile of the related species to particular values in agreement with observations. The defined values of the six sets of species-dependent coefficients, Q_i, q_i, U_i, u_i, W_i, and w_i used in eq (37) are listed in table 7. The values of q_i and U_i were selected so that for O_2, Ar, and He, the quantity $v_i/(D_i + K)$ becomes zero at exactly 86 km. For atomic oxygen, however, all six of these coefficients contribute to maximizing this quantity for $Z = 86$ km.

Molecular Nitrogen.—Molecular nitrogen (N_2) is the first species for which n is calculated since, on the average, the distribution of N_2 is close to that for static equilibrium, and hence, for this species, we may neglect the transport velocity, thereby eliminating the term $[v_i/(D_i + K)]$ from that version of eq (35) applying to N_2. This species is dominant up to and above the turbopause, and its molecular weight is close to the mean molecular weight in the lower thermosphere, where mixing still dominates the distribution process. We approximate the effect of mixing up to 100 km by two additional adjustments to eq (35), both adjustments implicit in $f(Z)$; i.e., neglecting K and replacing M_i by the mean molecular weight M which, for the altitude region, 86 to 100 km, is approximated by M_0. With these three adjustments, that version of eq (35) applying to N_2 reduces to

$$n(N_2) = n(N_2)_7 \cdot \frac{T_7}{T} \cdot \exp \left\{ -\int_{Z_7}^{Z} \frac{M \cdot g}{R^* \cdot T} \cdot dZ \right\} \quad (38)$$

where

$M = M_0$ for $Z \leq 100$ km, and

$M = M(N_2)$ for $Z > 100$ km.

Figure 5 shows a graph of $n(N_2)$ versus Z.

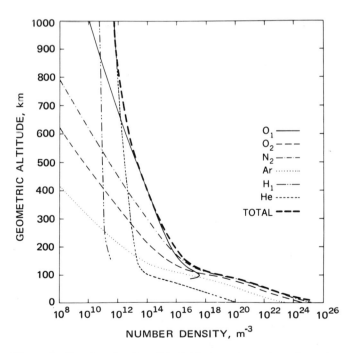

Figure 5. Number density of individual species and total number density as a function of geometric altitude

The species O, O_2, Ar, and He.—As noted above, after the calculation of $n(N_2)$ has been performed, the values of n_i for the next four species are calculated from eq (35) in the order O, O_2, Ar, and He.

In the case of O and O_2, the problem of mutual diffusion is simplified by considering N_2 as the stationary background gas (as described in the previous section). For Ar and He, which are minor constituents in the lower thermosphere, it is more realistic to use the sum of the number densities of N_2, O, and O_2 as the background gas in evaluating the molecular-diffusion coefficient D_i, and the mean-molecular weight M, except below 100 km, where M is taken to be the sea-level value M_0. This latter choice is to maintain consistency with the method for calculating $n(N_2)$.

In eq (37), defining $[v_i/(D_i + K)]$, the coefficients Q_i, q_i, U_i, u_i, W_i, and w_i, which, except for q_i are constant for a particular species, are each adjusted such that appropriate densities are obtained at 450 km for O and He, and at 150 km for O, O_2, He, and Ar. The constant q_i, and hence the second term of eq (37) is zero for all species except atomic oxygen, and is also zero for atomic oxygen above 97 km; the extra term for atomic oxygen is needed below 97 km to generate a maximum in the density-height profile at the selected height of 97 km. This maximum results from the increased loss of atomic oxygen by recombination at lower altitudes. The flux terms for O and O_2 are based on, and lead (qualitatively) to the same results as those derived from the much more detailed calculations by Colegrove et al. (1965), and Keneshea and Zimmerman (1970).

A further computational simplification is realized above 115 km where the eddy diffusion coefficient becomes zero. For these altitudes, the set of equations represented by eq (35) becomes uncoupled, and each member reduces to the sum of the barometric equation for the particular species plus the thermal-diffusion term and the velocity term. In the case of O, O_2, and Ar, the thermal diffusion term is zero. Also, as will be seen in Part 2, the velocity term $[v_i/(D_i + K)]$, becomes small above 120 km and, with the exception of atomic hydrogen, each species considered is nearly in diffusive equilibrium at these heights. For the present model, however, this situation becomes exactly true only at altitudes above 150 km.

The altitude profile of number density for each of the species O, O_2, Ar, and He is given in figure 5, along with that for N_2.

Atomic Hydrogen.—For various reasons, the height distribution of the number density of atomic hydrogen $n(H)$ is defined only for heights from 150 to 1000 km. Below 150 km, the concentration of H is negligible compared with the concentrations of O, O_2, Ar, and He. The defining expression for $n(H)$, like the expression for $n(N_2)$, $n(O)$, etc., is derived from eq (6). The solution for $n(H)$, however, is expressed in terms of the vertical flux $n(H) \cdot v(H)$ represented by ϕ, rather than in

terms of $v(H)$, because it is the flux which is considered known for H. In this model only that contribution to ϕ due to planetary escape from the exosphere is considered.

Since K is zero, for the altitude region of interest, the particular version of eq (6) applied to H is correspondingly simplified, and one possible solution to the resulting expression is

$$n(H) = \left[n(H)_{11} - \int_{Z_{11}}^{Z} \frac{\phi}{D(H)} \cdot \left(\frac{T}{T_{11}} \right)^{1 + \alpha(H)} \right.$$
$$\left. \cdot (\exp \tau) \cdot dZ \right] \cdot \left(\frac{T_{11}}{T} \right)^{1 + \alpha(H)} \cdot (\exp\text{-}\tau) \quad (39)$$

where

$n(H)_{11}$ = $8.0 \times 10^{10}\,m^{-3}$, the number density of H at $Z_{11} = 500$ km, as defined in table 2,

$D(H)$ = The molecular diffusion coefficient for hydrogen given by eq (8) in which the values of a_i and b_i for hydrogen are as defined in table 6,

ϕ = $7.2 \times 10^{11}\,m^{-2} \cdot s^{-1}$, the vertical flux of H, as defined in table 2,

T = $T(Z)$ as specified by eq (31),

T_{11} = 999.2356 K, the temperature derived from eq (31) for $z = Z_{11}$,

$\alpha(H)$ = The thermal diffusion coefficient for H, -0.25 (dimensionless), as defined in table 6, and

τ = $\tau(Z)$ defined in eq (40) below.

$$\tau = \int_{Z_{11}}^{Z} \frac{g \cdot M(H)}{R^* \cdot T} \cdot dZ. \quad (40)$$

Because $D(H)$ becomes very large compared with ϕ for heights above 500 km, the value of the integral term in eq (39) can be neglected at these heights, and atomic hydrogen is then essentially in diffusive equilibrium. Figure 5 depicts the graph of $n(H)$ as a function of Z.

Eq (35) through (39) permit the calculation of the number densities of the species N_2, O, O_2, Ar, He, and H, for heights above 150 km, and of the first five of these species for heights between 86 and 150 km, where $n(H)$ is insignificant compared with $n(N_2)$. These number densities permit the calculation of several atmospheric parameters in the height region 86 to 1000 km. The first is mean molecular weight using eq (20). These values of M, along with those implicit in table 8, for Z from 80 to 86 km, plus the invariant value, M_0, for heights from 0 to 80 km, are shown in figure 6.

The number densities of the several species also permit us now to compute total pressure for heights from 86 to 1000 km, using eq (33c). Figure 7 depicts these values as well as those for heights below 86 km computed from eq (33a) and (33b). Finally, these individual number densities permit the calculation of total number density, $N = \Sigma n_i$, at least at heights of 86 to 1000 km.

1.3.3. TOTAL NUMBER DENSITY.—From eq (2), (22), and (33c) it is apparent that total number density N, the number of neutral atmospheric gas particles per unit volume of the atmosphere may be expressed in any one of the three equivalent forms following:

$$N = \frac{M_0 \cdot N_A \cdot P}{T_M \cdot R^* \cdot M} = \frac{N_A \cdot P}{R^* \cdot T} = \Sigma n_i. \quad (41)$$

The three forms are selected to satisfy three types of calculations: (a) Those depending upon values of T_M, (b) Those depending upon values of T, and (c) Those depending upon values of Σn_i. This format will be followed in specifying the computational equations, insofar as possible, for the balance of the quantities discussed in this section. A graph of the altitude variation of N is presented in figure 5, along with the number densities of individual species. That portion of (41) involving T_M is of particular interest in calculating N for heights from 0 to 86 km.

1.3.4 MASS DENSITY.—From eq (1), (22), and (33c) one may write the following three forms of computational equations for mass density ρ:

$$\rho = \frac{P \cdot M_0}{R^* \cdot T_M} = \frac{P \cdot M}{R^* \cdot T} = \frac{\Sigma (n_i \cdot M_i)}{N_A}. \quad (42)$$

The altitude-dependent variations of this quantity are shown in figure 7 along with those of pressure.

1.3.5 MOLE VOLUME.—Mole volume v_m of air is defined as the volume of one mole of air, where one mole of air is the amount consisting of a number of neutral particles equal to N_A. In SI units, the quantity v_m should specify the number of cubic meters containing one kilomole of air. Since M has the dimensions of $kg/kmol$, and ρ has the dimensions of kg/m^3, the ratio M/ρ, with the units $m^3/kmol$, provides the definition of mole volume. In terms of eq (1), (22), and (33c), this ratio may be equated to the following series of expressions:

$$v_m = \frac{R^* \cdot M \cdot T_M}{M_0 \cdot P} = \frac{R^* \cdot T}{P} = \frac{N_A}{\Sigma n_i}. \quad (43)$$

This quantity, while not tabulated in this Standard, is shown graphically in figure 8.

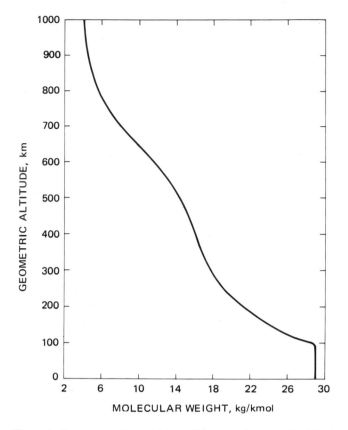

Figure 6. Mean molecular weight as a function of geometric altitude

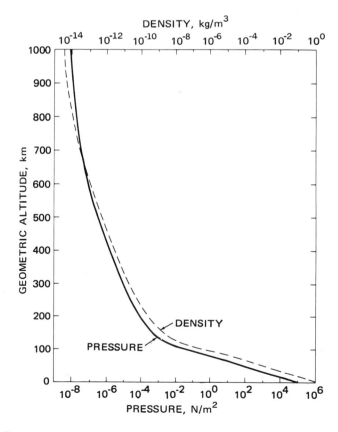

Figure 7. Total pressure and mass density as a function of geometric altitude

1.3.6　SCALE HEIGHT

Pressure Scale Height.—The quantity $H_p R^* \cdot T/(g \cdot M)$, which has dimensions of length, is a quantity commonly associated with the concept of scale height, and is the defining form of pressure scale height H_p used in this model, such that with eq (20) and (22) we may write

$$H_P = \frac{R^* \cdot T_M}{g \cdot M_0} = \frac{R^* \cdot T}{g \cdot M} = \frac{R^* \cdot T \cdot \Sigma n_i}{g \cdot \Sigma (n_i \cdot N_i)} \cdot (44)$$

The reciprocal of this quantity, which appears on the right-hand side of eq (5) is seen to equal the slope of the function $\ln P$ versus Z at height Z in the regions where hydrostatic equilibrium or diffusive equilibrium holds. In the present model, this condition is true for heights below 80 km (complete mixing) and essentially true above approximately 120 km, where diffusive equilibrium is nearly satisfied and where each individual species is governed by eq (4).

In the region 80 to 120 km, where the transition from a completely mixed atmosphere to one in diffusive equilibrium takes place, the situation is complicated by the competition between three processes: molecular diffusion, eddy diffusion, and dissociation of molecular oxygen. These processes result in a vertical transport, such that eq (4) and (5) are no longer exactly true in this 40-km layer. Since molecular nitrogen is the dominant species in this altitude range, however, and since this species has a zero transport velocity in this model, the pressure scale height is still a good indicator of the rate of change of the pressure in this height region.

It should be noted that eq (4) and (5) also become invalid at very high altitudes (the exospheric region) due to the infrequent collisions between neutral particles. Thus, in this region, the significance of H_P as a measure of $d\ln P/dZ$ again loses validity.

In eq (44) both g and T_M or all three of g, T, and M are functions of Z, such that H_P is the local value of geometric pressure scale height.

This quantity, which is the particular scale height tabulated in this Standard, and which is plotted in figure 9, is frequently but incorrectly associated with the altitude increment over which the pressure decreases by exactly a factor of $1/e$. The conditions necessary for the pressure to decrease by exactly that factor over an altitude increase of a single pressure scale height, would be for the variables T, g, and M all to remain constant over that altitude interval. Since g may never be constant over any altitude interval, this particular concept of pressure decrease can rarely if ever apply exactly to H_P.

Density Scale Height.—Because of the relationship between H_P and the slope of $\ln P$ versus Z, it is convenient to apply the name geometric den-

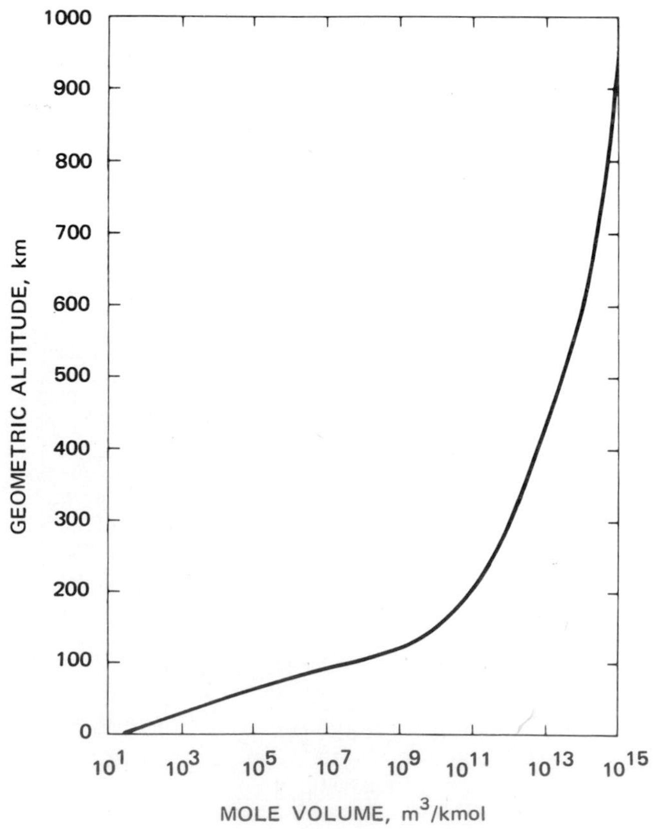

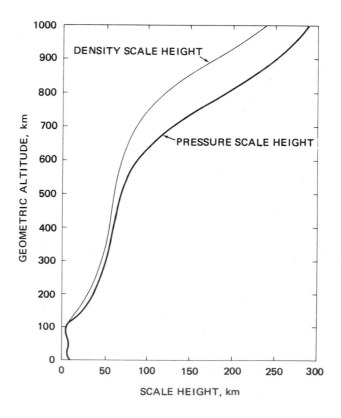

Figure 8.　Mole volume as a function of geometric altitude

Figure 9.　Pressure scale height and density scale height as a function of geometric altitude

sity scale height H_ρ to the negative reciprocal of the slope of $\ln\rho$ versus Z. Using the equation of state to relate $d\ln\rho$ to $d\ln P$, one may define

$$H_\rho = \frac{H_P}{1 + H_P \cdot \left(\dfrac{d\ln T_M}{dZ}\right)} = \frac{H_P}{1 + H_P \cdot \left(\dfrac{d\ln T}{dZ} - \dfrac{d\ln M}{dZ}\right)}.$$

(45)

The relationships implied between H_ρ and $d\ln\rho/dZ$ are subject to the same limitations as those between H_P and $d\ln P/dZ$ expressed above, i.e., H_ρ is only an approximation to $(d\ln\rho/dZ)^{-1}$ between 80 and 120 km, and in the exosphere, where the approximation becomes less valid with increasing altitude.

Within these limitations it is apparent that in layers where T_M does not change with changing altitude, i.e., where $(d\ln T_M/dZ) = 0$, H_ρ is equal to H_P. Within such layers, the slope of $\ln\rho$ versus Z, at any particular altitude Z, is identical to the slope of $\ln P$ versus Z.

While density scale height is not tabulated in this Standard, values of this quantity are shown graphically with H_P in figure 9.

1.3.7 MEAN AIR-PARTICLE SPEED.—The mean air-particle speed V is the arithmetic average of the speeds of all air particles in the volume element being considered. All particles are considered to be neutral. For a valid average to occur, there must, of course, be a sufficient number of particles involved to represent mean conditions. Pressure and temperature gradients within the volume must also be negligible. The analytical expression for V is closely related to that for the speed of sound, and is proportional to the ratio T/M. Thus, in terms of eq (20) and (22), we write

$$V = \left[\frac{8 \cdot R^* \cdot T_M}{\pi \cdot M_0}\right]^{1/2} = \left[\frac{8 \cdot R^* \cdot T}{\pi \cdot M}\right]^{1/2}$$

$$= \left[\frac{8 \cdot R^* \cdot T \cdot \Sigma n_i}{\pi \cdot \Sigma(n_i \cdot M_i)}\right]^{1/2}.$$

(46)

The variation of particle speed with geometric altitude is shown in figure 10.

1.3.8 MEAN FREE PATH.—The mean free path L is the mean value of the distances traveled by each of the neutral particles, in a selected volume, between successive collisions with other particles in that volume. As in the case of V, a meaningful average requires that the selected volume be big enough to contain a large number of particles. The computational form for L is

$$L = \frac{2^{1/2} \cdot R^* \cdot M \cdot T_M}{2\pi \cdot N_A \cdot \sigma^2 \cdot M_0 \cdot P} = \frac{2^{1/2} \cdot R^* \cdot T}{2\pi \cdot N_A \cdot \sigma^2 \cdot P}$$

$$= \frac{2^{1/2}}{2\pi \cdot \sigma^2 \cdot \Sigma n_i}$$

(47)

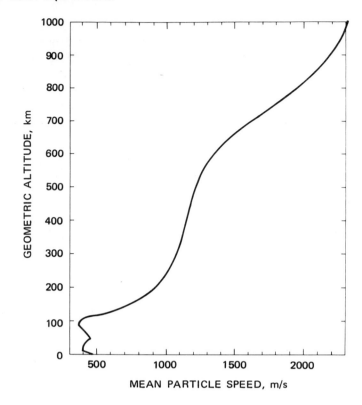

Figure 10. Mean air-particle speed as a function of geometric altitude

where σ is the effective collision diameter of the mean air molecules. The adopted value of σ, i.e., 3.65×10^{-10} m is suitable for that part of the atmosphere below about 86 km, which is dominated by N_2 and O_2. Above this height, the value of σ, which depends upon composition in a complicated manner, begins to change significantly so that tabulations with four significant figures are no longer valid. At great altitudes, this expression for L is valid only under assumptions that hold M, T_M, P, and σ constant throughout the volume used. Figure 11 depicts the mean free path in terms of altitude.

1.3.9 MEAN COLLISION FREQUENCY.—The mean collision frequency ν is the average speed of the air particles within a selected volume divided by the mean free path L of the particles within that volume. That is,

$$\nu = \frac{V}{L}$$

(48)

and in computational form:

$$\nu = 4N_A \cdot \sigma^2 \cdot \left[\frac{\pi \cdot M_0 \cdot P^2}{R^* \cdot M^2 \cdot T_M}\right]^{1/2}$$

$$= 4N_A \cdot \sigma^2 \cdot \left[\frac{\pi \cdot P^2}{R^* \cdot M \cdot T}\right]^{1/2}$$

$$= 4N_A \cdot \sigma^2 \cdot \left[\frac{\pi \cdot P^2 \cdot \Sigma n_i}{R^* \cdot T \cdot \Sigma(n_i \cdot M_i)}\right]^{1/2}.$$

(49)

Note that σ is again involved in this quantity, and hence ν has limitations similar to those of mean free path. The foregoing expressions are taken to apply to neutral particles only, since no considerations involving charged particles are introduced for purposes of developing the tables and graphs of this standard.

Figure 12 graphically displays the variation of collision frequency with altitude. See section 1.3.7 for a discussion of the assumptions under which eq (49) is valid at great altitudes.

1.3.10 SPEED OF SOUND.—The expression adopted for the speed of sound C_s is

$$C_s = \left(\frac{\gamma \cdot R^* \cdot T_M}{M_0}\right)^{1/2} \qquad (50)$$

where γ is the ratio of specific heat of air at constant pressure to that at constant volume; and is taken to be 1.40 exact (dimensionless), as defined in table 2. Eq (50) for speed of sound applies only when the sound wave is a small perturbation on the ambient condition. Calculated values for C_s have been found to vary slightly from experimentally determined values.

The limitations of the concept of speed of sound due to extreme attenuation are also of concern. The attenuation which exists at sea level for high frequencies applies to successively lower frequencies as atmospheric pressure decreases, or as the mean free path increases. For this reason, the concept of speed of sound (except for frequencies approaching zero) progressively loses its range of applicability at high altitudes. Hence, the main tables listing the values for speed of sound terminate at 86

km. Figure 13 shows the variation with altitude of the computed speed of sound.

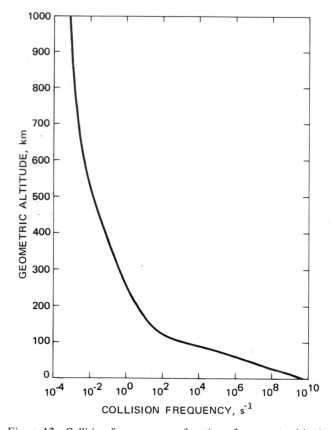

Figure 12. Collision frequency as a function of geometric altitude

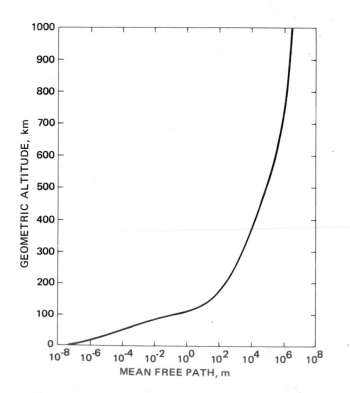

Figure 11. Mean free path as a function of geometric altitude

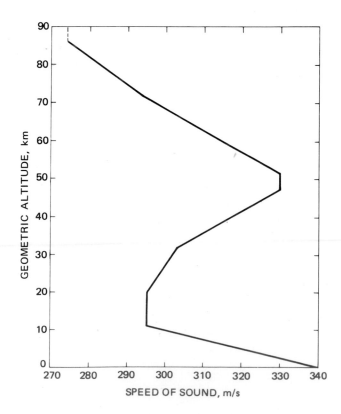

Figure 13. Speed of sound as a function of geometric altitude

1.3.11 DYNAMIC VISCOSITY.—The coefficient of dynamic viscosity μ (N · s/m²) is defined as a coefficient of internal friction developed where gas regions move adjacent to each other at different velocities. The following expression, basically from kinetic theory, but with constants derived from experiment, is used for computation of the tables:

$$\mu = \frac{\beta \cdot T^{3/2}}{T + S}. \qquad (51)$$

In this equation β is a constant equal to 1.458 × 10^{-6} kg/(s · m · K$^{1/2}$) and S is Sutherland's constant, equal to 110.4 K, both defined in table 2B. Because of the empirical nature of this equation, no attempt has been made to transform it into one involving T_M.

Eq (51) fails for conditions of very high and very low temperatures, and under conditions occurring at great altitudes. Consequently, tabular entries for coefficient of dynamic viscosity are terminated at 86 km. For these reasons caution is necessary in making measurements involving probes and other objects which are small with respect to the mean free path of molecules particularly in the region of 32 to 86 km.

The variation of dynamic viscosity with altitude is shown in figure 14.

1.3.12 KINEMATIC VISCOSITY.—Kinematic viscosity η is defined as the ratio of the dynamic viscosity of a gas to the density of that gas; that is,

$$\eta = \frac{\mu}{\rho}. \qquad (52)$$

Limitations of this equation are comparable to those associated with dynamic viscosity, and consequently tabular entries of kinematic viscosity are also terminated at the 86-km level. See figure 15 for a graphical representation of the variation of kinematic viscosity with altitude.

1.3.13 COEFFICIENT OF THERMAL CONDUCTIVITY.—The empirical expression adopted for purposes of developing tabular values of the coefficient of thermal conductivity k_t for heights up to the 86-km level is as follows:

$$k_t = \frac{2.64638 \times 10^{-3} \cdot T^{3/2}}{T + 245.4 \times 10^{-(12/T)}} \qquad (53)$$

This expression differs from that used in the U. S. Standard Atmosphere, 1962 in that the numerical constant has been adjusted to accommodate a conversion of the related energy unit from the temperature-dependent kilogram calorie to the invariant joule. Thus, the values of k_t in units of J/(m · s · K) or W/(m · K) are greater than the values of k_t in units of kcal/(m · s · K) by a factor of exactly 4.18580 × 10^3, when the kilocalorie is assumed to be the one for 15°C. Kinetic-theory de-

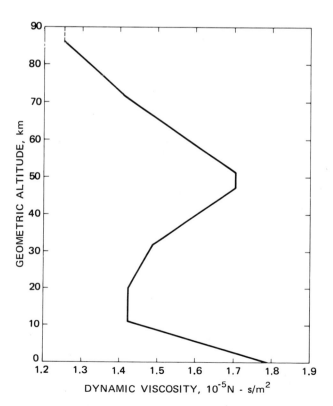

Figure 14. Dynamic viscosity as a function of geometric altitude

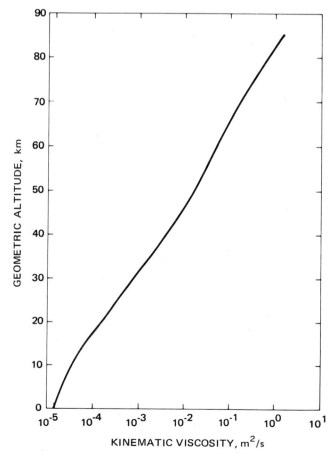

Figure 15. Kinematic viscosity as a function of geometric altitude

terminations of thermal conductivity of some monatomic gases agree well with observation. For these gases thermal conductivity is directly proportional to the dynamic viscosity. Modification of the simple theory has accounted in part for differences introduced by polyatomic molecules and by mixtures of gases. Tabular entry of values for coefficient of thermal conductivity is terminated at 86 km. The variation with height of this quantity is shown in figure 16.

1.4 SELECTED TABULAR VALUES OF ATMOSPHERIC PROPERTIES AND CONVERSION FACTORS FOR METRIC TO ENGLISH UNITS

1.4.1 SEA-LEVEL VALUES.—The sea-level values of fifteen of the atmospheric properties discussed in this Standard are listed in table 10. The sea-level values for g, P, and T are defined quantities; the remainder are quantities calculated from the preceding equations.

1.4.2 CONVERSION OF METRIC TO ENGLISH UNITS.—For those who have a need to work in the English System of units, the conversion factors

listed in table 11 are applicable to the atmospheric parameters tabulated or shown graphically in this Standard. For other transformations, see Mechtly (1973).

TABLE 10.—Seal-level values of atmospheric properties

Symbol	Sea-level value
$C_{s,0}$	3.40294×10^2 m/s
g_0	9.80665 m/s²
$H_{P,0}$	8.4345×10^3 m
$k_{t,0}$	2.5326×10^{-3} J/(s·m·K) or W/(m·K)
L_0	6.6328×10^{-8} m
$V_{m,0}$	2.3643×10^1 m³/kmol
M_0	2.89644×10^1 kg/kmol
N_0	2.5470×10^{25} m⁻³
P_0	1.01325×10^5 N/m²
T_0	2.8815×10^2 K
V_0	4.5894×10^2 m/s
η_0	1.4607×10^{-5} m²/s
μ_0	1.7894×10^{-5} kg/(m·s)
ν_0	6.9193×10^9 s⁻¹
ρ_0	1.2250 kg/m³

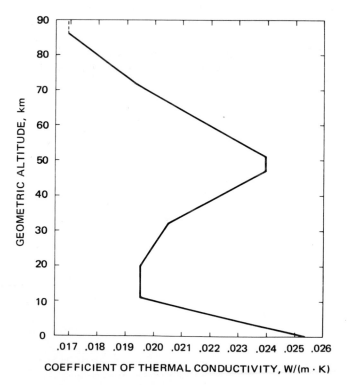

Figure 16. Coefficient of thermal conductivity as a function of geometric altitude

TABLE 11.—Metric to English conversion factors for properties of The U. S. Standard Atmosphere, 1976

Symbol	To convert from metric units	to English units	divide by
C_s	m/s	ft/s	$3.048^* \times 10^{-1}$
g	m/s²	ft/s²	$3.048^* \times 10^{-1}$
H_p	m	ft	$3.048^* \times 10^{-1}$
k_t	W/(m·K)	BTU/(ft·s·°R)	$6.226477504 \times 10^{-3}$
L	m	ft	$3.048^* \times 10^{-1}$
v_m	m³/kmol	ft³/lbmol	$6.242796057 \times 10^{-2}$
M	kg/kmol	lb/lbmol	1.000^*
N	m⁻³	ft⁻³	3.531466672×10^2
P	mb	in Hg (32°F)	3.386389×10^1
T or T_M	K	°R	$5/9^*$
V	m/s	ft/s	$3.048^* \times 10^{-1}$
η	m²/s	ft²/s	$9.290304 \times 10^{-2*}$
μ	N·s/m²	lb/(ft·s)	1.488163944
ν	s⁻¹	s⁻¹	1.000^*
ρ	kg/m³	lb/ft³	1.6018463×10^1

*exact definition

PART 2

Atmospheric Model

2.0 INTRODUCTION

In September 1971 The COESA Working Group reviewed the temperature and density data derived from recent satellite and rocket observations. This review revealed a need to revise the *U.S. Standard Atmosphere, 1962* (COESA 1962) at altitudes above 50 km. Data available for levels below 50 km were found to be in reasonably good agreement with the 1962 Standard.

2.1 MODEL AND DATA FOR ALTITUDES UP TO 86 KM

The number of available observations between 50 and 86 km on which to base a mean annual temperature-altitude profile for 45°N is still relatively small. The greatest number of observations at specific locations were obtained at Wallops Island (38°N) and Ft. Churchill (59°N). Even at these locations, however, the data for a given month vary from 1 to 20 observations for altitudes between 55 and 80 km, and from 0 to 12 for altitudes above 80 km. The unequal distribution of observations by month and time of day, as well as by location, makes it difficult to derive accurate estimates of the annual temperature cycle, particularly at altitudes above 80 km. However, new data were sufficient to indicate that the *U.S. Standard Atmosphere, 1962* needed to be revised at all altitudes above 50 km.

2.1.1 DATA SOURCES.—Mean annual temperature-altitude profiles for altitudes between 50 and 90 km were prepared from temperature data derived from grenade, pitot-static tube, and falling-sphere experiments conducted through June of 1972 at the locations shown in table 12. Annual means for 31° latitude were computed from observations at White Sands, Woomera, and Eglin, and

TABLE 12.—Rocket Launch Sites and Data Sources

Station	Location		Data Sources*
Natal, Brazil	6°S	35°W	A
Ascension Island	8°S	14°W	A
Eglin AFB, Florida	30°N	87°W	C
Woomera, Australia	31°S	137°E	D
White Sands, New Mexico	32°N	106°W	C
Wallops Island, Virginia	38°N	75°W	A,B
Ft. Churchill, Manitoba	59°N	94°W	A,B,C
Point Barrow, Alaska	71°N	157°W	A

*Data sources are given on page G 26.

for 8° latitude from observations at Natal and Ascension. The data for Woomera were combined with Northern Hemisphere data, using a 6-month change in date.

Mean annual temperature-altitude profiles prepared by Soviet meteorologists (data source E) from measurements taken with resistance thermometers on M-100 rockets at Volgograd (49°N) and Heiss Island, USSR (81°N) were also used in developing a mean annual temperature-altitude cross-section from equator to pole for altitudes between 50 and 80 km.

As with rocket thermistor measurements of temperature made in North America and elsewhere, the Soviets apply corrections compensating for aerodynamic heating of the sensor and for radiational and other nonambient heat sources. These corrections, based on a detailed evaluation of an appropriate heat transfer differential equation, typically range from 1 to 2 K near 40 km to many degrees above 55 km. Comparative investigations have shown that further systematic adjustment of the Soviet data is required, since in general the reported Soviet temperatures are low with respect to other measurements above 50 km. The data used here have been adjusted above 60 km by the Soviets, on the basis of their comparison of mean temperatures computed from their M-100 rocket measurements and means derived from grenade and pitot-static tube results.

2.1.2 DATA PROCESSING.—Mean annual temperatures for the various locations and altitudes were obtained by averaging 12 observed and/or interpolated mean monthly values. Both subjective and objective analyses of the distributions of observed mean monthly temperatures at levels between 50 and 100 km were employed. At locations and altitudes where observed values were available for only a few months or where values were missing for the extreme months, a subjective analysis appeared to provide a better estimate of the annual distribution of mean monthly values than that obtained by objective methods.

At altitudes and locations for which there were relatively complete sets of observed mean monthly temperatures, the mean monthly values were subjected to harmonic analysis for semiannual and annual cycles. The analyses give regression equations of the form:

$$T = \bar{T} + A_1 \sin (ix + \phi_1) + A_2 \sin (2ix + \phi_2), \quad (54)$$

where the bar indicates an arithmetic mean, x is $360°/$period, i is $0, 1, 2, \ldots, 11$, and 0 represents 15 January.

Examples of the curves representing the sum of the first and second harmonics, including equations giving the phase and amplitude of each cycle, are shown in figures 17 and 18 for the altitudes between 60 and 90 km at Ft. Churchill and Wallops Island. Table 13 gives the level of significance (F-test) of the annual and semiannual oscillations at each alti-

tude. An "X" indicates that the level of significance is beyond 25 percent.

The semiannual oscillation at Wallops is significant at the 5.0- and 0.1-percent level at 60 and 70 km, respectively. However, at Ft. Churchill it is not significant, even at the 25-percent level, at any of the altitudes shown. The annual oscillation at both locations is significant at the 5-percent level or better at all altitudes above 60 km. There is a change in phase of the annual temperature cycle between

TABLE 13.— Level of significance of annual and semiannual oscillations

Altitude (km)	WALLOPS oscillations (percent)		CHURCHILL oscillations (percent)	
	Annual	Semiannual	Annual	Semiannual
60	10	5.0	10	X
70	0.1	0.1	5.0	X
80	0.5	25.0	0.1	X
90	1.0	10.0	2.5	X

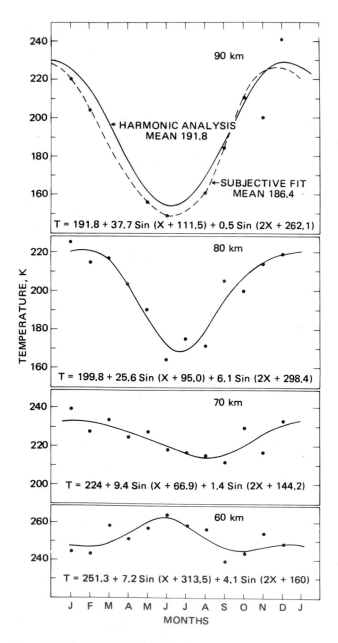

Figure 17. Harmonic analysis of median monthly temperatures at Ft. Churchill, Manitoba

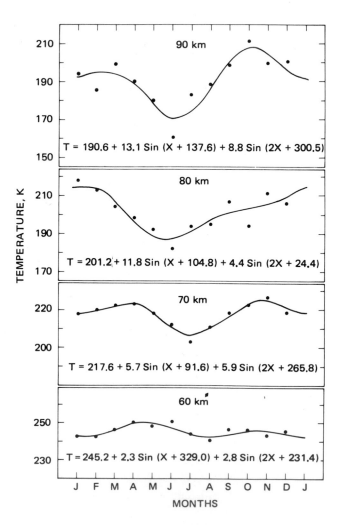

Figure 18. Harmonic analysis of median monthly temperatures at Wallops Island, Va.

60 and 65 km. At altitudes below 60 km the maximum mean monthly temperatures occur in summer, and above 65 km the maximums occur in winter. At altitudes between 60 and 65 km these two variations are partially self-cancelling, giving rise to a region of minimum variability (see figures 17 and 18).

Annual mean temperatures computed from harmonically smoothed mean monthly values were compared to annual means derived from curves that had been subjectively fitted to the observed mean monthly values. The differences between the mean annual values obtained by each method for altitudes between 50 and 85 km were less than 2K, and at most levels less than 1K. Differences were greater at 90 km, especially where 12 mean monthly values were not available. An example of the differences in annual means obtained by objective and subjective analyses is shown for the 90-km level at Ft. Churchill in figure 17. The subjetive analysis appears to provide a more realistic fit to the data; it provides an annual mean that is 5K colder than the objective analysis.

Curves showing the variation with latitude of the mean annual temperatures were drawn for various altitudes between 40 and 90 km. The 40–, 60–, and 80–km curves are shown in figure 19. Values interpolated from these curves for 45°N differ considerably from those for the *U. S. Standard Atmosphere, 1962* at altitudes above 50 km.

2.1.3 COMPARISON OF DATA WITH MODEL.—The temperature-altitude profile based on values interpolated for 45°N from the latitudinal temperature curves described in the preceding paragraph is shown by profile A in figure 20 for altitudes between 50 and 100 km. Mean annual values for Wallops Island (38°N) and Ft. Churchill (59°N) are also shown in figure 20, because interpolated values for 45°N are based primarily on the observations from these two locations. The vertical temperature gradients of the profile that is fitted to the data are linear with geopotential altitude.

The isothermal layer between 86 and 91 km, figure 20, represents the region of the mesopause and is based on the vertical distributions of mean annual values. The vertical structure of this isothermal region changes from day-to-day and month-to-month, varying from less than 1 km to more than 15 km in thickness. At times there appear to be several mesopauses with minimum temperatures occurring 10 to 15 km apart. The time cross-sections of mean monthly values for Ft. Churchill and Wallops Island, figures 21 and 22, respectively, indicate that the isothermal layer at the mesopause is best defined and thinnest in late spring and summer when temperatures are lowest.

The temperature-altitude profile adopted for this Standard (profile B of figure 20) is approximately

isothermal, in terms of T_M, for a few kilometers above 85 geopotential km; it is nearly 3 degrees colder than the interpolated values for this layer. The lower mesopause temperature was required so that computed N_2 densities would reasonably match the observed density data in the low thermosphere. The mesopause temperature selected is well within the limits of accuracy that can be assigned to values obtained from the observations available at this altitude.

Densities associated with the adopted temperature-altitude profile are shown in figure 23 as percentage departures from the *U. S. Standard Atmosphere, 1962* (COESA 1962) for altitudes between 50 and 100 km. Percentage departures of observed

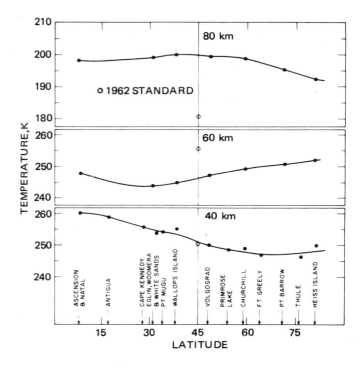

Figure 19. Mean annual temperature variation with latitude

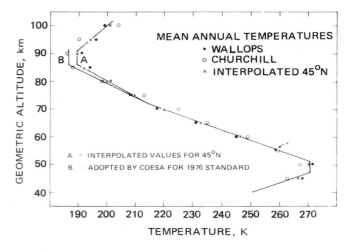

Figure 20. Temperature-altitude profile for the U.S. Standard Atmosphere, 1976

mean annual densities are also shown in figure 23 for Wallops Island and Ft. Churchill. Densities for this Standard are nearly the same as those for the *1962 Standard* for altitudes up to 60 km but are approximately 6 percent less between 79 and 80 km and 10 to 15 percent greater near 90 km. Observed latitudinal variations of the percent departures from the mean annual densities at levels between 40 and 90 km are shown in figure 24.

2.1.4 Systematic Variations And Observed And Inferred Extremes.— In the region 0 to 86 km, latitudinal and seasonal variations about the Standard are observed. In addition, both observation and inference show that extreme departures of considerable magnitude occur. This information is being developed in detail in a series of reference atmospheres which will extend to 90 km.

These reference atmospheres are being prepared under the direction of COESA to replace those described in the *U. S. Standard Atmosphere Supplements, 1966.* They will include mean monthly atmospheres for each 15° of latitude from Equator

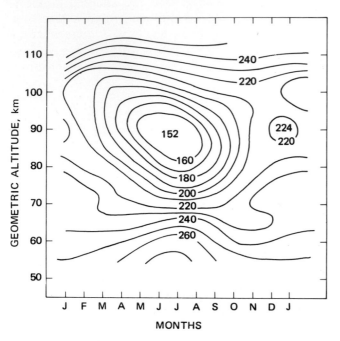

Figure 21. Cross-section of median monthly temperatures at Ft. Churchill, Manitoba

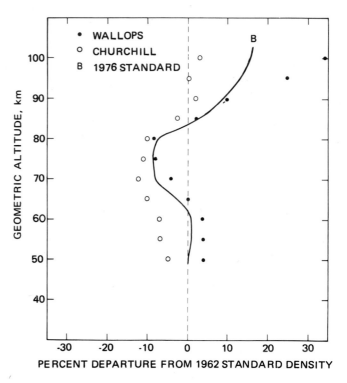

Figure 23. Mean annual density-altitude profiles

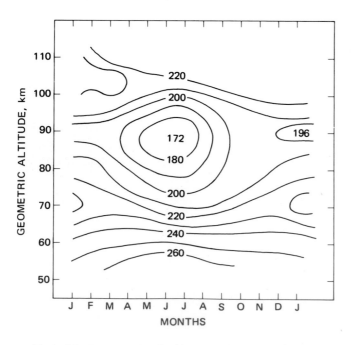

Figure 22. Cross-section of median monthly temperatures at Wallops Island, Va.

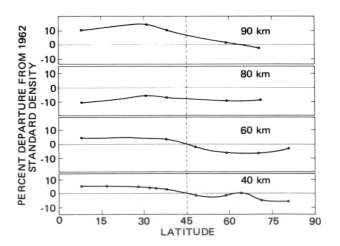

Figure 24. Mean annual density variation with latitude

to pole. Winter models at 60° and 75°N will depict typical conditions over both North America and Europe. These data will provide information to scientists and engineers on latitudinal, longitudinal, seasonal, and day-to-day changes in atmospheric structure that can be used to investigate the importance of such departures from the Standard in experiments and designs. Preliminary work on these reference atmospheres for latitudes from the Equator to the pole has yielded envelopes of mean monthly and extreme values of temperature and density which are discussed below for altitudes up to 90 km.

Temperature Variations.— The arrows in figure 25 show the lowest and highest mean monthly temperatures obtained for any location between the Equator and pole. Estimates of the one-percent maximum and minimum temperatures that occur during the warmest and coldest months, respectively, in the most extreme locations are shown by dashed lines. Values below 30 km are based on radiosonde observations and those between 30 and 50 km on meteorological rocket observations. Variations above 55 km are based on data derived primarily from grenade, falling-sphere, and pressure-gauge experiments. Available observations between 50 and 100 km on which to base estimates of the seasonal, latitudinal, and extreme variations are still relatively sparse. Errors associated with the direct and indirect temperature measurements are also larger above 50 km than at lower altitudes. Consequently, less confidence can be placed in the

estimated seasonal fluctuations and extreme values above 50 km.

Values shown for the various levels by envelope curves could not possibly be encountered at all altitudes at a given location and time. The warmest layers near the surface, for example, are associated with the coldest temperatures at the tropopause, and temperatures near the stratopause are negatively correlated with those at the mesopause.

At locations between 30 and 90°N, maximum mean monthly temperatures at altitudes below 25 km usually occur in June or July, and minimum values in December or January. In the upper stratosphere and lower mesosphere (30 to 60 km), semiannual and biennial oscillations complicate the annual temperature distributions. The magnitude of the annual cycle is largest in the polar regions and decreases toward the Equator, whereas the importance of the biennial and semiannual cycles is greatest near the Equator and decreases toward the poles. At mid and high latitudes the annual and semiannual cycles tend to obscure the biennial oscillation. Observations show that north of 25° latitude the combined annual and semiannual components shift the time of maximum temperature in the upper stratosphere to May or early June, and of minimum temperatures to November or early December. In the mesosphere, above 60 to 65 km, the maximum mean monthly temperatures generally occur in December or January and the minimum in June or July.

The largest departures from the Standard at

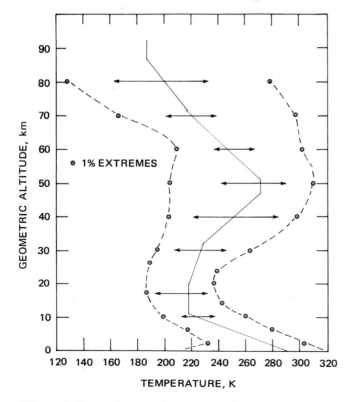

Figure 25. Range of systematic variability of temperature around the U.S. Standard Atmosphere, 1976

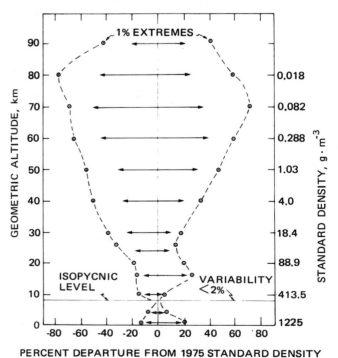

Figure 26. Range of systematic variability of density around the U.S. Standard Atmosphere, 1976

all altitudes between 25 and 90 km occur in arctic and sub-arctic regions.

Density Variations.—The estimated range of systematic changes (seasonal and latitudinal) in mean monthly densities is indicated by the horizontal arrows in figure 26 as percentage departure from the Standard. Estimates of the one-percent maximum and minimum densities that occur during months with the highest and lowest values in the most extreme locations are shown by dashed lines. Above 30 km both the largest negative and positive departures occur in arctic and sub-arctic regions. The negative departures represent winter and the positive departures summer conditions. Densities greater than standard are, however, occasionally observed in arctic latitudes *in winter*, during "sudden" warmings of the stratosphere and/or mesosphere (Quiroz 1970, 1974). Below 30 km the range cannot be depicted for all levels by the maximum and minimum seasonal values at any one latitude.

The minimum latitudinal and seasonal variability, less than 2 percent, occurs at the isopycnic level near 8 km. Other levels of minimum variability, much less pronounced than at the isopycnic level, are near 26 and 90 km. Levels of maximum seasonal and latitudinal variability occur near 15 and 70 km.

DATA SOURCES

DATA SOURCE A.

SMITH, W., KATCHEN, L., SACHER, P., SWARTZ, and THEON, J., 1964: Temperature, Pressure, Density and Wind Measurements with the Rocket Grenade Experiment, 1960–1963. *Technical Report* R-211, National Aeronautics and Space Administration, Washington, D.C.

SMITH, W., THEON, J., KATCHEN, L., and SWARTZ, P., 1966: Temperature, Pressure, Density and Wind Measurements in the Upper Stratosphere and Mesosphere, 1964. *Technical Report* R-245, National Aeronautics and Space Administration, Washington, D.C.

SMITH, W., THEON, J., SWARTZ, P., and KATCHEN, L., 1967: Temperature, Pressure, Density and Wind Measurements in the Upper Stratosphere and Mesosphere, 1965, *Technical Report* R-263, National Aeronautics and Space Administration, Washington, D.C.

SMITH, W., THEON, J. SWARTZ, P., and KATCHEN, L., 1968: Temperature, Pressure, Density and Wind Measurements in the Stratosphere and Mesosphere, 1966, *Technical Report* R-288, National Aeronautics and Space Administration, Washington, D.C.

SMITH, W., THEON, J., and SWARTZ, P., 1968: Temperature, Pressure, Density and Wind Measurements in the Stratosphere and Mesosphere, 1967, *Technical Report* R-306, National Aeronautics and Space Administration, Washington, D.C.

SMITH, W., THEON, J., CASEY, J., and HORVATH, J., 1970: Temperature, Pressure, Density and Wind Measurements in the Stratosphere and Mesosphere, 1968, *Technical Report* R-340, National Aeronautics and Space Administration, Washington, D.C.

SMITH, W.S., THEON, J.S., WRIGHT, D.U., JR., CASEY, J.F. and HORVATH, J.J., 1970: Measurements of the Structure and Circulation of the Stratosphere and Mesosphere, 1970, *Technical Report* R-391, National Aeronautics and Space Administration, Washington, D.C.

SMITH, W., THEON, J., CASEY, J., AZCARRAGA, A., and HORVATH, J., 1971: Temperature, Pressure, Density and Wind Measurements in the Stratosphere and Mesosphere, *Technical Report* R-360, National Aeronautics and Space Administration, Washington, D.C.

SMITH, W., THEON, J., WRIGHT, D., RAMSDEL, D., and HORVATH, J. 1974: Measurements of the Structure and Circulation of the Stratosphere and Mesosphere, 1971–2, *Technical Report* R-416, National Aeronautics and Space Administration, Washington, D.C.

DATA SOURCE B.

HORVATH, J.J., 1972: Neutral Atmospheric Structure Measurements by Pitot-Probe Technique, *05776-1-F*, University of Michigan, NASA Contract NAS5-3335, Ann Arbor, Michigan.

THEON, J.S., SMITH, W.S., CASEY, J.F., and KIRKWOOD, B.R., 1972: The Mean Observed Meteorological Structure and Circulation of the Stratosphere and Mesosphere, *Technical Report* R-375, National Aeronautics and Space Administration, Washington, D.C.

DATA SOURCE C.

FAIRE, A.C., and CHAMPION, K.S.W., 1965: Falling sphere measurement of atmospheric density, temperature and pressure up to 115 km. *Space Research*, V, North-Holland Publishing Co., Amsterdam, Netherlands.

FAIRE, A.C., and CHAMPION, K.S.W., 1966: High-Altitude rocket density measurements at Eglin AFB, Florida. *Space Research*, VI, North-Holland Publishing Co., Amsterdam, Netherlands.

FAIRE, A.C., and CHAMPION, K.S.W., 1967: Falling sphere measurements of atmospheric density, temperature, and pressure at Fort Churchill, Canada, and Eglin, Florida. *Space Research*, VII, North-Holland Publishing Co., Amsterdam, Netherlands.

FAIRE, A.C., and CHAMPION, K.S.W., 1968: Recent density temperature and pressure obtained at White Sands Missile Range compared with IQSY results. *Space Research*, VIII, North-Holland Publishing Co., Amsterdam, Netherlands.

FAIRE, A.C., and CHAMPION, K.S.W., 1969: Upper atmospheric parameters obtained from recent falling sphere measurements at Eglin, Florida. *Space Research*, IX, North-Holland Publishing Co., Amsterdam, Netherlands.

FAIRE, A.C., CHAMPION, K.S.W., and MURPHY, E.A., 1972: ABRES Density Variations. *AFCRL 72-0042*, Air Force Cambridge Research Laboratories, Bedford, Mass.

DATA SOURCE D.

GROVES, G.V., 1965: Diurnal variations in upper atmosphere wind and temperature structure of Woomera, 15–16 October 1963, *Space Research*, V, North-Holland Publishing Co., Amsterdam, Netherlands.

GROVES, G.V., 1966: Seasonal variations of temperature, pressure, density and winds to 80 km altitude at Woomera, 1957–1963. *Space Research*, VI, North-Holland Publishing Co., Amsterdam, Netherlands.

GROVES, G.V., 1967: Variations in upper atmosphere wind, temperature and pressure at Woomera during the night of 29/30 April 1965. *Space Research*, VII, North-Holland Publishing Co., Amsterdam, Netherlands.

JOHNSON, S.G., 1971: Measurements of the Basic Atmospheric Parameters of Woomera Using the Falling Sphere —1970. *W.R.E. Tech. Note* 50, Salisbury, S. Australia.

PEARSON, P.H.O., 1965: Falling Sphere Results for Carnarvon During July 1964, *W.R.E. Tech. Note* PAD 103 Salisbury, S. Australia.

PEARSON, P.H.O., 1969: Basic Atmospheric Parameters as Measured by Four Falling Sphere Experiments at Woomera, February to June 1966. *W.R.E. Tech. Note* SAD 211, Salisbury, S. Australia.

PEARSON, P.H.O., 1969: Basic Atmospheric Parameters as Measured by Four Falling Sphere Experiments at Woomera, July to November 1966. *W.R.E. Tech. Note* SAD 219, Salisbury, S. Australia.

ROFE, B., 1966: The Stratosphere and Mesosphere Circulation at Mid-latitudes of the Southern Hemisphere, *W.R.E. Tech. Note* SAD 115, Salisbury, S. Australia.

DATA SOURCE E.

U.S.S.R., 1970: Proposals for the Project of International Standard Atmospheric Models, International Standards Organization, *Draft document*, ISO/TC 20/SC6 (Secretariat-19) 24, Geneva, Switzerland.

2.2 THE MODEL FOR ALTITUDES ABOVE 86 KM

2.2.1 GENERAL CONSIDERATIONS.—Above 85 km, two processes are primarily responsible for a decrease in the mean molecular weight with increasing height: the first is the dissociation of molecular oxygen, and the second is diffusive separation, which becomes increasingly important relative to mixing in this height region. In this altitude region between approximately 85 and 120 km, the effect of height- and time-dependent, molecular-oxygen dissociation, and the competition between eddy and molecular diffusion combine to complicate the study of the height distribution of the atmospheric species, such that generation of numerical values for the altitude profiles of physical parameters necessitates a considerable amount of numerical computation. More specifically, atomic oxygen becomes appreciable above 85 km, and diffusive separation begins to be effective at an average height of about 100 km. Also, in the regime where molecular diffusion becomes significant (above about 85 km), the effect of vertical winds on the composition is important (Reber and Hays 1973).

Above approximately 120 km, it is relatively safe to assume that there is no further large-scale oxygen dissociation, and that (except for wind effects and atomic-hydrogen flow and production) diffusive equilibrium prevails. Under such conditions, as seen in Part 1, the simultaneous equations governing molecular diffusion are no longer interdependent, and these equations can then be applied to each atmospheric constituent separately. In this case, the computation of the individual density-height profiles presents no greater difficulty than that of the total pressure or density below 80 km, except for constituents such as atomic hydrogen, which have a nonnegligible vertical flow up to several hundred kilometers. The nonzero flux for atomic hydrogen results from two processes: planetary escape from the exosphere, and production due to chemical reactions in the lower thermosphere (Patterson 1966, Tinsley 1973) in accord-

ance with chemical equations in table 27 of Appendix C.

2.2.2 AVAILABILITY OF DATA.—In the altitude region, 50 to 90 km, atmospheric measurements of temperature, density, and pressure are made almost exclusively with rocket-borne instruments. These observations, described in Section 2.1, have served to develop an extensive set of thermodynamic data on which to base the lower boundary conditions for the model above 86 km. The region from 140 to 1000 km is one in which the thermodynamic properties are determined almost exclusively from satellite-related observations and radar incoherent scatter techniques. A vast amount of data has been accumulated for this height region. For altitudes between 90 and 140 km, however, there is only a very limited amount of atmospheric data from rocket soundings and incoherent scatter observations, and almost none from satellite observations. Furthermore, no unique observational technique has, to date, been developed for efficient observation of the thermodynamic and photochemical properties of this region of the earth's atmosphere.

2.2.3 PHILOSOPHY OF MODEL CONSTRUCTION.— In view of the necessity for computing individual density-altitude profiles for each atmospheric species in the heterosphere, the use of molecular-scale temperature T_M becomes impractical, and in this region kinetic temperature T is used as a governing parameter. In addition, the use of a linearly segmented temperature-height function, with discontinuous first derivatives, as in $T_M(H)$ below 86 km, is terminated in favor of one in which the first derivative is continuous from 86 to 1000 km. Furthermore, geometric altitude replaces geopotential altitude as the argument of the temperature-height function at heights of 86 km and above.

The transition from $T_M(H)$ to a function $T(Z)$ occurs at 86 geometric kilometers (84.8520 km'), where the value of T_M and the molecular-weight ratio, M/M_0, lead to $T = 186.8673$ K. The observed temperature-height profiles usually show large gradients at heights from 100 to 200 km. At greater altitudes, the gradients decrease with increasing height to about 500 km, where the temperature approaches an asymptote (usually referred to as the exospheric temperature, T_∞) which varies with solar activity, time of day, and several other parameters. In the present model, T_∞ is defined to be 1000 K, a value which is associated with mean solar conditions.

The form of the functions used to represent the mean profiles reflects the desire to make the Standard a useful, analytical tool:

a. The temperature is expressed as a smooth mathematical function of geometric altitude, with a continuous first derivative.

b. Functions representing the temperature profile are readily adjustable to allow approximation of various data sets.

c. Functions relating number densities to altitude are physically meaningful and analytically expressible.

Altitude profiles of both temperatures and gas-species number densities are consistent with inputs from a variety of sources:

a. At the 86-km boundary, the temperature and number densities match the model for heights below 86 km. Such a match is somewhat complicated by the fact that the model below 86 km is defined in terms of geopotential altitude and molecular-scale temperature, while above 86 km the model uses geometric altitude and kinetic temperature. The procedure used for establishing the match is discussed in Part 1, while the generation of the 86-km number densities is described in Appendix A.

b. In the altitude region between the lower boundary and about 130 km, temperature and mass-density profiles reflect the available data, which come largely from measurements made by rocket-borne pitot tubes Horvath 1972) and falling spheres (Theon 1972), and by the incoherent scatter technique (Wand 1972). The average value of the N_2 density above 150 km is reasonably well established, however, and this value strongly influences the choice of temperature profiles in the region below this altitude, particularly in the very low temperature region from about 85 to 92 km.

c. At 150 km the composition matches the Working Group recommendations shown in table 14.

d. The largest body of data available on the neutral composition of the upper thermosphere (as opposed to the larger data set available on total density) is that obtained from the quadrupole mass spectrometer on the OGO-6 satellite (e.g., Hedin et al. 1972 and 1974). These data refer primarily to

an altitude of 450 km; the values of N_2, O, He, and Ar, for this altitude, are given in table 14. They represent the OGO-6 data after adjustment to 45°N latitude, and to an exospheric temperature of 1000 K. The coefficients for the exponential segment of the temperature model above 120 km reflect this large and unique data set.

e. At altitudes above about 130 km, the total density and its scale height are consistent with the large body of data determined from satellite drag.

f. The number densities, eddy diffusion coefficients, flux terms, and temperature profile are consistent with those in the photochemical model of Keneshea and Zimmerman (1970) discussed in Appendix C, and based upon observation (Philbrick et al. 1973).

It must be emphasized that many of the parameters and profiles used and calculated for this Standard are dynamic by nature, and any steady-state description is only an approximation to the true state of affairs. Examples are the wave-like structure frequently observed in the temperature and gas densities as shown in figure 27 (Reber et al. 1975); the atomic-oxygen profile which appears to be extremely time dependent with significant

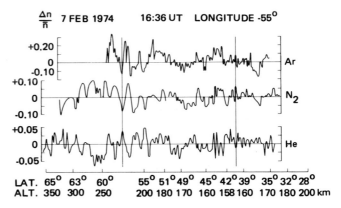

Figure 27. Wave-like structure of number-density profiles of Ar, N_2, and He, observed during a single satellite pass

TABLE 14.—Number densities, mass densities, and mean molecular weights of five species at selected heights

Gas	86 km (m⁻³)	120 km (m⁻³)	150 km (m⁻³)	450 km (m⁻³)
N_2	1.12979×10^{20}	3.7258×10^{17}	3.1240×10^{16}	1.0865×10^{12}
O (atomic)	8.60000×10^{16}	9.2741×10^{16}	1.7800×10^{16}	4.1633×10^{13}
O_2	3.03090×10^{19}	4.3950×10^{16}	2.7500×10^{15}	2.3676×10^{10}
He	7.58173×10^{14}	3.8879×10^{13}	2.1058×10^{13}	3.9479×10^{12}
Ar	1.35140×10^{18}	1.3661×10^{15}	5.0000×10^{13}	2.6583×10^{7}
H (atomic)	—	—	3.7544×10^{11}	8.4483×10^{10}
ρ	6.95788×10^{-6} kg·m⁻³	2.222×10^{-8} kg·m⁻³	2.074×10^{-9} kg·m⁻³	1.184×10^{-12} kg·m⁻³
M	28.95221 kg/kmole	26.205 kg/kmole	24.103 kg/kmole	15.247 kg/kmole

diurnal and seasonal components (e.g., George et al. 1972) ; and the helium profile which shows a strong annual component (Jacchia and Slowey 1967; Reber et al. 1968; Keating and Prior 1968; and Reber and Hays 1973). For the purpose of this model, temperature and number-density profiles are adjusted to represent average steady-state conditions.

2.2.4 TEMPERATURE-HEIGHT PROFILE.—The adopted temperature-height profile between 86 and 1000 km is described as follows :

a. For 86 to 91 km, the layer is assumed to be isothermal at 186.8673 K.

b. For 91 to 110 km, a segment of an ellipse is used, assuring a smooth monotonically increasing temperature-height function, with sufficient generality to match the temperature and its gradient at both end points. Equations are given in Part 1; derivations are contained in Appendix B.

c. The layer, 110 to 120 km, is represented by a straight-line segment in which the change in temperature with altitude, i.e., dT/dZ, is equal to 12 K/km.

d. The region, 120 to 1000 km, is represented by an exponential function in which T asymptotically approaches 1000 K at heights above 500 km. This form is well known, widely used, and permits the utilization of the Walker (1965) modification of the Bates (1959) technique for analytically representing upper-atmosphere number densities.

The equations for the temperature-height profile are given in Part 1. The adopted temperature-height profile from the surface to 1000 km is shown in figure 4. Variations in the temperature-height profiles, between 100 and 1000 km, for various degrees of solar and geomagnetic activity are presented in figure 28. Profile (A) gives the lowest temperatures expected at sunspot minimum; profile (B) represents average conditions at sunspot minimum; (C) represents average conditions at an average sunspot maximum; and (D) gives the highest temperatures to be expected during a period of exceptionally high solar and geomagnetic activity.

2.2.5 DENSITIES.—In this model, the steady-state vertical distribution of the number density n_i of a gas species with molecular weight M_i is governed by the vertical component of the momentum equation for that gas. Ideally, it is solved in conjunction with the equation of continuity (Colegrove et al. 1965; Keneshea and Zimmerman 1970; Reber and Hays 1973).

The equations used in the computation of the number-density profiles for the individual species, molecular nitrogen, atomic and molecular oxygen,

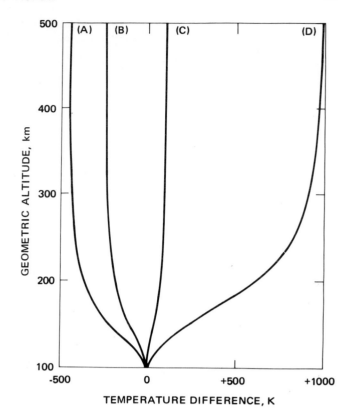

Figure 28. Departures of the temperature-altitude profiles from that of the present model for various degree of solar activity

helium, argon, and atomic hydrogen are discussed in Part 1. Number-density profiles based on the adopted temperature-height profile are shown in figure 5. Number-density profiles corresponding to the two extremes of temperature deviation (shown in figure 28) are depicted in figures 29 a, b, c, and d. Figure 29a presents number densities of the six species under conditions of minimum solar activity, while figure 29b shows number-density profiles of the same six species under conditions of maximum solar activity. Figure 29c depicts the possible range of variation of number densities of N_2, Ar, and He, from the Standard, while figure 29d shows the possible range of variation of number densities of O_2, O, and H from the Standard.

The total mass-density profile $\rho(Z)$ for the current model is shown in figure 7. Departures of the density-height profile from that of the present model in accordance with changes in exospheric temperatures are shown in figure 30. The four profiles shown in the diagram correspond to the four temperature difference profiles in figure 28.

2.2.6 MODEL COMPARED WITH OBSERVATIONS

Height Profiles of Temperature and N_2 Number Density.—As previously noted, the N_2 number density at any altitude is sensitive primarily to the temperatures at lower altitudes. This fact has serious implications when there are a number of data sets to be matched, as in the development of the temperature-height profile between 86 and 160 km.

The situation at 150 km, as of 1970, was sum-

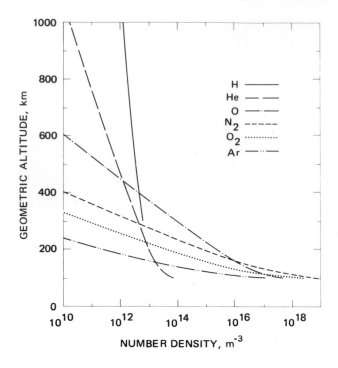

Figure 29a. Relative concentrations of atmospheric constituents during periods of minimum solar activity

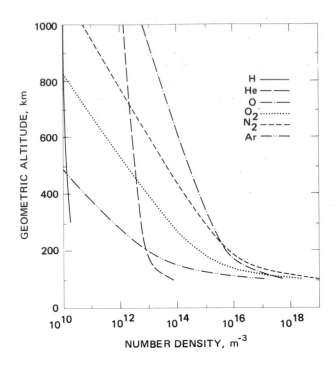

Figure 29b. Relative concentrations of atmosphere constituents during periods of maximum solar activity

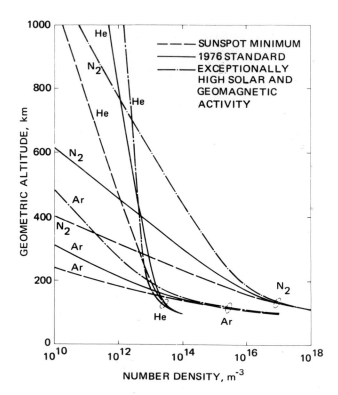

Figure 29c. Range of possible variation of number-density profiles of N_2, Ar, and He due to solar and geomagnetic activity

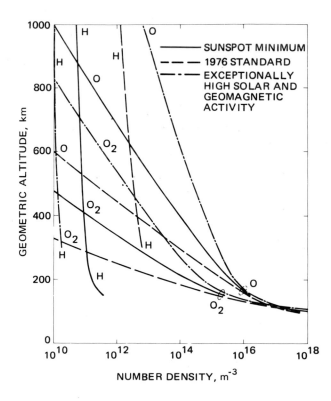

Figure 29d. Range of possible variation of number-density profiles of O_2, O, and H due to solar and geomagnetic activity

marized by von Zahn (1970) making use of the relevant density values as well as mass-spectroscopic and UV-extinction data available at the time. After evaluating the data, he concluded that the most consistent agreement between densities de-

termined from drag acceleration and those determined from mass spectroscopy, was obtained if one assumed that drag-determined densities were high by 10 percent and the values of atomic oxygen found by mass spectroscopy were low by an appre-

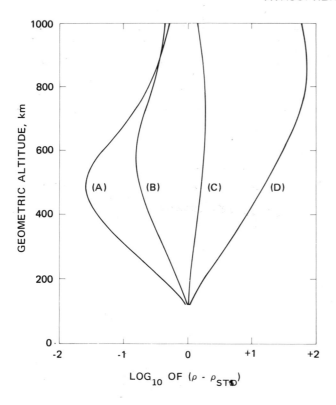

Figure 30. Departures of the density-altitude profiles from that of the standard for various degrees of solar activity

ciable factor. Accordingly, he estimated the species number densities, n_i, and the total mass density ρ, for 150-km altitude to be as follows: $n\ (N_2) = 2.6 \times 10^{16}$ m^{-3}, $n(O_2) = 2.5 \times 10^{15}$ m^{-3}, $n(Ar) = 5 \times 10^{13}$ m^{-3}, $n(O) = 2.3 \times 10^{16}$ m^{-3}, and $\rho = 1.96 \times 10^{-9}$ kg/m^3, where his $n(O)$ value represents an upward adjustment from available observed values. His drastic increase in the amount of atomic oxygen seemed justified in part by later measurements made at 120 km with a helium-cooled, rocket-borne mass spectrometer which gave an appreciably higher value of the concentration ratio of O to O_2 at 120 km than had ever been reported in the literature (Offermann and von Zahn 1971).

Nier (1972), on the other hand, pointed out that since atomic oxygen is a major constituent of the atmosphere in the neighborhood of 150 km, any arbitrary increase, such as by a factor of substantially more than two in its measured abundance relative to other constituents, would destroy the excellent agreement between mass-density scale heights computed from mass-spectrometer composition measurements and those found from drag measurements on low-altitude satellites such as OVI-15 (Champion et al. 1970a) and OVI-16 (Champion et al. 1970b). He subsequently reinforced his argument through laboratory experiments (Nier et al. 1972; and Lake and Nier 1973), in which it was shown that it was not likely that atomic-oxygen densities measured with instruments such as he and his colleagues previously used in rocket flights were low by more than a factor of two.

More recently, Taeusch and Carignan (1972), in an extrapolation of OGO-6 composition and drag-determined densities down to 150 km, concluded that the 150-km atomic-oxygen value given by von Zahn (1970) and employed by Jacchia in his 1971 model, was too high. They prefer a number about 20 percent lower, but still considerably above the average value found with rocket-borne mass spectrometers. Their $n(N_2)$ and $n(O_2)$ values at 150 km, on the other hand, are about 25 percent higher than values generally found with rocket-borne mass spectrometers.

Moe (1973) completed a comprehensive study of drag measurements with satellites as well as of published values of atmospheric composition by all methods, correcting drag measurements for effects due to accommodation coefficients, and composition measurements for possible errors in instruments due to surface effects. Moe's $n(N_2)$, $n(O_2)$, and $n(Ar)$ values at 150 km agree closely with those given by von Zahn (1970), which are essentially the abundances deduced from rocket-borne mass spectrometers. His $n(O)$ value, however, is about 20 percent lower than von Zahn's value, and is in agreement with values given by Taeusch and Carignan (1972).

The concentration of helium in the lower thermosphere at mid-latitudes is known to vary by a factor of as much as 10 between summer and winter. Also below 150 km, it appears not to be in diffusive equilibrium. The values presented in the present report fall between the extremes obtained in observations.

The temperature data in this layer of the atmosphere come mainly from recent pitot-tube measurements (Horvath 1972), and from incoherent-scatter data (e.g., Wand 1972). These two data sets are quite consistent in one particular feature: the mean temperature profile, between about 105 km and 125 km, for each data set, appears to have a constant gradient with an average value of about 15 K/m for the backscatter data, and about 18 K/km for the pitot-tube data. The adopted version of the temperature-height profile also exhibits a constant gradient in this region, but it is 12 K/km, only two-thirds of the larger of these two measured values. Attempts to incorporate higher gradients lead to unacceptably high values for N_2 densities above 150 km.

The lower-boundary parameters and the N_2 density at 150 km reflect the results of many measurements in which there is a high degree of confidence, so it is unlikely that these data have serious error. It is not clear whether the recent measurements of the temperature-height profile between 110 and 120 km suggest a gradient which is too large, or whether the three inputs are basically inconsistent in that they are not true averages over similar sets of conditions.

Dynamic Characteristics.—As noted earlier, most of the properties being modeled are time-dependent by nature, and steady-state description has to be used advisedly. Examples are the diurnal photochemical variations in the densities of atomic and molecular oxygen (Appendix C), and the longer-term, dynamically induced variations in helium and argon densities. The model described by the equations in Part 1 includes the provision for representing deviations from diffusive-equilibrium profiles in the middle thermosphere, deviations which are becoming more and more accepted as being physically real. Basic considerations for computing a time-dependent model are discussed in Appendix C.

Composition.—In the altitude range, 100–200 km, atmospheric densities computed from composition measurements made with rocket-borne mass spectrometers have usually been lower than values inferred from drag measurements on satellites. While it has been recognized that there might be some error in the drag coefficients upon which the drag measurements depend, the general feeling has been that the composition measurements were in error. In particular, because of the highly reactive nature of atomic oxygen, it has been assumed that this constituent was largely lost in mass-spectrometer ion sources, and hence, grossly underestimated. Early mass-spectrometric values such as those of Meadows and Townsend (1960) or Pokhunkov (1960) were extremely low, undoubtedly owing to the loss of atomic oxygen on the extensive surfaces of their instruments. With the advent of "open" source instruments, such as those of Schaefer (1963) and of Nier et al. (1964), much higher values were obtained. Even so, it was recognized that the losses might still be considerable.

Hall et al. (1965, 1967), using EUV extinction measurements made with rocket-borne UV spectrometers, found atomic-oxygen abundances in the altitude range, 150–200 km, to be considerably above those reported from rocket-borne mass-

spectrometer measurements. Results extrapolated downward from OSO-III measurements (Hinteregger and Hall 1969) gave similar results. The absolute numbers given are in some doubt, however, in view of the uncertainty in the absorption cross section employed for atomic oxygen (Moe 1970).

While some of the variations reported in $n(N_2)$, $n(O_2)$, and $n(Ar)$ measurements in the 100–200 km range are almost certainly due to errors in measurements, some must be attributed to true atmospheric variations. The adopted values of $n(N_2)$, $n(O_2)$, $n(Ar)$ at 150 km listed in table 14, and used in constructing the present model are nominal values, and are the best estimates available at the present time. Each is believed to have an uncertainty of less that 25 percent. Because of the uncertainty in the amount of atomic oxygen lost in rocket-borne mass spectrometers, the value of $n(O)$ at 150 km is based on two sources. The first of these is the set of data obtained from the downward extrapolation of measurements made at higher altitudes with satellite-borne instruments in which, it is believed, the atomic-oxygen loss can be properly evaluated (Hedin et al. 1973). The second source is the set of mass densities found from satellite drag and corrected for the other constituents (N_2, O_2, and Ar) which can be measured accurately. It appears likely that the $n(O)$ values given in table 14 are maximum values, as they are based on the assumption that atomic oxygen is strongly absorbed in mass spectrometers used in rocket studies of the lower thermosphere. This view may be too pessimistic, but it does not seem probable that values given could be high by a factor as large as two.

In the case of atomic hydrogen, a number density of 8.0×10^{10} m^{-3} at 500 km is consistent with satellite data (Meier and Mange 1970; Vidal-Madjar et al. 1973; and Brinton and Mayr 1971 and 1972) appropriate for an exospheric temperature of 1000 K. This value of $n(H)$ is approximately three times the value given in the earlier work of Kocharts and Nicolet (1963). This larger number density at 500 km serves as a boundary value for the calculation of $n(H)$ at other altitudes.

PART 3
Trace Constituents

3.0 INTRODUCTION

Standard concentrations for a number of atmospheric trace constituents are given in this chapter. No revised standards are proposed for the inert gases, which had the following values in the 1962 Standard Atmosphere:

Constituent	*Percent by volume*
Argon	0.934
Neon	0.001818
Helium	0.000524
Krypton	0.000114
Xenon	0.0000087

Substances that have not been measured, but whose concentrations can only be inferred from numerical models, are not included. Also, charged species, radionuclides, and isotopes are not included.

The amount of concentration data available for the trace substances varies greatly. For most substances statistical evaluation of the data was not appropriate so typical values and, when feasible, concentration ranges are provided. Standards for these substances are given and discussed in section 3.1 entitled "Miscellaneous Trace Constituents". Standards for near-surface concentrations are summarized in table 15. Much more data exist for ozone, water vapor, and fine particles, and these are treated in sections 3.2, 3.3, and 3.4.

TABLE 15.—Concentrations* of various tropospheric trace constituents near the earth's surface.

Constituent	Typical Concentration, parts per billion by volume (ppbv)
N_2O	270
NO	0.5
NO_2	1
H_2S	0.05
NH_3	4
H_2	500
CH_4	1500
SO_2	1
CO	190
CO_2	3.22×10^5
O_3	40

*Concentration ranges are discussed in the text when sufficient data are available to indicate a range.

3.1 MISCELLANEOUS TRACE CONSTITUENTS

3.1.1 MID-LATITUDE SURFACE OZONE.—Most ozone in unpolluted air near the earth's surface is believed to have been formed in the stratosphere and brought to the earth's surface by vertical transport processes. In polluted atmospheres the concentrations of ozone are often more than an order of magnitude greater than in the "natural" atmosphere, the ozone being produced by the action of sunlight on a mixture of hydrocarbons and oxides of nitrogen in air. Ripperton et al. (1970) and others have suggested that some ozone in unpolluted tropospheric air may be produced by smog-type reactions involving terpenes given off by plants.

The results of numerous studies of ozone concentrations in relatively unpolluted air near the earth's surface have been reviewed by Junge (1963) and more recent studies have given similar results. A typical concentration is 0.04 parts per million by volume (ppmv) and the range is about 0-0.1 ppmv.

3.1.2 NITROUS OXIDE.—Nitrous oxide (N_2O) has been measured by many scientists and the latest values (Hahn 1972, Lahue et al. 1973) fall around 270 parts per billion by volume (ppbv). Concentrations have been found to be constant to 10 km (Schütz et al. 1970), and at altitudes of 13 to 18 km the nitrous oxide decreases from 250 ppbv to 100 ppbv (Goldman et al. 1973). There is little or no variation with latitude. Recommended values are:

270 ppbv, ground level
270 ppbv, 0–10 km
250–100 ppbv, 13–18 km

3.1.3 NITRIC OXIDE AND NITROGEN DIOXIDE.—Although a large amount of data exists concerning nitric oxide (NO) and nitrogen dioxide (NO_2) in polluted atmospheres, there are few reliable data concerning the concentrations of these compounds in the relatively unpolluted lower troposphere. The data up to about 1968 were reviewed by Robinson and Robbins (1966). Lodge and Pate (1966) report values of 0.5 to 4 ppbv for NO_2 and 0 to 6 ppbv for NO. Lodge et al. (1960) found that in air above the Pacific Ocean and about halfway between San Francisco and Hawaii the concentration of NO_2 was less than 1 ppbv 94 percent of the time. O'Connor (1962) obtained concentrations of NO_2 in Ireland of about 0.3 ppbv. Ripperton et al. (1968) found concentrations of NO_2 of about 4 ppbv and of NO of about 2.6 ppbv. Hamilton et al. (1968) at Pike's Peak obtained NO_2 concentrations of about 4 ppbv and of NO of about 2.7 ppbv. Fischer et al. (1968) in the Antarctic found that the average concentration of NO_2 was less than 0.6 ppbv. A more recent paper by Pate et al. (1970) suggests a background concentration of 0.5 ppbv fo rboth NO_2 and NO based on measurements in Panama.

At least some of the higher values probably were for somewhat contaminated air. Thus the lower end of the concentration ranges is probably most appropriate for reference concentrations for unpolluted air. Until more data are available, 1 ppbv for NO_2 and 0.5 ppbv for NO seems reasonable.

Three groups have estimated concentrations of nitric oxide in the lower stratosphere. Toth et al. (1973) tentatively identified features of the sunset solar spectra measured from 12 km altitude as being due to NO and estimated concentrations in the altitude range of 15 to 20 km of about 10^9 molecules cm^{-3} (mixing ratios of about 0.2 to 0.5 ppbv). Ridley et al. (in press) used a chemiluminescent sensor to measure the NO concentration in the 15 to 20 km altitude range, obtaining concentrations of about 0.1 ppbv. Ackerman et al. (1973) attributed features of the solar spectrum measured from a balloon to NO, and estimated mixing ratios varying from about 0.1 ppbv at about 16 km to 5 ppbv at 40 km. These values must be considered to be tentative, and no standard or reference concentrations of NO are proposed.

The situation for stratospheric nitrogen dioxide is similar to that for NO. Ackerman and Muller (1972), using data of Goldman et al. (1970) and some additional data, estimated NO_2 concentrations between about 1 and 10 ppbv in the altitude range 12 to 28 km. The mixing ratio seemed to increase from 20 to 28 km, suggesting the presence of a stratospheric layer of NO_2. Harries (1973) analyzed sub-millimeter wavelength far-infrared emission spectra of the stratosphere made from a Concorde supersonic aircraft during a tour of the Far East in 1972. He estimated an NO_2 mixing ratio of about 20 ppbv but stated that the accuracy of this measurement is severely limited since the spectral assignments are somewhat uncertain and in addition source spectra data are of poor quality.

3.1.4 NITRIC ACID VAPOR.—Mixing ratios of nitric acid vapor in the stratosphere have been measured by Williams et al. (1972) and by Murcray et al. (1973) using infrared emission spectra, and by Cadle et al. (1970) and Lazrus et al. (1972), absorbing the nitric acid vapor on cellulose ("IPC") filters. Although the latter technique can hardly be considered to be a well-recognized method, surprisingly good agreement be-

tween the two methods was obtained. The mixing ratios are much higher in the lower stratosphere than in the troposphere and maintain relatively high mixing ratios to an altitude of at least 30 km. The mixing ratios are extremely variable, but a typical mixing ratio at mid-latitudes at about 18 km is 2 ppbv, and at 24 km, where there may be a maximum, is 5 ppbv.

Almost no information is available concerning nitric acid vapor in the troposphere. Several measurements are reported by Cadle et al. (1970) for mixing ratios of nitric acid vapor at 8 km near the Philippine Islands, again using the absorbing filter technique. A typical mixing ratio was 0.06 ppbv.

3.1.5 HYDROGEN SULFIDE.—The only data available are ground-level values of 0.05 ppbv measured at Boulder, Colo. (Natusch et al. 1972). These same values were also found for rural areas near St. Louis but the information is unpublished. No data are available for levels above the ground. Recommended value: 0.05 ppbv at ground level.

3.1.6 AMMONIA.—Georgii (1963) reported ammonia concentration values of 4 ppbv at Mauna Loa Observatory, Hawaii. Higher values were measured in urban centers. Other workers (Tsunogai et al. 1968) have measured ammonia concentrations above the ocean surface near Japan. They too found the mixing ratios to also be 4 ppbv. No data are available for ammonia concentrations vs altitude. Recommended value: 4 ppbv at ground level.

3.1.7 HYDROGEN.—English workers Glueckauf and Kitt (1957), found the concentration of hydrogen (H_2) at ground level in their area to be 600 ppbv. Recent measurements (Scholz et al. 1970) at Boulder, Colo. and in Arizona indicated values of 450 ppbv. Recommended value: 500 ppbv at ground level.

Available data indicate that the concentration of hydrogen in the troposphere can be considered constant at about 0.5 ppmv. The only stratospheric hydrogen profiles now available are those published by Ehhalt and Heidt (1972). Three profiles were published, all showing an increase in hydrogen concentration above the tropopause. Hydrogen mixing ratios reached a maximum at 28 km and decreased above, at least to 30 km, the highest altitude reached. The maximum concentration varied from about 0.6 to about 1.4 ppmv and for purposes of a reference atmosphere, might be considered to be 1.0 ppmv. A single measurement has been obtained by Scholz et al. (1970) (at 50 km), who obtained a mixing ratio of 0.4 ppmv.

3.1.8 METHANE.—Methane (CH_4) was discovered in the earth's atmosphere by Migeotte (1948) in 1948 by its absorption band in the telluric spectrum. Several recent spectroscopic measurements (Goldberg 1951, 1953) have yielded a nearly constant value of 1.2 cm standard temperature and pressure (STP), corresponding to a uniform mixing ratio of 1.5 ppmv.

Although early studies suggested that the mixing ratio is constant with altitude and is uniform over the globe, more recent work has indicated that this is not the case. Bainbridge and Heidt (1966) determined vertical profiles in the troposphere and lower stratosphere, concluding that the mixing ratio varies little with altitude in the troposphere, but decreases with increasing altitude in the stratosphere. The stratospheric mixing ratio at 23 km altitude was about 60–70 percent of the tropospheric average. Cavanaugh, Schadt, and Robinson (1969), using a flame ionization detector, found methane concentrations at Point Barrow, Alaska, varying from 1.4 to 1.65 ppmv. Measurements by Ehhalt (1967) at Scottsbluff, Nebraska, using gas chromatographic techniques, yielded a minimum concentration of 0.6 ppmv and a maximum concentration of 1.6 ppmv. Gas chromatographic analysis by Ehhalt, Heidt, and Martell (1972) of an air sample collected by a rocket-borne cryogenic sampler between 44 and 62 km altitude over White Sands, New Mexico, indicated a methane concentration of 0.25 ppmv. This concentration may be very nearly that at the stratopause, near an altitude of 48 km. This rapid decrease in methane concentration with increasing altitude in the stratosphere is consistent with suggestions by Cadle (1964), Cadle and Powers (1966), and Nicolet (1970), that methane is oxidized by $O(^3P)$ and $O(^1D)$ in the stratosphere and lower mesosphere. Recently, profiles for stratospheric methane have been reported by Ehhalt and Heidt (1972), by Ackerman and Muller (1972), and by Cumming and Lowe (1972). They gave markedly different results. For example, unlike the others, Cumming and Lowe found little decrease in the methane mixing ratio with increasing altitude in the lower stratosphere, but the concentrations averaged less than 1.0 ppmv. If their values are correct, there must have been a large concentration gradient near the tropopause.

A statistical analysis of the methane measurements is hardly justified since the results obtained by any one technique or at any one place are quite sparse. However, a concentration range at sea level of 0.6 to 1.6 ppmv with most of the values being close to 1.5 ppmv seems to be a reasonable standard.

Based on the measurements described above, table 16 is what we recommend at present with regard to the variation with altitude.

3.1.9 SULFUR DIOXIDE.—A major contribution to the atmospheric sulfur dioxide (SO_2) content is anthropogenic, from the combustion of fossil fuels. This makes it difficult to determine the sulfur dioxide content of the unpolluted atmosphere. Assuming that the anthropogenic effect would be minimal away from major land areas, the measure-

TABLE 16.—Reference concentrations of CH_4 assuming a constant mixing ratio in the troposphere of 1.5 ppmv and a linear decreasing mixing ratio with altitude in the stratosphere to a value of 0.25 ppmv at 50 km.

Altitude (km)	Mixing Ratio (ppmv)
0	1.5
10	1.5
20	1.3
30	0.9
40	0.6
50	0.25

ments reported in Georgii (1970), Georgii and Vitze (1971), and Büchen and Georgii (1971) for the mid-Atlantic were used to obtain zonal means. The mixing ratio for the 40–50° zone is given in table 17. Observations made elsewhere over the globe, for example in Antarctica by Fisher et al. (1968) and in the Canary Islands by Abel et al. (1969), give a mean global background mixing ratio $\leq 0.4 \times 10^{-3}$ ppmv. Observations in the troposphere and stratosphere are insufficient to determine representative values. A more detailed review of the information available on the sulfur dioxide distribution is given in Viebrock (1973). See table 17.

3.1.10 CARBON MONOXIDE.—Carbon monoxide (CO) has both anthropogenic and natural sources. The effects of anthropogenic sources on the surface values were minimized by using mid-ocean values. Robinson and Robbins (1969) estimated the latitudinal distribution over the Pacific Ocean, while Junge et al. (1971) published observations for the Atlantic Ocean. Both distributions gave a mixing ratio of 0.19 ppmv for the 40°–50° N latitude zone. Tropospheric carbon monoxide was measured by Seiler and Junge (1970). Their observations give a mean mixing ratio of 0.13 ppmv. Seiler and Warneck (1972) report a carbon monoxide mixing ratio of 0.04 ppmv for the lower stratosphere. A comprehensive review of the carbon monoxide distribution is given by Viebrock (1973). See table 17.

3.1.11 CARBON DIOXIDE.—Carbon dioxide and its variation with time in the earth's atmosphere have been observed for many years. The longest period of record is available from Mauna Loa, Hawaii (SCEP 1970 and Machta 1972). Keeling et al. (1968) and Bolin and Bischof (1970) have reported on carbon dioxide measurements in the troposphere. Though there are significant seasonal and latitudinal variations, on an annual mean basis the carbon dioxide appears to be well mixed throughout the troposphere. The annual mean mixing ratio for 1970 at Mauna Loa was 322 ppmv. Bolin and Bischof (1970) estimated that the carbon dioxide mixing ratio in the stratosphere was 0.6 ppmv less than in the troposphere. The mean carbon dioxide concentration in the troposphere has been increasing for many years; presumably as a result of man's activities. Although the rate of increase varies, the average rate of increase is at present (1972) about 0.2 percent per year. Machta (1972) and Bolin and Bischof (1970) using slightly different models estimate a 1980 carbon dioxide mixing ratio of 335 ppmv. A fuller discussion of the carbon dioxide distribution is given in Viebrock (1973). See table 17.

TABLE 17.—Annual mean mixing ratios of sulfur dioxide, carbon dioxide, and carbon monoxide for 45°N. All the mixing ratios are reported in parts per million by volume (ppmv).

Height (km)	Sulfur dioxide (SO$_2$)	Carbon monoxide (CO)	Carbon dioxide (CO$_2$)
Surface	1.2×10^{-3}*	0.19	322 (1970)
0–11 (Troposphere)	**	0.13	322 (1970)
11–20 (Lower Stratosphere)	**	0.04	321 (1970)

*tentative value
**insufficient data

3.2   SUMMARY OF A MID-LATITUDE OZONE MODEL

A mid-latitude, Northern-Hemisphere model of the ozone distribution in the troposphere, stratosphere, and lower mesosphere has been constructed (Krueger and Minzner 1976). Data from rocket soundings in the latitude range 45°N ± 15°, results from satellite ozone observations, and the results of balloon soundings at latitudes from 41 to 47°N have been merged to produce estimates of the annual mean ozone concentration and its variability at heights to 72 km. This model is a revision, for heights above 26 km, of the tentative Mid-Latitude Ozone Model, included in the *U. S. Standard Atmosphere Supplements, 1966* (Committee on Extension to the Standard Atmosphere, 1967), hereafter referred to as the 1966 Supplements. Such a revision is justified by the greater number of rocket soundings presently available, compared to the number available in 1966, as well as by the newly acquired ozone data from the Backscatter Ultraviolet (BUV) experiment on the Nimbus 4 satellite (Heath et al. 1973).

For heights below 27 km, the ozone model described herein is essentially unchanged from that of the 1966 Supplements. This portion of the model was computed from the mean mass-density values (in kg/m^3) and their standard deviations, as given in the 1966 Supplements. These data were originally obtained from the systematic program of weekly ozonesonde ascents made throughout the

year 1963 at: Seattle, Wash.; Fort Collins, Colo.; Madison, Wis.; and Bedford, Mass. (Hering and Borden 1964). Because of the location of these stations, the average of annual-mean profiles computed for each of these stations, after first averaging individual sounding data over 2-km vertical intervals, is considered here to represent a 45° average for the United States. Approximately 150 balloon ozonesonde ascents were used in the determination of this mean ozone profile.

For heights above 27 km, the ozone model was computed from a set of column densities of ozone, a quantity usually obtained from optical observations, and frequently expressed in units of centimeters of ozone, at standard temperature and pressure (STP), per unit vertical distance. In abbreviated form these units are expressed as atm-cm/km. The column density represents the amount of ozone per vertical kilometer column, at any height, reduced to STP conditions. The thickness of the resulting layer of pure ozone is then the measure of the column density. For example, a column density of 0.01 atm-cm/km corresponds to 2.14148×10^{-4} kg/(m$^2 \cdot$ km), or to 2.14148×10^{-7} kg/m^3. The height integral of the column density, called the total ozone and expressed in atm-cm (or m-atm-cm, the Dobson unit), is also a commonly used measure of ozone. The Dobson unit is defined as 10^{-5}m of ozone at 0°C, and at standard sea-level pressure.

The column densities of this model for heights above 32 km were determined from 12 daytime and 5 twilight rocket measurements of the ozone distribution (15 over North America and 2 over Japan), while the values for the height region from 28 to 32 km represent a composite of both rocket and balloon data. Latitude gradients, for correction of the mean rocket data, have been derived from the global BUV satellite data. These satellite data have not been used directly in the model because of height-resolution considerations. Such data will, however, be very valuable for extension of this model to other latitudes, and to establish variabilities for supplementary models.

The 17 rocket soundings used to develop the model comprise a subset selected from the 31 daytime and 6 twilight rocket soundings obtained through 1972 at sites between 30°N and 60°N. Seventeen soundings were chosen from the 37 soundings using a set of selection criteria established to allow computation of realistic mean values and standard deviations. These criteria include traceable absolute accuracy (either inherent in the technique or established by comparison with an absolute instrument), and a height resolution of 2 km or better. Soundings influenced by abnormal geophysical conditions or showing significant biases from the statistical distribution of the majority of the soundings were rejected.

The rocket model is based on tabular data furnished or published by Hilsenrath (1972); Krueger (1975); Ogawa (1972); Smith (1969); Craig (1965), after Johnson et al. (1962); Weeks et al. (1972); and Weeks and Smith (1968). The techniques have been described elsewhere by Hilsenrath et al. (1969); Krueger and McBride (1968); and Nagata, et al. (1971). Ten of the selected soundings were made at Wallops Island, Va. (38°N, 75°W); two are from Fort Churchill, Manitoba (59°N, 94°W); two are from Uchinoura, Japan (31°N, 131°E); and one sounding has come from each of the following: Point Mugu, Calif. (34°N, 119°W); Primrose Lake, Alberta (55°N, 110° W); and White Sands Missile Range, N. M. (32°N, 107°W). Fourteen of the soundings were made during the years 1968–1970, the others in 1972, 1966, and 1949.

The mean latitude of these rocket soundings is 38°N. The latitudinal gradient derived from the satellite data provided the means for adjusting the rocket model in the height region of 26 to 40 km to an effective latitude of 45°N. The greatest adjustment (−15 percent) was applied at 28 to 30 km. The adjusted rocket model merges cleanly with the balloon data defining the 1966 model. In the region of overlap, 28 to 34 km, the mean values of these two data sets have been used. The differences between these two data sets, however, are all less than 5 percent at corresponding heights.

The data for the combined model come principally from the North American continent. The balloon observations were taken in the 51° longitude band between Seattle, Wash. and Bedford, Mass., and all but two of the rocket soundings (those at Uchinoura, Japan) were made in the United States and Canada. The two Japanese soundings did not differ significantly from those over North America. On the basis of this limited evidence, the model above 30 km is tentatively taken to represent mean mid-latitude conditions around the Northern Hemisphere. Additional data will be needed to verify this assumption.

The amount of information about secular changes is very limited. Near the tropopause, large inter-annual changes would be expected because of the dominant effects of meteorological transport processes on the ozone distribution. At altitudes above 35 km, changes might be expected due to variations in the solar spectrum during the solar cycle. The quantity of ozone data is far from adequate to establish such trends. It should be noted that the present Model, for heights above 30 km, is weighted towards the solar maximum conditions which existed in the late 1960's.

Table 18 defines the mid-latitude ozone model in height increments of 2 kilometers. The ozone mass densities $\rho(O_3)$, which are the basis for the lower portion of the model (<27 km), and the ozone column densities $\varepsilon(O_3)$, which are the basic data for the upper portion of the model (>27 km) have both been transformed into a common continuous profile of ozone number densities $n(O_3)$, with corresponding standard deviations σ. These transformations were accomplished using equations and values of physical constants given in table 19. The values of N, R^*, and V_0 are those given by Mechtly (1973), and are consistent with an atomic weight scale based on $C^{12} = 12.000$ (Taylor et al. 1969). The values of $M(O_3)$ and M, based on the same atomic weight scale, are taken from the *U. S. Standard Atmosphere, 1962* (Committee on the Extension to the Standard Atmosphere, 1962). The values of σ for heights below 27 km were transformed from the standard deviations of ρ (O_3) given in the 1966 Supplements to the U. S. Standard Atmosphere, whereas the values of σ for higher altitudes are derived principally from the data which determined $\varepsilon(O_3)$.

The percent-variability column represents 100 times the value of σ divided by $n(O_3)$. The values in the remaining columns, i.e., the values of $\varepsilon(O_3)$ below 27 km, the value of $\rho(O_3)$ above 27 km, and the entire range of values for ozone partial pressure $p(O_3)$ and for ozone mass mixing ratio $r(O_3)$ (or, equivalently, density mixing ratio) were computed from the appropriate basic data sets in accordance with equations and constants given in table 19. In addition to $\rho(O_3)$ or $\varepsilon(O_3)$ the computations of $p(O_3)$ and $r(O_3)$ require, respectively, the 1976 Standard-Atmosphere values of temperature T and air mass density ρ_s. While not given in table 18, it should be noted that pressure mixing ratio (or equivalently volume mixing ratio $r'(O_3)$ may be computed by multiplying values of $r(O_3)$ by 0.603448, the ratio of the mean molecular weight of air to that of ozone.

The total ozone content of this model, 0.345 atm-cm, is about five percent more than that obtained with the global network of Dobson spectrophotometers for 45°N (London 1963). This is indicative of some longitudinal variation in the ozone densities in the lower stratosphere. The total ozone value of 0.345 atm-cm is equivalent to 7.39×10^{-3} kg/m², or 9.27×10^{22} molecules/m².

The height profile of number density for this mid-latitude ozone model is shown in figure 31. The ozone density reaches a maximum at a height of about 22 km, and, between 38 and 70 km, decreases nearly exponentially by three orders of magnitude in accordance with a mean scale height of about 4.6 km. In the height region 22 to 75 km, the number density decreases by more than four orders of magnitude. The variability is shown at

TABLE 18.—Mid-latitude ozone model

| Geometric Height Z, m | Geopotential Height H, m' | Number Density | | | Column Density atm-cm/km $\varepsilon(O_3)$ | Mass Density kg/m³ $\rho(O_3)$ | Partial Pressure mb $p(O_3)$ | Mass Mixing Ratio kg/kg $r(O_3)$ |
		Quantity m⁻³ $n(O_3)$	Variability m⁻³ σ	Percent Variability $100\sigma/n(O_3)$				
2000	1999	6.8 (+17)	3.8 (+17)	56	2.5 (−3)	5.4 (−8)	2.6 (−5)	5.4 (−8)
4000	3997	5.8	2.9	50	2.1	4.6	2.1	5.6
6000	5994	5.7	3.0	53	2.1	4.5	1.9	6.8
8000	7990	6.5	5.9	90	2.4	5.2	2.1	9.9
10000	9984	1.13 (+18)	1.23 (+18)	109	4.2	9.0	3.5	2.18 (−7)
12000	11977	2.02	1.58	78	7.5	1.61 (−7)	6.0	5.16
14000	13969	2.35	1.48	63	8.7	1.87	7.0	8.21
16000	15960	2.95	1.42	48	1.10 (−2)	2.35	8.8	1.41 (−6)
18000	17949	4.04	1.23	30	1.50	3.22	1.21 (−4)	2.65
20000	19937	4.77	0.98	21	1.77	3.80	1.43	4.27
22000	21924	4.86	0.82	17	1.81	3.87	1.47	6.0
24000	23910	4.54	0.61	14	1.69	3.62	1.38	7.77
26000	25894	4.03	0.55	14	1.49	3.21	1.24	9.39
28000	27877	3.24	0.45	14	1.20	2.57	1.00	1.02 (−5)
30000	29859	2.52	0.33	13	9.38 (−3)	2.01	7.88 (−5)	1.09
32000	31840	2.03	0.34	17	7.55	1.62	6.40	1.19
34000	33819	1.58	0.27	17	5.88	1.26	5.10	1.27
36000	35797	1.22	0.17	14	4.54	9.72 (−8)	4.03	1.34
38000	37774	8.73 (+17)	1.10 (+17)	13	3.25	6.96	2.95	1.30
40000	39750	6.07	0.79	13	2.26	4.84	2.10	1.21
42000	41724	3.98	0.44	11	1.48	3.17	1.40	1.06
44000	43698	2.74	0.49	18	1.02	2.18	9.89 (−6)	9.67 (−6)
46000	45669	1.69	0.36	21	6.29 (−4)	1.35	6.23	7.86
48000	47640	1.03	0.17	17	3.83	8.20 (−9)	3.85	6.23
50000	49610	6.64 (+16)	1.10 (+16)	17	2.47	5.29	2.48	5.15
52000	51578	3.84	0.7	18	1.43	3.06	1.43	3.8
54000	53545	2.55	0.68	27	9.49 (−5)	2.03	9.28 (−7)	3.18
56000	55511	1.61	0.37	32	6.00	1.28	5.74	2.58
58000	57476	1.12	0.29	26	4.17	8.93 (−10)	3.90	2.25
60000	59439	7.33 (+15)	2.5 (+15)	34	2.73	5.85	2.50	1.88
62000	61401	4.81	1.8	38	1.79	3.83	1.60	1.59
64000	63362	3.17	1.2	38	1.18	2.52	1.03	1.36
66000	65322	1.72	0.66	38	6.4 (−6)	1.37	5.5 (−8)	9.6 (−7)
68000	67280	7.5 (+14)	5.1 (+14)	68	2.8	6.0 (−11)	2.4	5.5
70000	69238	5.4	3.1	57	2.0	4.3	1.6	5.1
72000	71194	2.2	1.7	77	8.2 (−7)	1.8	6.5 (−9)	2.8
74000	73148	1.7	0.9	63	6.3	1.3	4.9	2.9

Total ozone amount = 0.345 atm-cm

successive levels, with bars representing plus and minus one standard deviation. The dashed bars indicate uncertainty in the statistical distribution of data at 8 to 16 km.

Because of the large range of ozone densities, it is frequently convenient to use the ratio of ozone density to air density (i.e., mixing ratio) as shown in figure 32. The greatest mixing ratios, approximately 1.5 × 10⁻⁵ kg/kg (15 µgm/gm), occur at about 35 km. Above and below this maximum, the values tend to fall off nearly symmetrically, de-

creasing by about 50 percent at 23 and 48 km. It is important to note that the height of the mixing-ratio maximum occurs about 15 km higher than the density maximum. The range of mixing ratios shown at each height level corresponds to plus and minus one sigma value.

The tabulated standard deviations of the data, upon which this mid-latitude ozone model is based, show apparent percentage variabilities ranging from near 10 percent to greater than 100 percent. The tropospheric variability derived from

TABLE 19.—Conversion of ozone units

Derived quantity	Basic quantity	
	Mass density $\rho(O_3)$ kg/m³	Column density $\varepsilon(O_3)$ atm-cm/km
Number density $n(O_8)$ m⁻³	$\dfrac{N_A}{M(O_3)}\cdot\rho(O_3)$ $1.25467 \times 10^{25}\cdot\rho(O_3)$	$10^{-5}\cdot\dfrac{N_A}{V_0}\cdot\varepsilon(O_3)$ $2.68684 \times 10^{20}\cdot\varepsilon_3$
Column density $\varepsilon(O_3)$ atm-cm/km	$10^5\cdot\dfrac{V_0}{M(O_3)}\cdot\rho(O_3)$ $4.66968 \times 10^4\cdot\rho(O_3)$	$\varepsilon(O_3)$
Mass density $\rho(O_3)$ kg/m³	$\rho(O_3)$	$10^{-5}\cdot\dfrac{M(O_3)}{V_0}\cdot\varepsilon(O_3)$ $2.14148 \times 10^{-5}\cdot\varepsilon(O_3)$
Partial pressure $p(O_3)$ N/m² or Pa mb	$\dfrac{R^*}{M(O_3)}\cdot T\cdot\rho(O_3)$ $1.73222 \times 10^2\cdot T\cdot\rho(O_3)$ $1.73222\cdot T\cdot\rho(O_3)$	$10^{-5}\dfrac{R^*}{V_0}\cdot T\cdot\varepsilon(O_3)$ $3.70951 \times 10^{-3}\cdot T\cdot\varepsilon(O_3)$ $3.70951 \times 10^{-5}\cdot T_3\cdot\varepsilon(O_3)$
Mass mixing ratio $r(O_3)$ dimensionless	$\dfrac{\rho(O_3)}{\rho_s}$	$10^{-5}\cdot\dfrac{M(O_3)\cdot\varepsilon(O_3)}{V_0\cdot\rho_s}$ $2.14148 \times 10^{-5}\cdot\varepsilon(O_3)/\rho_s$
Volume mixing ratio $r'(O_3)$ dimensionless	$\dfrac{\rho(O_3)\cdot M}{\rho_s\cdot M(O_3)}$ $6.03448 \times 10^{-1}\cdot\rho(O_3)/\rho_s$	$10^{-5}\cdot\dfrac{M\cdot\varepsilon(O_3)}{V_0\cdot\rho_s}$ $1.29227 \times 10^{-5}\cdot\varepsilon(O_3)/\rho_s$

Avogadro's Number $\qquad N_A \qquad = 6.022169 \times 10^{26}$ (molecules) kmol⁻¹
Universal gas constant $\qquad R^* \qquad = 8.31432 \times 10^3$ N·m/(K·kmol)
Volume of ideal gas at STP $\qquad V_0 \qquad = 22.4136$ m³/kmol
Molecular weight of O_3 $\qquad M(O_3) \quad = 47.9982$ kg/kmol
Mean Molecular weight of air $\qquad M \qquad = 28.9644$ kg/kmol
Mean Molecular weight ratio $\qquad M(O_3)M = 1.65714$
Temperature of the U.S. Standard Atmosphere T (K) at height Z
Density of the U.S. Standard Atmosphere ρ_s (kg/m³) at height Z
1.0 Pa $= 1.0$ N/m² $= 0.01$ mb

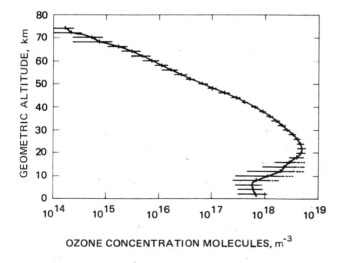

Figure 31. Mid-latitude ozone model density as a function of height

balloon ozonesondes is of the order of 50 percent. At heights from 8 to 16 km, the variability (also from balloon data) is found to increase significantly, reaching a maximum in excess of 100 percent at 10 km.

This large variability is due both to large-scale mixing processes in the atmosphere, and to changes in tropopause height with latitude. Tropospheric ozone profiles tend toward a constant mixing ratio (leading to a decrease of ozone density with height), while in the lower stratosphere the mixing ratio (and density) increases rapidly with height. The mid-latitude ozone-height profiles may contain elements of a low-latitude profile, with a minimum near 16 km (approximately 100 mb), and elements of a high-latitude profile, with a minimum at a height of about 10 km (approximately 250 mb). This situation is the result of transport to mid-latitudes of high-latitude tropospheric and lower stratospheric air, with its high-latitude ozone signature. Thus, one or more secondary ozone maxima of the type shown in figure 33 may result. This figure shows results of simultaneous ozone and temperature soundings at Boulder, Colo. on January 13, 1964 (Dütsch 1966). Here a distinct secondary maximum is found near 150 mb (13 km), under the primary maximum at 80 mb (22 km). Such secondary maxima, found most frequently in the winter and spring, are the cause of the large vari-

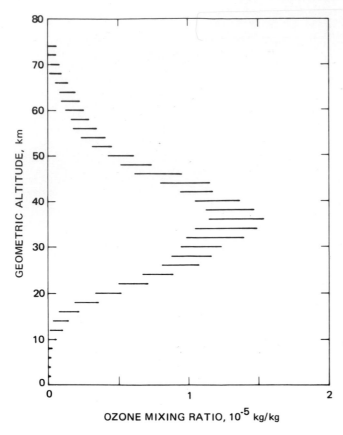

Figure 32. Mixing ratio as a function of height from mid-latitude ozone model

ment techniques of 1974. The densities are derived principally from instruments with known absolute accuracy, and are thus believed to be definitive. The variabilities are based on a relatively small data set and therefore need refinement. Clearly, a need exists for further models which include seasonal, latitudinal, and secular dependences. These extensions of the model will depend on systematic, in-situ, rocket and balloon soundings coordinated with continued satellite monitoring.

3.3   WATER VAPOR

3.3.1   SURFACE LAYERS.—The water-vapor content of any volume of atmosphere is dependent upon its proximity to sources and sinks of moisture. Most water vapor in the atmosphere enters it through the boundary layer of air by vaporization from major bodies of water. Water in both liquid and solid state has a vapor pressure which increases exponentially with its surface temperature. If this temperature exceeds the dew point of the overlying air, vaporization can proceed until the air attains a saturation temperature (dew point) equal to the water temperature. Usually, slightly lower dew points become equilibrium values since advection and mixing of drier air from land masses and upward diffusion of surface-layer water vapor act as controlling factors.

The warmest body of water of significant size, the Persian Gulf with summer surface temperatures of 35°C, is responsible for the highest atmospheric water-vapor content. The highest accepted weather-observatory dew point, 34°C, has been recorded on its shores at Sharjah, Saudi Arabia (Salmela and Grantham 1972).

Because relative humidity alone is not a physically meaningful indicator of atmospheric water vapor, humidity values have been reduced to mixing ratio (the mass of water vapor per unit mass of dry air). Mixing ratio is used herein because it is one of the most conservative indicators of moisture, not changing with either vertical or horizontal air movement unless vapor is physically added or removed from the air. The mixing ratio associated with the record high dew point of 34°C, assuming a typical sea-level atmospheric pressure of about 1000 mb, is 3.5×10^4 parts per million by mass (ppmm). Higher mixing ratios could be obtained only by the artificial heating of water and would be very localized. Even hot springs in desert areas would not create higher values of any appreciable areal extent because the vapor would be quickly diffused into the drier surrounding air.

This physical limit of maximum water vapor near the earth's surface is generally accepted and is well supported by simple, accurate, voluminous observations. The analogous limit for minimum humidity at the earth's surface is based upon a dif-

ability in the mid-latitude ozone model at heights from 8 to 16 km.

Above the 22-km ozone maximum, the variability decreases to 14 percent in the balloon data, and is approximately 15 percent in the rocket data up to 52 km. The variabilities assessed from the satellite data are near 11 percent between 30 and 52 km, a value lower than that for the rocket model. This situation may be due in part to the greater smoothing of the ozone profile associated with the satellite technique. This difference may also be due to the fact that the satellite data represent the results of a single instrument, while the rocket model is derived from a multiplicity of instruments flown by several experimenters.

Between 52 and 66 km, the percentage variability in the rocket model increases to approximately 35 percent, and is greater than 50 percent at 68 to 74 km. These increases are due to the addition at these heights of twilight data which exhibit a much greater variability than that existing in daytime data. Diurnal changes, which would lead to a higher apparent variability, have been predicted from theory at altitudes above 55 km. Therefore, the reliability of the model is considerably degraded at these altitudes.

The ozone densities and variabilities in this mid-latitude ozone model are consistant with the knowledge and the state of the art of ozone measure

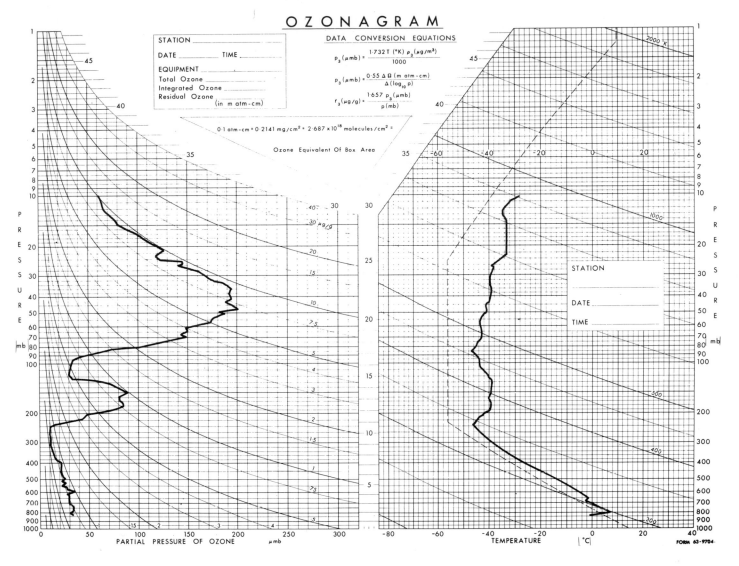

Figure 33. Simultaneously measured temperature-height and ozone-height profiles

ferent physical process. The sink involves atmospheric temperatures rather than water-body temperatures. The amount of water vapor that air can contain decreases exponentially with falling temperature, halving with a decrease of about 10°C at normal temperatures and 5°C at very cold temperatures. Therefore, cooling condenses out water vapor, and air with the lowest temperature contains the smallest amount of water vapor.

The lowest surface temperature on record is a −88.2°C at Vostok, Antarctica, altitude 3470 meters (Riordan 1970). At a frost point of −88°C, the mixing ratio at Vostok would be 0.1 ppmm, an order of magnitude lower than that often considered typical of the stratosphere. Thus, it is apparent that the water vapor over the earth's surface has a range of more than five orders of magnitude. These extremes are given in table 20 for the surface. In general, surface-layer water vapor decreases as latitude increases, though there are many variations due to local sources and sinks.

3.3.2 TROPOSPHERE.—Tropospheric relative humidity and associated temperature are measured routinely over much of the world by standard meteorological soundings (radiosondes). Unfortunately, most radiosondes lose their sensitivity as temperatures approach −40°C. Consequently, some polar winter soundings with surface temperatures below or near this value provide no humidity data. Even under the warmest atmospheric conditions, radiosonde humidity observations seldom exceed an altitude of 10 km. Though high accuracy cannot be claimed for individual relative-humidity sensors, and limitations are imposed by the associated temperature, the vast amount of data provides a reasonably complete picture for the distribution of water vapor up to 8 km. A humidity atlas (Gringorten et al. 1966) has been prepared using these data. It provides the 5-, 25-, 50-, 75-, and 95-percentile humidity values up to the 400-mb pressure surface over the Northern Hemisphere, roughly 6 to 8 km. Only research data are available for higher tropospheric altitudes, and these are generally associated with attempts to measure humidity in the stratosphere.

Recent studies by Richard and Snelling (1971) present radiosonde extremes and the 1-percent probable high and low values for areas which have the highest and lowest humidities at each altitude for the most extreme month. Grantham and Sissenwine (1970) extend the 1-percent high values to 80 km by subjective evaluation of research soundings and associated temperatures in nacreous clouds (25 km) and noctilucent clouds (80 km).

Radiosonde data around the world from the humidity atlas (Gringorten et al. 1966) and high-altitude research data were analyzed by Sissenwine, et al. (1968a, 1969b) and used to depict typical mid-latitude conditions from the surface upward into the stratosphere. Table 20 provides mean humidity values as well as world-wide extremes, and values exceeded in 99 percent (1 percent low) and 1 percent (1 percent high) of the observations, together with the data sources. Also indicated is the tropopause for humidity near 15 km. This is the level where the steady decrease in humidity with increasing altitude ends in most research soundings. It is located within the isothermal layer in this U. S. Standard Atmosphere, 1976 which starts at 11 km, the synthetic bottom of the stratosphere at mid-latitudes, and ends at 20 km.

3.3.3 STRATOSPHERE.—Very low temperatures in the lower stratosphere, —80°C or colder in the tropics to —48°C over the summer poles, and the very small amount of water vapor that even saturated air at these temperatures could retain, make water-vapor measurements very difficult. Consequently, much controversy has developed over the true values of mixing ratio in the stratosphere. One logical approach is to examine possible sources and sinks of water vapor and relate these to empirical observations, rejecting those that are physically impossible or obviously unreliable because of crude observing techniques and/or poor equipment.

Simplified theory of the general circulation of the atmosphere reveals that an acknowledged source of water vapor for the stratosphere is the moist air mass that rises over equatorial regions in the Hadley cell, a major feature in global circulation. In general, the temperature of the air above the tropopause increases with altitude. Since rising air cools adiabatically, penetration into the stratosphere causes it to become denser than surrounding air. As a result, it loses its buoyancy and descends back to the level of equal density. Thus, the tropopause establishes a lid over the troposphere and, in general, suppresses upward motion of the tropospheric air into the stratosphere. However,

at equatorial latitudes, the total energy received at the surface from solar radiation is sufficient for nearly continuous penetration through this lid. This equatorial tropospheric air moves poleward after penetrating into the stratosphere, cooling and subsiding so that it eventually returns to the troposphere and moves toward the Equator making a continuous loop. An interesting feature of this theory is that it supports a sink as well as a source of water vapor in the stratosphere.

The tropics have the coldest tropopause of any latitude, and it varies little over the year. Typical equatorial tropopause temperatures are —80°C to —82°C, with variations of only a few degrees. Since dew/frost points cannot exceed saturation temperature, most of the water vapor present in the ascending moist tropical air is condensed out into clouds and precipitation before reaching the tropopause. Since the tropopause occurs near 16 km where the pressure is very close to 100 mb, a mixing ratio of 2 to 3 ppmm is established, dependent upon the exact frost-point temperature and pressure.

From 1942 to 1947, British investigations of stratospheric humidity with an aircraft-carried, manually operated frost-point instrument (Brewer 1949) indicated that a 2-ppmm mixing ratio was typical for all latitudes at the peak altitude of the aircraft, 10 to 12 km. A small number of higher values were rejected. A follow-on aircraft program[*] in 1962, using the same instrumentation as the earlier program, did indicate considerable variability at higher altitude. Values in the lower stratosphere sometimes attained 10 ppmm.

Mastenbrook (1968, 1971), an investigator responsible for a most extensive stratospheric humidity sounding program carried out with an automatic optical frost-point sensor, and Mastenbrook and Purdy (1972) have recently indicated an upward trend from the value of 2 ppmm, considered typical in the original investigations, to 3 ppmm in 1971. A slight warming in the tropical tropopause may be responsible for raising this value to 3 ppmm. However, later unpublished data by Mastenbrook (Reiter in press) do not continue this trend. He found that variations with altitude, time, or location were small.

Many scientists have considered the stratospheric water-vapor mixing ratio to be constrained within the range 1 to 3 ppmm. On the other hand, many early investigators who used balloons as the platform for their sensors found more water vapor and much variability in the stratosphere. However, much of the data is challengeable. Outgassing from the balloon carrier was often a source of contamina-

---

*Private communication with member of *British Meteorological Research Committee*, which included an unpublished research report by W. T. Roach with graphs and cross sections of flight data.

tion when observations were made from sensors suspended beneath rising balloons. There is extensive discussion of most of these data in works already cited, and by Gutnick (1961), who described the controversy more than a dozen years ago in his article "How Dry is the Sky?"

In an attempt to resolve these differences, a series of 17 balloons, launched near 45°N, provided mixing ratios using an automatic alpha-radiation, frost-point sensor (Sissenwine et al. 1968a, 1968b). These soundings support the 3-ppmm value in the lowest part of the stratosphere if mixing ratio is computed from the average frost point, −80°C at the 100-mb level. This sensing technique should be reliable, since extreme precautions were taken to avoid water-vapor contamination. In addition, an inflight recorder provided internal checks on the heat-sink temperature, recorder calibration, etc. However, frost-point errors of a degree or so could have gone undetected despite careful editing of the soundings. Because of the nature of the measurements, such errors would be biased toward higher frost points.

The important feature of these 17 flights is that the water-vapor mixing ratio increases to about 6 times the tropopause value as altitude increases to 25 km. As noted, an error in any one of the 17 soundings could exaggerate the magnitude of the values, but the shape of the vertical profile, showing a maximum at 25 km, is of primary importance to this review. This maximum is followed by a decrease to the highest altitude observed, 32 km. To extrapolate to higher altitudes, a temperature of −130°C, found in the presence of noctilucent clouds (Theon 1967), was used to establish the vapor pressure at 80 km. It yields a mixing ratio of 0.6 ppmm. Figure 34 depicts the average profile up to 32 km (mean for Chico, Calif., at 40°N). It also shows Gutnick's average of pre-1961 soundings and the 2-ppmm "Dry Sky" profile. Table 21 presents alternative versions of stratospheric humidity, with version b extrapolated through the mesosphere on the basis of the meager evidence cited above.

An increase of mixing ratio above the tropopause may be questioned in the absence of an identifiable source of water vapor. Sissenwine et al. (1972) have attempted to establish a water-vapor balance in the stratosphere, which includes vapor passing through the tropical tropopause in the Hadley cell and introduces an additional source consistent with an increase up to 25 km. In their vapor-budget calculations, they consider amounts available by vaporization of convective clouds which penetrate the tropopause quite routinely in thunderstorms. Based on a climatology of hourly radar precipitation echoes observed at 31 U.S. sites from continuously operated (10-cm wavelength) storm ra-

dars, Kantor and Grantham (1968) compute that 3.6×10^{10} kg of convective clouds penetrate the tropopause daily over land areas in the Northern Hemisphere between 25° and 50°N. Vaporization of 1 percent of these clouds would raise the equilibrium mixing ratios by 1 ppmm if the vapor were distributed uniformly through the 16- to 32-km layer of the stratosphere. Sissenwine et al. (1972) also show that only a small percentage of these clouds (about 5 percent) need be vaporized to provide the actual vapor required to account for the increase in mixing ratio up to 25 km. Evidence of vaporization from such clouds has also been provided by other investigators (Kuhn et al. 1971; Barrett et al. 1972). Recent (1972) spectroscopic soundings (Murcray et al. 1972) also support a mixing-ratio maximum near 25 km.

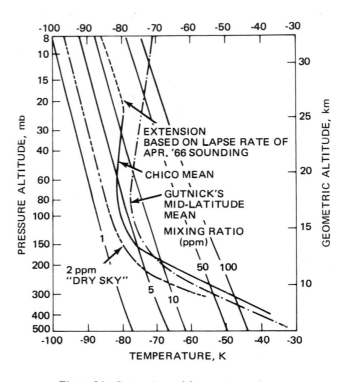

Figure 34. Comparison of frost-point profiles

There have been other theories suggesting a source of water vapor in the stratosphere. For example, about 10 years ago Rangarajan (1963) related earlier speculation with regard to the origin of water vapor (that the entire hydrogen content of the earth's oceans is of solar origin) to the high stratospheric humidities then being obtained (Gutnick 1961). He postulated that a chemical reaction involving hydrogen, together with subsidence over the polar area, could impart water vapor to the mid-stratosphere. However, there is now little support for most of the high-humidity observations. More recently, Scholz et al. (1970), utilizing a rocket platform, measured methane, hydrogen, and water vapor in an air sample for an

18-km thick layer averaging about 50 km in altitude. They suggested that most methane is consumed in the lower stratosphere, concluding that water vapor at altitudes up to 50 km from methane could approach 6 ppmm. This value does not differ substantially from that shown for 50 km in version b of table 21. In November 1972 a Department of Transportation Climatic Impact Assessment Program panel discussion of stratospheric aeronomy was conducted by many of the world's outstanding experts, including Nicolet (Belgium), Crutzen (Sweden), London (USA), and McElroy (USA). McElroy emphasized the importance of accounting for the mass of methane reaching the stratosphere from the earth's surface. He suggested that the "190 K" frost point in the stratosphere (water vapor of about 2 ppmm) does not allow for additional water vapor which would be formed by methane reacting with oxygen in the stratosphere. Yet he considers this an important source of water vapor.

The foregoing indicates considerable conflict in humidity values deemed representative of the stratosphere. As a result, two alternative vertical profiles have been presented in table 21. The true profile may lie somewhere between these two representations.

TABLE 20.—Water vapor in the troposphere and lower stratosphere (parts per million by mass)

Alt* (km)	Record low	1-percent low	Midlat. mean	1-percent high	Record high
Sfc	00.1[a]	5.0[a]	4686[c]	30,000[e]	35,000[e]
1	24.0[b]	27.0[b]	3700[c]	29,000[b]	31,000[b]
2	21.0[b]	31.0[b]	2843[c]	24,000[b]	28,000[b]
4	16.0[b]	24.0[b]	1268[c]	18,000[b]	22,000[b]
6	6.2[b]	12.0[b]	554[c]	7,700[b]	8,900[b]
8	6.1[b]	6.1[b]	216[c]	4,300[b]	4,700[b]
10		5.3[g]	43.2[d]	1,300[f]	
12		1.2[g]	11.3[d]	230[f]	
14		1.5[g]	3.3[d]	48[f]	
16		1.0[g]	3.3[d]	38[f]	

*Altitudes are based on Standard Atmosphere pressures.

Sources

[a] Based on saturation at record-cold temperature for Antarctica (Riordan 1970) and 1-percent coldest month for cold basin in Siberia, —62° (Salmela and Sissenwine 1970).

[b] Extreme from radiosonde data in most extreme (high and low) humid areas and most extreme month (Richard and Snelling 1971, Sissenwine and Cormier 1972).

[c] 45N latitude annual average of radiosonde data (Gringorten et al. 1966).

[d] Average of 17 alpha-radiation year-round mid-latitude soundings (Sissenwine et al. 1968a, 1968b).

[e] Surface psychrometric records for August along Gulf of Persia (Sissenwine and Cormier 1972).

[f] Special study of humidity extremes with some credence (Grantham and Sissenwine 1970).

[g] Assuming saturation at 1-percent cold radiosonde temperatures over coldest area and coldest month (Richard and Snelling 1971).

TABLE 21.—Alternative mixing ratios of water vapor in the natural stratosphere and mesosphere (parts per million by mass)

Altitude (km)	Hadley circulation only[a]	Hadley circulation plus possible contributions from thunderstorms, etc.[b]
16	2 to 3	3.3
18	2 to 3	3.3
20	2 to 3	4.5
22	2 to 3	7.2
24	2 to 3	11.6
26	2 to 3	18.6
28	2 to 3	18.2
30	2 to 3	17.6
32		16.8
35		15.4
40		12.2
45		11.1
50		7.6
55		4.9
60		3.8
65		2.3
70		1.4
75		1.1
80		0.6

[a] These values are typical of many optical frost-point measurements by Mastenbrook (1968, 1971), and Mastenbrook and Purdy (1972) and are in agreement with the theory that the only water vapor in the stratosphere is that in air ascending through the tropical tropopause.

[b] This is the average of 17 year-round alpha-radiation frost-point measurements by Sissenwine et al. (1968a, 1968b), and supports the possibility of a natural stratospheric source of water vapor (Sissenwine et al. 1968b). Values above 32 km are extrapolated to be in agreement with frost points from temperature observed in noctilucent clouds at 80 km.

Note: Values under column b are based on average frost point at the 100-mb level since frost point was directly computed. When individual mixing ratios are computed and averaged, they exceed the values under b by 0.8 ppmm at 16 km but the difference falls to zero by 26 km.

3.4　STANDARD AEROSOL

3.4.1　INTRODUCTION.—Because the concepts of mass conservation and continuity do not apply to atmospheric aerosols, assigning mean values to the parameters is more difficult than providing mean values for the fluid system. To understand the global aerosol, it is necessary to have knowledge of the production and transport, as well as of the chemical and physical mechanisms that modify and remove the particles from the atmosphere. Unfortunately, neither the experimental nor the theoretical techniques which are presently available are adequate for this task. This summary is based primarily on experimental measurements which, although not sufficiently detailed to be reliable as global estimates, are the only data available.

Measurements made by Blifford (1970) on tropospheric aerosols at a number of different geographical locations and at altitudes up to the tropopause have revealed considerable variability which has not been satisfactorily explained. In order to provide meaningful summary of the available information, data for measurements made over the mid-continnental United States, and over the open ocean in air masses with maritime trajectories have been averaged separately. The resulting average logarithmic distribution functions dN/d (log R) [cm^{-3}] vs R are shown in figure 35, where N is the number concentration of the particles, and R the particle radius.

A range of values of the average aerosol size-distribution function for different tropospheric altitudes is given rather than the results of individual measurements. Since the data were obtained using aircraft flying at constant pressure altitude and because the vertical concentration of particles is strongly influenced by the source at the earth's surface, the data were corrected to indicate true sampling height above the ground.

The greater variability found for the mid-troposphere and the relatively large decrease of particle number in the first few kilometers is readily seen. In the upper troposphere, the land and sea aerosols tend to have similar distributions and there is a significant decrease in the relative number of large particles. Except near the surface, the number concentration of particles measured over land is usually greater than it is over the ocean.

Although size distribution data for the stratosphere are sparse, some information on total particle number is available. Figure 36 has been adapted from the work of Rosen, who made a large number of measurements using balloon-borne, light-scattering counters. The shaded area encompasses the range of values for both summer and winter. The size distribution of particles in the stratosphere is not well known, but from determinations of the life time of the particles, it is inferred that they are of the order of 0.1 μm or less in mean radius.

3.4.2 SOURCES.—Table 22a gives estimates of the production rate of aerosols from various sources (Hidy and Brock 1972), along with some corresponding estimated lifetimes. Since a standard atmosphere implies a steady state, one approach to the problem is to consider an aerosol system whose physical and chemical properties and transport are expressed in the equilibrium concept of residence time. In this case, the steady-state concentrations can be computed from the above estimates of the daily production rate by the formula:

$$C_i = S_i + S_i \sum_{j-1}^{\infty} e^{-j/T} \qquad (55)$$

where C_i = the equilibrium concentration of the

aerosol, i, S_i = production rate of aerosol i, and T_i = the residence time of the aerosol i. The right-hand side of equation 55 is a series with j progressing from 1 to ∞ by steps of unity. The results of this simple computation using the data of table 22a are given in table 22b. It appears that the three major sources which contribute over 60 percent of the total mass are vegetation, soil dust, and sea spray. Although sea-salt aerosol is ubiquitous over the oceans, the available evidence indicates that it is confined to low altitudes and does not penetrate very far inland.

There is experimental evidence for inferring that the deserts are the most important sources of soil aerosol, with the wind controlling the distribution. Unfortunately, there is very little information available from which to construct patterns of the

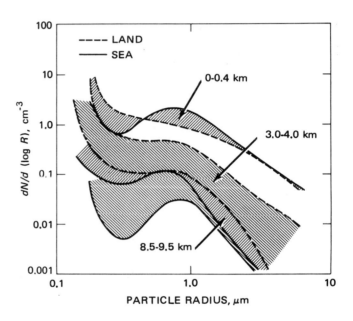

Figure 35. Average tropospheric aerosol particle size distributions

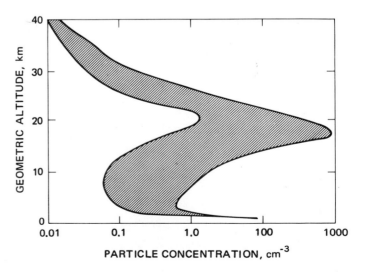

Figure 36. Average stratospheric aerosol particle number as a function of altitude

TABLE 22a.—A steady-state model of tropospheric aerosol composition

Source	Estimated production rate (tons/day)	Estimated residence time (days)
Dust rise by wind	10^6	15
Sea spray	3×10^6	2
Extraterrestrial (meteoric dust)	550	30
Volcanic dust (intermittent)	10^4	15
Forest fires (intermittent)	4×10^5	15
Vegetation	3×10^6	5
Sulfur cycle	10^6	5
Nitrogen cycle ammonia	7×10^5	5
$NO_x \rightarrow NO_3$	10^6	5
Volcano volatiles	10^3	15
Combustion and industrial	3×10^5	5
Cultivation dust rise	10^3	5
Hydrocarbon vapor	7×10^3	5
Anthropogenic sulfates	3×10^5	5
Anthropogenic nitrates	6×10^4	5
Anthropogenic ammonia	3×10^3	5

TABLE 22b.—A steady-state tropospheric aerosol composition

Source	Steady state total (tons)	Percent of total
Dust rise by wind	1.6×10^7	24.1
Sea spray	7.6×10^6	11.9
Extraterrestrial (meteoric dust)	1.5×10^3	—
Volcanic dust (intermittent)	1.6×10^5	0.2
Forest fires (intermittent)	6.2×10^6	9.9
Vegetation	1.7×10^7	25.8
Sulfur cycle	5.5×10^6	8.6
Nitrogen cycle ammonia	3.9×10^6	6.0
$NO_x \rightarrow NO_3$	5.5×10^6	7.7
Volcano volatiles	1.6×10^4	—
Combustion and industrial	1.7×10^6	2.6
Cultivation dust rise	5.5×10^3	—
Hydrocarbon vapors	3.9×10^4	0.1
Anthropogenic sulfates	1.7×10^6	2.6
Anthropogenic nitrates	3.3×10^5	0.5
Anthropogenic ammonia	1.7×10^4	—

TABLE 23.—Representative concentrations ($\mu g/m^3$) of elements from earlier literature compared with the lowest altitude observations of Gillette and Blifford (1971)

Element	From the literature						Gillette and Blifford (1971)				
	East Chicago (One measurement) [a]	Niles, Mich. (One measurement) [a]	Cambridge, Mass. (average) [b]	Chilton, Berks (average) [c]	Urban (mode) [d]	Non-Urban (mode) [d]	Scottsbluff, Nebraska (average)	Death Valley, Calif. (average)	Pacific offshore (average)	Chicago, Ill. (One measurement)	Orinoco Delta (average one altitude)
Chlorine Cl			0.5	2.2			0.61 ± 0.42	0.44 ± 0.28	1.3 ± 0.73	0.79	0.44 ± 0.23
Sulfur S	13.0 ± 8.0	11.0 ± 5.0			~ 4	1.6	0.11 ± 0.05	0.31 ± 0.15	0.24 ± 0.14	0.20	0.23 ± 0.42
Potassium K	1.42 ± 0.15	0.75 ± 0.1					0.31 ± 0.15	0.29 ± 0.14	0.34 ± 0.10	0.38	0.26 ± 0.33
Sodium Na	0.46 ± 0.04	0.17 ± 0.02	0.8	0.85			1.27	0.30 ± 0.33	0.38	0.35	0.26 ± 0.46
Silicon Si							0.74 ± 0.45	0.54 ± 0.48	0.48 ± 0.30		
Calcium Ca	7.00 ± 0.7	1.00 ± 0.2	~ 2				0.20 ± 0.11	0.13 ± 0.11	0.41 ± 0.35	2.2	0.32 ± 0.54
Titanium Ti	0.19 ± 0.04	0.12 ± 0.03			~ 0.03	~ 0.01	0.02 ± 0.02	0.12 ± 0.10	0.06 ± 0.06	0.13	0.07 ± 0.21

Data sources:

[a] Dams, R., Robbins, J. A., Rahn, K. A., and Winchester, J. W., 1970: Nondestructive neutron activation analysis of air pollution particulates. *Analytical Chemistry*, 42, pp. 861–867.

[b] Zoller, W. H., and Gordon, G. E., 1970: Instrumental neutron activation analyses of atmospheric pollutants utilizing Ge(Li) γ-ray detectors. *Analytical Chemistry*, 42, pp. 257–265.

[c] Keane, J. R., and Fisher, E. M. R., 1968: Analysis of trace elements in air-borne particulates, by neutron activation and Gamma ray spectrometry. *Atmospheric Environment*, 2, pp. 603–614.

[d] McMullen, T. B., Faoro, R. B., and Morgan, G., 1970: Profile of pollutant fractions in nonurban suspended particulate matter. *Journal of the Air Pollution Control Association*, 20, pp. 369–372.

global deposition. It would appear that the largest and most interesting variations will occur in the Monsoon region of Asia.

Although there is evidence that near the surface, coastal aerosols are influenced by the trajectories of air masses, no such relationship has been demonstrated for higher tropospheric altitudes (Blifford and Gillette 1972). Dust from the Sahara is frequently observed in the Southern Atlantic, and deposits of dust of Asian origin have been found in Hawaii. Uniformity of chemical composition and size distribution suggest that in the middle and upper troposphere, the major aerosol component is of soil origin.

Various gases in the atmosphere are converted into particles by chemical reactions. Terpenes and other essential oils emitted by plants are believed to be oxidized to form compounds of high molecular weight that condense to form gummy particles. Sulfur dioxide is oxidized and hydrated to form sulfuric acid droplets which in turn can react with ammonia to form ammonium sulfate.

3.4.3 CHEMICAL COMPOSITION. — Relatively little information about the chemical composition of aerosols in the troposphere is available, most of the reported measurements having been made near the ground in urban locations. Some representative values for the concentration of selected elements in aerosols near the surface are given in table 23. Table 24 gives the altitude distribution of six elemental constituents of atmospheric aerosols measured by Gillette and Blifford (1971) in non-pollution situations over land and over the ocean. Profiles for most of the elements indicate that there is a marked decrease from the surface values in the first few hundred meters.

Over the ocean, chlorine (chloride) predominates near the surface. Above the boundary layer, the concentrations of all six elements measured become more uniform with altitude. In maritime situations the concentrations tend to be about half those over land. At the lower altitudes, the concentration of the elements characteristic of soils (Si, K, Ca) may be quite variable. Correlations between the elements originating in the soil provide support for the hypothesis that in the middle and upper troposphere, a large fraction of the aerosol originates from wind-blown dust.

TABLE 24.—Average mass (μgm/m³) of elemental constituents of atmospheric aerosols (0.01μm $\leqq$ r $<$10μm)*

Altitude (km)	Land	Ocean
Chlorine		
0.015–0.915	0.42(11)	1.79(3)
1.5 –3.0	0.52(20)	0.30(3)
3.7 –6.1	0.24(21)	0.31(3)
7.6 –9.1	0.23(20)	0.45(7)
Sulfur		
0.015–0.915	0.32(10)	0.36(1)
1.5 –3.0	0.22(18)	0.09(4)
3.7 –6.1	0.09(17)	0.08(5)
7.6 –9.1	0.09(17)	0.06(7)
Potassium		
0.015–0.915	0.22(10)	0.30(3)
1.5 –3.0	0.20(21)	0.05(3)
3.7 –6.1	0.09(25)	0.10(5)
7.6 –9.1	0.09(20)	0.08(7)
Silicon		
0.051–0.915	0.43(10)	0.29(3)
1.5 –3.0	0.38(26)	0.11(4)
3.7 –6.1	0.17(22)	0.10(6)
7.6 –9.1	0.20(23)	0.10(6)
Calcium		
0.051–0.915	0.44(8)	0.13(3)
1.5 –3.0	0.19(25)	0.07(2)
3.7 –6.1	0.09(22)	0.04(4)
7.6 –9.1	0.12(17)	0.07(7)
Titanium		
0.051–0.915	0.07(11)	0.03(3)
1.5 –3.0	0.04(24)	0.02(3)
3.7 –6.1	0.02(22)	0.01(7)
7.6 –9.1	0.04(20)	0.03(7)

*The numbers in parentheses refer to the number of observations.

The major constituent of stratospheric particles seems to be impure sulfuric acid droplets with silicates making up much of the remainder. The concentrations are extremely variable with altitude and time. A highly stratified layer of the particles exists at altitudes of about 16 to 20 km. The highest concentrations of particles throughout the lower stratosphere occur shortly after major volcanic eruptions. This subject has been reviewed by Cadle (1972).

PART 4
Main Tables

TABLE I

Temperature, pressure, and density for geopotential and geometric altitudes in metric units.*

TABLE II

Acceleration due to gravity, pressure scale height, number density, mean particle speed, mean collision frequency, mean free path, and mean molecular weight for geopotential and geometric altitudes in metric units.*

TABLE III

Sound speed, dynamic viscosity, kinematic viscosity, and thermal conductivity for geopotential and geometric altitudes in metric units.*

TABLE IV

Temperature, pressure, and density for geopotential and geometric altitudes in feet. Table entries in metric units.*

TABLE V

Gravity ratio, number density, mean collision frequency, mean free path, sound speed, viscosity ratio, thermal conductivity ratio for geopotential and geometric altitudes in feet. Table entries in metric units.*

TABLE VI

Geopotential altitude in meters as a function of pressure in millibars.

TABLE VII

Geopotential altitude in feet as a function of pressure in millibars.

TABLE VIII

Atmospheric composition in terms of number density for nitrogen, atomic oxygen, molecular oxygen, argon, helium, and atomic hydrogen.*

For further information and details of the computer programs used to generate these tables, contact the Environmental Science Information Center, Environmental Data Service, National Oceanic and Atmospheric Administration, Washington, D.C. 20235.

---

*A one- or two-digit number (preceded by a plus or minus sign) following the initial entry of each block indicates the power of ten by which that entry and each succeeding entry of that block should be multiplied. A change of power occurring within a block is indicated by a similar notation.

Table I
Geopotential Altitude, Metric Units

Altitude		Temperature			Pressure			Density	
H (m)	Z (m)	T (K)	t (°C)	T$_M$ (K)	P (mb)	P (torr)	P/P$_0$	ρ (kg/m³)	ρ/ρ$_0$
-5000	-4996	320.650	47.500	320.650	1.7768 ◆ 3	1.3327 ◆ 3	1.7536 ◆ 0	1.9305 ◆ 0	1.5759 ◆ 0
-4950	-4946	320.325	47.175	320.325	1.7674	1.3256	1.7443	1.9222	1.5691
-4900	-4896	320.000	46.850	320.000	1.7580	1.3186	1.7350	1.9139	1.5623
-4850	-4846	319.675	46.525	319.675	1.7486	1.3115	1.7257	1.9056	1.5556
-4800	-4796	319.350	46.200	319.350	1.7393	1.3046	1.7165	1.8974	1.5489
-4750	-4746	319.025	45.875	319.025	1.7300	1.2976	1.7074	1.8892	1.5422
-4700	-4697	318.700	45.550	318.700	1.7208	1.2907	1.6983	1.8810	1.5355
-4650	-4647	318.375	45.225	318.375	1.7116	1.2838	1.6892	1.8728	1.5289
-4600	-4597	318.050	44.900	318.050	1.7024	1.2769	1.6801	1.8647	1.5222
-4550	-4547	317.725	44.575	317.725	1.6933	1.2700	1.6711	1.8566	1.5156
-4500	-4497	317.400	44.250	317.400	1.6842 ◆ 3	1.2632 ◆ 3	1.6622 ◆ 0	1.8486 ◆ 0	1.5090 ◆ 0
-4450	-4447	317.075	43.925	317.075	1.6751	1.2564	1.6532	1.8405	1.5025
-4400	-4397	316.750	43.600	316.750	1.6661	1.2497	1.6443	1.8325	1.4959
-4350	-4347	316.425	43.275	316.425	1.6572	1.2430	1.6355	1.8245	1.4894
-4300	-4297	316.100	42.950	316.100	1.6482	1.2363	1.6267	1.8166	1.4829
-4250	-4247	315.775	42.625	315.775	1.6394	1.2296	1.6179	1.8086	1.4764
-4200	-4197	315.450	42.300	315.450	1.6305	1.2230	1.6092	1.8007	1.4700
-4150	-4147	315.125	41.975	315.125	1.6217	1.2164	1.6005	1.7928	1.4635
-4100	-4097	314.800	41.650	314.800	1.6129	1.2098	1.5918	1.7850	1.4571
-4050	-4047	314.475	41.325	314.475	1.6042	1.2032	1.5832	1.7771	1.4507
-4000	-3997	314.150	41.000	314.150	1.5955 ◆ 3	1.1967 ◆ 3	1.5746 ◆ 0	1.7693 ◆ 0	1.4444 ◆ 0
-3950	-3948	313.825	40.675	313.825	1.5868	1.1902	1.5661	1.7616	1.4380
-3900	-3898	313.500	40.350	313.500	1.5782	1.1837	1.5576	1.7538	1.4317
-3850	-3848	313.175	40.025	313.175	1.5696	1.1773	1.5491	1.7461	1.4254
-3800	-3798	312.850	39.700	312.850	1.5611	1.1709	1.5407	1.7384	1.4191
-3750	-3748	312.525	39.375	312.525	1.5526	1.1645	1.5323	1.7307	1.4128
-3700	-3698	312.200	39.050	312.200	1.5441	1.1582	1.5239	1.7231	1.4066
-3650	-3648	311.875	38.725	311.875	1.5357	1.1519	1.5156	1.7154	1.4004
-3600	-3598	311.550	38.400	311.550	1.5273	1.1456	1.5073	1.7078	1.3942
-3550	-3548	311.225	38.075	311.225	1.5189	1.1393	1.4991	1.7003	1.3880
-3500	-3498	310.900	37.750	310.900	1.5106 ◆ 3	1.1331 ◆ 3	1.4909 ◆ 0	1.6927 ◆ 0	1.3818 ◆ 0
-3450	-3448	310.575	37.425	310.575	1.5023	1.1268	1.4827	1.6852	1.3757
-3400	-3398	310.250	37.100	310.250	1.4941	1.1207	1.4746	1.6777	1.3696
-3350	-3348	309.925	36.775	309.925	1.4859	1.1145	1.4665	1.6703	1.3635
-3300	-3298	309.600	36.450	309.600	1.4777	1.1084	1.4584	1.6628	1.3574
-3250	-3248	309.275	36.125	309.275	1.4696	1.1023	1.4504	1.6554	1.3513
-3200	-3198	308.950	35.800	308.950	1.4615	1.0962	1.4424	1.6480	1.3453
-3150	-3148	308.625	35.475	308.625	1.4534	1.0901	1.4344	1.6406	1.3393
-3100	-3098	308.300	35.150	308.300	1.4454	1.0841	1.4265	1.6333	1.3333
-3050	-3049	307.975	34.825	307.975	1.4374	1.0781	1.4186	1.6260	1.3273
-3000	-2999	307.650	34.500	307.650	1.4295 ◆ 3	1.0722 ◆ 3	1.4108 ◆ 0	1.6187 ◆ 0	1.3214 ◆ 0
-2950	-2949	307.325	34.175	307.325	1.4215	1.0662	1.4029	1.6114	1.3155
-2900	-2899	307.000	33.850	307.000	1.4136	1.0603	1.3952	1.6042	1.3095
-2850	-2849	306.675	33.525	306.675	1.4058	1.0544	1.3874	1.5970	1.3037
-2800	-2799	306.350	33.200	306.350	1.3980	1.0486	1.3797	1.5898	1.2978
-2750	-2749	306.025	32.875	306.025	1.3902	1.0427	1.3720	1.5826	1.2919
-2700	-2699	305.700	32.550	305.700	1.3825	1.0369	1.3644	1.5755	1.2861
-2650	-2649	305.375	32.225	305.375	1.3748	1.0311	1.3568	1.5684	1.2803
-2600	-2599	305.050	31.900	305.050	1.3671	1.0254	1.3492	1.5613	1.2745
-2550	-2549	304.725	31.575	304.725	1.3594	1.0197	1.3417	1.5542	1.2687
-2500	-2499	304.400	31.250	304.400	1.3518 ◆ 3	1.0140 ◆ 3	1.3342 ◆ 0	1.5472 ◆ 0	1.2630 ◆ 0
-2450	-2449	304.075	30.925	304.075	1.3443	1.0083	1.3267	1.5401	1.2573
-2400	-2399	303.750	30.600	303.750	1.3367	1.0026	1.3193	1.5332	1.2516
-2350	-2349	303.425	30.275	303.425	1.3292	9.9705 ◆ 2	1.3119	1.5262	1.2459
-2300	-2299	303.100	29.950	303.100	1.3218	9.9145	1.3045	1.5192	1.2402
-2250	-2249	302.775	29.625	302.775	1.3143	9.8587	1.2972	1.5123	1.2345
-2200	-2199	302.450	29.300	302.450	1.3069	9.8032	1.2899	1.5054	1.2289
-2150	-2149	302.125	28.975	302.125	1.2996	9.7480	1.2826	1.4986	1.2233
-2100	-2099	301.800	28.650	301.800	1.2922	9.6930	1.2753	1.4917	1.2177
-2050	-2049	301.475	28.325	301.475	1.2850	9.6383	1.2681	1.4849	1.2121
-2000	-1999	301.150	28.000	301.150	1.2777 ◆ 3	9.5838 ◆ 2	1.2610 ◆ 0	1.4781 ◆ 0	1.2066 ◆ 0
-1950	-1949	300.825	27.675	300.825	1.2705	9.5295	1.2538	1.4713	1.2011
-1900	-1899	300.500	27.350	300.500	1.2633	9.4755	1.2467	1.4645	1.1955
-1850	-1849	300.175	27.025	300.175	1.2561	9.4218	1.2397	1.4578	1.1901
-1800	-1799	299.850	26.700	299.850	1.2490	9.3683	1.2326	1.4511	1.1846
-1750	-1750	299.525	26.375	299.525	1.2419	9.3151	1.2256	1.4444	1.1791
-1700	-1700	299.200	26.050	299.200	1.2348	9.2621	1.2186	1.4378	1.1737
-1650	-1650	298.875	25.725	298.875	1.2278	9.2093	1.2117	1.4311	1.1683
-1600	-1600	298.550	25.400	298.550	1.2208	9.1568	1.2048	1.4245	1.1629
-1550	-1550	298.225	25.075	298.225	1.2138	9.1045	1.1979	1.4179	1.1575
-1500	-1500	297.900	24.750	297.900	1.2069 ◆ 3	9.0525 ◆ 2	1.1911 ◆ 0	1.4114 ◆ 0	1.1521 ◆ 0
-1450	-1450	297.575	24.425	297.575	1.2000	9.0007	1.1843	1.4048	1.1468
-1400	-1400	297.250	24.100	297.250	1.1931	8.9492	1.1775	1.3983	1.1415
-1350	-1350	296.925	23.775	296.925	1.1862	8.8979	1.1707	1.3918	1.1362
-1300	-1300	296.600	23.450	296.600	1.1794	8.8468	1.1640	1.3853	1.1309
-1250	-1250	296.275	23.125	296.275	1.1727	8.7960	1.1573	1.3789	1.1256
-1200	-1200	295.950	22.800	295.950	1.1659	8.7454	1.1507	1.3725	1.1204
-1150	-1150	295.625	22.475	295.625	1.1592	8.6950	1.1440	1.3661	1.1152
-1100	-1100	295.300	22.150	295.300	1.1525	8.6449	1.1374	1.3597	1.1099
-1050	-1050	294.975	21.825	294.975	1.1459	8.5950	1.1309	1.3533	1.1048

Table I
Geometric Altitude, Metric Units

Altitude		Temperature			Pressure			Density	
Z (m)	H (m)	T (K)	t (°C)	T_M (K)	P (mb)	P (torr)	P/P_0	ρ (kg/m³)	ρ/ρ_0
-5000	-5004	320.676	47.526	320.676	1.7776 + 3	1.3333 + 3	1.7543 + 0	1.9311 + 0	1.5764 + 0
-4950	-4954	320.350	47.200	320.350	1.7681	1.3262	1.7450	1.9228	1.5696
-4900	-4904	320.025	46.875	320.025	1.7587	1.3191	1.7357	1.9145	1.5629
-4850	-4854	319.699	46.549	319.699	1.7493	1.3121	1.7264	1.9062	1.5561
-4800	-4804	319.374	46.224	319.374	1.7400	1.3051	1.7172	1.8980	1.5494
-4750	-4754	319.048	45.898	319.048	1.7307	1.2981	1.7080	1.8898	1.5427
-4700	-4703	318.723	45.573	318.723	1.7214	1.2911	1.6989	1.8816	1.5360
-4650	-4653	318.397	45.247	318.397	1.7122	1.2842	1.6898	1.8734	1.5293
-4600	-4603	318.072	44.922	318.072	1.7030	1.2773	1.6807	1.8653	1.5227
-4550	-4553	317.746	44.596	317.746	1.6939	1.2705	1.6717	1.8572	1.5160
-4500	-4503	317.421	44.271	317.421	1.6848 + 3	1.2637 + 3	1.6627 + 0	1.8491 + 0	1.5094 + 0
-4450	-4453	317.095	43.945	317.095	1.6757	1.2569	1.6538	1.8410	1.5029
-4400	-4403	316.770	43.620	316.770	1.6667	1.2501	1.6449	1.8330	1.4963
-4350	-4353	316.444	43.294	316.444	1.6577	1.2434	1.6360	1.8250	1.4898
-4300	-4303	316.119	42.969	316.119	1.6488	1.2367	1.6272	1.8170	1.4833
-4250	-4253	315.793	42.643	315.793	1.6399	1.2300	1.6184	1.8091	1.4768
-4200	-4203	315.468	42.318	315.468	1.6310	1.2233	1.6097	1.8011	1.4703
-4150	-4153	315.143	41.993	315.143	1.6222	1.2167	1.6010	1.7933	1.4639
-4100	-4103	314.817	41.667	314.817	1.6134	1.2101	1.5923	1.7854	1.4575
-4050	-4053	314.492	41.342	314.492	1.6046	1.2036	1.5837	1.7775	1.4511
-4000	-4003	314.166	41.016	314.166	1.5959 + 3	1.1970 + 3	1.5751 + 0	1.7697 + 0	1.4447 + 0
-3950	-3952	313.841	40.691	313.841	1.5873	1.1905	1.5665	1.7619	1.4383
-3900	-3902	313.516	40.366	313.516	1.5786	1.1841	1.5580	1.7542	1.4320
-3850	-3852	313.190	40.040	313.190	1.5700	1.1776	1.5495	1.7464	1.4257
-3800	-3802	312.865	39.715	312.865	1.5615	1.1712	1.5411	1.7387	1.4194
-3750	-3752	312.539	39.389	312.539	1.5530	1.1648	1.5327	1.7311	1.4131
-3700	-3702	312.214	39.064	312.214	1.5445	1.1584	1.5243	1.7234	1.4069
-3650	-3652	311.889	38.739	311.889	1.5360	1.1521	1.5160	1.7158	1.4006
-3600	-3602	311.563	38.413	311.563	1.5276	1.1458	1.5077	1.7082	1.3944
-3550	-3552	311.238	38.088	311.238	1.5193	1.1395	1.4994	1.7006	1.3882
-3500	-3502	310.913	37.763	310.913	1.5109 + 3	1.1333 + 3	1.4912 + 0	1.6930 + 0	1.3821 + 0
-3450	-3452	310.587	37.437	310.587	1.5027	1.1271	1.4830	1.6855	1.3759
-3400	-3402	310.262	37.112	310.262	1.4944	1.1209	1.4749	1.6780	1.3698
-3350	-3352	309.936	36.786	309.936	1.4862	1.1147	1.4667	1.6705	1.3637
-3300	-3302	309.611	36.461	309.611	1.4780	1.1086	1.4587	1.6631	1.3576
-3250	-3252	309.286	36.136	309.286	1.4699	1.1025	1.4506	1.6556	1.3515
-3200	-3202	308.960	35.810	308.960	1.4617	1.0964	1.4426	1.6482	1.3455
-3150	-3152	308.635	35.485	308.635	1.4537	1.0903	1.4347	1.6409	1.3395
-3100	-3102	308.310	35.160	308.310	1.4456	1.0843	1.4267	1.6335	1.3335
-3050	-3051	307.985	34.835	307.985	1.4376	1.0783	1.4188	1.6262	1.3275
-3000	-3001	307.659	34.509	307.659	1.4297 + 3	1.0723 + 3	1.4110 + 0	1.6189 + 0	1.3216 + 0
-2950	-2951	307.334	34.184	307.334	1.4217	1.0664	1.4032	1.6116	1.3156
-2900	-2901	307.009	33.859	307.009	1.4139	1.0605	1.3954	1.6044	1.3097
-2850	-2851	306.683	33.533	306.683	1.4060	1.0546	1.3876	1.5972	1.3038
-2800	-2801	306.358	33.208	306.358	1.3982	1.0487	1.3799	1.5900	1.2979
-2750	-2751	306.033	32.883	306.033	1.3904	1.0429	1.3722	1.5828	1.2921
-2700	-2701	305.707	32.557	305.707	1.3826	1.0371	1.3646	1.5756	1.2862
-2650	-2651	305.382	32.232	305.382	1.3749	1.0313	1.3570	1.5685	1.2804
-2600	-2601	305.057	31.907	305.057	1.3673	1.0255	1.3494	1.5614	1.2746
-2550	-2551	304.732	31.582	304.732	1.3596	1.0198	1.3418	1.5544	1.2689
-2500	-2501	304.406	31.256	304.406	1.3520 + 3	1.0141 + 3	1.3343 + 0	1.5473 + 0	1.2631 + 0
-2450	-2451	304.081	30.931	304.081	1.3444	1.0084	1.3268	1.5403	1.2574
-2400	-2401	303.756	30.606	303.756	1.3369	1.0027	1.3194	1.5333	1.2517
-2350	-2351	303.431	30.281	303.431	1.3294	9.9714 + 2	1.3120	1.5263	1.2460
-2300	-2301	303.105	29.955	303.105	1.3219	9.9154	1.3046	1.5194	1.2403
-2250	-2251	302.780	29.630	302.780	1.3145	9.8596	1.2973	1.5124	1.2346
-2200	-2201	302.455	29.305	302.455	1.3071	9.8041	1.2900	1.5055	1.2290
-2150	-2151	302.130	28.980	302.130	1.2997	9.7488	1.2827	1.4986	1.2234
-2100	-2101	301.805	28.655	301.805	1.2924	9.6937	1.2754	1.4918	1.2178
-2050	-2051	301.479	28.329	301.479	1.2850	9.6390	1.2682	1.4850	1.2122
-2000	-2001	301.154	28.004	301.154	1.2778 + 3	9.5845 + 2	1.2611 + 0	1.4782 + 0	1.2067 + 0
-1950	-1951	300.829	27.679	300.829	1.2705	9.5302	1.2539	1.4714	1.2011
-1900	-1901	300.504	27.354	300.504	1.2633	9.4762	1.2468	1.4646	1.1956
-1850	-1851	300.179	27.029	300.179	1.2562	9.4224	1.2397	1.4579	1.1901
-1800	-1801	299.853	26.703	299.853	1.2490	9.3689	1.2327	1.4512	1.1846
-1750	-1750	299.528	26.378	299.528	1.2419	9.3156	1.2257	1.4445	1.1792
-1700	-1700	299.203	26.053	299.203	1.2349	9.2625	1.2187	1.4378	1.1737
-1650	-1650	298.878	25.728	298.878	1.2278	9.2098	1.2118	1.4312	1.1683
-1600	-1600	298.553	25.403	298.553	1.2208	9.1572	1.2049	1.4246	1.1629
-1550	-1550	298.227	25.077	298.227	1.2138	9.1049	1.1980	1.4180	1.1575
-1500	-1500	297.902	24.752	297.902	1.2069 + 3	9.0529 + 2	1.1911 + 0	1.4114 + 0	1.1522 + 0
-1450	-1450	297.577	24.427	297.577	1.2000	9.0011	1.1843	1.4049	1.1468
-1400	-1400	297.252	24.102	297.252	1.1931	8.9495	1.1775	1.3984	1.1415
-1350	-1350	296.927	23.777	296.927	1.1863	8.8982	1.1708	1.3919	1.1362
-1300	-1300	296.602	23.452	296.602	1.1795	8.8471	1.1640	1.3854	1.1309
-1250	-1250	296.277	23.127	296.277	1.1727	8.7962	1.1574	1.3789	1.1257
-1200	-1200	295.951	22.801	295.951	1.1659	8.7456	1.1507	1.3725	1.1204
-1150	-1150	295.626	22.476	295.626	1.1592	8.6952	1.1441	1.3661	1.1152
-1100	-1100	295.301	22.151	295.301	1.1525	8.6451	1.1375	1.3597	1.1100
-1050	-1050	294.976	21.826	294.976	1.1459	8.5952	1.1309	1.3534	1.1048

Table I
Geopotential Altitude, Metric Units

Altitude		Temperature			Pressure			Density	
H (m)	Z (m)	T (K)	t (°C)	T_M (K)	P (mb)	P (torr)	P/P_0	ρ (kg/m³)	ρ/ρ_0
-1000	-1000	294.650	21.500	294.650	1.1392 + 3	8.5453 + 2	1.1243 + 0	1.3470 + 0	1.0996 + 0
-950	-950	294.325	21.175	294.325	1.1327	8.4959	1.1178	1.3407	1.0944
-900	-900	294.000	20.850	294.000	1.1261	8.4467	1.1114	1.3344	1.0893
-850	-850	293.675	20.525	293.675	1.1196	8.3978	1.1049	1.3281	1.0842
-800	-800	293.350	20.200	293.350	1.1131	8.3490	1.0985	1.3219	1.0791
-750	-750	293.025	19.875	293.025	1.1066	8.3005	1.0921	1.3157	1.0740
-700	-700	292.700	19.550	292.700	1.1002	8.2523	1.0858	1.3095	1.0690
-650	-650	292.375	19.225	292.375	1.0938	8.2042	1.0795	1.3033	1.0639
-600	-600	292.050	18.900	292.050	1.0874	8.1564	1.0732	1.2971	1.0589
-550	-550	291.725	18.575	291.725	1.0810	8.1088	1.0669	1.2910	1.0539
-500	-500	291.400	18.250	291.400	1.0747 + 3	8.0614 + 2	1.0607 + 0	1.2849 + 0	1.0489 + 0
-450	-450	291.075	17.925	291.075	1.0684	8.0143	1.0545	1.2788	1.0439
-400	-400	290.750	17.600	290.750	1.0622	7.9674	1.0483	1.2727	1.0390
-350	-350	290.425	17.275	290.425	1.0560	7.9207	1.0421	1.2667	1.0340
-300	-300	290.100	16.950	290.100	1.0498	7.8742	1.0360	1.2607	1.0291
-250	-250	289.775	16.625	289.775	1.0436	7.8279	1.0299	1.2547	1.0242
-200	-200	289.450	16.300	289.450	1.0375	7.7819	1.0239	1.2487	1.0193
-150	-150	289.125	15.975	289.125	1.0313	7.7361	1.0179	1.2427	1.0145
-100	-100	288.800	15.650	288.800	1.0253	7.6905	1.0119	1.2368	1.0096
-50	-50	288.475	15.325	288.475	1.0192	7.6451	1.0059	1.2309	1.0048
0	0	288.150	15.000	288.150	1.01325 + 3	7.60000 + 2	1.00000 + 0	1.2250 + 0	1.0000 + 0
50	50	287.825	14.675	287.825	1.0072	7.5550	9.9408 - 1	1.2191	9.9521 - 1
100	100	287.500	14.350	287.500	1.0012	7.5103	9.8820	1.2133	9.9043
150	150	287.175	14.025	287.175	9.9535 + 2	7.4658	9.8234	1.2075	9.8568
200	200	286.850	13.700	286.850	9.8945	7.4215	9.7651	1.2017	9.8094
250	250	286.525	13.375	286.525	9.8357	7.3774	9.7071	1.1959	9.7622
300	300	286.200	13.050	286.200	9.7772	7.3335	9.6494	1.1901	9.7151
350	350	285.875	12.725	285.875	9.7190	7.2898	9.5919	1.1844	9.6683
400	400	285.550	12.400	285.550	9.6611	7.2464	9.5347	1.1786	9.6216
450	450	285.225	12.075	285.225	9.6034	7.2031	9.4778	1.1729	9.5751
500	500	284.900	11.750	284.900	9.5460 + 2	7.1601 + 2	9.4212 - 1	1.1673 + 0	9.5287 - 1
550	550	284.575	11.425	284.575	9.4889	7.1173	9.3649	1.1616	9.4826
600	600	284.250	11.100	284.250	9.4321	7.0747	9.3088	1.1560	9.4365
650	650	283.925	10.775	283.925	9.3756	7.0322	9.2530	1.1504	9.3907
700	700	283.600	10.450	283.600	9.3193	6.9900	9.1974	1.1448	9.3451
750	750	283.275	10.125	283.275	9.2633	6.9480	9.1422	1.1392	9.2996
800	800	282.950	9.800	282.950	9.2076	6.9062	9.0872	1.1336	9.2542
850	850	282.625	9.475	282.625	9.1521	6.8647	9.0325	1.1281	9.2091
900	900	282.300	9.150	282.300	9.0970	6.8233	8.9780	1.1226	9.1641
950	950	281.975	8.825	281.975	9.0420	6.7821	8.9238	1.1171	9.1193
1000	1000	281.650	8.500	281.650	8.9874 + 2	6.7411 + 2	8.8699 - 1	1.1116 + 0	9.0746 - 1
1050	1050	281.325	8.175	281.325	8.9330	6.7003	8.8162	1.1062	9.0302
1100	1100	281.000	7.850	281.000	8.8789	6.6597	8.7628	1.1008	8.9858
1150	1150	280.675	7.525	280.675	8.8251	6.6193	8.7097	1.0954	8.9417
1200	1200	280.350	7.200	280.350	8.7715	6.5792	8.6568	1.0900	8.8977
1250	1250	280.025	6.875	280.025	8.7182	6.5392	8.6042	1.0846	8.8539
1300	1300	279.700	6.550	279.700	8.6651	6.4994	8.5518	1.0793	8.8102
1350	1350	279.375	6.225	279.375	8.6124	6.4598	8.4997	1.0739	8.7668
1400	1400	279.050	5.900	279.050	8.5598	6.4204	8.4479	1.0686	8.7234
1450	1450	278.725	5.575	278.725	8.5076	6.3812	8.3963	1.0633	8.6803
1500	1500	278.400	5.250	278.400	8.4555 + 2	6.3422 + 2	8.3450 - 1	1.0581 + 0	8.6373 - 1
1550	1550	278.075	4.925	278.075	8.4038	6.3034	8.2939	1.0528	8.5945
1600	1600	277.750	4.600	277.750	8.3523	6.2647	8.2431	1.0476	8.5518
1650	1650	277.425	4.275	277.425	8.3011	6.2263	8.1925	1.0424	8.5093
1700	1700	277.100	3.950	277.100	8.2501	6.1881	8.1422	1.0372	8.4669
1750	1750	276.775	3.625	276.775	8.1993	6.1500	8.0921	1.0320	8.4248
1800	1801	276.450	3.300	276.450	8.1489	6.1121	8.0423	1.0269	8.3827
1850	1851	276.125	2.975	276.125	8.0986	6.0745	7.9927	1.0218	8.3409
1900	1901	275.800	2.650	275.800	8.0487	6.0370	7.9434	1.0166	8.2992
1950	1951	275.475	2.325	275.475	7.9989	5.9997	7.8943	1.0116	8.2576
2000	2001	275.150	2.000	275.150	7.9495 + 2	5.9626 + 2	7.8455 - 1	1.0065 + 0	8.2162 - 1
2050	2051	274.825	1.675	274.825	7.9002	5.9257	7.7969	1.0014	8.1750
2100	2101	274.500	1.350	274.500	7.8513	5.8889	7.7486	9.9641 - 1	8.1340
2150	2151	274.175	1.025	274.175	7.8025	5.8524	7.7005	9.9140	8.0931
2200	2201	273.850	.700	273.850	7.7540	5.8160	7.6526	9.8641	8.0523
2250	2251	273.525	.375	273.525	7.7058	5.7798	7.6050	9.8143	8.0117
2300	2301	273.200	.050	273.200	7.6578	5.7438	7.5577	9.7648	7.9713
2350	2351	272.875	-.275	272.875	7.6100	5.7080	7.5105	9.7155	7.9310
2400	2401	272.550	-.600	272.550	7.5625	5.6723	7.4636	9.6663	7.8909
2450	2451	272.225	-.925	272.225	7.5152	5.6369	7.4170	9.6174	7.8509
2500	2501	271.900	-1.250	271.900	7.4682 + 2	5.6016 + 2	7.3705 - 1	9.5686 - 1	7.8111 - 1
2550	2551	271.575	-1.575	271.575	7.4214	5.5665	7.3244	9.5200	7.7714
2600	2601	271.250	-1.900	271.250	7.3748	5.5316	7.2784	9.4716	7.7319
2650	2651	270.925	-2.225	270.925	7.3285	5.4968	7.2327	9.4234	7.6926
2700	2701	270.600	-2.550	270.600	7.2824	5.4623	7.1872	9.3754	7.6534
2750	2751	270.275	-2.875	270.275	7.2366	5.4279	7.1419	9.3276	7.6143
2800	2801	269.950	-3.200	269.950	7.1910	5.3936	7.0969	9.2799	7.5755
2850	2851	269.625	-3.525	269.625	7.1456	5.3596	7.0521	9.2325	7.5367
2900	2901	269.300	-3.850	269.300	7.1004	5.3257	7.0076	9.1852	7.4981
2950	2951	268.975	-4.175	268.975	7.0555	5.2920	6.9632	9.1381	7.4597

Table I
Geometric Altitude, Metric Units

Altitude		Temperature			Pressure			Density	
Z (m)	H (m)	T (K)	t (°C)	T_M (K)	P (mb)	P (torr)	P/P_0	ρ (kg/m³)	ρ/ρ_0
-1000	-1000	294.651	21.501	294.651	1.1393 ♦ 3	8.5455 ♦ 2	1.1244 ♦ 0	1.3470 ♦ 0	1.0996 ♦ 0
-950	-950	294.326	21.176	294.326	1.1327	8.4961	1.1179	1.3407	1.0945
-900	-900	294.001	20.851	294.001	1.1261	8.4468	1.1114	1.3344	1.0893
-850	-850	293.676	20.526	293.676	1.1196	8.3979	1.1049	1.3281	1.0842
-800	-800	293.351	20.201	293.351	1.1131	8.3491	1.0985	1.3219	1.0791
-750	-750	293.026	19.876	293.026	1.1066	8.3006	1.0921	1.3157	1.0740
-700	-700	292.701	19.551	292.701	1.1002	8.2523	1.0858	1.3095	1.0690
-650	-650	292.375	19.225	292.375	1.0938	8.2043	1.0795	1.3033	1.0639
-600	-600	292.050	18.900	292.050	1.0874	8.1564	1.0732	1.2971	1.0589
-550	-550	291.725	18.575	291.725	1.0810	8.1088	1.0669	1.2910	1.0539
-500	-500	291.400	18.250	291.400	1.0747 ♦ 3	8.0615 ♦ 2	1.0607 ♦ 0	1.2849 ♦ 0	1.0489 ♦ 0
-450	-450	291.075	17.925	291.075	1.0684	8.0143	1.0545	1.2788	1.0439
-400	-400	290.750	17.600	290.750	1.0622	7.9674	1.0483	1.2727	1.0390
-350	-350	290.425	17.275	290.425	1.0560	7.9207	1.0422	1.2667	1.0340
-300	-300	290.100	16.950	290.100	1.0498	7.8742	1.0360	1.2607	1.0291
-250	-250	289.775	16.625	289.775	1.0436	7.8279	1.0299	1.2547	1.0242
-200	-200	289.450	16.300	289.450	1.0375	7.7819	1.0239	1.2487	1.0193
-150	-150	289.125	15.975	289.125	1.0314	7.7361	1.0179	1.2427	1.0145
-100	-100	288.800	15.650	288.800	1.0253	7.6905	1.0119	1.2368	1.0096
-50	-50	288.475	15.325	288.475	1.0192	7.6451	1.0059	1.2309	1.0048
0	0	288.150	15.000	288.150	1.01325 ♦ 3	7.60000 ♦ 2	1.00000 ♦ 0	1.2250 ♦ 0	1.0000 ♦ 0
50	50	287.825	14.675	287.825	1.0072	7.5550	9.9408 - 1	1.2191	9.9521 - 1
100	100	287.500	14.350	287.500	1.0012	7.5103	9.8820	1.2133	9.9044
150	150	287.175	14.025	287.175	9.9535 ♦ 2	7.4658	9.8234	1.2075	9.8568
200	200	286.850	13.700	286.850	9.8945	7.4215	9.7651	1.2017	9.8094
250	250	286.525	13.375	286.525	9.8357	7.3774	9.7071	1.1959	9.7622
300	300	286.200	13.050	286.200	9.7772	7.3335	9.6494	1.1901	9.7152
350	350	285.875	12.725	285.875	9.7190	7.2898	9.5919	1.1844	9.6683
400	400	285.550	12.400	285.550	9.6611	7.2464	9.5348	1.1786	9.6216
450	450	285.225	12.075	285.225	9.6034	7.2032	9.4779	1.1730	9.5751
500	500	284.900	11.750	284.900	9.5461 ♦ 2	7.1601 ♦ 2	9.4212 - 1	1.1673 ♦ 0	9.5288 - 1
550	550	284.575	11.425	284.575	9.4890	7.1173	9.3649	1.1616	9.4826
600	600	284.250	11.100	284.250	9.4322	7.0747	9.3088	1.1560	9.4366
650	650	283.925	10.775	283.925	9.3756	7.0323	9.2530	1.1504	9.3908
700	700	283.601	10.451	283.601	9.3194	6.9901	9.1975	1.1448	9.3451
750	750	283.276	10.126	283.276	9.2634	6.9481	9.1423	1.1392	9.2996
800	800	282.951	9.801	282.951	9.2077	6.9063	9.0873	1.1337	9.2543
850	850	282.626	9.476	282.626	9.1523	6.8648	9.0326	1.1281	9.2092
900	900	282.301	9.151	282.301	9.0971	6.8234	8.9781	1.1226	9.1642
950	950	281.976	8.826	281.976	9.0422	6.7822	8.9240	1.1171	9.1194
1000	1000	281.651	8.501	281.651	8.9876 ♦ 2	6.7412 ♦ 2	8.8700 - 1	1.1117 ♦ 0	9.0748 - 1
1050	1050	281.326	8.176	281.326	8.9332	6.7005	8.8164	1.1062	9.0303
1100	1100	281.001	7.851	281.001	8.8791	6.6599	8.7630	1.1008	8.9860
1150	1150	280.676	7.526	280.676	8.8253	6.6195	8.7099	1.0954	8.9419
1200	1200	280.351	7.201	280.351	8.7717	6.5793	8.6570	1.0900	8.8979
1250	1250	280.027	6.877	280.027	8.7185	6.5394	8.6044	1.0846	8.8541
1300	1300	279.702	6.552	279.702	8.6654	6.4996	8.5521	1.0793	8.8105
1350	1350	279.377	6.227	279.377	8.6127	6.4600	8.5000	1.0740	8.7670
1400	1400	279.052	5.902	279.052	8.5602	6.4206	8.4482	1.0687	8.7237
1450	1450	278.727	5.577	278.727	8.5079	6.3814	8.3966	1.0634	8.6806
1500	1500	278.402	5.252	278.402	8.4559 ♦ 2	6.3424 ♦ 2	8.3453 - 1	1.0581 ♦ 0	8.6376 - 1
1550	1550	278.077	4.927	278.077	8.4042	6.3036	8.2943	1.0529	8.5948
1600	1600	277.753	4.603	277.753	8.3527	6.2650	8.2435	1.0476	8.5521
1650	1650	277.428	4.278	277.428	8.3015	6.2266	8.1929	1.0424	8.5096
1700	1700	277.103	3.953	277.103	8.2505	6.1884	8.1427	1.0372	8.4673
1750	1750	276.778	3.628	276.778	8.1998	6.1504	8.0926	1.0321	8.4252
1800	1799	276.453	3.303	276.453	8.1494	6.1125	8.0428	1.0269	8.3832
1850	1849	276.128	2.978	276.128	8.0992	6.0749	7.9933	1.0218	8.3413
1900	1899	275.804	2.654	275.804	8.0492	6.0374	7.9440	1.0167	8.2996
1950	1949	275.479	2.329	275.479	7.9995	6.0001	7.8949	1.0116	8.2581
2000	1999	275.154	2.004	275.154	7.9501 ♦ 2	5.9630 ♦ 2	7.8461 - 1	1.0066 ♦ 0	8.2168 - 1
2050	2049	274.829	1.679	274.829	7.9009	5.9261	7.7976	1.0015	8.1756
2100	2099	274.505	1.355	274.505	7.8519	5.8894	7.7493	9.9648 - 1	8.1345
2150	2149	274.180	1.030	274.180	7.8032	5.8529	7.7012	9.9147	8.0936
2200	2199	273.855	.705	273.855	7.7548	5.8165	7.6534	9.8648	8.0529
2250	2249	273.530	.380	273.530	7.7066	5.7804	7.6058	9.8151	8.0124
2300	2299	273.205	.055	273.205	7.6586	5.7444	7.5584	9.7656	7.9719
2350	2349	272.881	-.269	272.881	7.6109	5.7086	7.5113	9.7163	7.9317
2400	2399	272.556	-.594	272.556	7.5634	5.6730	7.4645	9.6672	7.8916
2450	2449	272.231	-.919	272.231	7.5161	5.6375	7.4178	9.6183	7.8517
2500	2499	271.906	-1.244	271.906	7.4691 ♦ 2	5.6023 ♦ 2	7.3715 - 1	9.5695 - 1	7.8119 - 1
2550	2549	271.582	-1.568	271.582	7.4224	5.5672	7.3253	9.5210	7.7722
2600	2599	271.257	-1.893	271.257	7.3758	5.5323	7.2794	9.4726	7.7328
2650	2649	270.932	-2.218	270.932	7.3295	5.4976	7.2337	9.4245	7.6934
2700	2699	270.607	-2.543	270.607	7.2835	5.4631	7.1882	9.3765	7.6543
2750	2749	270.283	-2.867	270.283	7.2377	5.4287	7.1430	9.3287	7.6153
2800	2799	269.958	-3.192	269.958	7.1921	5.3945	7.0980	9.2811	7.5764
2850	2849	269.633	-3.517	269.633	7.1467	5.3605	7.0533	9.2337	7.5377
2900	2899	269.309	-3.841	269.309	7.1016	5.3266	7.0087	9.1865	7.4991
2950	2949	268.984	-4.166	268.984	7.0567	5.2930	6.9644	9.1394	7.4607

Table I
Geopotential Altitude, Metric Units

Altitude		Temperature			Pressure			Density	
H (m)	Z (m)	T (K)	t (°C)	T_M (K)	P (mb)	P (torr)	P/P_0	ρ (kg/m³)	ρ/ρ_0
3000	3001	268.650	−4.500	268.650	7.0108 +2	5.2585 +2	6.9191 −1	9.0912 −1	7.4214 −1
3050	3051	268.325	−4.825	268.325	6.9663	5.2252	6.8752	9.0445	7.3833
3100	3102	268.000	−5.150	268.000	6.9221	5.1920	6.8316	8.9980	7.3453
3150	3152	267.675	−5.475	267.675	6.8781	5.1590	6.7882	8.9516	7.3075
3200	3202	267.350	−5.800	267.350	6.8343	5.1262	6.7450	8.9055	7.2698
3250	3252	267.025	−6.125	267.025	6.7908	5.0935	6.7020	8.8595	7.2322
3300	3302	266.700	−6.450	266.700	6.7474	5.0610	6.6592	8.8137	7.1948
3350	3352	266.375	−6.775	266.375	6.7043	5.0287	6.6167	8.7681	7.1576
3400	3402	266.050	−7.100	266.050	6.6615	4.9965	6.5743	8.7226	7.1205
3450	3452	265.725	−7.425	265.725	6.6188	4.9645	6.5322	8.6774	7.0836
3500	3502	265.400	−7.750	265.400	6.5764 +2	4.9327 +2	6.4904 −1	8.6323 −1	7.0468 −1
3550	3552	265.075	−8.075	265.075	6.5341	4.9010	6.4487	8.5874	7.0101
3600	3602	264.750	−8.400	264.750	6.4921	4.8695	6.4072	8.5427	6.9736
3650	3652	264.425	−8.725	264.425	6.4504	4.8382	6.3660	8.4981	6.9372
3700	3702	264.100	−9.050	264.100	6.4088	4.8070	6.3250	8.4538	6.9010
3750	3752	263.775	−9.375	263.775	6.3675	4.7760	6.2842	8.4096	6.8650
3800	3802	263.450	−9.700	263.450	6.3263	4.7451	6.2436	8.3656	6.8290
3850	3852	263.125	−10.025	263.125	6.2854	4.7144	6.2032	8.3217	6.7933
3900	3902	262.800	−10.350	262.800	6.2447	4.6839	6.1631	8.2781	6.7576
3950	3952	262.475	−10.675	262.475	6.2042	4.6536	6.1231	8.2346	6.7221
4000	4003	262.150	−11.000	262.150	6.1640 +2	4.6233 +2	6.0834 −1	8.1913 −1	6.6868 −1
4050	4053	261.825	−11.325	261.825	6.1239	4.5933	6.0438	8.1482	6.6516
4100	4103	261.500	−11.650	261.500	6.0841	4.5634	6.0045	8.1052	6.6165
4150	4153	261.175	−11.975	261.175	6.0444	4.5337	5.9654	8.0624	6.5816
4200	4203	260.850	−12.300	260.850	6.0050	4.5041	5.9265	8.0198	6.5468
4250	4253	260.525	−12.625	260.525	5.9658	4.4747	5.8878	7.9774	6.5121
4300	4303	260.200	−12.950	260.200	5.9268	4.4454	5.8493	7.9351	6.4776
4350	4353	259.875	−13.275	259.875	5.8880	4.4163	5.8110	7.8930	6.4433
4400	4403	259.550	−13.600	259.550	5.8494	4.3874	5.7729	7.8511	6.4090
4450	4453	259.225	−13.925	259.225	5.8110	4.3586	5.7350	7.8093	6.3750
4500	4503	258.900	−14.250	258.900	5.7728 +2	4.3299 +2	5.6973 −1	7.7677 −1	6.3410 −1
4550	4553	258.575	−14.575	258.575	5.7348	4.3014	5.6598	7.7263	6.3072
4600	4603	258.250	−14.900	258.250	5.6970	4.2731	5.6225	7.6851	6.2735
4650	4653	257.925	−15.225	257.925	5.6594	4.2449	5.5854	7.6440	6.2400
4700	4703	257.600	−15.550	257.600	5.6220	4.2169	5.5485	7.6031	6.2066
4750	4754	257.275	−15.875	257.275	5.5849	4.1890	5.5118	7.5624	6.1734
4800	4804	256.950	−16.200	256.950	5.5479	4.1612	5.4753	7.5218	6.1402
4850	4854	256.625	−16.525	256.625	5.5111	4.1337	5.4390	7.4814	6.1073
4900	4904	256.300	−16.850	256.300	5.4745	4.1062	5.4029	7.4411	6.0744
4950	4954	255.975	−17.175	255.975	5.4381	4.0789	5.3670	7.4011	6.0417
5000	5004	255.650	−17.500	255.650	5.4019 +2	4.0518 +2	5.3313 −1	7.3612 −1	6.0091 −1
5050	5054	255.325	−17.825	255.325	5.3659	4.0248	5.2958	7.3214	5.9767
5100	5104	255.000	−18.150	255.000	5.3301	3.9979	5.2604	7.2818	5.9444
5150	5154	254.675	−18.475	254.675	5.2945	3.9712	5.2253	7.2424	5.9122
5200	5204	254.350	−18.800	254.350	5.2591	3.9447	5.1903	7.2032	5.8801
5250	5254	254.025	−19.125	254.025	5.2239	3.9182	5.1556	7.1641	5.8482
5300	5304	253.700	−19.450	253.700	5.1889	3.8920	5.1210	7.1252	5.8164
5350	5355	253.375	−19.775	253.375	5.1540	3.8658	5.0866	7.0864	5.7848
5400	5405	253.050	−20.100	253.050	5.1194	3.8398	5.0524	7.0478	5.7533
5450	5455	252.725	−20.425	252.725	5.0849	3.8140	5.0184	7.0093	5.7219
5500	5505	252.400	−20.750	252.400	5.0506 +2	3.7883 +2	4.9846 −1	6.9711 −1	5.6907 −1
5550	5555	252.075	−21.075	252.075	5.0165	3.7627	4.9509	6.9329	5.6595
5600	5605	251.750	−21.400	251.750	4.9826	3.7373	4.9175	6.8950	5.6285
5650	5655	251.425	−21.725	251.425	4.9489	3.7120	4.8842	6.8572	5.5977
5700	5705	251.100	−22.050	251.100	4.9154	3.6868	4.8511	6.8195	5.5670
5750	5755	250.775	−22.375	250.775	4.8820	3.6618	4.8182	6.7820	5.5364
5800	5805	250.450	−22.700	250.450	4.8489	3.6370	4.7855	6.7447	5.5059
5850	5855	250.125	−23.025	250.125	4.8159	3.6122	4.7529	6.7075	5.4755
5900	5905	249.800	−23.350	249.800	4.7831	3.5876	4.7206	6.6705	5.4453
5950	5956	249.475	−23.675	249.475	4.7505	3.5631	4.6884	6.6337	5.4152
6000	6006	249.150	−24.000	249.150	4.7181 +2	3.5388 +2	4.6564 −1	6.5970 −1	5.3853 −1
6050	6056	248.825	−24.325	248.825	4.6858	3.5146	4.6245	6.5604	5.3554
6100	6106	248.500	−24.650	248.500	4.6537	3.4906	4.5929	6.5240	5.3257
6150	6156	248.175	−24.975	248.175	4.6218	3.4666	4.5614	6.4878	5.2962
6200	6206	247.850	−25.300	247.850	4.5901	3.4428	4.5301	6.4517	5.2667
6250	6256	247.525	−25.625	247.525	4.5585	3.4192	4.4989	6.4158	5.2374
6300	6306	247.200	−25.950	247.200	4.5272	3.3956	4.4680	6.3800	5.2082
6350	6356	246.875	−26.275	246.875	4.4960	3.3722	4.4372	6.3444	5.1791
6400	6406	246.550	−26.600	246.550	4.4650	3.3490	4.4066	6.3089	5.1501
6450	6457	246.225	−26.925	246.225	4.4341	3.3258	4.3761	6.2736	5.1213
6500	6507	245.900	−27.250	245.900	4.4034 +2	3.3028 +2	4.3459 −1	6.2384 −1	5.0926 −1
6550	6557	245.575	−27.575	245.575	4.3729	3.2800	4.3157	6.2034	5.0640
6600	6607	245.250	−27.900	245.250	4.3426	3.2572	4.2858	6.1686	5.0356
6650	6657	244.925	−28.225	244.925	4.3124	3.2346	4.2560	6.1338	5.0072
6700	6707	244.600	−28.550	244.600	4.2824	3.2121	4.2264	6.0993	4.9790
6750	6757	244.275	−28.875	244.275	4.2526	3.1897	4.1970	6.0649	4.9509
6800	6807	243.950	−29.200	243.950	4.2230	3.1675	4.1677	6.0306	4.9229
6850	6857	243.625	−29.525	243.625	4.1935	3.1454	4.1386	5.9965	4.8951
6900	6907	243.300	−29.850	243.300	4.1642	3.1234	4.1097	5.9625	4.8674
6950	6958	242.975	−30.175	242.975	4.1350	3.1015	4.0809	5.9287	4.8397

Table I
Geometric Altitude, Metric Units

Altitude		Temperature			Pressure			Density	
Z (m)	H (m)	T (K)	t (°C)	T_M (K)	P (mb)	P (torr)	P/P_0	ρ (kg/m³)	ρ/ρ_0
3000	2999	268.659	−4.491	268.659	7.0121 +2	5.2595 +2	6.9204 −1	9.0925 −1	7.4225 −1
3050	3049	268.335	−4.815	268.335	6.9676	5.2261	6.8765	9.0459	7.3844
3100	3098	268.010	−5.140	268.010	6.9234	5.1930	6.8329	8.9994	7.3464
3150	3148	267.685	−5.465	267.685	6.8795	5.1600	6.7895	8.9531	7.3086
3200	3198	267.360	−5.790	267.360	6.8357	5.1272	6.7463	8.9069	7.2710
3250	3248	267.036	−6.114	267.036	6.7922	5.0946	6.7034	8.8610	7.2335
3300	3298	266.711	−6.439	266.711	6.7489	5.0621	6.6607	8.8152	7.1961
3350	3348	266.386	−6.764	266.386	6.7059	5.0298	6.6182	8.7697	7.1589
3400	3398	266.062	−7.088	266.062	6.6630	4.9977	6.5759	8.7243	7.1219
3450	3448	265.737	−7.413	265.737	6.6204	4.9657	6.5338	8.6791	7.0849
3500	3498	265.413	−7.737	265.413	6.5780 +2	4.9339 +2	6.4920 −1	8.6340 −1	7.0482 −1
3550	3548	265.088	−8.062	265.088	6.5358	4.9022	6.4503	8.5892	7.0116
3600	3598	264.763	−8.387	264.763	6.4939	4.8708	6.4089	8.5445	6.9751
3650	3648	264.439	−8.711	264.439	6.4521	4.8395	6.3677	8.5000	6.9388
3700	3698	264.114	−9.036	264.114	6.4106	4.8083	6.3268	8.4557	6.9026
3750	3748	263.789	−9.361	263.789	6.3693	4.7773	6.2860	8.4115	6.8666
3800	3798	263.465	−9.685	263.465	6.3282	4.7465	6.2454	8.3676	6.8307
3850	3848	263.140	−10.010	263.140	6.2873	4.7159	6.2051	8.3238	6.7949
3900	3898	262.816	−10.334	262.816	6.2467	4.6854	6.1650	8.2802	6.7593
3950	3948	262.491	−10.659	262.491	6.2062	4.6550	6.1251	8.2367	6.7239
4000	3997	262.166	−10.984	262.166	6.1660 +2	4.6249 +2	6.0854 −1	8.1935 −1	6.6885 −1
4050	4047	261.842	−11.308	261.842	6.1260	4.5948	6.0459	8.1504	6.6534
4100	4097	261.517	−11.633	261.517	6.0862	4.5650	6.0066	8.1075	6.6183
4150	4147	261.193	−11.957	261.193	6.0466	4.5353	5.9675	8.0647	6.5835
4200	4197	260.868	−12.282	260.868	6.0072	4.5057	5.9286	8.0222	6.5487
4250	4247	260.543	−12.607	260.543	5.9680	4.4764	5.8900	7.9798	6.5141
4300	4297	260.219	−12.931	260.219	5.9290	4.4471	5.8515	7.9376	6.4796
4350	4347	259.894	−13.256	259.894	5.8903	4.4181	5.8132	7.8955	6.4453
4400	4397	259.570	−13.580	259.570	5.8517	4.3891	5.7752	7.8536	6.4111
4450	4447	259.245	−13.905	259.245	5.8134	4.3604	5.7373	7.8119	6.3771
4500	4497	258.921	−14.229	258.921	5.7752 +2	4.3317 +2	5.6997 −1	7.7704 −1	6.3432 −1
4550	4547	258.596	−14.554	258.596	5.7373	4.3033	5.6622	7.7290	6.3094
4600	4597	258.272	−14.878	258.272	5.6995	4.2750	5.6250	7.6878	6.2758
4650	4647	257.947	−15.203	257.947	5.6620	4.2468	5.5879	7.6468	6.2423
4700	4697	257.623	−15.527	257.623	5.6246	4.2188	5.5511	7.6059	6.2089
4750	4746	257.298	−15.852	257.298	5.5875	4.1910	5.5144	7.5652	6.1757
4800	4796	256.974	−16.176	256.974	5.5506	4.1633	5.4780	7.5247	6.1426
4850	4846	256.649	−16.501	256.649	5.5138	4.1357	5.4417	7.4844	6.1097
4900	4896	256.325	−16.825	256.325	5.4773	4.1083	5.4056	7.4442	6.0769
4950	4946	256.000	−17.150	256.000	5.4409	4.0810	5.3698	7.4042	6.0442
5000	4996	255.676	−17.474	255.676	5.4048 +2	4.0539 +2	5.3341 −1	7.3643 −1	6.0117 −1
5050	5046	255.351	−17.799	255.351	5.3688	4.0269	5.2986	7.3246	5.9793
5100	5096	255.027	−18.123	255.027	5.3331	4.0001	5.2633	7.2851	5.9470
5150	5146	254.702	−18.448	254.702	5.2975	3.9734	5.2282	7.2457	5.9149
5200	5196	254.378	−18.772	254.378	5.2621	3.9469	5.1933	7.2065	5.8829
5250	5246	254.053	−19.097	254.053	5.2269	3.9205	5.1586	7.1675	5.8510
5300	5296	253.729	−19.421	253.729	5.1919	3.8943	5.1241	7.1286	5.8192
5350	5346	253.404	−19.746	253.404	5.1571	3.8682	5.0897	7.0899	5.7876
5400	5395	253.080	−20.070	253.080	5.1225	3.8422	5.0556	7.0513	5.7562
5450	5445	252.755	−20.395	252.755	5.0881	3.8164	5.0216	7.0129	5.7248
5500	5495	252.431	−20.719	252.431	5.0539 +2	3.7907 +2	4.9878 −1	6.9747 −1	5.6936 −1
5550	5545	252.106	−21.044	252.106	5.0198	3.7652	4.9542	6.9366	5.6625
5600	5595	251.782	−21.368	251.782	4.9860	3.7398	4.9208	6.8987	5.6316
5650	5645	251.458	−21.692	251.458	4.9523	3.7145	4.8875	6.8610	5.6008
5700	5695	251.133	−22.017	251.133	4.9188	3.6894	4.8545	6.8234	5.5701
5750	5745	250.809	−22.341	250.809	4.8855	3.6644	4.8216	6.7859	5.5395
5800	5795	250.484	−22.666	250.484	4.8524	3.6396	4.7889	6.7487	5.5091
5850	5845	250.160	−22.990	250.160	4.8194	3.6149	4.7564	6.7115	5.4788
5900	5895	249.836	−23.314	249.836	4.7867	3.5903	4.7241	6.6746	5.4486
5950	5944	249.511	−23.639	249.511	4.7541	3.5659	4.6919	6.6378	5.4186
6000	5994	249.187	−23.963	249.187	4.7217 +2	3.5416 +2	4.6600 −1	6.6011 −1	5.3887 −1
6050	6044	248.862	−24.288	248.862	4.6895	3.5174	4.6282	6.5646	5.3589
6100	6094	248.538	−24.612	248.538	4.6575	3.4934	4.5966	6.5283	5.3292
6150	6144	248.214	−24.936	248.214	4.6256	3.4695	4.5651	6.4921	5.2997
6200	6194	247.889	−25.261	247.889	4.5939	3.4457	4.5338	6.4561	5.2703
6250	6244	247.565	−25.585	247.565	4.5624	3.4221	4.5027	6.4202	5.2410
6300	6294	247.241	−25.909	247.241	4.5311	3.3986	4.4718	6.3845	5.2118
6350	6344	246.916	−26.234	246.916	4.4999	3.3752	4.4411	6.3489	5.1828
6400	6394	246.592	−26.558	246.592	4.4689	3.3520	4.4105	6.3135	5.1539
6450	6443	246.267	−26.883	246.267	4.4381	3.3289	4.3801	6.2782	5.1251
6500	6493	245.943	−27.207	245.943	4.4075 +2	3.3059 +2	4.3499 −1	6.2431 −1	5.0964 −1
6550	6543	245.619	−27.531	245.619	4.3770	3.2830	4.3198	6.2081	5.0679
6600	6593	245.294	−27.856	245.294	4.3467	3.2603	4.2899	6.1733	5.0394
6650	6643	244.970	−28.180	244.970	4.3166	3.2377	4.2602	6.1387	5.0112
6700	6693	244.646	−28.504	244.646	4.2867	3.2153	4.2306	6.1042	4.9830
6750	6743	244.322	−28.828	244.322	4.2569	3.1929	4.2012	6.0698	4.9549
6800	6793	243.997	−29.153	243.997	4.2273	3.1707	4.1720	6.0356	4.9270
6850	6843	243.673	−29.477	243.673	4.1978	3.1486	4.1429	6.0015	4.8992
6900	6893	243.349	−29.801	243.349	4.1685	3.1267	4.1140	5.9676	4.8715
6950	6942	243.024	−30.126	243.024	4.1394	3.1048	4.0853	5.9338	4.8439

Table I
Geopotential Altitude, Metric Units

Altitude		Temperature			Pressure			Density	
H (m)	Z (m)	T (K)	t (°C)	T_M (K)	P (mb)	P (torr)	P/P_0	ρ (kg/m³)	ρ/ρ_0
7000	7008	242.650	-30.500	242.650	4.1060 +2	3.0798 +2	4.0523 -1	5.8950 -1	4.8123 -1
7050	7058	242.325	-30.825	242.325	4.0772	3.0581	4.0239	5.8615	4.7849
7100	7108	242.000	-31.150	242.000	4.0485	3.0366	3.9956	5.8281	4.7576
7150	7158	241.675	-31.475	241.675	4.0200	3.0153	3.9675	5.7949	4.7305
7200	7208	241.350	-31.800	241.350	3.9917	2.9940	3.9395	5.7618	4.7035
7250	7258	241.025	-32.125	241.025	3.9635	2.9729	3.9117	5.7288	4.6766
7300	7308	240.700	-32.450	240.700	3.9355	2.9519	3.8841	5.6960	4.6498
7350	7359	240.375	-32.775	240.375	3.9077	2.9310	3.8566	5.6634	4.6231
7400	7409	240.050	-33.100	240.050	3.8800	2.9102	3.8293	5.6308	4.5966
7450	7459	239.725	-33.425	239.725	3.8525	2.8896	3.8021	5.5985	4.5702
7500	7509	239.400	-33.750	239.400	3.8251 +2	2.8690 +2	3.7751 -1	5.5662 -1	4.5439 -1
7550	7559	239.075	-34.075	239.075	3.7979	2.8486	3.7482	5.5341	4.5177
7600	7609	238.750	-34.400	238.750	3.7708	2.8283	3.7215	5.5022	4.4916
7650	7659	238.425	-34.725	238.425	3.7439	2.8082	3.6950	5.4704	4.4656
7700	7709	238.100	-35.050	238.100	3.7172	2.7881	3.6686	5.4387	4.4398
7750	7759	237.775	-35.375	237.775	3.6906	2.7682	3.6423	5.4072	4.4140
7800	7810	237.450	-35.700	237.450	3.6641	2.7483	3.6162	5.3758	4.3884
7850	7860	237.125	-36.025	237.125	3.6379	2.7286	3.5903	5.3446	4.3629
7900	7910	236.800	-36.350	236.800	3.6117	2.7090	3.5645	5.3135	4.3375
7950	7960	236.475	-36.675	236.475	3.5858	2.6895	3.5389	5.2825	4.3122
8000	8010	236.150	-37.000	236.150	3.5599 +2	2.6702 +2	3.5134 -1	5.2517 -1	4.2871 -1
8050	8060	235.825	-37.325	235.825	3.5343	2.6509	3.4880	5.2210	4.2620
8100	8110	235.500	-37.650	235.500	3.5087	2.6318	3.4628	5.1904	4.2371
8150	8160	235.175	-37.975	235.175	3.4834	2.6127	3.4378	5.1600	4.2123
8200	8211	234.850	-38.300	234.850	3.4581	2.5938	3.4129	5.1297	4.1875
8250	8261	234.525	-38.625	234.525	3.4330	2.5750	3.3882	5.0996	4.1629
8300	8311	234.200	-38.950	234.200	3.4081	2.5563	3.3635	5.0696	4.1384
8350	8361	233.875	-39.275	233.875	3.3833	2.5377	3.3391	5.0397	4.1140
8400	8411	233.550	-39.600	233.550	3.3587	2.5192	3.3148	5.0100	4.0898
8450	8461	233.225	-39.925	233.225	3.3342	2.5008	3.2906	4.9804	4.0656
8500	8511	232.900	-40.250	232.900	3.3099 +2	2.4826 +2	3.2666 -1	4.9509 -1	4.0415 -1
8550	8562	232.575	-40.575	232.575	3.2856	2.4644	3.2427	4.9216	4.0176
8600	8612	232.250	-40.900	232.250	3.2616	2.4464	3.2189	4.8924	3.9938
8650	8662	231.925	-41.225	231.925	3.2377	2.4284	3.1953	4.8633	3.9700
8700	8712	231.600	-41.550	231.600	3.2139	2.4106	3.1719	4.8344	3.9464
8750	8762	231.275	-41.875	231.275	3.1903	2.3929	3.1485	4.8055	3.9229
8800	8812	230.950	-42.200	230.950	3.1668	2.3753	3.1254	4.7769	3.8995
8850	8862	230.625	-42.525	230.625	3.1434	2.3577	3.1023	4.7483	3.8762
8900	8912	230.300	-42.850	230.300	3.1202	2.3403	3.0794	4.7199	3.8530
8950	8963	229.975	-43.175	229.975	3.0971	2.3230	3.0566	4.6916	3.8299
9000	9013	229.650	-43.500	229.650	3.0742 +2	2.3058 +2	3.0340 -1	4.6635 -1	3.8069 -1
9050	9063	229.325	-43.825	229.325	3.0514	2.2887	3.0115	4.6355	3.7840
9100	9113	229.000	-44.150	229.000	3.0287	2.2717	2.9891	4.6076	3.7613
9150	9163	228.675	-44.475	228.675	3.0062	2.2548	2.9669	4.5798	3.7386
9200	9213	228.350	-44.800	228.350	2.9838	2.2380	2.9448	4.5522	3.7160
9250	9263	228.025	-45.125	228.025	2.9616	2.2213	2.9228	4.5247	3.6936
9300	9314	227.700	-45.450	227.700	2.9395	2.2048	2.9010	4.4973	3.6712
9350	9364	227.375	-45.775	227.375	2.9175	2.1883	2.8793	4.4700	3.6490
9400	9414	227.050	-46.100	227.050	2.8956	2.1719	2.8578	4.4429	3.6268
9450	9464	226.725	-46.425	226.725	2.8739	2.1556	2.8363	4.4159	3.6048
9500	9514	226.400	-46.750	226.400	2.8523 +2	2.1394 +2	2.8150 -1	4.3890 -1	3.5829 -1
9550	9564	226.075	-47.075	226.075	2.8309	2.1233	2.7938	4.3623	3.5610
9600	9615	225.750	-47.400	225.750	2.8095	2.1073	2.7728	4.3356	3.5393
9650	9665	225.425	-47.725	225.425	2.7883	2.0914	2.7519	4.3091	3.5177
9700	9715	225.100	-48.050	225.100	2.7673	2.0756	2.7311	4.2827	3.4961
9750	9765	224.775	-48.375	224.775	2.7463	2.0599	2.7104	4.2565	3.4747
9800	9815	224.450	-48.700	224.450	2.7255	2.0443	2.6899	4.2304	3.4534
9850	9865	224.125	-49.025	224.125	2.7049	2.0288	2.6695	4.2044	3.4321
9900	9915	223.800	-49.350	223.800	2.6843	2.0134	2.6492	4.1785	3.4110
9950	9966	223.475	-49.675	223.475	2.6639	1.9981	2.6290	4.1527	3.3900
10000	10016	223.150	-50.000	223.150	2.6436 +2	1.9828 +2	2.6090 -1	4.1271 -1	3.3690 -1
10050	10066	222.825	-50.325	222.825	2.6234	1.9677	2.5891	4.1015	3.3482
10100	10116	222.500	-50.650	222.500	2.6034	1.9527	2.5693	4.0761	3.3275
10150	10166	222.175	-50.975	222.175	2.5834	1.9377	2.5496	4.0509	3.3068
10200	10216	221.850	-51.300	221.850	2.5636	1.9229	2.5301	4.0257	3.2863
10250	10267	221.525	-51.625	221.525	2.5439	1.9081	2.5107	4.0007	3.2659
10300	10317	221.200	-51.950	221.200	2.5244	1.8934	2.4914	3.9757	3.2455
10350	10367	220.875	-52.275	220.875	2.5050	1.8789	2.4722	3.9509	3.2253
10400	10417	220.550	-52.600	220.550	2.4856	1.8644	2.4531	3.9263	3.2051
10450	10467	220.225	-52.925	220.225	2.4665	1.8500	2.4342	3.9017	3.1851
10500	10517	219.900	-53.250	219.900	2.4474 +2	1.8357 +2	2.4154 -1	3.8773 -1	3.1651 -1
10550	10568	219.575	-53.575	219.575	2.4284	1.8215	2.3967	3.8529	3.1452
10600	10618	219.250	-53.900	219.250	2.4096	1.8073	2.3781	3.8287	3.1255
10650	10668	218.925	-54.225	218.925	2.3909	1.7933	2.3596	3.8046	3.1058
10700	10718	218.600	-54.550	218.600	2.3723	1.7794	2.3413	3.7806	3.0862
10750	10768	218.275	-54.875	218.275	2.3538	1.7655	2.3230	3.7568	3.0668
10800	10818	217.950	-55.200	217.950	2.3354	1.7517	2.3049	3.7330	3.0474
10850	10869	217.625	-55.525	217.625	2.3172	1.7380	2.2869	3.7094	3.0281
10900	10919	217.300	-55.850	217.300	2.2991	1.7244	2.2690	3.6859	3.0089
10950	10969	216.975	-56.175	216.975	2.2811	1.7109	2.2512	3.6625	2.9898

Table I
Geometric Altitude, Metric Units

Altitude		Temperature			Pressure			Density	
Z (m)	H (m)	T (K)	t (°C)	T_M (K)	P (mb)	P (torr)	P/P_0	ρ (kg/m³)	ρ/ρ_0
7000	6992	242.700	-30.450	242.700	4.1105 + 2	3.0831 + 2	4.0567 - 1	5.9002 - 1	4.8165 - 1
7050	7042	242.376	-30.774	242.376	4.0817	3.0615	4.0283	5.8667	4.7891
7100	7092	242.051	-31.099	242.051	4.0531	3.0400	4.0001	5.8334	4.7619
7150	7142	241.727	-31.423	241.727	4.0246	3.0187	3.9720	5.8002	4.7348
7200	7192	241.403	-31.747	241.403	3.9963	2.9975	3.9441	5.7671	4.7079
7250	7242	241.079	-32.071	241.079	3.9682	2.9764	3.9163	5.7343	4.6810
7300	7292	240.754	-32.396	240.754	3.9402	2.9554	3.8887	5.7015	4.6543
7350	7342	240.430	-32.720	240.430	3.9124	2.9345	3.8612	5.6689	4.6277
7400	7391	240.106	-33.044	240.106	3.8847	2.9138	3.8339	5.6364	4.6012
7450	7441	239.782	-33.368	239.782	3.8573	2.8932	3.8068	5.6041	4.5748
7500	7491	239.457	-33.693	239.457	3.8299 + 2	2.8727 + 2	3.7798 - 1	5.5719 - 1	4.5485 - 1
7550	7541	239.133	-34.017	239.133	3.8027	2.8523	3.7530	5.5399	4.5224
7600	7591	238.809	-34.341	238.809	3.7757	2.8320	3.7263	5.5080	4.4963
7650	7641	238.485	-34.665	238.485	3.7489	2.8119	3.6998	5.4762	4.4704
7700	7691	238.161	-34.989	238.161	3.7221	2.7918	3.6735	5.4446	4.4446
7750	7741	237.836	-35.314	237.836	3.6956	2.7719	3.6473	5.4131	4.4189
7800	7790	237.512	-35.638	237.512	3.6692	2.7521	3.6212	5.3818	4.3933
7850	7840	237.188	-35.962	237.188	3.6429	2.7324	3.5953	5.3506	4.3678
7900	7890	236.864	-36.286	236.864	3.6168	2.7128	3.5695	5.3196	4.3425
7950	7940	236.540	-36.610	236.540	3.5909	2.6934	3.5439	5.2886	4.3173
8000	7990	236.215	-36.935	236.215	3.5651 + 2	2.6740 + 2	3.5185 - 1	5.2579 - 1	4.2921 - 1
8050	8040	235.891	-37.259	235.891	3.5395	2.6548	3.4932	5.2272	4.2671
8100	8090	235.567	-37.583	235.567	3.5140	2.6357	3.4680	5.1967	4.2422
8150	8140	235.243	-37.907	235.243	3.4886	2.6167	3.4430	5.1664	4.2174
8200	8189	234.919	-38.231	234.919	3.4634	2.5978	3.4182	5.1361	4.1928
8250	8239	234.595	-38.555	234.595	3.4384	2.5790	3.3934	5.1060	4.1682
8300	8289	234.270	-38.880	234.270	3.4135	2.5603	3.3689	5.0761	4.1437
8350	8339	233.946	-39.204	233.946	3.3888	2.5418	3.3444	5.0462	4.1194
8400	8389	233.622	-39.528	233.622	3.3641	2.5233	3.3202	5.0166	4.0951
8450	8439	233.298	-39.852	233.298	3.3397	2.5050	3.2960	4.9870	4.0710
8500	8489	232.974	-40.176	232.974	3.3154 + 2	2.4867 + 2	3.2720 - 1	4.9576 - 1	4.0470 - 1
8550	8539	232.650	-40.500	232.650	3.2912	2.4686	3.2482	4.9283	4.0231
8600	8588	232.326	-40.824	232.326	3.2672	2.4506	3.2244	4.8991	3.9993
8650	8638	232.001	-41.149	232.001	3.2433	2.4326	3.2009	4.8701	3.9756
8700	8688	231.677	-41.473	231.677	3.2195	2.4148	3.1774	4.8412	3.9520
8750	8738	231.353	-41.797	231.353	3.1959	2.3971	3.1541	4.8125	3.9285
8800	8788	231.029	-42.121	231.029	3.1725	2.3795	3.1310	4.7838	3.9052
8850	8838	230.705	-42.445	230.705	3.1492	2.3620	3.1080	4.7553	3.8819
8900	8888	230.381	-42.769	230.381	3.1260	2.3447	3.0851	4.7270	3.8588
8950	8937	230.057	-43.093	230.057	3.1029	2.3274	3.0623	4.6987	3.8357
9000	8987	229.733	-43.417	229.733	3.0800 + 2	2.3102 + 2	3.0397 - 1	4.6706 - 1	3.8128 - 1
9050	9037	229.409	-43.741	229.409	3.0573	2.2931	3.0173	4.6427	3.7899
9100	9087	229.085	-44.065	229.085	3.0346	2.2761	2.9949	4.6148	3.7672
9150	9137	228.760	-44.390	228.760	3.0121	2.2593	2.9727	4.5871	3.7446
9200	9187	228.436	-44.714	228.436	2.9898	2.2425	2.9507	4.5595	3.7220
9250	9237	228.112	-45.038	228.112	2.9675	2.2258	2.9287	4.5320	3.6996
9300	9286	227.788	-45.362	227.788	2.9454	2.2093	2.9069	4.5047	3.6773
9350	9336	227.464	-45.686	227.464	2.9235	2.1928	2.8853	4.4775	3.6551
9400	9386	227.140	-46.010	227.140	2.9017	2.1764	2.8637	4.4504	3.6330
9450	9436	226.816	-46.334	226.816	2.8800	2.1601	2.8423	4.4234	3.6110
9500	9486	226.492	-46.658	226.492	2.8584 + 2	2.1440 + 2	2.8210 - 1	4.3966 - 1	3.5891 - 1
9550	9536	226.168	-46.982	226.168	2.8370	2.1279	2.7999	4.3699	3.5673
9600	9586	225.844	-47.306	225.844	2.8157	2.1119	2.7789	4.3433	3.5456
9650	9635	225.520	-47.630	225.520	2.7945	2.0961	2.7580	4.3169	3.5240
9700	9685	225.196	-47.954	225.196	2.7735	2.0803	2.7372	4.2905	3.5025
9750	9735	224.872	-48.278	224.872	2.7526	2.0646	2.7166	4.2643	3.4811
9800	9785	224.548	-48.602	224.548	2.7318	2.0490	2.6961	4.2382	3.4598
9850	9835	224.224	-48.926	224.224	2.7111	2.0335	2.6757	4.2123	3.4386
9900	9885	223.900	-49.250	223.900	2.6906	2.0181	2.6554	4.1864	3.4175
9950	9934	223.576	-49.574	223.576	2.6702	2.0028	2.6353	4.1607	3.3965
10000	9984	223.252	-49.898	223.252	2.6499 + 2	1.9876 + 2	2.6153 - 1	4.1351 - 1	3.3756 - 1
10050	10034	222.928	-50.222	222.928	2.6298	1.9725	2.5954	4.1096	3.3548
10100	10084	222.604	-50.546	222.604	2.6098	1.9575	2.5756	4.0843	3.3341
10150	10134	222.280	-50.870	222.280	2.5899	1.9425	2.5560	4.0590	3.3135
10200	10184	221.956	-51.194	221.956	2.5701	1.9277	2.5365	4.0339	3.2930
10250	10233	221.632	-51.518	221.632	2.5504	1.9130	2.5171	4.0089	3.2726
10300	10283	221.308	-51.842	221.308	2.5309	1.8983	2.4978	3.9840	3.2523
10350	10333	220.984	-52.166	220.984	2.5115	1.8838	2.4786	3.9593	3.2321
10400	10383	220.660	-52.490	220.660	2.4922	1.8693	2.4596	3.9346	3.2119
10450	10433	220.336	-52.814	220.336	2.4730	1.8549	2.4407	3.9101	3.1919
10500	10483	220.013	-53.137	220.013	2.4540 + 2	1.8406 + 2	2.4219 - 1	3.8857 - 1	3.1720 - 1
10550	10533	219.689	-53.461	219.689	2.4350	1.8264	2.4032	3.8614	3.1522
10600	10582	219.365	-53.785	219.365	2.4162	1.8123	2.3846	3.8372	3.1324
10650	10632	219.041	-54.109	219.041	2.3975	1.7983	2.3662	3.8132	3.1128
10700	10682	218.717	-54.433	218.717	2.3790	1.7844	2.3479	3.7892	3.0933
10750	10732	218.393	-54.757	218.393	2.3605	1.7705	2.3296	3.7654	3.0738
10800	10782	218.069	-55.081	218.069	2.3422	1.7568	2.3115	3.7417	3.0545
10850	10832	217.745	-55.405	217.745	2.3239	1.7431	2.2935	3.7181	3.0352
10900	10881	217.421	-55.729	217.421	2.3058	1.7295	2.2757	3.6946	3.0160
10950	10931	217.097	-56.053	217.097	2.2878	1.7160	2.2579	3.6713	2.9970

Table I
Geopotential Altitude, Metric Units

Altitude		Temperature			Pressure			Density	
H (m)	Z (m)	T (K)	t (°C)	T_M (K)	P (mb)	P (torr)	P/P_0	ρ (kg/m³)	ρ/ρ_0
11000	11019	216.650	−56.500	216.650	2.2632 + 2	1.6975 + 2	2.2336 − 1	3.6392 − 1	2.9708 − 1
11100	11119	216.650	−56.500	216.650	2.2277	1.6709	2.1986	3.5822	2.9243
11200	11220	216.650	−56.500	216.650	2.1929	1.6448	2.1642	3.5262	2.8785
11300	11320	216.650	−56.500	216.650	2.1586	1.6191	2.1304	3.4710	2.8335
11400	11420	216.650	−56.500	216.650	2.1248	1.5937	2.0970	3.4167	2.7892
11500	11521	216.650	−56.500	216.650	2.0916	1.5688	2.0642	3.3633	2.7455
11600	11621	216.650	−56.500	216.650	2.0588	1.5442	2.0319	3.3107	2.7026
11700	11722	216.650	−56.500	216.650	2.0266	1.5201	2.0001	3.2589	2.6603
11800	11822	216.650	−56.500	216.650	1.9949	1.4963	1.9688	3.2079	2.6187
11900	11922	216.650	−56.500	216.650	1.9637	1.4729	1.9380	3.1577	2.5777
12000	12023	216.650	−56.500	216.650	1.9330 + 2	1.4498 + 2	1.9077 − 1	3.1083 − 1	2.5374 − 1
12100	12123	216.650	−56.500	216.650	1.9027	1.4272	1.8779	3.0597	2.4977
12200	12223	216.650	−56.500	216.650	1.8730	1.4048	1.8485	3.0118	2.4586
12300	12324	216.650	−56.500	216.650	1.8437	1.3829	1.8196	2.9647	2.4201
12400	12424	216.650	−56.500	216.650	1.8148	1.3612	1.7911	2.9183	2.3823
12500	12525	216.650	−56.500	216.650	1.7864	1.3399	1.7631	2.8726	2.3450
12600	12625	216.650	−56.500	216.650	1.7585	1.3190	1.7355	2.8277	2.3083
12700	12725	216.650	−56.500	216.650	1.7310	1.2983	1.7083	2.7834	2.2722
12800	12826	216.650	−56.500	216.650	1.7039	1.2780	1.6816	2.7399	2.2366
12900	12926	216.650	−56.500	216.650	1.6772	1.2580	1.6553	2.6970	2.2017
13000	13027	216.650	−56.500	216.650	1.6510 + 2	1.2383 + 2	1.6294 − 1	2.6548 − 1	2.1672 − 1
13100	13127	216.650	−56.500	216.650	1.6252	1.2190	1.6039	2.6133	2.1333
13200	13227	216.650	−56.500	216.650	1.5997	1.1999	1.5788	2.5724	2.0999
13300	13328	216.650	−56.500	216.650	1.5747	1.1811	1.5541	2.5322	2.0671
13400	13428	216.650	−56.500	216.650	1.5501	1.1626	1.5298	2.4925	2.0347
13500	13529	216.650	−56.500	216.650	1.5258	1.1444	1.5059	2.4536	2.0029
13600	13629	216.650	−56.500	216.650	1.5019	1.1265	1.4823	2.4152	1.9716
13700	13730	216.650	−56.500	216.650	1.4784	1.1089	1.4591	2.3774	1.9407
13800	13830	216.650	−56.500	216.650	1.4553	1.0916	1.4363	2.3402	1.9104
13900	13930	216.650	−56.500	216.650	1.4325	1.0745	1.4138	2.3036	1.8805
14000	14031	216.650	−56.500	216.650	1.4101 + 2	1.0577 + 2	1.3917 − 1	2.2675 − 1	1.8510 − 1
14100	14131	216.650	−56.500	216.650	1.3881	1.0411	1.3699	2.2321	1.8221
14200	14232	216.650	−56.500	216.650	1.3663	1.0248	1.3485	2.1971	1.7936
14300	14332	216.650	−56.500	216.650	1.3450	1.0088	1.3274	2.1628	1.7655
14400	14433	216.650	−56.500	216.650	1.3239	9.9306 + 1	1.3066	2.1289	1.7379
14500	14533	216.650	−56.500	216.650	1.3032	9.7752	1.2862	2.0956	1.7107
14600	14634	216.650	−56.500	216.650	1.2828	9.6223	1.2660	2.0628	1.6839
14700	14734	216.650	−56.500	216.650	1.2628	9.4718	1.2462	2.0306	1.6576
14800	14835	216.650	−56.500	216.650	1.2430	9.3236	1.2267	1.9988	1.6317
14900	14935	216.650	−56.500	216.650	1.2235	9.1777	1.2075	1.9675	1.6061
15000	15035	216.650	−56.500	216.650	1.2044 + 2	9.0341 + 1	1.1887 − 1	1.9367 − 1	1.5810 − 1
15100	15136	216.650	−56.500	216.650	1.1856	8.8928	1.1701	1.9064	1.5563
15200	15236	216.650	−56.500	216.650	1.1670	8.7536	1.1518	1.8766	1.5319
15300	15337	216.650	−56.500	216.650	1.1488	8.6167	1.1337	1.8473	1.5080
15400	15437	216.650	−56.500	216.650	1.1308	8.4819	1.1160	1.8183	1.4844
15500	15538	216.650	−56.500	216.650	1.1131	8.3492	1.0985	1.7899	1.4611
15600	15638	216.650	−56.500	216.650	1.0957	8.2186	1.0813	1.7619	1.4383
15700	15739	216.650	−56.500	216.650	1.0785	8.0900	1.0644	1.7343	1.4158
15800	15839	216.650	−56.500	216.650	1.0617	7.9634	1.0478	1.7072	1.3936
15900	15940	216.650	−56.500	216.650	1.0450	7.8388	1.0314	1.6805	1.3718
16000	16040	216.650	−56.500	216.650	1.0287 + 2	7.7162 + 1	1.0152 − 1	1.6542 − 1	1.3504 − 1
16100	16141	216.650	−56.500	216.650	1.0126	7.5955	9.9940 − 2	1.6283	1.3292
16200	16241	216.650	−56.500	216.650	9.9680 + 1	7.4766	9.8377	1.6028	1.3084
16300	16342	216.650	−56.500	216.650	9.8121	7.3596	9.6838	1.5778	1.2880
16400	16442	216.650	−56.500	216.650	9.6586	7.2445	9.5323	1.5531	1.2678
16500	16543	216.650	−56.500	216.650	9.5074	7.1312	9.3831	1.5288	1.2480
16600	16643	216.650	−56.500	216.650	9.3587	7.0196	9.2363	1.5049	1.2285
16700	16744	216.650	−56.500	216.650	9.2123	6.9098	9.0918	1.4813	1.2092
16800	16845	216.650	−56.500	216.650	9.0682	6.8017	8.9496	1.4581	1.1903
16900	16945	216.650	−56.500	216.650	8.9263	6.6952	8.8096	1.4353	1.1717
17000	17046	216.650	−56.500	216.650	8.7866 + 1	6.5905 + 1	8.6717 − 2	1.4129 − 1	1.1534 − 1
17100	17146	216.650	−56.500	216.650	8.6492	6.4874	8.5361	1.3908	1.1353
17200	17247	216.650	−56.500	216.650	8.5138	6.3859	8.4025	1.3690	1.1176
17300	17347	216.650	−56.500	216.650	8.3806	6.2860	8.2710	1.3476	1.1001
17400	17448	216.650	−56.500	216.650	8.2495	6.1876	8.1416	1.3265	1.0829
17500	17548	216.650	−56.500	216.650	8.1205	6.0908	8.0143	1.3058	1.0659
17600	17649	216.650	−56.500	216.650	7.9934	5.9955	7.8889	1.2853	1.0492
17700	17749	216.650	−56.500	216.650	7.8684	5.9017	7.7655	1.2652	1.0328
17800	17850	216.650	−56.500	216.650	7.7452	5.8094	7.6440	1.2454	1.0167
17900	17951	216.650	−56.500	216.650	7.6241	5.7185	7.5244	1.2259	1.0008
18000	18051	216.650	−56.500	216.650	7.5048 + 1	5.6290 + 1	7.4067 − 2	1.2068 − 1	9.8511 − 2
18100	18152	216.650	−56.500	216.650	7.3874	5.5410	7.2908	1.1879	9.6970
18200	18252	216.650	−56.500	216.650	7.2718	5.4543	7.1767	1.1693	9.5453
18300	18353	216.650	−56.500	216.650	7.1580	5.3690	7.0644	1.1510	9.3959
18400	18453	216.650	−56.500	216.650	7.0460	5.2850	6.9539	1.1330	9.2489
18500	18554	216.650	−56.500	216.650	6.9358	5.2023	6.8451	1.1153	9.1042
18600	18655	216.650	−56.500	216.650	6.8273	5.1209	6.7380	1.0978	8.9618
18700	18755	216.650	−56.500	216.650	6.7205	5.0408	6.6326	1.0806	8.8216
18800	18856	216.650	−56.500	216.650	6.6153	4.9619	6.5288	1.0637	8.6836
18900	18956	216.650	−56.500	216.650	6.5118	4.8843	6.4267	1.0471	8.5477

Table I
Geometric Altitude, Metric Units

Altitude		Temperature			Pressure						Density			
Z (m)	H (m)	T (K)	t (°C)	T_M (K)	P (mb)		P (torr)		P/P_0		ρ (kg/m³)		ρ/ρ_0	
11000	10981	216.774	−56.376	216.774	2.2699	+ 2	1.7026	+ 2	2.2403	− 1	3.6480	− 1	2.9780	− 1
11100	11081	216.650	−56.500	216.650	2.2346		1.6760		2.2053		3.5932		2.9332	
11200	11180	216.650	−56.500	216.650	2.1997		1.6499		2.1710		3.5372		2.8875	
11300	11280	216.650	−56.500	216.650	2.1654		1.6242		2.1371		3.4820		2.8425	
11400	11380	216.650	−56.500	216.650	2.1317		1.5989		2.1038		3.4277		2.7982	
11500	11479	216.650	−56.500	216.650	2.0984		1.5739		2.0710		3.3743		2.7545	
11600	11579	216.650	−56.500	216.650	2.0657		1.5494		2.0387		3.3217		2.7116	
11700	11679	216.650	−56.500	216.650	2.0335		1.5252		2.0069		3.2699		2.6693	
11800	11778	216.650	−56.500	216.650	2.0018		1.5015		1.9756		3.2190		2.6277	
11900	11878	216.650	−56.500	216.650	1.9706		1.4781		1.9448		3.1688		2.5868	
12000	11977	216.650	−56.500	216.650	1.9399	+ 2	1.4550	+ 2	1.9145	− 1	3.1194	− 1	2.5464	− 1
12100	12077	216.650	−56.500	216.650	1.9097		1.4323		1.8847		3.0708		2.5067	
12200	12177	216.650	−56.500	216.650	1.8799		1.4100		1.8553		3.0229		2.4677	
12300	12276	216.650	−56.500	216.650	1.8506		1.3880		1.8264		2.9758		2.4292	
12400	12376	216.650	−56.500	216.650	1.8218		1.3664		1.7979		2.9294		2.3914	
12500	12475	216.650	−56.500	216.650	1.7934		1.3451		1.7699		2.8838		2.3541	
12600	12575	216.650	−56.500	216.650	1.7654		1.3242		1.7423		2.8388		2.3174	
12700	12675	216.650	−56.500	216.650	1.7379		1.3035		1.7152		2.7946		2.2813	
12800	12774	216.650	−56.500	216.650	1.7108		1.2832		1.6884		2.7510		2.2457	
12900	12874	216.650	−56.500	216.650	1.6842		1.2632		1.6621		2.7082		2.2107	
13000	12973	216.650	−56.500	216.650	1.6579	+ 2	1.2435	+ 2	1.6362	− 1	2.6660	− 1	2.1763	− 1
13100	13073	216.650	−56.500	216.650	1.6321		1.2241		1.6107		2.6244		2.1424	
13200	13173	216.650	−56.500	216.650	1.6066		1.2051		1.5856		2.5835		2.1090	
13300	13272	216.650	−56.500	216.650	1.5816		1.1863		1.5609		2.5433		2.0761	
13400	13372	216.650	−56.500	216.650	1.5570		1.1678		1.5366		2.5037		2.0438	
13500	13471	216.650	−56.500	216.650	1.5327		1.1496		1.5127		2.4646		2.0120	
13600	13571	216.650	−56.500	216.650	1.5088		1.1317		1.4891		2.4263		1.9806	
13700	13671	216.650	−56.500	216.650	1.4853		1.1141		1.4659		2.3885		1.9498	
13800	13770	216.650	−56.500	216.650	1.4622		1.0967		1.4431		2.3512		1.9194	
13900	13870	216.650	−56.500	216.650	1.4394		1.0796		1.4206		2.3146		1.8895	
14000	13969	216.650	−56.500	216.650	1.4170	+ 2	1.0628	+ 2	1.3985	− 1	2.2786	− 1	1.8601	− 1
14100	14069	216.650	−56.500	216.650	1.3949		1.0463		1.3767		2.2431		1.8311	
14200	14168	216.650	−56.500	216.650	1.3732		1.0300		1.3552		2.2081		1.8026	
14300	14268	216.650	−56.500	216.650	1.3518		1.0139		1.3341		2.1737		1.7745	
14400	14367	216.650	−56.500	216.650	1.3307		9.9817	+ 1	1.3133		2.1399		1.7468	
14500	14467	216.650	−56.500	216.650	1.3100		9.8262		1.2929		2.1066		1.7196	
14600	14567	216.650	−56.500	216.650	1.2896		9.6732		1.2727		2.0737		1.6929	
14700	14666	216.650	−56.500	216.650	1.2695		9.5226		1.2529		2.0414		1.6665	
14800	14766	216.650	−56.500	216.650	1.2498		9.3743		1.2334		2.0097		1.6405	
14900	14865	216.650	−56.500	216.650	1.2303		9.2283		1.2142		1.9784		1.6150	
15000	14965	216.650	−56.500	216.650	1.2111	+ 2	9.0846	+ 1	1.1953	− 1	1.9476	− 1	1.5898	− 1
15100	15064	216.650	−56.500	216.650	1.1923		8.9431		1.1767		1.9172		1.5651	
15200	15164	216.650	−56.500	216.650	1.1737		8.8038		1.1584		1.8874		1.5407	
15300	15263	216.650	−56.500	216.650	1.1554		8.6668		1.1403		1.8580		1.5167	
15400	15363	216.650	−56.500	216.650	1.1374		8.5318		1.1226		1.8291		1.4931	
15500	15462	216.650	−56.500	216.650	1.1197		8.3990		1.1051		1.8006		1.4699	
15600	15562	216.650	−56.500	216.650	1.1023		8.2682		1.0879		1.7725		1.4470	
15700	15661	216.650	−56.500	216.650	1.0851		8.1395		1.0709		1.7449		1.4244	
15800	15761	216.650	−56.500	216.650	1.0682		8.0128		1.0543		1.7178		1.4023	
15900	15860	216.650	−56.500	216.650	1.0516		7.8880		1.0379		1.6910		1.3804	
16000	15960	216.650	−56.500	216.650	1.0352	+ 2	7.7652	+ 1	1.0217	− 1	1.6647	− 1	1.3589	− 1
16100	16059	216.650	−56.500	216.650	1.0191		7.6443		1.0058		1.6388		1.3378	
16200	16159	216.650	−56.500	216.650	1.0033		7.5253		9.9018	− 2	1.6133		1.3170	
16300	16258	216.650	−56.500	216.650	9.8768	+ 1	7.4082		9.7476		1.5882		1.2965	
16400	16358	216.650	−56.500	216.650	9.7231		7.2929		9.5959		1.5635		1.2763	
16500	16457	216.650	−56.500	216.650	9.5717		7.1794		9.4465		1.5391		1.2564	
16600	16557	216.650	−56.500	216.650	9.4227		7.0676		9.2995		1.5152		1.2369	
16700	16656	216.650	−56.500	216.650	9.2761		6.9576		9.1548		1.4916		1.2176	
16800	16756	216.650	−56.500	216.650	9.1317		6.8493		9.0123		1.4684		1.1987	
16900	16855	216.650	−56.500	216.650	8.9896		6.7427		8.8720		1.4455		1.1800	
17000	16955	216.650	−56.500	216.650	8.8497	+ 1	6.6378	+ 1	8.7340	− 2	1.4230	− 1	1.1616	− 1
17100	17054	216.650	−56.500	216.650	8.7120		6.5345		8.5980		1.4009		1.1436	
17200	17154	216.650	−56.500	216.650	8.5764		6.4328		8.4642		1.3791		1.1258	
17300	17253	216.650	−56.500	216.650	8.4429		6.3327		8.3325		1.3576		1.1083	
17400	17352	216.650	−56.500	216.650	8.3115		6.2342		8.2029		1.3365		1.0910	
17500	17452	216.650	−56.500	216.650	8.1822		6.1372		8.0752		1.3157		1.0740	
17600	17551	216.650	−56.500	216.650	8.0549		6.0417		7.9496		1.2952		1.0573	
17700	17651	216.650	−56.500	216.650	7.9296		5.9477		7.8259		1.2751		1.0409	
17800	17750	216.650	−56.500	216.650	7.8062		5.8551		7.7041		1.2552		1.0247	
17900	17850	216.650	−56.500	216.650	7.6847		5.7640		7.5843		1.2357		1.0087	
18000	17949	216.650	−56.500	216.650	7.5652	+ 1	5.6743	+ 1	7.4663	− 2	1.2165	− 1	9.9304	− 2
18100	18049	216.650	−56.500	216.650	7.4475		5.5861		7.3501		1.1975		9.7759	
18200	18148	216.650	−56.500	216.650	7.3316		5.4992		7.2358		1.1789		9.6238	
18300	18247	216.650	−56.500	216.650	7.2176		5.4136		7.1232		1.1606		9.4741	
18400	18347	216.650	−56.500	216.650	7.1053		5.3294		7.0124		1.1425		9.3267	
18500	18446	216.650	−56.500	216.650	6.9948		5.2465		6.9033		1.1248		9.1816	
18600	18546	216.650	−56.500	216.650	6.8860		5.1649		6.7959		1.1073		9.0388	
18700	18645	216.650	−56.500	216.650	6.7789		5.0845		6.6902		1.0900		8.8982	
18800	18745	216.650	−56.500	216.650	6.6734		5.0055		6.5862		1.0731		8.7598	
18900	18844	216.650	−56.500	216.650	6.5696		4.9276		6.4837		1.0564		8.6236	

Table I
Geopotential Altitude, Metric Units

Altitude		Temperature			Pressure			Density	
H (m)	Z (m)	T (K)	t (°C)	T_M (K)	P (mb)	P (torr)	P/P_0	ρ (kg/m³)	ρ/ρ_0
19000	19057	216.650	-56.500	216.650	6.4100 ·1	4.8078 ·1	6.3261 -2	1.0307 -1	8.4140 -2
19100	19158	216.650	-56.500	216.650	6.3097	4.7326	6.2272	1.0146	8.2823
19200	19258	216.650	-56.500	216.650	6.2110	4.6586	6.1297	9.9871 -2	8.1528
19300	19359	216.650	-56.500	216.650	6.1138	4.5857	6.0338	9.8309	8.0252
19400	19459	216.650	-56.500	216.650	6.0181	4.5140	5.9394	9.6771	7.8997
19500	19560	216.650	-56.500	216.650	5.9240	4.4433	5.8465	9.5257	7.7761
19600	19661	216.650	-56.500	216.650	5.8313	4.3738	5.7550	9.3767	7.6544
19700	19761	216.650	-56.500	216.650	5.7401	4.3054	5.6650	9.2300	7.5347
19800	19862	216.650	-56.500	216.650	5.6503	4.2380	5.5764	9.0856	7.4168
19900	19962	216.650	-56.500	216.650	5.5619	4.1717	5.4891	8.9434	7.3007
20000	20063	216.650	-56.500	216.650	5.4748 ·1	4.1065 ·1	5.4032 -2	8.8035 -2	7.1865 -2
20100	20164	216.750	-56.400	216.750	5.3892	4.0422	5.3187	8.6618	7.0708
20200	20264	216.850	-56.300	216.850	5.3049	3.9790	5.2356	8.5224	6.9571
20300	20365	216.950	-56.200	216.950	5.2220	3.9168	5.1538	8.3854	6.8452
20400	20466	217.050	-56.100	217.050	5.1405	3.8557	5.0732	8.2506	6.7352
20500	20566	217.150	-56.000	217.150	5.0602	3.7955	4.9940	8.1180	6.6270
20600	20667	217.250	-55.900	217.250	4.9812	3.7362	4.9161	7.9877	6.5205
20700	20768	217.350	-55.800	217.350	4.9035	3.6779	4.8394	7.8595	6.4159
20800	20868	217.450	-55.700	217.450	4.8271	3.6206	4.7640	7.7334	6.3129
20900	20969	217.550	-55.600	217.550	4.7519	3.5642	4.6897	7.6093	6.2117
21000	21070	217.650	-55.500	217.650	4.6778 ·1	3.5087 ·1	4.6167 -2	7.4874 -2	6.1121 -2
21100	21170	217.750	-55.400	217.750	4.6050	3.4540	4.5448	7.3674	6.0142
21200	21271	217.850	-55.300	217.850	4.5333	3.4003	4.4740	7.2494	5.9179
21300	21372	217.950	-55.200	217.950	4.4628	3.3474	4.4044	7.1334	5.8232
21400	21472	218.050	-55.100	218.050	4.3934	3.2953	4.3360	7.0192	5.7300
21500	21573	218.150	-55.000	218.150	4.3251	3.2441	4.2686	6.9070	5.6383
21600	21674	218.250	-54.900	218.250	4.2579	3.1937	4.2023	6.7965	5.5482
21700	21774	218.350	-54.800	218.350	4.1918	3.1441	4.1370	6.6879	5.4595
21800	21875	218.450	-54.700	218.450	4.1268	3.0953	4.0728	6.5811	5.3724
21900	21976	218.550	-54.600	218.550	4.0627	3.0473	4.0096	6.4761	5.2866
22000	22076	218.650	-54.500	218.650	3.9997 ·1	3.0000 ·1	3.9474 -2	6.3727 -2	5.2022 -2
22100	22177	218.750	-54.400	218.750	3.9377	2.9535	3.8862	6.2711	5.1193
22200	22278	218.850	-54.300	218.850	3.8767	2.9078	3.8260	6.1711	5.0376
22300	22379	218.950	-54.200	218.950	3.8167	2.8627	3.7668	6.0728	4.9574
22400	22479	219.050	-54.100	219.050	3.7576	2.8184	3.7085	5.9760	4.8784
22500	22580	219.150	-54.000	219.150	3.6995	2.7748	3.6511	5.8809	4.8007
22600	22681	219.250	-53.900	219.250	3.6423	2.7319	3.5946	5.7873	4.7243
22700	22781	219.350	-53.800	219.350	3.5860	2.6897	3.5391	5.6953	4.6492
22800	22882	219.450	-53.700	219.450	3.5306	2.6481	3.4844	5.6047	4.5753
22900	22983	219.550	-53.600	219.550	3.4760	2.6072	3.4306	5.5156	4.5026
23000	23084	219.650	-53.500	219.650	3.4224 ·1	2.5670 ·1	3.3776 -2	5.4280 -2	4.4310 -2
23100	23184	219.750	-53.400	219.750	3.3696	2.5274	3.3255	5.3418	4.3607
23200	23285	219.850	-53.300	219.850	3.3176	2.4884	3.2742	5.2571	4.2915
23300	23386	219.950	-53.200	219.950	3.2665	2.4500	3.2237	5.1737	4.2234
23400	23486	220.050	-53.100	220.050	3.2161	2.4123	3.1741	5.0916	4.1564
23500	23587	220.150	-53.000	220.150	3.1666	2.3751	3.1252	5.0109	4.0906
23600	23688	220.250	-52.900	220.250	3.1178	2.3386	3.0771	4.9316	4.0258
23700	23789	220.350	-52.800	220.350	3.0699	2.3026	3.0297	4.8535	3.9620
23800	23889	220.450	-52.700	220.450	3.0226	2.2672	2.9831	4.7766	3.8993
23900	23990	220.550	-52.600	220.550	2.9762	2.2323	2.9373	4.7011	3.8376
24000	24091	220.650	-52.500	220.650	2.9304 ·1	2.1980 ·1	2.8921 -2	4.6267 -2	3.7769 -2
24100	24192	220.750	-52.400	220.750	2.8854	2.1642	2.8477	4.5536	3.7172
24200	24292	220.850	-52.300	220.850	2.8411	2.1310	2.8040	4.4817	3.6585
24300	24393	220.950	-52.200	220.950	2.7975	2.0983	2.7609	4.4109	3.6007
24400	24494	221.050	-52.100	221.050	2.7546	2.0661	2.7186	4.3413	3.5439
24500	24595	221.150	-52.000	221.150	2.7124	2.0344	2.6769	4.2728	3.4880
24600	24696	221.250	-51.900	221.250	2.6708	2.0033	2.6359	4.2054	3.4330
24700	24796	221.350	-51.800	221.350	2.6299	1.9726	2.5955	4.1391	3.3788
24800	24897	221.450	-51.700	221.450	2.5896	1.9424	2.5558	4.0739	3.3256
24900	24998	221.550	-51.600	221.550	2.5500	1.9126	2.5166	4.0097	3.2732
25000	25099	221.650	-51.500	221.650	2.5110 ·1	1.8834 ·1	2.4781 -2	3.9466 -2	3.2217 -2
25100	25200	221.750	-51.400	221.750	2.4726	1.8546	2.4402	3.8845	3.1710
25200	25300	221.850	-51.300	221.850	2.4348	1.8262	2.4029	3.8234	3.1211
25300	25401	221.950	-51.200	221.950	2.3976	1.7983	2.3662	3.7633	3.0721
25400	25502	222.050	-51.100	222.050	2.3610	1.7709	2.3301	3.7041	3.0238
25500	25603	222.150	-51.000	222.150	2.3249	1.7438	2.2945	3.6460	2.9763
25600	25704	222.250	-50.900	222.250	2.2895	1.7172	2.2595	3.5887	2.9296
25700	25804	222.350	-50.800	222.350	2.2545	1.6910	2.2251	3.5324	2.8836
25800	25905	222.450	-50.700	222.450	2.2202	1.6653	2.1911	3.4770	2.8383
25900	26006	222.550	-50.600	222.550	2.1863	1.6399	2.1578	3.4225	2.7938
26000	26107	222.650	-50.500	222.650	2.1530 ·1	1.6149 ·1	2.1249 -2	3.3688 -2	2.7501 -2
26100	26203	222.750	-50.400	222.750	2.1203	1.5903	2.0925	3.3160	2.7070
26200	26308	222.850	-50.300	222.850	2.0880	1.5661	2.0607	3.2641	2.6646
26300	26409	222.950	-50.200	222.950	2.0562	1.5423	2.0294	3.2130	2.6229
26400	26510	223.050	-50.100	223.050	2.0250	1.5188	1.9985	3.1628	2.5819
26500	26611	223.150	-50.000	223.150	1.9942	1.4958	1.9681	3.1133	2.5415
26600	26712	223.250	-49.900	223.250	1.9639	1.4730	1.9382	3.0646	2.5018
26700	26813	223.350	-49.800	223.350	1.9341	1.4507	1.9088	3.0168	2.4627
26800	26913	223.450	-49.700	223.450	1.9047	1.4287	1.8798	2.9697	2.4242
26900	27014	223.550	-49.600	223.550	1.8758	1.4070	1.8513	2.9233	2.3864

Table I
Geometric Altitude, Metric Units

Altitude		Temperature			Pressure			Density	
Z (m)	H (m)	T (K)	t (°C)	T_M (K)	P (mb)	P (torr)	P/P_0	ρ (kg/m³)	ρ/ρ_0
19000	18943	216.650	-56.500	216.650	6.4674 +1	4.8510 +1	6.3829 -2	1.0400 -1	8.4894 -2
19100	19043	216.650	-56.500	216.650	6.3669	4.7755	6.2836	1.0238	8.3574
19200	19142	216.650	-56.500	216.650	6.2678	4.7013	6.1859	1.0079	8.2274
19300	19242	216.650	-56.500	216.650	6.1704	4.6281	6.0897	9.9219 -2	8.0995
19400	19341	216.650	-56.500	216.650	6.0744	4.5562	5.9950	9.7676	7.9735
19500	19440	216.650	-56.500	216.650	5.9799	4.4853	5.9017	9.6157	7.8495
19600	19540	216.650	-56.500	216.650	5.8870	4.4156	5.8100	9.4662	7.7275
19700	19639	216.650	-56.500	216.650	5.7954	4.3469	5.7196	9.3190	7.6073
19800	19739	216.650	-56.500	216.650	5.7053	4.2793	5.6307	9.1741	7.4890
19900	19838	216.650	-56.500	216.650	5.6166	4.2128	5.5431	9.0314	7.3726
20000	19937	216.650	-56.500	216.650	5.5293 +1	4.1473 +1	5.4570 -2	8.8910 -2	7.2580 -2
20100	20037	216.687	-56.463	216.687	5.4433	4.0828	5.3721	8.7513	7.1439
20200	20136	216.786	-56.364	216.786	5.3587	4.0193	5.2886	8.6113	7.0297
20300	20235	216.885	-56.265	216.885	5.2755	3.9569	5.2065	8.4737	6.9173
20400	20335	216.985	-56.165	216.985	5.1936	3.8955	5.1256	8.3383	6.8068
20500	20434	217.084	-56.066	217.084	5.1130	3.8350	5.0461	8.2052	6.6981
20600	20533	217.183	-55.967	217.183	5.0336	3.7755	4.9678	8.0742	6.5912
20700	20633	217.283	-55.867	217.283	4.9556	3.7170	4.8908	7.9454	6.4860
20800	20732	217.382	-55.768	217.382	4.8788	3.6594	4.8150	7.8187	6.3826
20900	20832	217.482	-55.668	217.482	4.8033	3.6027	4.7404	7.6941	6.2809
21000	20931	217.581	-55.569	217.581	4.7289 +1	3.5469 +1	4.6671 -2	7.5715 -2	6.1808 -2
21100	21030	217.680	-55.470	217.680	4.6557	3.4921	4.5948	7.4509	6.0824
21200	21130	217.780	-55.370	217.780	4.5837	3.4381	4.5238	7.3324	5.9856
21300	21229	217.879	-55.271	217.879	4.5129	3.3849	4.4538	7.2157	5.8904
21400	21328	217.978	-55.172	217.978	4.4431	3.3326	4.3850	7.1010	5.7967
21500	21428	218.078	-55.072	218.078	4.3745	3.2811	4.3173	6.9881	5.7046
21600	21527	218.177	-54.973	218.177	4.3070	3.2305	4.2507	6.8771	5.6140
21700	21626	218.276	-54.874	218.276	4.2405	3.1806	4.1851	6.7680	5.5249
21800	21725	218.375	-54.775	218.375	4.1751	3.1316	4.1205	6.6606	5.4372
21900	21825	218.475	-54.675	218.475	4.1108	3.0833	4.0570	6.5549	5.3509
22000	21924	218.574	-54.576	218.574	4.0475 +1	3.0358 +1	3.9945 -2	6.4510 -2	5.2661 -2
22100	22023	218.673	-54.477	218.673	3.9851	2.9891	3.9330	6.3488	5.1827
22200	22123	218.773	-54.377	218.773	3.9238	2.9431	3.8725	6.2482	5.1006
22300	22222	218.872	-54.278	218.872	3.8634	2.8978	3.8129	6.1493	5.0198
22400	22321	218.971	-54.179	218.971	3.8040	2.8532	3.7543	6.0520	4.9404
22500	22421	219.071	-54.079	219.071	3.7455	2.8094	3.6966	5.9563	4.8623
22600	22520	219.170	-53.980	219.170	3.6880	2.7662	3.6398	5.8621	4.7854
22700	22619	219.269	-53.881	219.269	3.6314	2.7237	3.5839	5.7695	4.7098
22800	22719	219.369	-53.781	219.369	3.5757	2.6819	3.5289	5.6784	4.6354
22900	22818	219.468	-53.682	219.468	3.5208	2.6408	3.4748	5.5888	4.5622
23000	22917	219.567	-53.583	219.567	3.4668 +1	2.6003 +1	3.4215 -2	5.5006 -2	4.4903 -2
23100	23016	219.666	-53.484	219.666	3.4137	2.5605	3.3690	5.4138	4.4195
23200	23116	219.766	-53.384	219.766	3.3614	2.5212	3.3174	5.3285	4.3498
23300	23215	219.865	-53.285	219.865	3.3099	2.4826	3.2666	5.2445	4.2813
23400	23314	219.964	-53.186	219.964	3.2593	2.4446	3.2167	5.1620	4.2138
23500	23413	220.063	-53.087	220.063	3.2094	2.4073	3.1675	5.0807	4.1475
23600	23513	220.163	-52.987	220.163	3.1604	2.3705	3.1190	5.0008	4.0823
23700	23612	220.262	-52.888	220.262	3.1121	2.3342	3.0714	4.9221	4.0181
23800	23711	220.361	-52.789	220.361	3.0645	2.2986	3.0245	4.8448	3.9549
23900	23810	220.460	-52.690	220.460	3.0177	2.2635	2.9783	4.7687	3.8928
24000	23910	220.560	-52.590	220.560	2.9717 +1	2.2289 +1	2.9328 -2	4.6938 -2	3.8317 -2
24100	24009	220.659	-52.491	220.659	2.9264	2.1949	2.8881	4.6201	3.7715
24200	24108	220.758	-52.392	220.758	2.8818	2.1615	2.8441	4.5476	3.7124
24300	24207	220.857	-52.293	220.857	2.8379	2.1286	2.8007	4.4763	3.6542
24400	24307	220.957	-52.193	220.957	2.7946	2.0961	2.7581	4.4062	3.5969
24500	24406	221.056	-52.094	221.056	2.7521	2.0642	2.7161	4.3372	3.5405
24600	24505	221.155	-51.995	221.155	2.7102	2.0328	2.6748	4.2693	3.4851
24700	24604	221.254	-51.896	221.254	2.6690	2.0019	2.6341	4.2024	3.4306
24800	24704	221.354	-51.796	221.354	2.6284	1.9715	2.5940	4.1367	3.3769
24900	24803	221.453	-51.697	221.453	2.5885	1.9415	2.5546	4.0720	3.3241
25000	24902	221.552	-51.598	221.552	2.5492 +1	1.9120 +1	2.5158 -2	4.0084 -2	3.2722 -2
25100	25001	221.651	-51.499	221.651	2.5105	1.8830	2.4776	3.9458	3.2210
25200	25100	221.750	-51.400	221.750	2.4724	1.8544	2.4401	3.8842	3.1708
25300	25200	221.850	-51.300	221.850	2.4349	1.8263	2.4031	3.8236	3.1213
25400	25299	221.949	-51.201	221.949	2.3980	1.7986	2.3666	3.7639	3.0726
25500	25398	222.048	-51.102	222.048	2.3617	1.7714	2.3308	3.7052	3.0247
25600	25497	222.147	-51.003	222.147	2.3259	1.7445	2.2955	3.6475	2.9776
25700	25597	222.247	-50.903	222.247	2.2907	1.7181	2.2607	3.5907	2.9312
25800	25696	222.346	-50.804	222.346	2.2560	1.6921	2.2265	3.5348	2.8855
25900	25795	222.445	-50.705	222.445	2.2219	1.6666	2.1929	3.4798	2.8406
26000	25894	222.544	-50.606	222.544	2.1883 +1	1.6414 +1	2.1597 -2	3.4257 -2	2.7965 -2
26100	25993	222.643	-50.507	222.643	2.1553	1.6166	2.1271	3.3724	2.7530
26200	26092	222.742	-50.408	222.742	2.1227	1.5922	2.0950	3.3200	2.7102
26300	26192	222.842	-50.308	222.842	2.0907	1.5681	2.0633	3.2684	2.6681
26400	26291	222.941	-50.209	222.941	2.0591	1.5445	2.0322	3.2177	2.6267
26500	26390	223.040	-50.110	223.040	2.0281	1.5212	2.0016	3.1678	2.5859
26600	26489	223.139	-50.011	223.139	1.9975	1.4983	1.9714	3.1186	2.5458
26700	26588	223.238	-49.912	223.238	1.9674	1.4757	1.9417	3.0703	2.5064
26800	26687	223.337	-49.813	223.337	1.9378	1.4535	1.9125	3.0227	2.4675
26900	26787	223.437	-49.713	223.437	1.9086	1.4316	1.8837	2.9759	2.4293

Table I
Geopotential Altitude, Metric Units

Altitude		Temperature			Pressure			Density	
H (m)	Z (m)	T (K)	t (°C)	T_M (K)	P (mb)	P (torr)	P/P_0	ρ (kg/m³)	ρ/ρ_0
27000	27115	223.650	-49.500	223.650	1.8474 +1	1.3857 +1	1.8232 -2	2.8777 -2	2.3491 -2
27100	27216	223.750	-49.400	223.750	1.8194	1.3647	1.7956	2.8328	2.3125
27200	27317	223.850	-49.300	223.850	1.7918	1.3440	1.7684	2.7886	2.2764
27300	27418	223.950	-49.200	223.950	1.7647	1.3236	1.7416	2.7452	2.2410
27400	27519	224.050	-49.100	224.050	1.7380	1.3036	1.7153	2.7024	2.2061
27500	27619	224.150	-49.000	224.150	1.7117	1.2839	1.6893	2.6604	2.1717
27600	27720	224.250	-48.900	224.250	1.6858	1.2645	1.6638	2.6190	2.1379
27700	27821	224.350	-48.800	224.350	1.6603	1.2453	1.6386	2.5782	2.1047
27800	27922	224.450	-48.700	224.450	1.6352	1.2265	1.6139	2.5381	2.0720
27900	28023	224.550	-48.600	224.550	1.6106	1.2080	1.5895	2.4987	2.0398
28000	28124	224.650	-48.500	224.650	1.5862 +1	1.1898 +1	1.5655 -2	2.4599 -2	2.0081 -2
28100	28225	224.750	-48.400	224.750	1.5623	1.1718	1.5419	2.4217	1.9769
28200	28326	224.850	-48.300	224.850	1.5387	1.1541	1.5186	2.3841	1.9462
28300	28427	224.950	-48.200	224.950	1.5155	1.1367	1.4957	2.3471	1.9160
28400	28527	225.050	-48.100	225.050	1.4927	1.1196	1.4732	2.3107	1.8863
28500	28628	225.150	-48.000	225.150	1.4702	1.1027	1.4510	2.2749	1.8571
28600	28729	225.250	-47.900	225.250	1.4481	1.0861	1.4291	2.2397	1.8283
28700	28830	225.350	-47.800	225.350	1.4263	1.0698	1.4076	2.2050	1.8000
28800	28931	225.450	-47.700	225.450	1.4048	1.0537	1.3865	2.1708	1.7721
28900	29032	225.550	-47.600	225.550	1.3837	1.0379	1.3656	2.1373	1.7447
29000	29133	225.650	-47.500	225.650	1.3629 +1	1.0223 +1	1.3451 -2	2.1042 -2	1.7177 -2
29100	29234	225.750	-47.400	225.750	1.3424	1.0069	1.3249	2.0717	1.6912
29200	29335	225.850	-47.300	225.850	1.3223	9.9182 +0	1.3050	2.0397	1.6650
29300	29436	225.950	-47.200	225.950	1.3024	9.7694	1.2854	2.0082	1.6393
29400	29537	226.050	-47.100	226.050	1.2829	9.6228	1.2661	1.9772	1.6140
29500	29638	226.150	-47.000	226.150	1.2637	9.4785	1.2471	1.9466	1.5891
29600	29738	226.250	-46.900	226.250	1.2447	9.3364	1.2284	1.9166	1.5646
29700	29839	226.350	-46.800	226.350	1.2261	9.1965	1.2100	1.8871	1.5405
29800	29940	226.450	-46.700	226.450	1.2077	9.0588	1.1919	1.8580	1.5167
29900	30041	226.550	-46.600	226.550	1.1896	8.9232	1.1741	1.8294	1.4934
30000	30142	226.650	-46.500	226.650	1.1718 +1	8.7897 +0	1.1565 -2	1.8012 -2	1.4704 -2
30100	30243	226.750	-46.400	226.750	1.1543	8.6582	1.1392	1.7735	1.4477
30200	30344	226.850	-46.300	226.850	1.1370	8.5288	1.1222	1.7462	1.4255
30300	30445	226.950	-46.200	226.950	1.1200	8.4013	1.1054	1.7193	1.4035
30400	30546	227.050	-46.100	227.050	1.1033	8.2758	1.0889	1.6929	1.3820
30500	30647	227.150	-46.000	227.150	1.0868	8.1522	1.0726	1.6669	1.3607
30600	30748	227.250	-45.900	227.250	1.0706	8.0306	1.0566	1.6413	1.3398
30700	30849	227.350	-45.800	227.350	1.0546	7.9108	1.0408	1.6161	1.3193
30800	30950	227.450	-45.700	227.450	1.0389	7.7928	1.0253	1.5913	1.2990
30900	31051	227.550	-45.600	227.550	1.0234	7.6767	1.0100	1.5669	1.2791
31000	31152	227.650	-45.500	227.650	1.0082 +1	7.5623 +0	9.9504 -3	1.5429 -2	1.2595 -2
31100	31253	227.750	-45.400	227.750	9.9321 +0	7.4497	9.8022	1.5192	1.2402
31200	31354	227.850	-45.300	227.850	9.7843	7.3388	9.6563	1.4960	1.2212
31300	31455	227.950	-45.200	227.950	9.6387	7.2296	9.5127	1.4731	1.2025
31400	31556	228.050	-45.100	228.050	9.4954	7.1221	9.3712	1.4505	1.1841
31500	31657	228.150	-45.000	228.150	9.3542	7.0162	9.2319	1.4283	1.1660
31600	31758	228.250	-44.900	228.250	9.2152	6.9120	9.0947	1.4065	1.1481
31700	31859	228.350	-44.800	228.350	9.0783	6.8093	8.9596	1.3850	1.1306
31800	31960	228.450	-44.700	228.450	8.9435	6.7082	8.8266	1.3638	1.1133
31900	32061	228.550	-44.600	228.550	8.8108	6.6086	8.6956	1.3430	1.0963
32000	32162	228.650	-44.500	228.650	8.6801 +0	6.5106 +0	8.5666 -3	1.3225 -2	1.0796 -2
32200	32364	229.210	-43.940	229.210	8.4249	6.3192	8.3147	1.2805	1.0453
32400	32566	229.770	-43.380	229.770	8.1777	6.1338	8.0708	1.2399	1.0122
32600	32768	230.330	-42.820	230.330	7.9384	5.9543	7.8346	1.2007	9.8014 -3
32800	32970	230.890	-42.260	230.890	7.7067	5.7805	7.6059	1.1628	9.4922
33000	33172	231.450	-41.700	231.450	7.4822	5.6121	7.3844	1.1262	9.1935
33200	33374	232.010	-41.140	232.010	7.2648	5.4491	7.1698	1.0908	8.9048
33400	33576	232.570	-40.580	232.570	7.0542	5.2911	6.9620	1.0567	8.6259
33600	33779	233.130	-40.020	233.130	6.8503	5.1381	6.7607	1.0236	8.3563
33800	33981	233.690	-39.460	233.690	6.6526	4.9899	6.5656	9.9173 -3	8.0958
34000	34183	234.250	-38.900	234.250	6.4612 +0	4.8463 +0	6.3767 -3	9.6089 -3	7.8440 -3
34200	34385	234.810	-38.340	234.810	6.2756	4.7071	6.1936	9.3107	7.6006
34400	34587	235.370	-37.780	235.370	6.0959	4.5723	6.0162	9.0225	7.3653
34600	34789	235.930	-37.220	235.930	5.9217	4.4416	5.8442	8.7438	7.1378
34800	34992	236.490	-36.660	236.490	5.7528	4.3150	5.6776	8.4744	6.9179
35000	35194	237.050	-36.100	237.050	5.5892	4.1922	5.5161	8.2139	6.7052
35200	35396	237.610	-35.540	237.610	5.4306	4.0732	5.3595	7.9620	6.4996
35400	35598	238.170	-34.980	238.170	5.2768	3.9579	5.2078	7.7184	6.3007
35600	35801	238.730	-34.420	238.730	5.1277	3.8461	5.0607	7.4828	6.1084
35800	36003	239.290	-33.860	239.290	4.9832	3.7377	4.9181	7.2549	5.9223
36000	36205	239.850	-33.300	239.850	4.8431 +0	3.6326 +0	4.7798 -3	7.0344 -3	5.7424 -3
36200	36407	240.410	-32.740	240.410	4.7072	3.5307	4.6457	6.8211	5.5683
36400	36610	240.970	-32.180	240.970	4.5755	3.4319	4.5157	6.6148	5.3999
36600	36812	241.530	-31.620	241.530	4.4477	3.3361	4.3896	6.4152	5.2369
36800	37014	242.090	-31.060	242.090	4.3238	3.2431	4.2673	6.2220	5.0792
37000	37217	242.650	-30.500	242.650	4.2036	3.1530	4.1486	6.0351	4.9266
37200	37419	243.210	-29.940	243.210	4.0870	3.0655	4.0336	5.8542	4.7790
37400	37621	243.770	-29.380	243.770	3.9739	2.9807	3.9220	5.6792	4.6361
37600	37824	244.330	-28.820	244.330	3.8642	2.8984	3.8137	5.5097	4.4977
37800	38026	244.890	-28.260	244.890	3.7578	2.8186	3.7086	5.3457	4.3638

Table I
Geometric Altitude, Metric Units

Altitude		Temperature			Pressure						Density			
Z (m)	H (m)	T (K)	t (°C)	T_M (K)	P (mb)		P (torr)		P/P_0		ρ (kg/m³)		ρ/ρ_0	
27000	26886	223.536	-49.614	223.536	1.8799	+ 1	1.4100	+ 1	1.8553	- 2	2.9298	- 2	2.3917	- 2
27100	26985	223.635	-49.515	223.635	1.8517		1.3888		1.8274		2.8845		2.3547	
27200	27084	223.734	-49.416	223.734	1.8238		1.3680		1.8000		2.8399		2.3183	
27300	27183	223.833	-49.317	223.833	1.7964		1.3474		1.7729		2.7960		2.2824	
27400	27282	223.932	-49.218	223.932	1.7695		1.3272		1.7463		2.7528		2.2472	
27500	27382	224.032	-49.118	224.032	1.7429		1.3073		1.7201		2.7103		2.2125	
27600	27481	224.131	-49.019	224.131	1.7168		1.2877		1.6943		2.6684		2.1783	
27700	27580	224.230	-48.920	224.230	1.6910		1.2684		1.6689		2.6273		2.1447	
27800	27679	224.329	-48.821	224.329	1.6657		1.2493		1.6439		2.5867		2.1116	
27900	27778	224.428	-48.722	224.428	1.6407		1.2306		1.6193		2.5469		2.0791	
28000	27877	224.527	-48.623	224.527	1.6161	+ 1	1.2122	+ 1	1.5950	- 2	2.5076	- 2	2.0470	- 2
28100	27976	224.626	-48.524	224.626	1.5920		1.1941		1.5711		2.4690		2.0155	
28200	28075	224.725	-48.425	224.725	1.5681		1.1762		1.5476		2.4310		1.9845	
28300	28175	224.825	-48.325	224.825	1.5447		1.1586		1.5245		2.3936		1.9540	
28400	28274	224.924	-48.226	224.924	1.5216		1.1413		1.5017		2.3568		1.9239	
28500	28373	225.023	-48.127	225.023	1.4989		1.1242		1.4793		2.3206		1.8943	
28600	28472	225.122	-48.028	225.122	1.4765		1.1075		1.4572		2.2849		1.8652	
28700	28571	225.221	-47.929	225.221	1.4545		1.0909		1.4354		2.2498		1.8366	
28800	28670	225.320	-47.830	225.320	1.4328		1.0747		1.4140		2.2153		1.8084	
28900	28769	225.419	-47.731	225.419	1.4114		1.0586		1.3930		2.1813		1.7807	
29000	28868	225.518	-47.632	225.518	1.3904	+ 1	1.0429	+ 1	1.3722	- 2	2.1478	- 2	1.7533	- 2
29100	28967	225.617	-47.533	225.617	1.3697		1.0273		1.3517		2.1149		1.7265	
29200	29066	225.716	-47.434	225.716	1.3493		1.0120		1.3316		2.0825		1.7000	
29300	29166	225.816	-47.334	225.816	1.3292		9.9700	+ 0	1.3118		2.0506		1.6740	
29400	29265	225.915	-47.235	225.915	1.3094		9.8217		1.2923		2.0192		1.6484	
29500	29364	226.014	-47.136	226.014	1.2899		9.6757		1.2731		1.9883		1.6231	
29600	29463	226.113	-47.037	226.113	1.2708		9.5319		1.2542		1.9579		1.5983	
29700	29562	226.212	-46.938	226.212	1.2519		9.3903		1.2355		1.9280		1.5739	
29800	29661	226.311	-46.839	226.311	1.2333		9.2509		1.2172		1.8986		1.5498	
29900	29760	226.410	-46.740	226.410	1.2150		9.1136		1.1991		1.8696		1.5262	
30000	29859	226.509	-46.641	226.509	1.1970	+ 1	8.9784	+ 0	1.1813	- 2	1.8410	- 2	1.5029	- 2
30100	29958	226.608	-46.542	226.608	1.1792		8.8453		1.1638		1.8129		1.4799	
30200	30057	226.707	-46.443	226.707	1.1618		8.7142		1.1466		1.7853		1.4574	
30300	30156	226.806	-46.344	226.806	1.1445		8.5851		1.1296		1.7581		1.4352	
30400	30255	226.905	-46.245	226.905	1.1276		8.4580		1.1129		1.7313		1.4133	
30500	30354	227.004	-46.146	227.004	1.1109		8.3329		1.0964		1.7049		1.3918	
30600	30453	227.103	-46.047	227.103	1.0945		8.2096		1.0802		1.6790		1.3706	
30700	30552	227.202	-45.948	227.202	1.0783		8.0882		1.0642		1.6534		1.3497	
30800	30651	227.301	-45.849	227.301	1.0624		7.9687		1.0485		1.6283		1.3292	
30900	30751	227.401	-45.749	227.401	1.0467		7.8510		1.0330		1.6035		1.3090	
31000	30850	227.500	-45.650	227.500	1.0312	+ 1	7.7351	+ 0	1.0177	- 2	1.5792	- 2	1.2891	- 2
31100	30949	227.599	-45.551	227.599	1.0160		7.6209		1.0027		1.5552		1.2695	
31200	31048	227.698	-45.452	227.698	1.0010		7.5085		9.8796	- 3	1.5316		1.2503	
31300	31147	227.797	-45.353	227.797	9.8629	+ 0	7.3978		9.7339		1.5083		1.2313	
31400	31246	227.896	-45.254	227.896	9.7175		7.2887		9.5905		1.4855		1.2126	
31500	31345	227.995	-45.155	227.995	9.5744		7.1814		9.4492		1.4629		1.1942	
31600	31444	228.094	-45.056	228.094	9.4334		7.0756		9.3101		1.4408		1.1761	
31700	31543	228.193	-44.957	228.193	9.2946		6.9715		9.1730		1.4190		1.1583	
31800	31642	228.292	-44.858	228.292	9.1579		6.8690		9.0381		1.3975		1.1408	
31900	31741	228.391	-44.759	228.391	9.0232		6.7680		8.9052		1.3763		1.1235	
32000	31840	228.490	-44.660	228.490	8.8906	+ 0	6.6685	+ 0	8.7743	- 3	1.3555	- 2	1.1065	- 2
32200	32038	228.756	-44.394	228.756	8.6314		6.4741		8.5185		1.3145		1.0730	
32400	32236	229.310	-43.840	229.310	8.3802		6.2857		8.2706		1.2731		1.0393	
32600	32434	229.864	-43.286	229.864	8.1369		6.1032		8.0305		1.2332		1.0067	
32800	32632	230.419	-42.731	230.419	7.9013		5.9265		7.7980		1.1946		9.7518	- 3
33000	32830	230.973	-42.177	230.973	7.6730		5.7552		7.5727		1.1573		9.4474	
33200	33027	231.527	-41.623	231.527	7.4519		5.5894		7.3545		1.1213		9.1532	
33400	33225	232.081	-41.069	232.081	7.2377		5.4287		7.1431		1.0864		8.8688	
33600	33423	232.635	-40.515	232.635	7.0301		5.2730		6.9382		1.0528		8.5939	
33800	33621	233.189	-39.961	233.189	6.8290		5.1222		6.7397		1.0202		8.3282	
34000	33819	233.743	-39.407	233.743	6.6341	+ 0	4.9760	+ 0	6.5473	- 3	9.8874	- 3	8.0714	- 3
34200	34017	234.298	-38.852	234.298	6.4452		4.8343		6.3609		9.5832		7.8230	
34400	34215	234.852	-38.298	234.852	6.2621		4.6970		6.1802		9.2890		7.5829	
34600	34413	235.406	-37.744	235.406	6.0847		4.5639		6.0051		9.0045		7.3507	
34800	34611	235.959	-37.191	235.959	5.9127		4.4348		5.8353		8.7295		7.1261	
35000	34808	236.513	-36.637	236.513	5.7459		4.3098		5.6708		8.4634		6.9089	
35200	35006	237.067	-36.083	237.067	5.5842		4.1885		5.5112		8.2061		6.6988	
35400	35204	237.621	-35.529	237.621	5.4275		4.0709		5.3565		7.9571		6.4956	
35600	35402	238.175	-34.975	238.175	5.2755		3.9569		5.2065		7.7163		6.2990	
35800	35599	238.729	-34.421	238.729	5.1281		3.8464		5.0611		7.4833		6.1088	
36000	35797	239.282	-33.868	239.282	4.9852	+ 0	3.7392	+ 0	4.9200	- 3	7.2579	- 3	5.9248	- 3
36200	35995	239.836	-33.314	239.836	4.8466		3.6352		4.7832		7.0398		5.7468	
36400	36193	240.390	-32.760	240.390	4.7121		3.5344		4.6505		6.8288		5.5745	
36600	36390	240.943	-32.207	240.943	4.5817		3.4365		4.5218		6.6245		5.4078	
36800	36588	241.497	-31.653	241.497	4.4552		3.3416		4.3969		6.4268		5.2464	
37000	36786	242.050	-31.100	242.050	4.3324		3.2496		4.2758		6.2355		5.0902	
37200	36984	242.604	-30.546	242.604	4.2134		3.1603		4.1583		6.0503		4.9390	
37400	37181	243.157	-29.993	243.157	4.0978		3.0736		4.0442		5.8710		4.7926	
37600	37379	243.711	-29.439	243.711	3.9857		2.9895		3.9336		5.6974		4.6509	
37800	37577	244.264	-28.886	244.264	3.8769		2.9079		3.8262		5.5293		4.5137	

Table I
Geopotential Altitude, Metric Units

Altitude		Temperature			Pressure			Density	
H (m)	Z (m)	T (K)	t (°C)	T_M (K)	P (mb)	P (torr)	P/P_0	ρ (kg/m³)	ρ/ρ_0
38000	38229	245.450	−27.700	245.450	3.6545 +0	2.7411 +0	3.6067 −3	5.1869 −3	4.2342 −3
38200	38431	246.010	−27.140	246.010	3.5543	2.6659	3.5078	5.0332	4.1087
38400	38633	246.570	−26.580	246.570	3.4570	2.5930	3.4118	4.8844	3.9872
38600	38836	247.130	−26.020	247.130	3.3626	2.5222	3.3187	4.7402	3.8696
38800	39038	247.690	−25.460	247.690	3.2711	2.4535	3.2283	4.6007	3.7557
39000	39241	248.250	−24.900	248.250	3.1822	2.3868	3.1405	4.4656	3.6454
39200	39443	248.810	−24.340	248.810	3.0959	2.3221	3.0554	4.3347	3.5385
39400	39646	249.370	−23.780	249.370	3.0121	2.2592	2.9727	4.2079	3.4350
39600	39848	249.930	−23.220	249.930	2.9308	2.1982	2.8924	4.0852	3.3348
39800	40051	250.490	−22.660	250.490	2.8518	2.1390	2.8145	3.9662	3.2377
40000	40253	251.050	−22.100	251.050	2.7752 +0	2.0815 +0	2.7389 −3	3.8510 −3	3.1437 −3
40200	40456	251.610	−21.540	251.610	2.7007	2.0257	2.6654	3.7394	3.0526
40400	40658	252.170	−20.980	252.170	2.6285	1.9715	2.5941	3.6312	2.9643
40600	40861	252.730	−20.420	252.730	2.5583	1.9188	2.5248	3.5264	2.8787
40800	41064	253.290	−19.860	253.290	2.4901	1.8677	2.4575	3.4249	2.7958
41000	41266	253.850	−19.300	253.850	2.4239	1.8181	2.3922	3.3265	2.7155
41200	41469	254.410	−18.740	254.410	2.3596	1.7698	2.3287	3.2311	2.6376
41400	41671	254.970	−18.180	254.970	2.2971	1.7230	2.2671	3.1387	2.5622
41600	41874	255.530	−17.620	255.530	2.2365	1.6775	2.2072	3.0491	2.4890
41800	42077	256.090	−17.060	256.090	2.1775	1.6333	2.1490	2.9622	2.4181
42000	42279	256.650	−16.500	256.650	2.1202 +0	1.5903 +0	2.0925 −3	2.8780 −3	2.3494 −3
42200	42482	257.210	−15.940	257.210	2.0646	1.5486	2.0376	2.7964	2.2828
42400	42685	257.770	−15.380	257.770	2.0105	1.5080	1.9842	2.7172	2.2182
42600	42887	258.330	−14.820	258.330	1.9580	1.4686	1.9324	2.6405	2.1555
42800	43090	258.890	−14.260	258.890	1.9069	1.4303	1.8820	2.5661	2.0948
43000	43293	259.450	−13.700	259.450	1.8573	1.3931	1.8330	2.4939	2.0359
43200	43496	260.010	−13.140	260.010	1.8091	1.3569	1.7854	2.4239	1.9787
43400	43698	260.570	−12.580	260.570	1.7622	1.3218	1.7392	2.3561	1.9233
43600	43901	261.130	−12.020	261.130	1.7167	1.2876	1.6942	2.2902	1.8696
43800	44104	261.690	−11.460	261.690	1.6724	1.2544	1.6505	2.2264	1.8174
44000	44307	262.250	−10.900	262.250	1.6293 +0	1.2221 +0	1.6080 −3	2.1644 −3	1.7669 −3
44200	44510	262.810	−10.340	262.810	1.5875	1.1907	1.5667	2.1043	1.7178
44400	44712	263.370	−9.780	263.370	1.5468	1.1602	1.5265	2.0460	1.6702
44600	44915	263.930	−9.220	263.930	1.5072	1.1305	1.4875	1.9894	1.6240
44800	45118	264.490	−8.660	264.490	1.4687	1.1016	1.4495	1.9346	1.5792
45000	45321	265.050	−8.100	265.050	1.4313	1.0735	1.4126	1.8813	1.5357
45200	45524	265.610	−7.540	265.610	1.3949	1.0463	1.3767	1.8296	1.4935
45400	45727	266.170	−6.980	266.170	1.3595	1.0197	1.3417	1.7794	1.4526
45600	45929	266.730	−6.420	266.730	1.3251	9.9394 −1	1.3078	1.7307	1.4128
45800	46132	267.290	−5.860	267.290	1.2916	9.6883	1.2747	1.6835	1.3743
46000	46335	267.850	−5.300	267.850	1.2591 +0	9.4440 −1	1.2426 −3	1.6376 −3	1.3368 −3
46200	46538	268.410	−4.740	268.410	1.2274	9.2064	1.2113	1.5931	1.3005
46400	46741	268.970	−4.180	268.970	1.1966	8.9752	1.1809	1.5498	1.2652
46600	46944	269.530	−3.620	269.530	1.1666	8.7503	1.1513	1.5079	1.2309
46800	47147	270.090	−3.060	270.090	1.1374	8.5315	1.1225	1.4671	1.1976
47000	47350	270.650	−2.500	270.650	1.1090	8.3186	1.0945	1.4275	1.1653
47200	47553	270.650	−2.500	270.650	1.0814	8.1112	1.0672	1.3919	1.1363
47400	47756	270.650	−2.500	270.650	1.0544	7.9090	1.0406	1.3572	1.1080
47600	47959	270.650	−2.500	270.650	1.0281	7.7118	1.0147	1.3234	1.0803
47800	48162	270.650	−2.500	270.650	1.0025	7.5196	9.8942 −4	1.2904	1.0534
48000	48365	270.650	−2.500	270.650	9.7754 −1	7.3321 −1	9.6476 −4	1.2582 −3	1.0271 −3
48200	48568	270.650	−2.500	270.650	9.5317	7.1493	9.4071	1.2269	1.0015
48400	48771	270.650	−2.500	270.650	9.2941	6.9711	9.1725	1.1963	9.7657 −4
48600	48974	270.650	−2.500	270.650	9.0624	6.7973	8.9439	1.1665	9.5222
48800	49178	270.650	−2.500	270.650	8.8365	6.6279	8.7209	1.1374	9.2848
49000	49381	270.650	−2.500	270.650	8.6162	6.4626	8.5035	1.1090	9.0534
49200	49584	270.650	−2.500	270.650	8.4014	6.3015	8.2915	1.0814	8.8277
49400	49787	270.650	−2.500	270.650	8.1919	6.1444	8.0848	1.0544	8.6076
49600	49990	270.650	−2.500	270.650	7.9877	5.9913	7.8833	1.0281	8.3930
49800	50193	270.650	−2.500	270.650	7.7886	5.8419	7.6867	1.0025	8.1838
50000	50396	270.650	−2.500	270.650	7.5944 −1	5.6963 −1	7.4951 −4	9.7752 −4	7.9798 −4
50500	50904	270.650	−2.500	270.650	7.1299	5.3479	7.0367	9.1774	7.4917
51000	51413	270.650	−2.500	270.650	6.6938	5.0208	6.6063	8.6160	7.0335
51500	51921	269.250	−3.900	269.250	6.2834	4.7129	6.2012	8.1298	6.6366
52000	52429	267.850	−5.300	267.850	5.8962	4.4225	5.8191	7.6687	6.2601
52500	52937	266.450	−6.700	266.450	5.5310	4.1485	5.4586	7.2315	5.9032
53000	53446	265.050	−8.100	265.050	5.1866	3.8903	5.1188	6.8171	5.5650
53500	53954	263.650	−9.500	263.650	4.8621	3.6468	4.7985	6.4245	5.2445
54000	54463	262.250	−10.900	262.250	4.5563	3.4175	4.4967	6.0525	4.9408
54500	54971	260.850	−12.300	260.850	4.2682	3.2014	4.2124	5.7003	4.6533
55000	55480	259.450	−13.700	259.450	3.9969 −1	2.9979 −1	3.9447 −4	5.3668 −4	4.3811 −4
55500	55989	258.050	−15.100	258.050	3.7416	2.8064	3.6927	5.0512	4.1235
56000	56498	256.650	−16.500	256.650	3.5013	2.6262	3.4555	4.7526	3.8797
56500	57007	255.250	−17.900	255.250	3.2753	2.4566	3.2324	4.4702	3.6491
57000	57516	253.850	−19.300	253.850	3.0627	2.2972	3.0226	4.2031	3.4311
57500	58025	252.450	−20.700	252.450	2.8628	2.1473	2.8254	3.9506	3.2250
58000	58534	251.050	−22.100	251.050	2.6750	2.0064	2.6401	3.7121	3.0303
58500	59043	249.650	−23.500	249.650	2.4986	1.8741	2.4659	3.4867	2.8463
59000	59553	248.250	−24.900	248.250	2.3329	1.7498	2.3024	3.2738	2.6725
59500	60062	246.850	−26.300	246.850	2.1774	1.6331	2.1489	3.0729	2.5085

Table I
Geometric Altitude, Metric Units

Altitude		Temperature			Pressure			Density	
Z (m)	H (m)	T (K)	t (°C)	T_M (K)	P (mb)	P (torr)	P/P_0	ρ (kg/m³)	ρ/ρ_0
38000	37774	244.818	-28.332	244.818	3.7713 + 0	2.8287 + 0	3.7220 - 3	5.3666 - 3	4.3809 - 3
38200	37972	245.371	-27.779	245.371	3.6689	2.7519	3.6209	5.2090	4.2522
38400	38169	245.924	-27.226	245.924	3.5694	2.6773	3.5227	5.0564	4.1277
38600	38367	246.478	-26.672	246.478	3.4729	2.6049	3.4275	4.9086	4.0070
38800	38565	247.031	-26.119	247.031	3.3792	2.5346	3.3350	4.7654	3.8901
39000	38762	247.584	-25.566	247.584	3.2882	2.4663	3.2452	4.6268	3.7769
39200	38960	248.137	-25.013	248.137	3.1998	2.4001	3.1580	4.4924	3.6673
39400	39157	248.690	-24.460	248.690	3.1141	2.3357	3.0734	4.3623	3.5611
39600	39355	249.243	-23.907	249.243	3.0308	2.2733	2.9912	4.2362	3.4581
39800	39552	249.797	-23.353	249.797	2.9499	2.2126	2.9114	4.1141	3.3584
40000	39750	250.350	-22.800	250.350	2.8714 + 0	2.1537 + 0	2.8338 - 3	3.9957 - 3	3.2618 - 3
40200	39947	250.903	-22.247	250.903	2.7951	2.0965	2.7586	3.8810	3.1681
40400	40145	251.456	-21.694	251.456	2.7210	2.0409	2.6855	3.7698	3.0774
40600	40342	252.008	-21.142	252.008	2.6491	1.9870	2.6144	3.6621	2.9894
40800	40540	252.561	-20.589	252.561	2.5792	1.9345	2.5455	3.5576	2.9042
41000	40737	253.114	-20.036	253.114	2.5113	1.8836	2.4784	3.4564	2.8216
41200	40935	253.667	-19.483	253.667	2.4453	1.8341	2.4133	3.3583	2.7415
41400	41132	254.220	-18.930	254.220	2.3812	1.7861	2.3501	3.2632	2.6638
41600	41330	254.773	-18.377	254.773	2.3189	1.7393	2.2886	3.1709	2.5885
41800	41527	255.325	-17.825	255.325	2.2584	1.6939	2.2289	3.0815	2.5155
42000	41724	255.878	-17.272	255.878	2.1996 + 0	1.6498 + 0	2.1709 - 3	2.9948 - 3	2.4447 - 3
42200	41922	256.431	-16.719	256.431	2.1425	1.6070	2.1145	2.9107	2.3761
42400	42119	256.983	-16.167	256.983	2.0869	1.5653	2.0596	2.8291	2.3095
42600	42316	257.536	-15.614	257.536	2.0329	1.5248	2.0064	2.7500	2.2449
42800	42514	258.088	-15.062	258.088	1.9805	1.4855	1.9546	2.6733	2.1823
43000	42711	258.641	-14.509	258.641	1.9295	1.4472	1.9042	2.5989	2.1216
43200	42908	259.193	-13.957	259.193	1.8799	1.4100	1.8553	2.5267	2.0626
43400	43106	259.746	-13.404	259.746	1.8317	1.3739	1.8077	2.4567	2.0055
43600	43303	260.298	-12.852	260.298	1.7848	1.3387	1.7615	2.3887	1.9500
43800	43500	260.851	-12.299	260.851	1.7392	1.3045	1.7165	2.3228	1.8962
44000	43698	261.403	-11.747	261.403	1.6949 + 0	1.2713 + 0	1.6728 - 3	2.2589 - 3	1.8440 - 3
44200	43895	261.955	-11.195	261.955	1.6518	1.2390	1.6302	2.1968	1.7933
44400	44092	262.508	-10.642	262.508	1.6099	1.2075	1.5889	2.1366	1.7441
44600	44289	263.060	-10.090	263.060	1.5692	1.1770	1.5486	2.0781	1.6964
44800	44486	263.612	-9.538	263.612	1.5295	1.1472	1.5095	2.0214	1.6501
45000	44684	264.164	-8.986	264.164	1.4910	1.1183	1.4715	1.9663	1.6051
45200	44881	264.716	-8.434	264.716	1.4535	1.0902	1.4345	1.9128	1.5615
45400	45078	265.268	-7.882	265.268	1.4170	1.0628	1.3984	1.8609	1.5191
45600	45275	265.821	-7.329	265.821	1.3815	1.0362	1.3634	1.8106	1.4780
45800	45472	266.373	-6.777	266.373	1.3470	1.0103	1.3293	1.7616	1.4381
46000	45669	266.925	-6.225	266.925	1.3134 + 0	9.8513 - 1	1.2962 - 3	1.7142 - 3	1.3993 - 3
46200	45867	267.477	-5.673	267.477	1.2807	9.6061	1.2639	1.6680	1.3617
46400	46064	268.028	-5.122	268.028	1.2489	9.3675	1.2325	1.6233	1.3251
46600	46261	268.580	-4.570	268.580	1.2179	9.1354	1.2020	1.5798	1.2896
46800	46458	269.132	-4.018	269.132	1.1878	8.9094	1.1722	1.5375	1.2551
47000	46655	269.684	-3.466	269.684	1.1585	8.6895	1.1433	1.4965	1.2217
47200	46852	270.236	-2.914	270.236	1.1300	8.4755	1.1152	1.4567	1.1891
47400	47049	270.650	-2.500	270.650	1.1022	8.2671	1.0877	1.4187	1.1581
47600	47246	270.650	-2.500	270.650	1.0751	8.0641	1.0610	1.3839	1.1297
47800	47443	270.650	-2.500	270.650	1.0487	7.8660	1.0350	1.3499	1.1019
48000	47640	270.650	-2.500	270.650	1.0229 + 0	7.6728 - 1	1.0095 - 3	1.3167 - 3	1.0749 - 3
48200	47837	270.650	-2.500	270.650	9.9783 - 1	7.4843	9.8478 - 4	1.2844	1.0485
48400	48034	270.650	-2.500	270.650	9.7332	7.3005	9.6059	1.2528	1.0227
48600	48231	270.650	-2.500	270.650	9.4942	7.1212	9.3700	1.2221	9.9760 - 4
48800	48428	270.650	-2.500	270.650	9.2610	6.9463	9.1399	1.1920	9.7310
49000	48625	270.650	-2.500	270.650	9.0336	6.7758	8.9155	1.1628	9.4920
49200	48822	270.650	-2.500	270.650	8.8118	6.6094	8.6966	1.1342	9.2590
49400	49019	270.650	-2.500	270.650	8.5955	6.4471	8.4831	1.1064	9.0317
49600	49216	270.650	-2.500	270.650	8.3845	6.2889	8.2748	1.0792	8.8099
49800	49413	270.650	-2.500	270.650	8.1786	6.1345	8.0717	1.0527	8.5937
50000	49610	270.650	-2.500	270.650	7.9779 - 1	5.9839 - 1	7.8735 - 4	1.0269 - 3	8.3827 - 4
50500	50102	270.650	-2.500	270.650	7.4973	5.6234	7.3993	9.6503 - 4	7.8778
51000	50594	270.650	-2.500	270.650	7.0458	5.2847	6.9536	9.0690	7.4033
51500	51086	270.409	-2.741	270.409	6.6214	4.9665	6.5349	8.5305	6.9637
52000	51578	269.031	-4.119	269.031	6.2214	4.6664	6.1401	8.0562	6.5765
52500	52070	267.654	-5.496	267.654	5.8438	4.3832	5.7674	7.6061	6.2091
53000	52562	266.277	-6.873	266.277	5.4873	4.1158	5.4156	7.1791	5.8605
53500	53053	264.900	-8.250	264.900	5.1510	3.8636	5.0836	6.7741	5.5299
54000	53545	263.524	-9.626	263.524	4.8337	3.6256	4.7705	6.3901	5.2164
54500	54037	262.147	-11.003	262.147	4.5345	3.4012	4.4752	6.0260	4.9192
55000	54528	260.771	-12.379	260.771	4.2525 - 1	3.1896 - 1	4.1969 - 4	5.6810 - 4	4.6376 - 4
55500	55020	259.395	-13.755	259.395	3.9866	2.9902	3.9345	5.3541	4.3707
56000	55511	258.019	-15.131	258.019	3.7362	2.8024	3.6873	5.0445	4.1180
56500	56002	256.644	-16.506	256.644	3.5003	2.6254	3.4545	4.7513	3.8786
57000	56493	255.268	-17.882	255.268	3.2782	2.4588	3.2353	4.4738	3.6521
57500	56985	253.893	-19.257	253.893	3.0691	2.3020	3.0289	4.2112	3.4377
58000	57476	252.518	-20.632	252.518	2.8723	2.1544	2.8348	3.9627	3.2348
58500	57967	251.144	-22.006	251.144	2.6872	2.0156	2.6521	3.7276	3.0430
59000	58457	249.769	-23.381	249.769	2.5132	1.8850	2.4803	3.5054	2.8615
59500	58948	248.395	-24.755	248.395	2.3496	1.7623	2.3189	3.2953	2.6900

Table I
Geopotential Altitude, Metric Units

Altitude		Temperature			Pressure			Density	
H (m)	Z (m)	T (K)	t (°C)	T_M (K)	P (mb)	P (torr)	P/P_0	ρ (kg/m³)	ρ/ρ_0
60000	60572	245.450	−27.700	245.450	2.0314 −1	1.5236 −1	2.0048 −4	2.8832 −4	2.3536 −4
60500	61081	244.050	−29.100	244.050	1.8944	1.4209	1.8697	2.7043	2.2076
61000	61591	242.650	−30.500	242.650	1.7660	1.3246	1.7429	2.5355	2.0698
61500	62101	241.250	−31.900	241.250	1.6456	1.2343	1.6241	2.3764	1.9399
62000	62611	239.850	−33.300	239.850	1.5328	1.1497	1.5128	2.2264	1.8175
62500	63121	238.450	−34.700	238.450	1.4271	1.0704	1.4085	2.0851	1.7021
63000	63631	237.050	−36.100	237.050	1.3282	9.9627 −2	1.3108	1.9520	1.5935
63500	64141	235.650	−37.500	235.650	1.2356	9.2681	1.2194	1.8267	1.4912
64000	64651	234.250	−38.900	234.250	1.1489	8.6181	1.1339	1.7087	1.3949
64500	65161	232.850	−40.300	232.850	1.0679	8.0103	1.0539	1.5978	1.3043
65000	65672	231.450	−41.700	231.450	9.9220 −2	7.4421 −2	9.7922 −5	1.4934 −4	1.2191 −4
65500	66182	230.050	−43.100	230.050	9.2140	6.9111	9.0935	1.3953	1.1390
66000	66692	228.650	−44.500	228.650	8.5527	6.4150	8.4408	1.3031	1.0637
66500	67203	227.250	−45.900	227.250	7.9352	5.9519	7.8314	1.2165	9.9302 −5
67000	67714	225.850	−47.300	225.850	7.3589	5.5196	7.2627	1.1351	9.2661
67500	68224	224.450	−48.700	224.450	6.8212	5.1163	6.7320	1.0587	8.6427
68000	68735	223.050	−50.100	223.050	6.3199	4.7403	6.2372	9.8707 −5	8.0577
68500	69246	221.650	−51.500	221.650	5.8525	4.3897	5.7760	9.1985	7.5090
69000	69757	220.250	−52.900	220.250	5.4171	4.0632	5.3463	8.5683	6.9945
69500	70268	218.850	−54.300	218.850	5.0116	3.7590	4.9461	7.9776	6.5124
70000	70779	217.450	−55.700	217.450	4.6342 −2	3.4759 −2	4.5736 −5	7.4243 −5	6.0606 −5
70500	71291	216.050	−57.100	216.050	4.2830	3.2125	4.2270	6.9061	5.6376
71000	71802	214.650	−58.500	214.650	3.9564	2.9675	3.9046	6.4211	5.2417
71500	72313	213.650	−59.500	213.650	3.6530	2.7400	3.6053	5.9566	4.8625
72000	72825	212.650	−60.500	212.650	3.3717	2.5290	3.3276	5.5237	4.5091
72500	73336	211.650	−61.500	211.650	3.1109	2.3333	3.0702	5.1205	4.1800
73000	73848	210.650	−62.500	210.650	2.8691	2.1520	2.8316	4.7449	3.8734
73500	74360	209.650	−63.500	209.650	2.6451	1.9840	2.6105	4.3954	3.5881
74000	74872	208.650	−64.500	208.650	2.4377	1.8284	2.4058	4.0701	3.3225
74500	75384	207.650	−65.500	207.650	2.2456	1.6843	2.2162	3.7675	3.0755
75000	75896	206.650	−66.500	206.650	2.0679 −2	1.5510 −2	2.0408 −5	3.4861 −5	2.8458 −5
75500	76408	205.650	−67.500	205.650	1.9034	1.4277	1.8785	3.2245	2.6322
76000	76920	204.650	−68.500	204.650	1.7514	1.3136	1.7284	2.9813	2.4337
76500	77432	203.650	−69.500	203.650	1.6108	1.2082	1.5897	2.7555	2.2494
77000	77944	202.650	−70.500	202.650	1.4809	1.1107	1.4615	2.5458	2.0782
77500	78457	201.650	−71.500	201.650	1.3609	1.0207	1.3431	2.3511	1.9193
78000	78969	200.650	−72.500	200.650	1.2501	9.3766 −3	1.2337	2.1705	1.7718
78500	79482	199.650	−73.500	199.650	1.1478	8.6096	1.1328	2.0029	1.6350
79000	79994	198.650	−74.500	198.650	1.0535	7.9019	1.0397	1.8475	1.5082
79500	80507	197.650	−75.500	197.650	9.6649 −3	7.2492	9.5385 −6	1.7035	1.3906
80000	81020	196.650	−76.500	196.650	8.8627 −3	6.6476 −3	8.7468 −6	1.5701 −5	1.2817 −5
80500	81533	195.650	−77.500	195.650	8.1236	6.0932	8.0173	1.4465	1.1808
81000	82046	194.650	−78.500	194.650	7.4427	5.5825	7.3454	1.3320	1.0874
81500	82559	193.650	−79.500	193.650	6.8159	5.1123	6.7268	1.2262	1.0009
82000	83072	192.650	−80.500	192.650	6.2390	4.6796	6.1574	1.1282	9.2098 −6
82500	83585	191.650	−81.500	191.650	5.7083	4.2816	5.6336	1.0376	8.4704
83000	84098	190.650	−82.500	190.650	5.2203	3.9155	5.1520	9.5390 −6	7.7869
83500	84611	189.650	−83.500	189.650	4.7718	3.5791	4.7094	8.7654	7.1554
84000	85125	188.650	−84.500	188.650	4.3598	3.2701	4.3027	8.0510	6.5722
84500	85638	187.650	−85.500	187.650	3.9814	2.9863	3.9293	7.3914	6.0338

Table I
Geometric Altitude, Metric Units

Altitude		Temperature			Pressure			Density	
Z (m)	H (m)	T (K)	t (°C)	T_M (K)	P (mb)	P (torr)	P/P_0	ρ (kg/m³)	ρ/ρ_0
60000	59439	247.021	-26.129	247.021	2.1958 - 1	1.6470 - 1	2.1671 - 4	3.0968 - 4	2.5280 - 4
60500	59930	245.647	-27.503	245.647	2.0514	1.5386	2.0245	2.9093	2.3749
61000	60420	244.274	-28.876	244.274	1.9157	1.4369	1.8907	2.7321	2.2303
61500	60911	242.900	-30.250	242.900	1.7883	1.3414	1.7650	2.5649	2.0938
62000	61401	241.527	-31.623	241.527	1.6688	1.2517	1.6470	2.4071	1.9650
62500	61891	240.154	-32.996	240.154	1.5567	1.1676	1.5363	2.2582	1.8434
63000	62382	238.781	-34.369	238.781	1.4515	1.0887	1.4325	2.1178	1.7288
63500	62872	237.409	-35.741	237.409	1.3529	1.0148	1.3352	1.9853	1.6207
64000	63362	236.036	-37.114	236.036	1.2605	9.4551 - 2	1.2441	1.8605	1.5188
64500	63852	234.664	-38.486	234.664	1.1740	8.8059	1.1586	1.7429	1.4228
65000	64342	233.292	-39.858	233.292	1.0929 - 1	8.1979 - 2	1.0786 - 4	1.6321 - 4	1.3323 - 4
65500	64832	231.921	-41.229	231.921	1.0170	7.6288	1.0037	1.5278	1.2472
66000	65322	230.549	-42.601	230.549	9.4609 - 2	7.0962	9.3372 - 5	1.4296	1.1670
66500	65811	229.178	-43.972	229.178	8.7967	6.5981	8.6817	1.3372	1.0916
67000	66301	227.807	-45.343	227.807	8.1757	6.1323	8.0688	1.2503	1.0206
67500	66791	226.436	-46.714	226.436	7.5953	5.6969	7.4959	1.1685	9.5390 - 5
68000	67280	225.065	-48.085	225.065	7.0529	5.2901	6.9607	1.0917	8.9118
68500	67770	223.695	-49.455	223.695	6.5465	4.9102	6.4609	1.0195	8.3225
69000	68259	222.325	-50.825	222.325	6.0736	4.5556	5.9942	9.5171 - 5	7.7690
69500	68748	220.955	-52.195	220.955	5.6324	4.2247	5.5588	8.8804	7.2493
70000	69238	219.585	-53.565	219.585	5.2209 - 2	3.9160 - 2	5.1526 - 5	8.2829 - 5	6.7616 - 5
70500	69727	218.215	-54.935	218.215	4.8372	3.6282	4.7739	7.7223	6.3039
71000	70216	216.846	-56.304	216.846	4.4795	3.3599	4.4210	7.1966	5.8747
71500	70705	215.477	-57.673	215.477	4.1464	3.1100	4.0922	6.7037	5.4724
72000	71194	214.263	-58.887	214.263	3.8362	2.8774	3.7861	6.2374	5.0917
72500	71682	213.285	-59.865	213.285	3.5479	2.6612	3.5015	5.7951	4.7307
73000	72171	212.308	-60.842	212.308	3.2802	2.4603	3.2373	5.3824	4.3938
73500	72660	211.330	-61.820	211.330	3.0316	2.2739	2.9919	4.9975	4.0796
74000	73148	210.353	-62.797	210.353	2.8008	2.1008	2.7642	4.6386	3.7866
74500	73637	209.376	-63.774	209.376	2.5867	1.9402	2.5529	4.3040	3.5134
75000	74125	208.399	-64.751	208.399	2.3881 - 2	1.7912 - 2	2.3569 - 5	3.9921 - 5	3.2589 - 5
75500	74614	207.423	-65.727	207.423	2.2040	1.6531	2.1751	3.7016	3.0218
76000	75102	206.446	-66.704	206.446	2.0333	1.5251	2.0067	3.4311	2.8009
76500	75590	205.469	-67.681	205.469	1.8751	1.4064	1.8506	3.1792	2.5953
77000	76078	204.493	-68.657	204.493	1.7286	1.2965	1.7060	2.9448	2.4039
77500	76566	203.517	-69.633	203.517	1.5929	1.1948	1.5721	2.7267	2.2259
78000	77054	202.541	-70.609	202.541	1.4673	1.1006	1.4481	2.5239	2.0603
78500	77542	201.565	-71.585	201.565	1.3511	1.0134	1.3335	2.3353	1.9063
79000	78030	200.590	-72.560	200.590	1.2437	9.3285 - 3	1.2274	2.1600	1.7632
79500	78518	199.614	-73.536	199.614	1.1443	8.5832	1.1293	1.9971	1.6303
80000	79006	198.639	-74.511	198.639	1.0524 - 2	7.8942 - 3	1.0387 - 5	1.8458 - 5	1.5068 - 5
80500	79493	197.663	-75.487	197.663	9.6761 - 3	7.2577	9.5496 - 6	1.7054	1.3921
81000	79981	196.688	-76.462	196.688	8.8923	6.6698	8.7761	1.5750	1.2857
81500	80468	195.713	-77.437	195.713	8.1687	6.1270	8.0619	1.4540	1.1870
82000	80956	194.739	-78.411	194.739	7.5009	5.6261	7.4028	1.3418	1.0954
82500	81443	193.764	-79.386	193.764	6.8848	5.1640	6.7948	1.2378	1.0105
83000	81930	192.790	-80.360	192.790	6.3167	4.7379	6.2341	1.1414	9.3178 - 6
83500	82417	191.815	-81.335	191.815	5.7930	4.3451	5.7172	1.0521	8.5887
84000	82904	190.841	-82.309	190.841	5.3105	3.9832	5.2410	9.6940 - 6	7.9134
84500	83391	189.867	-83.283	189.867	4.8660	3.6498	4.8024	8.9282	7.2883
85000	83878	188.893	-84.257	188.893	4.4568 - 3	3.3429 - 3	4.3985 - 6	8.2196 - 6	6.7099 - 6
85500	84365	187.920	-85.230	187.920	4.0802	3.0604	4.0269	7.5641	6.1747

Table I
Geometric Altitude, Metric Units

Altitude		Temperature			Pressure			Density	
Z (m)	H (m)	T (K)	t (°C)	T_M (K)	P (mb)	P (torr)	P/P_0	ρ (kg/m³)	ρ/ρ_0
86000	84852	186.87	−86.28	186.95	3.7338− 3	2.8006− 3	3.6850− 6	6.958− 6	5.680− 6
86500	85339	186.87	−86.28	186.96	3.4163	2.5624	3.3716	6.366	5.196
87000	85825	186.87	−86.28	186.98	3.1259	2.3446	3.0850	5.824	4.754
87500	86312	186.87	−86.28	187.00	2.8602	2.1454	2.8228	5.328	4.350
88000	86798	186.87	−86.28	187.03	2.6173	1.9631	2.5831	4.875	3.980
88500	87285	186.87	−86.28	187.06	2.3951	1.7965	2.3638	4.460	3.641
89000	87771	186.87	−86.28	187.11	2.1919	1.6440	2.1632	4.081	3.331
89500	88257	186.87	−86.28	187.16	2.0060	1.5046	1.9797	3.734	3.048
90000	88744	186.87	−86.28	187.21	1.8359− 3	1.3771− 3	1.8119− 6	3.416− 6	2.789− 6
90500	89230	186.87	−86.28	187.28	1.6804	1.2604	1.6584	3.126	2.552
91000	89716	186.87	−86.28	187.36	1.5381	1.1536	1.5179	2.860	2.335
91500	90202	186.89	−86.26	187.47	1.4078	1.0560	1.3894	2.616	2.136
92000	90688	186.96	−86.19	187.64	1.2887	9.6662− 4	1.2719	2.393	1.953
92500	91173	187.08	−86.07	187.87	1.1798	8.8490	1.1643	2.188	1.786
93000	91659	187.25	−85.90	188.16	1.0801	8.1014	1.0660	2.000	1.632
93500	92145	187.47	−85.68	188.51	9.8896− 4	7.4178	9.7602− 7	1.828	1.492
94000	92630	187.74	−85.41	188.92	9.0560	6.7925	8.9375	1.670	1.363
94500	93116	188.05	−85.10	189.39	8.2937	6.2208	8.1852	1.526	1.245
95000	93601	188.42	−84.73	189.92	7.5966− 4	5.6979− 4	7.4973− 7	1.393− 6	1.137− 6
95500	94087	188.84	−84.31	190.52	6.9592	5.2199	6.8682	1.273	1.039
96000	94572	189.31	−83.84	191.17	6.3765	4.7828	6.2932	1.162	9.486− 7
96500	95057	189.83	−83.32	191.90	5.8439	4.3833	5.7675	1.061	8.660
97000	95542	190.40	−82.75	192.69	5.3571	4.0181	5.2870	9.685− 7	7.906
97500	96027	191.04	−82.11	193.55	4.9122	3.6844	4.8480	8.842	7.218
98000	96512	191.72	−81.43	194.48	4.5057	3.3795	4.4468	8.071	6.588
98500	96997	192.47	−80.68	195.49	4.1342	3.1009	4.0802	7.367	6.014
99000	97482	193.28	−79.87	196.58	3.7948	2.8463	3.7452	6.725	5.490
99500	97967	194.15	−79.00	197.74	3.4846	2.6137	3.4390	6.139	5.011
100000	98451	195.08	−78.07	198.99	3.2011− 4	2.4010− 4	3.1593− 7	5.604− 7	4.575− 7
101000	99420	197.16	−75.99	201.75	2.7192	2.0396	2.6837	4.695	3.833
102000	100389	199.53	−73.62	204.88	2.3144	1.7359	2.2841	3.935	3.212
103000	101358	202.23	−70.92	208.42	1.9742	1.4808	1.9484	3.300	2.694
104000	102326	205.31	−67.84	212.41	1.6882	1.2663	1.6661	2.769	2.260
105000	103294	208.84	−64.31	216.93	1.4477	1.0859	1.4288	2.325	1.898
106000	104261	212.89	−60.26	222.09	1.2454	9.3411− 5	1.2291	1.954	1.595
107000	105229	217.63	−55.52	228.02	1.0751	8.0642	1.0611	1.643	1.341
108000	106196	223.29	−49.86	235.00	9.3188− 5	6.9897	9.1970− 8	1.381	1.128
109000	107162	230.33	−42.82	243.53	8.1142	6.0862	8.0081	1.161	9.475− 8
110000	108129	240.00	−33.15	254.93	7.1042− 5	5.3286− 5	7.0113− 8	9.708− 8	7.925− 8
111000	109095	252.00	−21.15	268.91	6.2614	4.6965	6.1796	8.111	6.622
112000	110061	264.00	−9.15	283.00	5.5547	4.1664	5.4821	6.838	5.582
113000	111026	276.00	2.85	297.17	4.9570	3.7180	4.8922	5.811	4.744
114000	111992	288.00	14.85	311.40	4.4473	3.3358	4.3892	4.975	4.061
115000	112957	300.00	26.85	325.69	4.0096	3.0075	3.9572	4.289	3.501
116000	113921	312.00	38.85	340.04	3.6312	2.7236	3.5837	3.720	3.037
117000	114885	324.00	50.85	354.43	3.3022	2.4768	3.2590	3.246	2.650
118000	115849	336.00	62.85	368.88	3.0144	2.2610	2.9750	2.847	2.324
119000	116813	348.00	74.85	383.37	2.7615	2.0713	2.7254	2.509	2.048
120000	117777	360.00	86.85	397.91	2.5382− 5	1.9038− 5	2.5050− 8	2.222− 8	1.814− 8
121000	118740	371.89	98.74	412.38	2.3401	1.7552	2.3095	1.977	1.614
122000	119703	383.55	110.40	426.66	2.1635	1.6228	2.1352	1.767	1.442
123000	120665	394.99	121.84	440.74	2.0055	1.5043	1.9793	1.585	1.294
124000	121627	406.22	133.07	454.64	1.8635	1.3977	1.8391	1.428	1.166
125000	122589	417.23	144.08	468.35	1.7354	1.3016	1.7127	1.291	1.054
126000	123551	428.04	154.89	481.89	1.6194	1.2147	1.5983	1.171	9.557− 9
127000	124512	438.64	165.49	495.26	1.5141	1.1357	1.4943	1.065	8.694
128000	125473	449.04	175.89	508.46	1.4183	1.0638	1.3997	9.717− 9	7.932
129000	126434	459.25	186.10	521.49	1.3307	9.9810− 6	1.3133	8.889	7.257
130000	127395	469.27	196.12	534.36	1.2505− 5	9.3795− 6	1.2341− 8	8.152− 9	6.655− 9
131000	128355	479.09	205.94	547.08	1.1769	8.8275	1.1615	7.494	6.118
132000	129315	488.74	215.59	559.64	1.1092	8.3196	1.0947	6.904	5.636
133000	130274	498.20	225.05	572.06	1.0468	7.8513	1.0331	6.374	5.204
134000	131234	507.48	234.33	584.32	9.8907− 6	7.4187	9.7614− 9	5.897	4.814
135000	132193	516.59	243.44	596.44	9.3568	7.0182	9.2345	5.465	4.461
136000	133151	525.53	252.38	608.42	8.8617	6.6468	8.7459	5.074	4.142
137000	134110	534.29	261.14	620.25	8.4018	6.3019	8.2919	4.719	3.852
138000	135068	542.90	269.75	631.95	7.9739	5.9809	7.8696	4.396	3.588
139000	136026	551.34	278.19	643.51	7.5751	5.6818	7.4760	4.101	3.348
140000	136983	559.63	286.48	654.94	7.2028− 6	5.4026− 6	7.1087− 9	3.831− 9	3.128− 9
141000	137940	567.76	294.61	666.23	6.8550	5.1416	6.7653	3.584	2.926
142000	138897	575.73	302.58	677.40	6.5294	4.8974	6.4440	3.358	2.741
143000	139854	583.56	310.41	688.44	6.2243	4.6686	6.1429	3.150	2.571
144000	140810	591.24	318.09	699.36	5.9380	4.4539	5.8604	2.958	2.415
145000	141766	598.78	325.63	710.15	5.6691	4.2522	5.5950	2.781	2.270
146000	142722	606.17	333.02	720.82	5.4162	4.0625	5.3454	2.618	2.137
147000	143677	613.43	340.28	731.38	5.1781	3.8839	5.1104	2.466	2.013
148000	144633	620.55	347.40	741.81	4.9538	3.7156	4.8890	2.326	1.899
149000	145587	627.54	354.39	752.14	4.7421	3.5569	4.6801	2.196	1.793

Table I
Geometric Altitude, Metric Units

Altitude		Temperature			Pressure			Density	
Z (m)	H (m)	T (K)	t (°C)	T_M (K)	P (mb)	P (torr)	P/P_0	ρ (kg/m³)	ρ/ρ_0
150000	146542	634.39	361.24	762.35	4.5422- 6	3.4070- 6	4.4828- 9	2.076- 9	1.694- 9
151000	147496	641.12	367.97	772.45	4.3533	3.2653	4.2964	1.963	1.603
152000	148450	647.72	374.57	782.44	4.1746	3.1312	4.1200	1.859	1.517
153000	149404	654.20	381.05	792.32	4.0054	3.0043	3.9530	1.761	1.438
154000	150357	660.56	387.41	802.10	3.8451	2.8840	3.7948	1.670	1.363
155000	151311	666.80	393.65	811.77	3.6930	2.7700	3.6447	1.585	1.294
156000	152263	672.92	399.77	821.34	3.5487	2.6617	3.5023	1.505	1.229
157000	153216	678.93	405.78	830.81	3.4116	2.5589	3.3670	1.431	1.168
158000	154168	684.83	411.68	840.18	3.2813	2.4612	3.2384	1.361	1.111
159000	155120	690.61	417.46	849.45	3.1574	2.3683	3.1161	1.295	1.057
160000	156072	696.29	423.14	858.63	3.0395- 6	2.2798- 6	2.9997- 9	1.233- 9	1.007- 9
161000	157023	701.86	428.71	867.71	2.9272	2.1956	2.8889	1.175	9.593- 10
162000	157974	707.33	434.18	876.70	2.8201	2.1153	2.7833	1.121	9.148
163000	158925	712.70	439.55	885.60	2.7181	2.0387	2.6825	1.069	8.728
164000	159875	717.96	444.81	894.41	2.6207	1.9657	2.5864	1.021	8.333
165000	160826	723.13	449.98	903.13	2.5278	1.8960	2.4947	9.750- 10	7.959
166000	161775	728.20	455.05	911.77	2.4390	1.8294	2.4071	9.319	7.607
167000	162725	733.18	460.03	920.32	2.3541	1.7657	2.3233	8.911	7.274
168000	163674	738.07	464.92	928.78	2.2730	1.7049	2.2432	8.525	6.960
169000	164623	742.86	469.71	937.16	2.1953	1.6466	2.1666	8.161	6.662
170000	165572	747.57	474.42	945.46	2.1210- 6	1.5909- 6	2.0933- 9	7.815- 10	6.380- 10
171000	166521	752.18	479.03	953.68	2.0499	1.5375	2.0231	7.488	6.113
172000	167469	756.71	483.56	961.82	1.9817	1.4864	1.9558	7.178	5.859
173000	168417	761.16	488.01	969.89	1.9164	1.4374	1.8913	6.883	5.619
174000	169364	765.53	492.38	977.87	1.8537	1.3904	1.8295	6.604	5.391
175000	170311	769.81	496.66	985.78	1.7936	1.3453	1.7702	6.339	5.174
176000	171258	774.01	500.86	993.62	1.7360	1.3021	1.7132	6.086	4.968
177000	172205	778.14	504.99	1001.38	1.6806	1.2605	1.6586	5.846	4.773
178000	173151	782.19	509.04	1009.07	1.6274	1.2206	1.6061	5.618	4.586
179000	174098	786.17	513.02	1016.69	1.5763	1.1823	1.5557	5.401	4.409
180000	175043	790.07	516.92	1024.24	1.5271- 6	1.1455- 6	1.5072- 9	5.194- 10	4.240- 10
181000	175989	793.89	520.74	1031.72	1.4799	1.1100	1.4606	4.997	4.079
182000	176934	797.65	524.50	1039.13	1.4345	1.0759	1.4157	4.809	3.926
183000	177879	801.34	528.19	1046.47	1.3907	1.0431	1.3726	4.630	3.779
184000	178824	804.96	531.81	1053.75	1.3487	1.0116	1.3310	4.459	3.640
185000	179768	808.51	535.36	1060.96	1.3081	9.8117- 7	1.2910	4.295	3.506
186000	180712	812.00	538.85	1068.11	1.2691	9.5189	1.2525	4.139	3.379
187000	181656	815.42	542.27	1075.19	1.2315	9.2368	1.2154	3.990	3.257
188000	182600	818.78	545.63	1082.21	1.1952	8.9649	1.1796	3.847	3.141
189000	183543	822.08	548.93	1089.17	1.1603	8.7028	1.1451	3.711	3.029
190000	184486	825.31	552.16	1096.07	1.1266- 6	8.4499- 7	1.1118- 9	3.581- 10	2.923- 10
191000	185428	828.49	555.34	1102.90	1.0940	8.2060	1.0797	3.456	2.821
192000	186371	831.61	558.46	1109.68	1.0627	7.9707	1.0488	3.336	2.723
193000	187313	834.67	561.52	1116.40	1.0324	7.7435	1.0189	3.222	2.630
194000	188255	837.67	564.52	1123.06	1.0031	7.5242	9.9003- 10	3.112	2.540
195000	189196	840.62	567.47	1129.67	9.7491- 7	7.3124	9.6216	3.006	2.454
196000	190137	843.51	570.36	1136.21	9.4763	7.1078	9.3524	2.905	2.372
197000	191078	846.35	573.20	1142.71	9.2127	6.9101	9.0922	2.809	2.293
198000	192019	849.14	575.99	1149.14	8.9580	6.7190	8.8408	2.716	2.217
199000	192959	851.87	578.72	1155.52	8.7117	6.5343	8.5978	2.626	2.144
200000	193899	854.56	581.41	1161.85	8.4736- 7	6.3557- 7	8.3628- 10	2.541- 10	2.074- 10
201000	194839	857.20	584.05	1168.13	8.2432	6.1829	8.1355	2.458	2.007
202000	195779	859.78	586.63	1174.35	8.0204	6.0158	7.9156	2.379	1.942
203000	196718	862.32	589.17	1180.52	7.8048	5.8541	7.7028	2.303	1.880
204000	197657	864.82	591.67	1186.64	7.5962	5.6976	7.4968	2.230	1.820
205000	198595	867.26	594.11	1192.71	7.3942	5.5461	7.2975	2.160	1.763
206000	199534	869.67	596.52	1198.73	7.1986	5.3994	7.1045	2.092	1.708
207000	200472	872.02	598.87	1204.70	7.0092	5.2573	6.9175	2.027	1.655
208000	201410	874.34	601.19	1210.62	6.8257	5.1197	6.7364	1.964	1.603
209000	202347	876.61	603.46	1216.49	6.6479	4.9863	6.5610	1.904	1.554
210000	203284	878.84	605.69	1222.31	6.4756- 7	4.8571- 7	6.3910- 10	1.846- 10	1.507- 10
211000	204221	881.03	607.88	1228.09	6.3087	4.7319	6.2262	1.790	1.461
212000	205158	883.18	610.03	1233.82	6.1468	4.6105	6.0664	1.736	1.417
213000	206094	885.29	612.14	1239.50	5.9899	4.4928	5.9115	1.683	1.374
214000	207030	887.36	614.21	1245.14	5.8377	4.3786	5.7613	1.633	1.333
215000	207966	889.39	616.24	1250.73	5.6900	4.2679	5.6156	1.585	1.294
216000	208902	891.39	618.24	1256.27	5.5468	4.1604	5.4743	1.538	1.256
217000	209837	893.35	620.20	1261.77	5.4078	4.0562	5.3371	1.493	1.219
218000	210772	895.27	622.12	1267.23	5.2729	3.9550	5.2040	1.450	1.183
219000	211706	897.16	624.01	1272.65	5.1420	3.8568	5.0748	1.408	1.149
220000	212641	899.01	625.86	1278.02	5.0149- 7	3.7615- 7	4.9494- 10	1.367- 10	1.116- 10
221000	213575	900.83	627.68	1283.34	4.8915	3.6689	4.8276	1.328	1.084
222000	214509	902.62	629.47	1288.63	4.7717	3.5791	4.7093	1.290	1.053
223000	215442	904.37	631.22	1293.87	4.6553	3.4918	4.5944	1.253	1.023
224000	216375	906.09	632.94	1299.07	4.5422	3.4069	4.4828	1.218	9.943- 11
225000	217308	907.78	634.63	1304.23	4.4324	3.3245	4.3744	1.184	9.665
226000	218241	909.44	636.29	1309.35	4.3256	3.2445	4.2690	1.151	9.395
227000	219173	911.07	637.92	1314.43	4.2219	3.1667	4.1666	1.119	9.134
228000	220105	912.67	639.52	1319.47	4.1210	3.0910	4.0671	1.088	8.882
229000	221037	914.24	641.09	1324.47	4.0230	3.0175	3.9704	1.058	8.638

70

Table I
Geometric Altitude, Metric Units

Altitude		Temperature			Pressure			Density	
Z (m)	H (m)	T (K)	t (°C)	T_M (K)	P (mb)	P (torr)	P/P_0	ρ (kg/m³)	ρ/ρ_0
230000	221969	915.78	642.63	1329.43	3.9276- 7	2.9460- 7	3.8763- 10	1.029- 10	8.402- 11
231000	222900	917.29	644.14	1334.35	3.8349	2.8764	3.7848	1.001	8.173
232000	223831	918.78	645.63	1339.23	3.7448	2.8088	3.6958	9.741- 11	7.952
233000	224762	920.24	647.09	1344.07	3.6571	2.7430	3.6093	9.479	7.738
234000	225692	921.67	648.52	1348.87	3.5718	2.6791	3.5251	9.225	7.530
235000	226622	923.07	649.92	1353.64	3.4888	2.6168	3.4432	8.979	7.329
236000	227552	924.45	651.30	1358.37	3.4080	2.5562	3.3634	8.740	7.135
237000	228481	925.81	652.66	1363.06	3.3294	2.4973	3.2859	8.509	6.946
238000	229411	927.14	653.99	1367.71	3.2529	2.4399	3.2103	8.285	6.764
239000	230340	928.44	655.29	1372.33	3.1784	2.3840	3.1368	8.068	6.586
240000	231268	929.73	656.58	1376.91	3.1059- 7	2.3296- 7	3.0653- 10	7.858- 11	6.415- 11
241000	232197	930.98	657.83	1381.46	3.0353	2.2767	2.9956	7.654	6.248
242000	233125	932.22	659.07	1385.97	2.9665	2.2251	2.9277	7.456	6.087
243000	234053	933.43	660.28	1390.45	2.8996	2.1749	2.8616	7.265	5.930
244000	234980	934.62	661.47	1394.88	2.8343	2.1259	2.7973	7.079	5.779
245000	235908	935.79	662.64	1399.29	2.7708	2.0783	2.7346	6.898	5.631
246000	236835	936.94	663.79	1403.66	2.7089	2.0318	2.6735	6.723	5.488
247000	237761	938.07	664.92	1407.99	2.6486	1.9866	2.6139	6.553	5.350
248000	238688	939.18	666.03	1412.30	2.5898	1.9425	2.5559	6.388	5.215
249000	239614	940.26	667.11	1416.56	2.5325	1.8995	2.4994	6.228	5.084
250000	240540	941.33	668.18	1420.80	2.4767- 7	1.8577- 7	2.4443- 10	6.073- 11	4.957- 11
251000	241466	942.38	669.23	1425.00	2.4222	1.8168	2.3906	5.922	4.834
252000	242391	943.41	670.26	1429.16	2.3692	1.7770	2.3382	5.775	4.714
253000	243316	944.42	671.27	1433.30	2.3175	1.7382	2.2871	5.633	4.598
254000	244241	945.41	672.26	1437.40	2.2670	1.7004	2.2374	5.494	4.485
255000	245165	946.38	673.23	1441.47	2.2178	1.6635	2.1888	5.360	4.375
256000	246089	947.34	674.19	1445.51	2.1698	1.6275	2.1415	5.229	4.269
257000	247013	948.28	675.13	1449.51	2.1230	1.5924	2.0953	5.102	4.165
258000	247937	949.20	676.05	1453.49	2.0774	1.5582	2.0502	4.979	4.064
259000	248860	950.10	676.95	1457.43	2.0328	1.5248	2.0063	4.859	3.967
260000	249784	950.99	677.84	1461.34	1.9894- 7	1.4922- 7	1.9634- 10	4.742- 11	3.871- 11
261000	250706	951.86	678.71	1465.22	1.9470	1.4604	1.9215	4.629	3.779
262000	251629	952.72	679.57	1469.07	1.9056	1.4293	1.8807	4.519	3.689
263000	252551	953.56	680.41	1472.89	1.8652	1.3990	1.8408	4.412	3.601
264000	253473	954.39	681.24	1476.68	1.8258	1.3695	1.8020	4.307	3.516
265000	254395	955.20	682.05	1480.44	1.7874	1.3406	1.7640	4.206	3.433
266000	255316	955.99	682.84	1484.17	1.7498	1.3125	1.7269	4.107	3.353
267000	256237	956.78	683.63	1487.87	1.7131	1.2850	1.6907	4.011	3.274
268000	257158	957.54	684.39	1491.54	1.6773	1.2581	1.6554	3.918	3.198
269000	258079	958.30	685.15	1495.18	1.6424	1.2319	1.6209	3.827	3.124
270000	258999	959.04	685.89	1498.80	1.6083- 7	1.2063- 7	1.5872- 10	3.738- 11	3.052- 11
271000	259919	959.77	686.62	1502.38	1.5749	1.1813	1.5543	3.652	2.981
272000	260839	960.48	687.33	1505.94	1.5424	1.1569	1.5222	3.568	2.913
273000	261758	961.18	688.03	1509.46	1.5106	1.1330	1.4908	3.486	2.846
274000	262678	961.87	688.72	1512.96	1.4795	1.1097	1.4602	3.407	2.781
275000	263597	962.54	689.39	1516.43	1.4492	1.0870	1.4302	3.329	2.718
276000	264515	963.21	690.06	1519.88	1.4195	1.0647	1.4010	3.254	2.656
277000	265434	963.86	690.71	1523.30	1.3906	1.0430	1.3724	3.180	2.596
278000	266352	964.50	691.35	1526.68	1.3623	1.0218	1.3444	3.108	2.538
279000	267269	965.13	691.98	1530.05	1.3346	1.0010	1.3171	3.039	2.481
280000	268187	965.75	692.60	1533.38	1.3076- 7	9.8075- 8	1.2905- 10	2.971- 11	2.425- 11
281000	269104	966.35	693.20	1536.69	1.2811	9.6093	1.2644	2.904	2.371
282000	270021	966.95	693.80	1539.98	1.2553	9.4156	1.2389	2.840	2.318
283000	270938	967.53	694.38	1543.23	1.2301	9.2263	1.2140	2.777	2.267
284000	271854	968.11	694.96	1546.47	1.2054	9.0412	1.1896	2.715	2.217
285000	272771	968.67	695.52	1549.67	1.1813	8.8603	1.1658	2.656	2.168
286000	273686	969.22	696.07	1552.85	1.1577	8.6834	1.1426	2.597	2.120
287000	274602	969.77	696.62	1556.01	1.1346	8.5104	1.1198	2.540	2.074
288000	275517	970.30	697.15	1559.14	1.1121	8.3413	1.0975	2.485	2.028
289000	276432	970.83	697.68	1562.24	1.0900	8.1759	1.0758	2.431	1.984
290000	277347	971.34	698.19	1565.32	1.0685- 7	8.0141- 8	1.0545- 10	2.378- 11	1.941- 11
291000	278262	971.85	698.70	1568.38	1.0474	7.8559	1.0337	2.326	1.899
292000	279176	972.34	699.19	1571.41	1.0267	7.7012	1.0133	2.276	1.858
293000	280090	972.83	699.68	1574.42	1.0066	7.5498	9.9340- 11	2.227	1.818
294000	281004	973.31	700.16	1577.41	9.8682- 8	7.4018	9.7392	2.179	1.779
295000	281917	973.78	700.63	1580.37	9.6751	7.2569	9.5486	2.133	1.741
296000	282830	974.24	701.09	1583.31	9.4862	7.1152	9.3622	2.087	1.704
297000	283743	974.70	701.55	1586.22	9.3014	6.9766	9.1797	2.043	1.668
298000	284656	975.14	701.99	1589.12	9.1205	6.8410	9.0013	1.999	1.632
299000	285568	975.58	702.43	1591.99	8.9436	6.7082	8.8266	1.957	1.598
300000	286480	976.01	702.86	1594.83	8.7704- 8	6.5783- 8	8.6557- 11	1.916- 11	1.564- 11
302000	288303	976.84	703.69	1600.46	8.4351	6.3268	8.3248	1.836	1.499
304000	290125	977.65	704.50	1606.00	8.1139	6.0859	8.0078	1.760	1.437
306000	291946	978.43	705.28	1611.46	7.8061	5.8551	7.7040	1.688	1.378
308000	293766	979.18	706.03	1616.84	7.5112	5.6338	7.4129	1.618	1.321
310000	295585	979.90	706.75	1622.13	7.2285	5.4218	7.1339	1.552	1.267
312000	297403	980.60	707.45	1627.34	6.9574	5.2185	6.8664	1.489	1.216
314000	299220	981.28	708.13	1632.47	6.6975	5.0235	6.6099	1.429	1.167
316000	301035	981.93	708.78	1637.53	6.4482	4.8365	6.3639	1.372	1.120
318000	302850	982.55	709.40	1642.51	6.2090	4.6572	6.1278	1.317	1.075

Table I
Geometric Altitude, Metric Units

Altitude		Temperature			Pressure			Density	
Z (m)	H (m)	T (K)	t (°C)	T_M (K)	P (mb)	P (torr)	P/P_0	ρ (kg/m³)	ρ/ρ_0
320000	304663	983.16	710.01	1647.42	5.9796- 8	4.4850- 8	5.9014- 11	1.264- 11	1.032- 11
322000	306476	983.74	710.59	1652.26	5.7593	4.3199	5.6840	1.214	9.913- 12
324000	308287	984.31	711.16	1657.03	5.5480	4.1613	5.4754	1.166	9.521
326000	310097	984.85	711.70	1661.73	5.3450	4.0091	5.2751	1.121	9.147
328000	311906	985.37	712.22	1666.37	5.1502	3.8629	5.0828	1.077	8.789
330000	313714	985.88	712.73	1670.94	4.9630	3.7226	4.8981	1.035	8.447
332000	315521	986.37	713.22	1675.45	4.7833	3.5877	4.7207	9.946- 12	8.119
334000	317327	986.84	713.69	1679.90	4.6106	3.4582	4.5503	9.561	7.805
336000	319132	987.29	714.14	1684.29	4.4447	3.3338	4.3865	9.193	7.505
338000	320935	987.73	714.58	1688.62	4.2852	3.2142	4.2292	8.841	7.217
340000	322738	988.15	715.00	1692.90	4.1320- 8	3.0992- 8	4.0779- 11	8.503- 12	6.941- 12
342000	324539	988.56	715.41	1697.13	3.9846	2.9887	3.9325	8.179	6.677
344000	326340	988.96	715.81	1701.30	3.8430	2.8825	3.7927	7.869	6.424
346000	328139	989.34	716.19	1705.42	3.7068	2.7803	3.6583	7.572	6.181
348000	329938	989.70	716.55	1709.50	3.5758	2.6821	3.5290	7.287	5.948
350000	331735	990.06	716.91	1713.53	3.4498	2.5876	3.4047	7.014	5.725
352000	333531	990.40	717.25	1717.51	3.3286	2.4966	3.2851	6.751	5.511
354000	335326	990.73	717.58	1721.46	3.2120	2.4092	3.1700	6.500	5.306
356000	337120	991.05	717.90	1725.36	3.0998	2.3250	3.0592	6.259	5.109
358000	338913	991.35	718.20	1729.22	2.9918	2.2440	2.9526	6.027	4.920
360000	340705	991.65	718.50	1733.05	2.8878- 8	2.1661- 8	2.8501- 11	5.805- 12	4.739- 12
362000	342496	991.94	718.79	1736.84	2.7878	2.0910	2.7513	5.592	4.565
364000	344286	992.21	719.06	1740.59	2.6915	2.0188	2.6563	5.387	4.397
366000	346074	992.48	719.33	1744.32	2.5987	1.9492	2.5647	5.190	4.237
368000	347862	992.74	719.59	1748.02	2.5094	1.8822	2.4766	5.001	4.083
370000	349648	992.98	719.83	1751.68	2.4234	1.8177	2.3917	4.820	3.934
372000	351434	993.22	720.07	1755.32	2.3405	1.7556	2.3099	4.645	3.792
374000	353218	993.46	720.31	1758.94	2.2607	1.6957	2.2312	4.478	3.655
376000	355002	993.68	720.53	1762.53	2.1839	1.6380	2.1553	4.316	3.524
378000	356784	993.89	720.74	1766.10	2.1098	1.5825	2.0822	4.162	3.397
380000	358565	994.10	720.95	1769.66	2.0384- 8	1.5289- 8	2.0117- 11	4.013- 12	3.276- 12
382000	360346	994.30	721.15	1773.19	1.9696	1.4773	1.9439	3.870	3.159
384000	362125	994.50	721.35	1776.71	1.9033	1.4276	1.8784	3.732	3.046
386000	363903	994.68	721.53	1780.22	1.8394	1.3797	1.8153	3.599	2.938
388000	365680	994.86	721.71	1783.72	1.7778	1.3335	1.7545	3.472	2.834
390000	367456	995.04	721.89	1787.20	1.7184	1.2889	1.6959	3.350	2.734
392000	369231	995.21	722.06	1790.68	1.6611	1.2460	1.6394	3.232	2.638
394000	371005	995.37	722.22	1794.15	1.6059	1.2045	1.5849	3.118	2.545
396000	372778	995.53	722.38	1797.61	1.5527	1.1646	1.5324	3.009	2.456
398000	374549	995.68	722.53	1801.08	1.5013	1.1261	1.4817	2.904	2.370
400000	376320	995.83	722.68	1804.54	1.4518- 8	1.0889- 8	1.4328- 11	2.803- 12	2.288- 12
402000	378090	995.97	722.82	1808.00	1.4040	1.0531	1.3856	2.705	2.208
404000	379858	996.10	722.95	1811.47	1.3579	1.0185	1.3401	2.611	2.132
406000	381626	996.23	723.08	1814.94	1.3134	9.8514- 9	1.2962	2.521	2.058
408000	383392	996.36	723.21	1818.41	1.2705	9.5295	1.2539	2.434	1.987
410000	385158	996.49	723.34	1821.90	1.2291	9.2189	1.2130	2.350	1.918
412000	386922	996.60	723.45	1825.39	1.1891	8.9192	1.1736	2.269	1.853
414000	388686	996.72	723.57	1828.90	1.1506	8.6299	1.1355	2.192	1.789
416000	390448	996.83	723.68	1832.42	1.1133	8.3507	1.0988	2.117	1.728
418000	392210	996.94	723.79	1835.96	1.0774	8.0812	1.0633	2.044	1.669
420000	393970	997.04	723.89	1839.52	1.0427- 8	7.8211- 9	1.0291- 11	1.975- 12	1.612- 12
422000	395729	997.14	723.99	1843.09	1.0092	7.5699	9.9605- 12	1.908	1.557
424000	397487	997.24	724.09	1846.69	9.7692- 9	7.3275	9.6414	1.843	1.504
426000	399245	997.33	724.18	1850.31	9.4570	7.0933	9.3333	1.781	1.453
428000	401001	997.42	724.27	1853.96	9.1556	6.8673	9.0359	1.720	1.404
430000	402756	997.50	724.35	1857.63	8.8645	6.6489	8.7486	1.662	1.357
432000	404510	997.59	724.44	1861.33	8.5834	6.4381	8.4712	1.606	1.311
434000	406263	997.67	724.52	1865.07	8.3119	6.2345	8.2032	1.553	1.267
436000	408015	997.75	724.60	1868.83	8.0497	6.0378	7.9444	1.501	1.225
438000	409766	997.82	724.67	1872.64	7.7964	5.8478	7.6944	1.450	1.184
440000	411516	997.90	724.75	1876.48	7.5517- 9	5.6642- 9	7.4529- 12	1.402- 12	1.144- 12
442000	413265	997.97	724.82	1880.36	7.3153	5.4869	7.2196	1.355	1.106
444000	415013	998.03	724.88	1884.28	7.0869	5.3156	6.9942	1.310	1.070
446000	416760	998.10	724.95	1888.24	6.8662	5.1500	6.7764	1.267	1.034
448000	418505	998.16	725.01	1892.25	6.6529	4.9901	6.5659	1.225	9.998- 13
450000	420250	998.22	725.07	1896.31	6.4468	4.8355	6.3625	1.184	9.668
452000	421994	998.28	725.13	1900.42	6.2477	4.6861	6.1660	1.145	9.349
454000	423737	998.34	725.19	1904.58	6.0552	4.5418	5.9760	1.108	9.041
456000	425478	998.40	725.25	1908.79	5.8691	4.4022	5.7924	1.071	8.744
458000	427219	998.45	725.30	1913.06	5.6893	4.2673	5.6149	1.036	8.457
460000	428959	998.50	725.35	1917.39	5.5155- 9	4.1370- 9	5.4434- 12	1.002- 12	8.180- 13
462000	430698	998.55	725.40	1921.77	5.3474	4.0109	5.2775	9.694- 13	7.913
464000	432435	998.60	725.45	1926.22	5.1850	3.8891	5.1172	9.377	7.655
466000	434172	998.65	725.50	1930.74	5.0279	3.7712	4.9621	9.072	7.406
468000	435907	998.69	725.54	1935.32	4.8760	3.6573	4.8123	8.777	7.165
470000	437642	998.73	725.58	1939.97	4.7292	3.5472	4.6673	8.492	6.932
472000	439376	998.78	725.63	1944.70	4.5871	3.4406	4.5272	8.217	6.708
474000	441108	998.82	725.67	1949.50	4.4498	3.3376	4.3916	7.952	6.491
476000	442840	998.86	725.71	1954.37	4.3170	3.2380	4.2605	7.695	6.282
478000	444570	998.89	725.74	1959.32	4.1885	3.1416	4.1337	7.447	6.079

Table I
Geometric Altitude, Metric Units

Altitude		Temperature			Pressure			Density	
Z (m)	H (m)	T (K)	t (°C)	T_M (K)	P (mb)	P (torr)	P/P_0	ρ (kg/m³)	ρ/ρ_0
480000	446300	998.93	725.78	1964.36	4.0642- 9	3.0484- 9	4.0111- 12	7.208- 13	5.884- 13
482000	448028	998.97	725.82	1969.47	3.9440	2.9583	3.8925	6.976	5.695
484000	449756	999.00	725.85	1974.68	3.8278	2.8711	3.7777	6.753	5.513
486000	451482	999.03	725.88	1979.97	3.7153	2.7867	3.6667	6.537	5.336
488000	453208	999.07	725.92	1985.35	3.6064	2.7051	3.5593	6.328	5.166
490000	454932	999.10	725.95	1990.83	3.5011	2.6261	3.4554	6.127	5.001
492000	456656	999.13	725.98	1996.40	3.3993	2.5497	3.3548	5.932	4.842
494000	458378	999.15	726.00	2002.07	3.3007	2.4757	3.2575	5.743	4.688
496000	460100	999.18	726.03	2007.84	3.2053	2.4041	3.1633	5.561	4.540
498000	461820	999.21	726.06	2013.71	3.1129	2.3349	3.0722	5.385	4.396
500000	463540	999.24	726.09	2019.69	3.0236- 9	2.2679- 9	2.9840- 12	5.215- 13	4.257- 13
505000	467834	999.30	726.15	2035.12	2.8125	2.1096	2.7757	4.814	3.930
510000	472122	999.35	726.20	2051.27	2.6179	1.9636	2.5837	4.446	3.629
515000	476404	999.40	726.25	2068.18	2.4385	1.8290	2.4066	4.107	3.353
520000	480679	999.45	726.30	2085.90	2.2729	1.7048	2.2431	3.796	3.099
525000	484949	999.50	726.35	2104.47	2.1200	1.5901	2.0923	3.509	2.865
530000	489212	999.54	726.39	2123.94	1.9789	1.4843	1.9530	3.246	2.650
535000	493469	999.57	726.42	2144.35	1.8485	1.3865	1.8244	3.003	2.452
540000	497719	999.61	726.46	2165.75	1.7281	1.2962	1.7055	2.780	2.269
545000	501964	999.64	726.49	2188.18	1.6167	1.2126	1.5956	2.574	2.101
550000	506202	999.67	726.52	2211.70	1.5137- 9	1.1354- 9	1.4939- 12	2.384- 13	1.946- 13
555000	510435	999.69	726.54	2236.35	1.4184	1.0639	1.3999	2.210	1.804
560000	514661	999.72	726.57	2262.18	1.3303	9.9778- 10	1.3129	2.049	1.672
565000	518881	999.74	726.59	2289.24	1.2486	9.3652	1.2323	1.900	1.551
570000	523095	999.76	726.61	2317.58	1.1729	8.7978	1.1576	1.763	1.439
575000	527303	999.78	726.63	2347.24	1.1028	8.2719	1.0884	1.637	1.336
580000	531505	999.80	726.65	2378.28	1.0378	7.7843	1.0243	1.520	1.241
585000	535701	999.81	726.66	2410.74	9.7752- 10	7.3320	9.6473- 13	1.413	1.153
590000	539890	999.83	726.68	2444.66	9.2155	6.9122	9.0950	1.313	1.072
595000	544074	999.84	726.69	2480.10	8.6958	6.5224	8.5821	1.221	9.971- 14
600000	548252	999.85	726.70	2517.10	8.2130- 10	6.1602- 10	8.1056- 13	1.137- 13	9.279- 14
605000	552424	999.86	726.71	2555.69	7.7642	5.8236	7.6626	1.058	8.640
610000	556589	999.88	726.72	2595.92	7.3468	5.5106	7.2507	9.859- 14	8.048
615000	560749	999.88	726.73	2637.82	6.9585	5.2193	6.8675	9.190	7.502
620000	564903	999.89	726.74	2681.43	6.5969	4.9481	6.5106	8.571	6.996
625000	569051	999.90	726.75	2726.78	6.2601	4.6954	6.1782	7.998	6.529
630000	573193	999.91	726.76	2773.89	5.9461	4.4600	5.8684	7.468	6.096
635000	577329	999.92	726.77	2822.79	5.6533	4.2404	5.5794	6.977	5.695
640000	581459	999.92	726.77	2873.49	5.3801	4.0354	5.3097	6.523	5.325
645000	585583	999.93	726.78	2926.01	5.1249	3.8440	5.0579	6.102	4.981
650000	589701	999.93	726.78	2980.36	4.8865- 10	3.6651- 10	4.8226- 13	5.712- 14	4.663- 14
655000	593814	999.94	726.79	3036.53	4.6635	3.4979	4.6025	5.350	4.368
660000	597920	999.94	726.79	3094.52	4.4549	3.3414	4.3966	5.015	4.094
665000	602021	999.95	726.80	3154.32	4.2595	3.1949	4.2038	4.704	3.840
670000	606116	999.95	726.80	3215.92	4.0765	3.0576	4.0232	4.416	3.605
675000	610205	999.96	726.81	3279.29	3.9048	2.9289	3.8538	4.148	3.386
680000	614288	999.96	726.81	3344.39	3.7438	2.8081	3.6948	3.900	3.183
685000	618365	999.96	726.81	3411.19	3.5925	2.6946	3.5455	3.669	2.995
690000	622437	999.97	726.82	3479.64	3.4504	2.5880	3.4052	3.454	2.820
695000	626503	999.97	726.82	3549.69	3.3166	2.4877	3.2733	3.255	2.657
700000	630563	999.97	726.82	3621.27	3.1908- 10	2.3933- 10	3.1491- 13	3.070- 14	2.506- 14
705000	634617	999.97	726.82	3694.31	3.0722	2.3043	3.0320	2.897	2.365
710000	638666	999.97	726.82	3768.74	2.9604	2.2205	2.9217	2.736	2.234
715000	642709	999.98	726.83	3844.47	2.8549	2.1414	2.8176	2.587	2.112
720000	646746	999.98	726.83	3921.41	2.7553	2.0666	2.7193	2.448	1.998
725000	650778	999.98	726.83	3999.46	2.6611	1.9960	2.6263	2.318	1.892
730000	654803	999.98	726.83	4078.53	2.5720	1.9292	2.5384	2.197	1.793
735000	658824	999.98	726.83	4158.49	2.4877	1.8659	2.4551	2.084	1.701
740000	662838	999.98	726.83	4239.25	2.4077	1.8059	2.3762	1.979	1.615
745000	666847	999.99	726.84	4320.67	2.3319	1.7491	2.3014	1.880	1.535
750000	670850	999.99	726.84	4402.64	2.2599- 10	1.6951- 10	2.2303- 13	1.788- 14	1.460- 14
755000	674848	999.99	726.84	4485.04	2.1915	1.6438	2.1628	1.702	1.390
760000	678840	999.99	726.84	4567.74	2.1265	1.5950	2.0987	1.622	1.324
765000	682826	999.99	726.84	4650.61	2.0645	1.5485	2.0375	1.547	1.262
770000	686807	999.99	726.84	4733.52	2.0056	1.5043	1.9793	1.476	1.205
775000	690782	999.99	726.84	4816.36	1.9493	1.4621	1.9238	1.410	1.151
780000	694751	999.99	726.84	4898.99	1.8957	1.4219	1.8709	1.348	1.100
785000	698715	999.99	726.84	4981.29	1.8444	1.3834	1.8203	1.290	1.053
790000	702674	999.99	726.84	5063.15	1.7954	1.3467	1.7719	1.235	1.008
795000	706627	999.99	726.84	5144.44	1.7485	1.3115	1.7256	1.184	9.666- 15
800000	710574	999.99	726.84	5225.06	1.7036- 10	1.2778- 10	1.6813- 13	1.136- 14	9.272- 15
805000	714516	999.99	726.84	5304.89	1.6606	1.2456	1.6389	1.091	8.902
810000	718452	999.99	726.84	5383.84	1.6193	1.2146	1.5982	1.048	8.554
815000	722383	1000.00	726.85	5461.80	1.5797	1.1849	1.5591	1.008	8.225
820000	726309	1000.00	726.85	5538.70	1.5417	1.1564	1.5215	9.697- 15	7.916
825000	730229	1000.00	726.85	5614.45	1.5051	1.1289	1.4854	9.339	7.624
830000	734143	1000.00	726.85	5688.96	1.4699	1.1025	1.4507	9.001	7.348
835000	738052	1000.00	726.85	5762.18	1.4360	1.0771	1.4172	8.682	7.087
840000	741956	1000.00	726.85	5834.03	1.4034	1.0526	1.3850	8.380	6.841
845000	745854	1000.00	726.85	5904.47	1.3719	1.0290	1.3539	8.094	6.607

Table I
Geometric Altitude, Metric Units

Altitude		Temperature			Pressure			Density	
Z (m)	H (m)	T (K)	t (°C)	T_M (K)	P (mb)	P (torr)	P/P_0	ρ (kg/m³)	ρ/ρ_0
850000	749747	1000.00	726.85	5973.45	1.3415- 10	1.0062- 10	1.3240- 13	7.824- 15	6.387- 15
855000	753634	1000.00	726.85	6040.93	1.3122	9.8420- 11	1.2950	7.567	6.177
860000	757516	1000.00	726.85	6106.87	1.2838	9.6295	1.2670	7.324	5.978
865000	761393	1000.00	726.85	6171.24	1.2564	9.4240	1.2400	7.093	5.790
870000	765264	1000.00	726.85	6234.03	1.2299	9.2251	1.2138	6.873	5.611
875000	769130	1000.00	726.85	6295.22	1.2043	9.0327	1.1885	6.664	5.440
880000	772991	1000.00	726.85	6354.81	1.1794	8.8463	1.1640	6.465	5.278
885000	776846	1000.00	726.85	6412.78	1.1553	8.6657	1.1402	6.276	5.123
890000	780696	1000.00	726.85	6469.15	1.1320	8.4905	1.1172	6.096	4.976
895000	784541	1000.00	726.85	6523.92	1.1093	8.3206	1.0948	5.924	4.836
900000	788380	1000.00	726.85	6577.11	1.0873- 10	8.1556- 11	1.0731- 13	5.759- 15	4.701- 15
905000	792214	1000.00	726.85	6628.72	1.0660	7.9954	1.0520	5.602	4.573
910000	796043	1000.00	726.85	6678.78	1.0452	7.8398	1.0316	5.452	4.451
915000	799866	1000.00	726.85	6727.31	1.0250	7.6885	1.0116	5.308	4.333
920000	803685	1000.00	726.85	6774.34	1.0054	7.5414	9.9229- 14	5.170	4.221
925000	807498	1000.00	726.85	6819.90	9.8635- 11	7.3982	9.7345	5.038	4.113
930000	811305	1000.00	726.85	6864.02	9.6777	7.2589	9.5512	4.912	4.010
935000	815108	1000.00	726.85	6906.73	9.4968	7.1232	9.3727	4.790	3.910
940000	818905	1000.00	726.85	6948.07	9.3207	6.9911	9.1988	4.673	3.815
945000	822697	1000.00	726.85	6988.07	9.1490	6.8623	9.0293	4.561	3.723
950000	826484	1000.00	726.85	7026.78	8.9816- 11	6.7368- 11	8.8642- 14	4.453- 15	3.635- 15
955000	830266	1000.00	726.85	7064.22	8.8184	6.6143	8.7031	4.349	3.550
960000	834043	1000.00	726.85	7100.45	8.6592	6.4949	8.5460	4.248	3.468
965000	837814	1000.00	726.85	7135.49	8.5039	6.3784	8.3927	4.152	3.389
970000	841580	1000.00	726.85	7169.40	8.3523	6.2647	8.2431	4.058	3.313
975000	845342	1000.00	726.85	7202.21	8.2043	6.1537	8.0970	3.968	3.239
980000	849098	1000.00	726.85	7233.96	8.0597	6.0453	7.9543	3.881	3.168
985000	852849	1000.00	726.85	7264.68	7.9185	5.9393	7.8149	3.797	3.100
990000	856594	1000.00	726.85	7294.43	7.7805	5.8358	7.6788	3.716	3.033
995000	860335	1000.00	726.85	7323.24	7.6456	5.7347	7.5457	3.637	2.969
1000000	864071	1000.00	726.85	7351.15	7.5138- 11	5.6358- 11	7.4155- 14	3.561- 15	2.907- 15

Table II
Geopotential Altitude, Metric Units

Altitude		Accel. due to gravity	Pressure scale height	Number density	Particle speed	Collision frequency	Mean free path	Molecular weight
H (m)	Z (m)	g (m/s^2)	H$_p$ (m)	n (m^{-3})	V (m/s)	ν (s^{-1})	L (m)	M (kg/kmol)
-5000	-4996	9.8221	9371.1	4.0138 +25	484.14	1.1502 +10	4.2092 - 8	28.964
-4950	-4946	9.8219	9361.7	3.9965	483.89	1.1447	4.2274	28.964
-4900	-4896	9.8218	9352.4	3.9792	483.64	1.1391	4.2457	28.964
-4850	-4846	9.8216	9343.0	3.9621	483.40	1.1336	4.2641	28.964
-4800	-4796	9.8215	9333.7	3.9450	483.15	1.1282	4.2826	28.964
-4750	-4746	9.8213	9324.3	3.9279	482.91	1.1227	4.3012	28.964
-4700	-4697	9.8212	9315.0	3.9109	482.66	1.1173	4.3199	28.964
-4650	-4647	9.8210	9305.6	3.8939	482.41	1.1119	4.3387	28.964
-4600	-4597	9.8208	9296.3	3.8771	482.17	1.1065	4.3576	28.964
-4550	-4547	9.8207	9286.9	3.8602	481.92	1.1011	4.3766	28.964
-4500	-4497	9.8205	9277.6	3.8434 +25	481.68	1.0958 +10	4.3957 - 8	28.964
-4450	-4447	9.8204	9268.2	3.8267	481.43	1.0905	4.4149	28.964
-4400	-4397	9.8202	9258.9	3.8101	481.18	1.0852	4.4342	28.964
-4350	-4347	9.8201	9249.5	3.7935	480.94	1.0799	4.4536	28.964
-4300	-4297	9.8199	9240.1	3.7769	480.69	1.0746	4.4732	28.964
-4250	-4247	9.8198	9230.8	3.7604	480.44	1.0694	4.4928	28.964
-4200	-4197	9.8196	9221.4	3.7440	480.19	1.0641	4.5125	28.964
-4150	-4147	9.8195	9212.1	3.7276	479.95	1.0589	4.5324	28.964
-4100	-4097	9.8193	9202.7	3.7112	479.70	1.0537	4.5523	28.964
-4050	-4047	9.8191	9193.4	3.6950	479.45	1.0486	4.5724	28.964
-4000	-3997	9.8190	9184.0	3.6787 +25	479.20	1.0434 +10	4.5925 - 8	28.964
-3950	-3948	9.8188	9174.6	3.6626	478.96	1.0383	4.6128	28.964
-3900	-3898	9.8187	9165.3	3.6464	478.71	1.0332	4.6332	28.964
-3850	-3848	9.8185	9155.9	3.6304	478.46	1.0281	4.6537	28.964
-3800	-3798	9.8184	9146.6	3.6144	478.21	1.0231	4.6743	28.964
-3750	-3748	9.8182	9137.2	3.5984	477.96	1.0180	4.6950	28.964
-3700	-3698	9.8181	9127.9	3.5825	477.71	1.0130	4.7158	28.964
-3650	-3648	9.8179	9118.5	3.5667	477.46	1.0080	4.7368	28.964
-3600	-3598	9.8178	9109.1	3.5509	477.22	1.0030	4.7579	28.964
-3550	-3548	9.8176	9099.8	3.5352	476.97	9.9804 + 9	4.7790	28.964
-3500	-3498	9.8175	9090.4	3.5195 +25	476.72	9.9309 + 9	4.8003 - 8	28.964
-3450	-3448	9.8173	9081.1	3.5038	476.47	9.8816	4.8218	28.964
-3400	-3398	9.8171	9071.7	3.4883	476.22	9.8326	4.8433	28.964
-3350	-3348	9.8170	9062.3	3.4727	475.97	9.7837	4.8649	28.964
-3300	-3298	9.8168	9053.0	3.4573	475.72	9.7350	4.8867	28.964
-3250	-3248	9.8167	9043.6	3.4418	475.47	9.6865	4.9086	28.964
-3200	-3198	9.8165	9034.3	3.4265	475.22	9.6381	4.9306	28.964
-3150	-3148	9.8164	9024.9	3.4112	474.97	9.5900	4.9528	28.964
-3100	-3098	9.8162	9015.5	3.3959	474.72	9.5421	4.9750	28.964
-3050	-3049	9.8161	9006.2	3.3807	474.47	9.4943	4.9974	28.964
-3000	-2999	9.8159	8996.8	3.3655 +25	474.22	9.4468 + 9	5.0199 - 8	28.964
-2950	-2949	9.8158	8987.4	3.3504	473.97	9.3994	5.0425	28.964
-2900	-2899	9.8156	8978.1	3.3354	473.72	9.3522	5.0653	28.964
-2850	-2849	9.8154	8968.7	3.3204	473.47	9.3053	5.0882	28.964
-2800	-2799	9.8153	8959.4	3.3054	473.22	9.2584	5.1112	28.964
-2750	-2749	9.8151	8950.0	3.2905	472.97	9.2118	5.1343	28.964
-2700	-2699	9.8150	8940.6	3.2757	472.71	9.1654	5.1576	28.964
-2650	-2649	9.8148	8931.3	3.2609	472.46	9.1191	5.1810	28.964
-2600	-2599	9.8147	8921.9	3.2461	472.21	9.0731	5.2045	28.964
-2550	-2549	9.8145	8912.5	3.2314	471.96	9.0272	5.2282	28.964
-2500	-2499	9.8144	8903.2	3.2168 +25	471.71	8.9815 + 9	5.2520 - 8	28.964
-2450	-2449	9.8142	8893.8	3.2022	471.46	8.9360	5.2759	28.964
-2400	-2399	9.8141	8884.4	3.1877	471.20	8.8907	5.3000	28.964
-2350	-2349	9.8139	8875.1	3.1732	470.95	8.8455	5.3242	28.964
-2300	-2299	9.8137	8865.7	3.1587	470.70	8.8005	5.3485	28.964
-2250	-2249	9.8136	8856.3	3.1444	470.45	8.7557	5.3730	28.964
-2200	-2199	9.8134	8847.0	3.1300	470.19	8.7111	5.3976	28.964
-2150	-2149	9.8133	8837.6	3.1157	469.94	8.6667	5.4224	28.964
-2100	-2099	9.8131	8828.2	3.1015	469.69	8.6225	5.4473	28.964
-2050	-2049	9.8130	8818.9	3.0873	469.44	8.5784	5.4723	28.964
-2000	-1999	9.8128	8809.5	3.0732 +25	469.18	8.5345 + 9	5.4975 - 8	28.964
-1950	-1949	9.8127	8800.1	3.0591	468.93	8.4908	5.5228	28.964
-1900	-1899	9.8125	8790.8	3.0450	468.68	8.4472	5.5483	28.964
-1850	-1849	9.8124	8781.4	3.0310	468.42	8.4039	5.5739	28.964
-1800	-1799	9.8122	8772.0	3.0171	468.17	8.3607	5.5996	28.964
-1750	-1750	9.8121	8762.7	3.0032	467.92	8.3177	5.6256	28.964
-1700	-1700	9.8119	8753.3	2.9894	467.66	8.2749	5.6516	28.964
-1650	-1650	9.8117	8743.9	2.9756	467.41	8.2322	5.6778	28.964
-1600	-1600	9.8116	8734.5	2.9618	467.15	8.1897	5.7042	28.964
-1550	-1550	9.8114	8725.2	2.9481	466.90	8.1474	5.7307	28.964
-1500	-1500	9.8113	8715.8	2.9345 +25	466.64	8.1053 + 9	5.7573 - 8	28.964
-1450	-1450	9.8111	8706.4	2.9209	466.39	8.0633	5.7841	28.964
-1400	-1400	9.8110	8697.1	2.9073	466.14	8.0215	5.8111	28.964
-1350	-1350	9.8108	8687.7	2.8938	465.88	7.9799	5.8382	28.964
-1300	-1300	9.8107	8678.3	2.8804	465.63	7.9384	5.8655	28.964
-1250	-1250	9.8105	8668.9	2.8669	465.37	7.8971	5.8929	28.964
-1200	-1200	9.8104	8659.6	2.8536	465.11	7.8560	5.9205	28.964
-1150	-1150	9.8102	8650.2	2.8403	464.86	7.8151	5.9482	28.964
-1100	-1100	9.8100	8640.8	2.8270	464.60	7.7743	5.9762	28.964
-1050	-1050	9.8099	8631.4	2.8138	464.35	7.7337	6.0042	28.964

Table II
Geometric Altitude, Metric Units

Altitude		Accel. due to gravity	Pressure scale height	Number density	Particle speed	Collision frequency	Mean free path	Molecular weight
Z (m)	H (m)	g (m/s^2)	H$_P$ (m)	n (m^{-3})	V (m/s)	ν (s^{-1})	L (m)	M (kg/kmol)
-5000	-5004	9.8221	9371.8	4.0151 +25	484.15	1.1506 +10	4.2078 - 8	28.964
-4950	-4954	9.8219	9362.5	3.9978	483.91	1.1451	4.2260	28.964
-4900	-4904	9.8218	9353.1	3.9805	483.66	1.1396	4.2443	28.964
-4850	-4854	9.8216	9343.7	3.9633	483.42	1.1341	4.2627	28.964
-4800	-4804	9.8215	9334.4	3.9462	483.17	1.1286	4.2813	28.964
-4750	-4754	9.8213	9325.0	3.9291	482.92	1.1231	4.2999	28.964
-4700	-4703	9.8212	9315.6	3.9121	482.68	1.1177	4.3186	28.964
-4650	-4653	9.8210	9306.3	3.8951	482.43	1.1123	4.3374	28.964
-4600	-4603	9.8209	9296.9	3.8782	482.18	1.1069	4.3563	28.964
-4550	-4553	9.8207	9287.5	3.8613	481.94	1.1015	4.3754	28.964
-4500	-4503	9.8205	9278.2	3.8445 +25	481.69	1.0961 +10	4.3945 - 8	28.964
-4450	-4453	9.8204	9268.8	3.8278	481.44	1.0908	4.4137	28.964
-4400	-4403	9.8202	9259.4	3.8111	481.20	1.0855	4.4330	28.964
-4350	-4353	9.8201	9250.1	3.7944	480.95	1.0802	4.4525	28.964
-4300	-4303	9.8199	9240.7	3.7779	480.70	1.0749	4.4720	28.964
-4250	-4253	9.8198	9231.3	3.7613	480.46	1.0697	4.4917	28.964
-4200	-4203	9.8196	9222.0	3.7449	480.21	1.0644	4.5114	28.964
-4150	-4153	9.8195	9212.6	3.7285	479.96	1.0592	4.5313	28.964
-4100	-4103	9.8193	9203.2	3.7121	479.71	1.0540	4.5512	28.964
-4050	-4053	9.8192	9193.8	3.6958	479.46	1.0489	4.5713	28.964
-4000	-4003	9.8190	9184.5	3.6795 +25	479.22	1.0437 +10	4.5915 - 8	28.964
-3950	-3952	9.8188	9175.1	3.6634	478.97	1.0386	4.6118	28.964
-3900	-3902	9.8187	9165.7	3.6472	478.72	1.0335	4.6322	28.964
-3850	-3852	9.8185	9156.4	3.6311	478.47	1.0284	4.6527	28.964
-3800	-3802	9.8184	9147.0	3.6151	478.22	1.0233	4.6734	28.964
-3750	-3752	9.8182	9137.6	3.5991	477.97	1.0182	4.6941	28.964
-3700	-3702	9.8181	9128.3	3.5832	477.72	1.0132	4.7149	28.964
-3650	-3652	9.8179	9118.9	3.5673	477.48	1.0082	4.7359	28.964
-3600	-3602	9.8178	9109.5	3.5515	477.23	1.0032	4.7570	28.964
-3550	-3552	9.8176	9100.2	3.5358	476.98	9.9823 + 9	4.7782	28.964
-3500	-3502	9.8175	9090.8	3.5201 +25	476.73	9.9328 + 9	4.7995 - 8	28.964
-3450	-3452	9.8173	9081.4	3.5044	476.48	9.8835	4.8210	28.964
-3400	-3402	9.8171	9072.0	3.4888	476.23	9.8343	4.8425	28.964
-3350	-3352	9.8170	9062.7	3.4733	475.98	9.7854	4.8642	28.964
-3300	-3302	9.8168	9053.3	3.4578	475.73	9.7366	4.8860	28.964
-3250	-3252	9.8167	9043.9	3.4424	475.48	9.6881	4.9079	28.964
-3200	-3202	9.8165	9034.6	3.4270	475.23	9.6397	4.9299	28.964
-3150	-3152	9.8164	9025.2	3.4116	474.98	9.5915	4.9521	28.964
-3100	-3102	9.8162	9015.8	3.3964	474.73	9.5435	4.9743	28.964
-3050	-3051	9.8161	9006.4	3.3811	474.48	9.4957	4.9967	28.964
-3000	-3001	9.8159	8997.1	3.3660 +25	474.23	9.4481 + 9	5.0193 - 8	28.964
-2950	-2951	9.8158	8987.7	3.3508	473.98	9.4007	5.0419	28.964
-2900	-2901	9.8156	8978.3	3.3358	473.73	9.3535	5.0647	28.964
-2850	-2851	9.8154	8969.0	3.3208	473.47	9.3064	5.0876	28.964
-2800	-2801	9.8153	8959.6	3.3058	473.22	9.2596	5.1106	28.964
-2750	-2751	9.8151	8950.2	3.2909	472.97	9.2129	5.1338	28.964
-2700	-2701	9.8150	8940.8	3.2760	472.72	9.1665	5.1571	28.964
-2650	-2651	9.8148	8931.5	3.2612	472.47	9.1202	5.1805	28.964
-2600	-2601	9.8147	8922.1	3.2465	472.22	9.0741	5.2040	28.964
-2550	-2551	9.8145	8912.7	3.2317	471.97	9.0281	5.2277	28.964
-2500	-2501	9.8144	8903.4	3.2171 +25	471.71	8.9824 + 9	5.2515 - 8	28.964
-2450	-2451	9.8142	8894.0	3.2025	471.46	8.9368	5.2755	28.964
-2400	-2401	9.8141	8884.6	3.1879	471.21	8.8915	5.2996	28.964
-2350	-2351	9.8139	8875.2	3.1734	470.96	8.8463	5.3238	28.964
-2300	-2301	9.8138	8865.9	3.1590	470.70	8.8013	5.3481	28.964
-2250	-2251	9.8136	8856.5	3.1446	470.45	8.7565	5.3726	28.964
-2200	-2201	9.8134	8847.1	3.1302	470.20	8.7118	5.3973	28.964
-2150	-2151	9.8133	8837.7	3.1159	469.95	8.6674	5.4220	28.964
2100	2101	9 8131	8828 4	3 1017	469 69	8 6231	5 4469	28 964
-2000	-2001	9.8128	8809.6	3.0733 +25	469.19	8.5351 + 9	5.4972 - 8	28.964
-1950	-1951	9.8127	8800.2	3.0592	468.93	8.4913	5.5225	28.964
-1900	-1901	9.8125	8790.9	3.0452	468.68	8.4477	5.5480	28.964
-1850	-1851	9.8124	8781.5	3.0312	468.43	8.4044	5.5736	28.964
-1800	-1801	9.8122	8772.1	3.0172	468.17	8.3611	5.5994	28.964
-1750	-1750	9.8121	8762.7	3.0033	467.92	8.3181	5.6253	28.964
-1700	-1700	9.8119	8753.4	2.9895	467.66	8.2752	5.6514	28.964
-1650	-1650	9.8117	8744.0	2.9757	467.41	8.2326	5.6776	28.964
-1600	-1600	9.8116	8734.6	2.9619	467.16	8.1900	5.7039	28.964
-1550	-1550	9.8114	8725.2	2.9482	466.90	8.1477	5.7305	28.964
-1500	-1500	9.8113	8715.9	2.9346 +25	466.65	8.1056 + 9	5.7571 - 8	28.964
-1450	-1450	9.8111	8706.5	2.9210	466.39	8.0636	5.7839	28.964
-1400	-1400	9.8110	8697.1	2.9074	466.14	8.0217	5.8109	28.964
-1350	-1350	9.8108	8687.7	2.8939	465.88	7.9801	5.8380	28.964
-1300	-1300	9.8107	8678.4	2.8804	465.63	7.9386	5.8653	28.964
-1250	-1250	9.8105	8669.0	2.8670	465.37	7.8973	5.8928	28.964
-1200	-1200	9.8104	8659.6	2.8536	465.12	7.8562	5.9204	28.964
-1150	-1150	9.8102	8650.2	2.8403	464.86	7.8152	5.9481	28.964
-1100	-1100	9.8100	8640.9	2.8271	464.60	7.7744	5.9761	28.964
-1050	-1050	9.8099	8631.5	2.8138	464.35	7.7338	6.0041	28.964

Table II
Geopotential Altitude, Metric Units

Altitude		Accel. due to gravity	Pressure scale height	Number density	Particle speed	Collision frequency	Mean free path	Molecular weight
H (m)	Z (m)	g (m/s^2)	H$_p$ (m)	n (m^{-3})	V (m/s)	ν (s^{-1})	L (m)	M (kg/kmol)
-1000	-1000	9.8097	8622.1	2.8006 +25	464.09	7.6932 + 9	6.0325 - 8	28.964
-950	-950	9.8096	8612.7	2.7875	463.84	7.6530	6.0609	28.964
-900	-900	9.8094	8603.3	2.7744	463.58	7.6129	6.0894	28.964
-850	-850	9.8093	8593.9	2.7614	463.32	7.5729	6.1182	28.964
-800	-800	9.8091	8584.6	2.7484	463.07	7.5331	6.1471	28.964
-750	-750	9.8090	8575.2	2.7355	462.81	7.4935	6.1761	28.964
-700	-700	9.8088	8565.8	2.7226	462.55	7.4541	6.2054	28.964
-650	-650	9.8087	8556.4	2.7097	462.30	7.4148	6.2348	28.964
-600	-600	9.8085	8547.1	2.6969	462.04	7.3757	6.2644	28.964
-550	-550	9.8083	8537.7	2.6842	461.78	7.3367	6.2941	28.964
-500	-500	9.8082	8528.3	2.6715 +25	461.53	7.2979 + 9	6.3240 - 8	28.964
-450	-450	9.8080	8518.9	2.6588	461.27	7.2593	6.3542	28.964
-400	-400	9.8079	8509.5	2.6462	461.01	7.2209	6.3844	28.964
-350	-350	9.8077	8500.2	2.6337	460.75	7.1825	6.4149	28.964
-300	-300	9.8076	8490.8	2.6211	460.50	7.1444	6.4455	28.964
-250	-250	9.8074	8481.4	2.6087	460.24	7.1064	6.4764	28.964
-200	-200	9.8073	8472.0	2.5962	459.98	7.0686	6.5074	28.964
-150	-150	9.8071	8462.7	2.5839	459.72	7.0309	6.5386	28.964
-100	-100	9.8070	8453.3	2.5715	459.46	6.9934	6.5699	28.964
-50	-50	9.8068	8443.9	2.5592	459.20	6.9561	6.6015	28.964
0	0	9.8066	8434.5	2.5470 +25	458.94	6.9189 + 9	6.6332 - 8	28.964
50	50	9.8065	8425.1	2.5348	458.69	6.8818	6.6652	28.964
100	100	9.8063	8415.8	2.5226	458.43	6.8450	6.6973	28.964
150	150	9.8062	8406.4	2.5105	458.17	6.8082	6.7296	28.964
200	200	9.8060	8397.0	2.4984	457.91	6.7717	6.7621	28.964
250	250	9.8059	8387.6	2.4864	457.65	6.7353	6.7948	28.964
300	300	9.8057	8378.2	2.4744	457.39	6.6990	6.8277	28.964
350	350	9.8056	8368.8	2.4625	457.13	6.6629	6.8608	28.964
400	400	9.8054	8359.5	2.4506	456.87	6.6270	6.8941	28.964
450	450	9.8053	8350.1	2.4387	456.61	6.5912	6.9276	28.964
500	500	9.8051	8340.7	2.4269 +25	456.35	6.5555 + 9	6.9613 - 8	28.964
550	550	9.8050	8331.3	2.4152	456.09	6.5200	6.9952	28.964
600	600	9.8048	8321.9	2.4035	455.83	6.4847	7.0293	28.964
650	650	9.8046	8312.5	2.3918	455.57	6.4495	7.0636	28.964
700	700	9.8045	8303.2	2.3802	455.31	6.4145	7.0981	28.964
750	750	9.8043	8293.8	2.3686	455.05	6.3796	7.1328	28.964
800	800	9.8042	8284.4	2.3570	454.78	6.3448	7.1678	28.964
850	850	9.8040	8275.0	2.3455	454.52	6.3103	7.2029	28.964
900	900	9.8039	8265.6	2.3341	454.26	6.2758	7.2383	28.964
950	950	9.8037	8256.2	2.3227	454.00	6.2415	7.2739	28.964
1000	1000	9.8036	8246.8	2.3113 +25	453.74	6.2074 + 9	7.3096 - 8	28.964
1050	1050	9.8034	8237.5	2.3000	453.48	6.1734	7.3456	28.964
1100	1100	9.8033	8228.1	2.2887	453.22	6.1396	7.3819	28.964
1150	1150	9.8031	8218.7	2.2774	452.95	6.1059	7.4183	28.964
1200	1200	9.8029	8209.3	2.2662	452.69	6.0723	7.4550	28.964
1250	1250	9.8028	8199.9	2.2551	452.43	6.0389	7.4919	28.964
1300	1300	9.8026	8190.5	2.2439	452.17	6.0056	7.5290	28.964
1350	1350	9.8025	8181.1	2.2329	451.90	5.9725	7.5663	28.964
1400	1400	9.8023	8171.7	2.2218	451.64	5.9396	7.6039	28.964
1450	1450	9.8022	8162.4	2.2108	451.38	5.9067	7.6417	28.964
1500	1500	9.8020	8153.0	2.1999 +25	451.11	5.8741 + 9	7.6798 - 8	28.964
1550	1550	9.8019	8143.6	2.1890	450.85	5.8415	7.7180	28.964
1600	1600	9.8017	8134.2	2.1781	450.59	5.8091	7.7565	28.964
1650	1650	9.8016	8124.8	2.1673	450.32	5.7769	7.7953	28.964
1700	1700	9.8014	8115.4	2.1565	450.06	5.7447	7.8343	28.964
1750	1750	9.8013	8106.0	2.1458	449.79	5.7128	7.8735	28.964
1800	1801	9.8011	8096.6	2.1351	449.53	5.6809	7.9130	28.964
1850	1851	9.8009	8087.2	2.1244	449.27	5.6492	7.9527	28.964
1900	1901	9.8008	8077.8	2.1138	449.00	5.6177	7.9926	28.964
1950	1951	9.8006	8068.5	2.1032	448.74	5.5863	8.0329	28.964
2000	2001	9.8005	8059.1	2.0927 +25	448.47	5.5550 + 9	8.0733 - 8	28.964
2050	2051	9.8003	8049.7	2.0822	448.21	5.5239	8.1140	28.964
2100	2101	9.8002	8040.3	2.0717	447.94	5.4929	8.1550	28.964
2150	2151	9.8000	8030.9	2.0613	447.68	5.4620	8.1962	28.964
2200	2201	9.7999	8021.5	2.0509	447.41	5.4313	8.2377	28.964
2250	2251	9.7997	8012.1	2.0406	447.15	5.4007	8.2794	28.964
2300	2301	9.7996	8002.7	2.0303	446.88	5.3702	8.3214	28.964
2350	2351	9.7994	7993.3	2.0200	446.61	5.3399	8.3637	28.964
2400	2401	9.7992	7983.9	2.0098	446.35	5.3098	8.4062	28.964
2450	2451	9.7991	7974.5	1.9996	446.08	5.2797	8.4490	28.964
2500	2501	9.7989	7965.1	1.9895 +25	445.82	5.2498 + 9	8.4921 - 8	28.964
2550	2551	9.7988	7955.7	1.9794	445.55	5.2200	8.5354	28.964
2600	2601	9.7986	7946.3	1.9693	445.28	5.1904	8.5790	28.964
2650	2651	9.7985	7936.9	1.9593	445.02	5.1609	8.6229	28.964
2700	2701	9.7983	7927.5	1.9493	444.75	5.1315	8.6671	28.964
2750	2751	9.7982	7918.1	1.9394	444.48	5.1022	8.7115	28.964
2800	2801	9.7980	7908.7	1.9294	444.21	5.0731	8.7562	28.964
2850	2851	9.7979	7899.3	1.9196	443.95	5.0441	8.8012	28.964
2900	2901	9.7977	7889.9	1.9098	443.68	5.0153	8.8465	28.964
2950	2951	9.7976	7880.6	1.9000	443.41	4.9866	8.8921	28.964

Table II
Geometric Altitude, Metric Units

Altitude Z (m)	H (m)	Accel. due to gravity g (m/s²)	Pressure scale height H_p (m)	Number density n (m⁻³)	Particle speed V (m/s)	Collision frequency ν (s⁻¹)	Mean free path L (m)	Molecular weight M (kg/kmol)
-1000	-1000	9.8097	8622.1	2.8007 +25	464.09	7.6934 + 9	6.0324 - 8	28.964
-950	-950	9.8096	8612.7	2.7875	463.84	7.6531	6.0608	28.964
-900	-900	9.8094	8603.3	2.7745	463.58	7.6130	6.0894	28.964
-850	-850	9.8093	8594.0	2.7614	463.32	7.5730	6.1181	28.964
-800	-800	9.8091	8584.6	2.7484	463.07	7.5332	6.1470	28.964
-750	-750	9.8090	8575.2	2.7355	462.81	7.4936	6.1761	28.964
-700	-700	9.8088	8565.8	2.7226	462.55	7.4542	6.2053	28.964
-650	-650	9.8087	8556.4	2.7098	462.30	7.4149	6.2347	28.964
-600	-600	9.8085	8547.1	2.6970	462.04	7.3757	6.2643	28.964
-550	-550	9.8083	8537.7	2.6842	461.78	7.3368	6.2941	28.964
-500	-500	9.8082	8528.3	2.6715 +25	461.53	7.2980 + 9	6.3240 - 8	28.964
-450	-450	9.8080	8518.9	2.6588	461.27	7.2593	6.3541	28.964
-400	-400	9.8079	8509.6	2.6462	461.01	7.2209	6.3844	28.964
-350	-350	9.8077	8500.2	2.6337	460.75	7.1826	6.4149	28.964
-300	-300	9.8076	8490.8	2.6211	460.50	7.1444	6.4455	28.964
-250	-250	9.8074	8481.4	2.6087	460.24	7.1064	6.4764	28.964
-200	-200	9.8073	8472.0	2.5962	459.98	7.0686	6.5074	28.964
-150	-150	9.8071	8462.7	2.5839	459.72	7.0309	6.5386	28.964
-100	-100	9.8070	8453.3	2.5715	459.46	6.9934	6.5699	28.964
-50	-50	9.8068	8443.9	2.5592	459.20	6.9561	6.6015	28.964
0	0	9.8066	8434.5	2.5470 +25	458.94	6.9189 + 9	6.6332 - 8	28.964
50	50	9.8065	8425.1	2.5348	458.69	6.8818	6.6652	28.964
100	100	9.8063	8415.8	2.5226	458.43	6.8450	6.6973	28.964
150	150	9.8062	8406.4	2.5105	458.17	6.8082	6.7296	28.964
200	200	9.8060	8397.0	2.4984	457.91	6.7717	6.7621	28.964
250	250	9.8059	8387.6	2.4864	457.65	6.7353	6.7948	28.964
300	300	9.8057	8378.2	2.4744	457.39	6.6990	6.8277	28.964
350	350	9.8056	8368.8	2.4625	457.13	6.6629	6.8608	28.964
400	400	9.8054	8359.5	2.4506	456.87	6.6270	6.8941	28.964
450	450	9.8053	8350.1	2.4388	456.61	6.5912	6.9276	28.964
500	500	9.8051	8340.7	2.4269 +25	456.35	6.5555 + 9	6.9613 - 8	28.964
550	550	9.8050	8331.3	2.4152	456.09	6.5201	6.9952	28.964
600	600	9.8048	8321.9	2.4035	455.83	6.4847	7.0293	28.964
650	650	9.8046	8312.6	2.3918	455.57	6.4496	7.0636	28.964
700	700	9.8045	8303.2	2.3802	455.31	6.4145	7.0981	28.964
750	750	9.8043	8293.8	2.3686	455.05	6.3796	7.1328	28.964
800	800	9.8042	8284.4	2.3571	454.79	6.3449	7.1677	28.964
850	850	9.8040	8275.0	2.3456	454.52	6.3103	7.2028	28.964
900	900	9.8039	8265.6	2.3341	454.26	6.2759	7.2382	28.964
950	950	9.8037	8256.3	2.3227	454.00	6.2416	7.2738	28.964
1000	1000	9.8036	8246.9	2.3113 +25	453.74	6.2075 + 9	7.3095 - 8	28.964
1050	1050	9.8034	8237.5	2.3000	453.48	6.1735	7.3455	28.964
1100	1100	9.8033	8228.1	2.2887	453.22	6.1397	7.3817	28.964
1150	1150	9.8031	8218.7	2.2775	452.95	6.1060	7.4182	28.964
1200	1200	9.8029	8209.3	2.2663	452.69	6.0725	7.4548	28.964
1250	1250	9.8028	8200.0	2.2551	452.43	6.0391	7.4917	28.964
1300	1300	9.8026	8190.6	2.2440	452.17	6.0058	7.5288	28.964
1350	1350	9.8025	8181.2	2.2329	451.90	5.9727	7.5661	28.964
1400	1400	9.8023	8171.8	2.2219	451.64	5.9398	7.6037	28.964
1450	1450	9.8022	8162.4	2.2109	451.38	5.9070	7.6415	28.964
1500	1500	9.8020	8153.0	2.2000 +25	451.12	5.8743 + 9	7.6795 - 8	28.964
1550	1550	9.8019	8143.6	2.1891	450.85	5.8418	7.7177	28.964
1600	1600	9.8017	8134.3	2.1782	450.59	5.8094	7.7562	28.964
1650	1650	9.8016	8124.9	2.1674	450.33	5.7771	7.7950	28.964
1700	1700	9.8014	8115.5	2.1566	450.06	5.7450	7.8339	28.964
1750	1750	9.8013	8106.1	2.1459	449.80	5.7131	7.8731	28.964
1800	1799	9.8011	8096.7	2.1352	449.53	5.6813	7.9126	28.964
1850	1849	9.8009	8087.3	2.1245	449.27	5.6496	7.9523	28.964
1900	1899	9.8008	8078.0	2.1139	449.01	5.6180	7.9922	28.964
1950	1949	9.8006	8068.6	2.1033	448.74	5.5867	8.0324	28.964
2000	1999	9.8005	8059.2	2.0928 +25	448.48	5.5554 + 9	8.0728 - 8	28.964
2050	2049	9.8003	8049.8	2.0823	448.21	5.5243	8.1135	28.964
2100	2099	9.8002	8040.4	2.0718	447.95	5.4933	8.1544	28.964
2150	2149	9.8000	8031.0	2.0614	447.68	5.4625	8.1956	28.964
2200	2199	9.7999	8021.6	2.0511	447.42	5.4317	8.2371	28.964
2250	2249	9.7997	8012.2	2.0407	447.15	5.4012	8.2788	28.964
2300	2299	9.7996	8002.9	2.0304	446.89	5.3708	8.3207	28.964
2350	2349	9.7994	7993.5	2.0202	446.62	5.3405	8.3629	28.964
2400	2399	9.7992	7984.1	2.0100	446.35	5.3103	8.4054	28.964
2450	2449	9.7991	7974.7	1.9998	446.09	5.2803	8.4482	28.964
2500	2499	9.7989	7965.3	1.9897 +25	445.82	5.2504 + 9	8.4912 - 8	28.964
2550	2549	9.7988	7955.9	1.9796	445.56	5.2206	8.5345	28.964
2600	2599	9.7986	7946.5	1.9695	445.29	5.1910	8.5781	28.964
2650	2649	9.7985	7937.1	1.9595	445.02	5.1615	8.6219	28.964
2700	2699	9.7983	7927.8	1.9495	444.76	5.1322	8.6660	28.964
2750	2749	9.7982	7918.4	1.9396	444.49	5.1029	8.7104	28.964
2800	2799	9.7980	7909.0	1.9297	444.22	5.0738	8.7551	28.964
2850	2849	9.7979	7899.6	1.9198	443.95	5.0449	8.8001	28.964
2900	2899	9.7977	7890.2	1.9100	443.69	5.0161	8.8453	28.964
2950	2949	9.7976	7880.8	1.9002	443.42	4.9874	8.8909	28.964

Table II
Geopotential Altitude, Metric Units

Altitude		Accel. due to gravity	Pressure scale height	Number density		Particle speed	Collision frequency		Mean free path		Molecular weight
H (m)	Z (m)	g (m/s²)	H_p (m)	n (m⁻³)		V (m/s)	ν (s⁻¹)		L (m)		M (kg/kmol)
3000	3001	9.7974	7871.2	1.8902	+25	443.14	4.9580	+9	8.9380	−8	28.964
3050	3051	9.7972	7861.8	1.8805		442.88	4.9295		8.9841		28.964
3100	3102	9.7971	7852.4	1.8708		442.61	4.9012		9.0306		28.964
3150	3152	9.7969	7843.0	1.8612		442.34	4.8730		9.0774		28.964
3200	3202	9.7968	7833.6	1.8516		442.07	4.8449		9.1244		28.964
3250	3252	9.7966	7824.2	1.8420		441.80	4.8170		9.1718		28.964
3300	3302	9.7965	7814.8	1.8325		441.53	4.7892		9.2194		28.964
3350	3352	9.7963	7805.4	1.8230		441.26	4.7615		9.2674		28.964
3400	3402	9.7962	7796.0	1.8136		440.99	4.7339		9.3157		28.964
3450	3452	9.7960	7786.6	1.8042		440.72	4.7065		9.3643		28.964
3500	3502	9.7959	7777.2	1.7948	+25	440.46	4.6791	+9	9.4132	−8	28.964
3550	3552	9.7957	7767.8	1.7855		440.19	4.6520		9.4624		28.964
3600	3602	9.7955	7758.4	1.7762		439.92	4.6249		9.5119		28.964
3650	3652	9.7954	7749.0	1.7669		439.65	4.5980		9.5618		28.964
3700	3702	9.7952	7739.5	1.7577		439.38	4.5711		9.6119		28.964
3750	3752	9.7951	7730.1	1.7485		439.10	4.5444		9.6624		28.964
3800	3802	9.7949	7720.7	1.7393		438.83	4.5179		9.7133		28.964
3850	3852	9.7948	7711.3	1.7302		438.56	4.4914		9.7644		28.964
3900	3902	9.7946	7701.9	1.7211		438.29	4.4651		9.8159		28.964
3950	3952	9.7945	7692.5	1.7121		438.02	4.4389		9.8678		28.964
4000	4003	9.7943	7683.1	1.7031	+25	437.75	4.4128	+9	9.9199	−8	28.964
4050	4053	9.7942	7673.7	1.6941		437.48	4.3869		9.9724		28.964
4100	4103	9.7940	7664.3	1.6852		437.21	4.3610		1.0025	−7	28.964
4150	4153	9.7938	7654.9	1.6763		436.94	4.3353		1.0079		28.964
4200	4203	9.7937	7645.5	1.6674		436.66	4.3097		1.0132		28.964
4250	4253	9.7935	7636.1	1.6586		436.39	4.2842		1.0186		28.964
4300	4303	9.7934	7626.7	1.6498		436.12	4.2589		1.0240		28.964
4350	4353	9.7932	7617.3	1.6411		435.85	4.2336		1.0295		28.964
4400	4403	9.7931	7607.9	1.6324		435.57	4.2085		1.0350		28.964
4450	4453	9.7929	7598.5	1.6237		435.30	4.1835		1.0405		28.964
4500	4503	9.7928	7589.1	1.6150	+25	435.03	4.1586	+9	1.0461	−7	28.964
4550	4553	9.7926	7579.7	1.6064		434.75	4.1339		1.0517		28.964
4600	4603	9.7925	7570.3	1.5979		434.48	4.1092		1.0573		28.964
4650	4653	9.7923	7560.8	1.5893		434.21	4.0847		1.0630		28.964
4700	4703	9.7922	7551.4	1.5808		433.93	4.0603		1.0687		28.964
4750	4754	9.7920	7542.0	1.5723		433.66	4.0360		1.0745		28.964
4800	4804	9.7918	7532.6	1.5639		433.39	4.0118		1.0803		28.964
4850	4854	9.7917	7523.2	1.5555		433.11	3.9877		1.0861		28.964
4900	4904	9.7915	7513.8	1.5471		432.84	3.9637		1.0920		28.964
4950	4954	9.7914	7504.4	1.5388		432.56	3.9399		1.0979		28.964
5000	5004	9.7912	7495.0	1.5305	+25	432.29	3.9161	+9	1.1039	−7	28.964
5050	5054	9.7911	7485.6	1.5222		432.01	3.8925		1.1099		28.964
5100	5104	9.7909	7476.2	1.5140		431.74	3.8690		1.1159		28.964
5150	5154	9.7908	7466.8	1.5058		431.46	3.8456		1.1220		28.964
5200	5204	9.7906	7457.3	1.4977		431.19	3.8223		1.1281		28.964
5250	5254	9.7905	7447.9	1.4895		430.91	3.7992		1.1342		28.964
5300	5304	9.7903	7438.5	1.4814		430.64	3.7761		1.1404		28.964
5350	5355	9.7901	7429.1	1.4734		430.36	3.7532		1.1467		28.964
5400	5405	9.7900	7419.7	1.4653		430.09	3.7303		1.1529		28.964
5450	5455	9.7898	7410.3	1.4574		429.81	3.7076		1.1593		28.964
5500	5505	9.7897	7400.9	1.4494	+25	429.53	3.6850	+9	1.1656	−7	28.964
5550	5555	9.7895	7391.5	1.4415		429.26	3.6625		1.1720		28.964
5600	5605	9.7894	7382.0	1.4336		428.98	3.6400		1.1785		28.964
5650	5655	9.7892	7372.6	1.4257		428.70	3.6178		1.1850		28.964
5700	5705	9.7891	7363.2	1.4179		428.42	3.5956		1.1915		28.964
5750	5755	9.7889	7353.8	1.4101		428.15	3.5735		1.1981		28.964
5800	5805	9.7888	7344.4	1.4023		427.87	3.5515		1.2048		28.964
5850	5855	9.7886	7335.0	1.3946		427.59	3.5297		1.2114		28.964
5900	5905	9.7885	7325.6	1.3869		427.31	3.5079		1.2182		28.964
5950	5956	9.7883	7316.1	1.3792		427.04	3.4862		1.2249		28.964
6000	6006	9.7881	7306.7	1.3716	+25	426.76	3.4647	+9	1.2317	−7	28.964
6050	6056	9.7880	7297.3	1.3640		426.48	3.4433		1.2386		28.964
6100	6106	9.7878	7287.9	1.3565		426.20	3.4219		1.2455		28.964
6150	6156	9.7877	7278.5	1.3489		425.92	3.4007		1.2525		28.964
6200	6206	9.7875	7269.1	1.3414		425.64	3.3796		1.2595		28.964
6250	6256	9.7874	7259.6	1.3339		425.36	3.3585		1.2665		28.964
6300	6306	9.7872	7250.2	1.3265		425.08	3.3376		1.2736		28.964
6350	6356	9.7871	7240.8	1.3191		424.81	3.3168		1.2808		28.964
6400	6406	9.7869	7231.4	1.3117		424.53	3.2961		1.2880		28.964
6450	6457	9.7868	7222.0	1.3044		424.25	3.2755		1.2952		28.964
6500	6507	9.7866	7212.5	1.2971	+25	423.97	3.2550	+9	1.3025	−7	28.964
6550	6557	9.7865	7203.1	1.2898		423.69	3.2345		1.3099		28.964
6600	6607	9.7863	7193.7	1.2825		423.40	3.2142		1.3173		28.964
6650	6657	9.7861	7184.3	1.2753		423.12	3.1940		1.3247		28.964
6700	6707	9.7860	7174.9	1.2681		422.84	3.1739		1.3322		28.964
6750	6757	9.7858	7165.4	1.2610		422.56	3.1539		1.3398		28.964
6800	6807	9.7857	7156.0	1.2539		422.28	3.1340		1.3474		28.964
6850	6857	9.7855	7146.6	1.2468		422.00	3.1142		1.3551		28.964
6900	6907	9.7854	7137.2	1.2397		421.72	3.0945		1.3628		28.964
6950	6958	9.7852	7127.8	1.2327		421.44	3.0749		1.3706		28.964

Table II
Geometric Altitude, Metric Units

Altitude		Accel. due to gravity	Pressure scale height	Number density	Particle speed	Collision frequency	Mean free path	Molecular weight
H (m)	Z (m)	g (m/s^2)	H$_P$ (m)	n (m^{-3})	V (m/s)	ν (s^{-1})	L (m)	M (kg/kmol)
3000	2999	9.7974	7871.4	1.8905 +25	443.15	4.9588 + 9	8.9367 − 8	28.964
3050	3049	9.7972	7862.0	1.8808	442.88	4.9304	8.9828	28.964
3100	3098	9.7971	7852.6	1.8711	442.62	4.9020	9.0292	28.964
3150	3148	9.7969	7843.3	1.8615	442.35	4.8739	9.0759	28.964
3200	3198	9.7968	7833.9	1.8519	442.08	4.8458	9.1229	28.964
3250	3248	9.7966	7824.5	1.8423	441.81	4.8179	9.1702	28.964
3300	3298	9.7965	7815.1	1.8328	441.54	4.7901	9.2178	28.964
3350	3348	9.7963	7805.7	1.8234	441.27	4.7624	9.2657	28.964
3400	3398	9.7962	7796.3	1.8139	441.00	4.7349	9.3139	28.964
3450	3448	9.7960	7786.9	1.8045	440.73	4.7075	9.3624	28.964
3500	3498	9.7959	7777.5	1.7952 +25	440.47	4.6802 + 9	9.4113 − 8	28.964
3550	3548	9.7957	7768.1	1.7858	440.20	4.6530	9.4604	28.964
3600	3598	9.7956	7758.7	1.7765	439.93	4.6260	9.5099	28.964
3650	3648	9.7954	7749.3	1.7673	439.66	4.5991	9.5597	28.964
3700	3698	9.7952	7740.0	1.7581	439.39	4.5723	9.6098	28.964
3750	3748	9.7951	7730.6	1.7489	439.12	4.5456	9.6602	28.964
3800	3798	9.7949	7721.2	1.7398	438.85	4.5191	9.7110	28.964
3850	3848	9.7948	7711.8	1.7306	438.58	4.4927	9.7620	28.964
3900	3898	9.7946	7702.4	1.7216	438.31	4.4664	9.8135	28.964
3950	3948	9.7945	7693.0	1.7125	438.03	4.4402	9.8652	28.964
4000	3997	9.7943	7683.6	1.7036 +25	437.76	4.4141 + 9	9.9173 − 8	28.964
4050	4047	9.7942	7674.2	1.6946	437.49	4.3882	9.9697	28.964
4100	4097	9.7940	7664.8	1.6857	437.22	4.3624	1.0022 − 7	28.964
4150	4147	9.7939	7655.4	1.6768	436.95	4.3367	1.0076	28.964
4200	4197	9.7937	7646.0	1.6679	436.68	4.3111	1.0129	28.964
4250	4247	9.7936	7636.6	1.6591	436.41	4.2857	1.0183	28.964
4300	4297	9.7934	7627.2	1.6503	436.13	4.2604	1.0237	28.964
4350	4347	9.7932	7617.9	1.6416	435.86	4.2351	1.0292	28.964
4400	4397	9.7931	7608.5	1.6329	435.59	4.2101	1.0346	28.964
4450	4447	9.7929	7599.1	1.6242	435.32	4.1851	1.0402	28.964
4500	4497	9.7928	7589.7	1.6156 +25	435.05	4.1602 + 9	1.0457 − 7	28.964
4550	4547	9.7926	7580.3	1.6070	434.77	4.1355	1.0513	28.964
4600	4597	9.7925	7570.9	1.5984	434.50	4.1109	1.0570	28.964
4650	4647	9.7923	7561.5	1.5899	434.23	4.0863	1.0626	28.964
4700	4697	9.7922	7552.1	1.5814	433.95	4.0619	1.0683	28.964
4750	4746	9.7920	7542.7	1.5729	433.68	4.0377	1.0741	28.964
4800	4796	9.7919	7533.3	1.5645	433.41	4.0135	1.0799	28.964
4850	4846	9.7917	7523.9	1.5561	433.13	3.9895	1.0857	28.964
4900	4896	9.7915	7514.5	1.5478	432.86	3.9655	1.0916	28.964
4950	4946	9.7914	7505.1	1.5394	432.58	3.9417	1.0975	28.964
5000	4996	9.7912	7495.7	1.5312 +25	432.31	3.9180 + 9	1.1034 − 7	28.964
5050	5046	9.7911	7486.3	1.5229	432.04	3.8944	1.1094	28.964
5100	5096	9.7909	7476.9	1.5147	431.76	3.8709	1.1154	28.964
5150	5146	9.7908	7467.5	1.5065	431.49	3.8476	1.1215	28.964
5200	5196	9.7906	7458.1	1.4983	431.21	3.8243	1.1276	28.964
5250	5246	9.7905	7448.7	1.4902	430.94	3.8012	1.1337	28.964
5300	5296	9.7903	7439.4	1.4821	430.66	3.7781	1.1399	28.964
5350	5346	9.7902	7430.0	1.4741	430.39	3.7552	1.1461	28.964
5400	5395	9.7900	7420.6	1.4661	430.11	3.7324	1.1524	28.964
5450	5445	9.7899	7411.2	1.4581	429.83	3.7097	1.1587	28.964
5500	5495	9.7897	7401.8	1.4502 +25	429.56	3.6871 + 9	1.1650 − 7	28.964
5550	5545	9.7895	7392.4	1.4422	429.28	3.6646	1.1714	28.964
5600	5595	9.7894	7383.0	1.4344	429.01	3.6423	1.1779	28.964
5650	5645	9.7892	7373.6	1.4265	428.73	3.6200	1.1843	28.964
5700	5695	9.7891	7364.2	1.4187	428.45	3.5978	1.1909	28.964
5750	5745	9.7889	7354.8	1.4109	428.18	3.5758	1.1974	28.964
5800	5795	9.7888	7345.4	1.4032	427.90	3.5538	1.2040	28.964
5850	5845	9.7886	7336.0	1.3954	427.62	3.5320	1.2107	28.964
5900	5895	9.7885	7326.6	1.3878	427.34	3.5103	1.2174	28.964
5950	5944	9.7883	7317.2	1.3801	427.07	3.4886	1.2242	28.964
6000	5994	9.7882	7307.8	1.3725 +25	426.79	3.4671 + 9	1.2310 − 7	28.964
6050	6044	9.7880	7298.4	1.3649	426.51	3.4457	1.2378	28.964
6100	6094	9.7879	7289.0	1.3573	426.23	3.4244	1.2447	28.964
6150	6144	9.7877	7279.6	1.3498	425.96	3.4032	1.2516	28.964
6200	6194	9.7875	7270.2	1.3423	425.68	3.3821	1.2586	28.964
6250	6244	9.7874	7260.8	1.3349	425.40	3.3611	1.2656	28.964
6300	6294	9.7872	7251.4	1.3274	425.12	3.3402	1.2727	28.964
6350	6344	9.7871	7242.0	1.3200	424.84	3.3194	1.2799	28.964
6400	6394	9.7869	7232.6	1.3127	424.56	3.2987	1.2870	28.964
6450	6443	9.7868	7223.2	1.3053	424.28	3.2782	1.2943	28.964
6500	6493	9.7866	7213.8	1.2980 +25	424.00	3.2577 + 9	1.3016 − 7	28.964
6550	6543	9.7865	7204.4	1.2908	423.72	3.2373	1.3089	28.964
6600	6593	9.7863	7195.0	1.2835	423.44	3.2170	1.3163	28.964
6650	6643	9.7862	7185.6	1.2763	423.16	3.1968	1.3237	28.964
6700	6693	9.7860	7176.2	1.2692	422.88	3.1768	1.3312	28.964
6750	6743	9.7859	7166.8	1.2620	422.60	3.1568	1.3387	28.964
6800	6793	9.7857	7157.4	1.2549	422.32	3.1369	1.3463	28.964
6850	6843	9.7855	7148.0	1.2478	422.04	3.1171	1.3539	28.964
6900	6893	9.7854	7138.6	1.2408	421.76	3.0974	1.3616	28.964
6950	6942	9.7852	7129.2	1.2337	421.48	3.0779	1.3694	28.964

Table II
Geopotential Altitude, Metric Units

Altitude		Accel. due to gravity	Pressure scale height	Number density	Particle speed	Collision frequency	Mean free path	Molecular weight
H (m)	Z (m)	g (m/s²)	H_P (m)	n (m⁻³)	V (m/s)	ν (s⁻¹)	L (m)	M (kg/kmol)
7000	7008	9.7851	7118.3	1.2257 +25	421.15	3.0554 + 9	1.3784 − 7	28.964
7050	7058	9.7849	7108.9	1.2187	420.87	3.0360	1.3863	28.964
7100	7108	9.7848	7099.5	1.2118	420.59	3.0166	1.3942	28.964
7150	7158	9.7846	7090.1	1.2048	420.31	2.9974	1.4022	28.964
7200	7208	9.7844	7080.7	1.1980	420.02	2.9783	1.4103	28.964
7250	7258	9.7843	7071.2	1.1911	419.74	2.9593	1.4184	28.964
7300	7308	9.7841	7061.8	1.1843	419.46	2.9403	1.4266	28.964
7350	7359	9.7840	7052.4	1.1775	419.18	2.9215	1.4348	28.964
7400	7409	9.7838	7043.0	1.1707	418.89	2.9028	1.4431	28.964
7450	7459	9.7837	7033.5	1.1640	418.61	2.8841	1.4514	28.964
7500	7509	9.7835	7024.1	1.1573 +25	418.32	2.8656 + 9	1.4598 − 7	28.964
7550	7559	9.7834	7014.7	1.1506	418.04	2.8471	1.4683	28.964
7600	7609	9.7832	7005.3	1.1440	417.76	2.8288	1.4768	28.964
7650	7659	9.7831	6995.8	1.1374	417.47	2.8105	1.4854	28.964
7700	7709	9.7829	6986.4	1.1308	417.19	2.7923	1.4940	28.964
7750	7759	9.7828	6977.0	1.1242	416.90	2.7743	1.5028	28.964
7800	7810	9.7826	6967.6	1.1177	416.62	2.7563	1.5115	28.964
7850	7860	9.7824	6958.1	1.1112	416.33	2.7384	1.5204	28.964
7900	7910	9.7823	6948.7	1.1048	416.05	2.7206	1.5293	28.964
7950	7960	9.7821	6939.3	1.0983	415.76	2.7029	1.5382	28.964
8000	8010	9.7820	6929.8	1.0919 +25	415.48	2.6852 + 9	1.5473 − 7	28.964
8050	8060	9.7818	6920.4	1.0855	415.19	2.6677	1.5564	28.964
8100	8110	9.7817	6911.0	1.0792	414.90	2.6503	1.5655	28.964
8150	8160	9.7815	6901.6	1.0728	414.62	2.6329	1.5747	28.964
8200	8211	9.7814	6892.1	1.0666	414.33	2.6157	1.5840	28.964
8250	8261	9.7812	6882.7	1.0603	414.04	2.5985	1.5934	28.964
8300	8311	9.7811	6873.3	1.0540	413.76	2.5814	1.6028	28.964
8350	8361	9.7809	6863.8	1.0478	413.47	2.5644	1.6123	28.964
8400	8411	9.7807	6854.4	1.0417	413.18	2.5475	1.6219	28.964
8450	8461	9.7806	6845.0	1.0355	412.89	2.5307	1.6315	28.964
8500	8511	9.7804	6835.5	1.0294 +25	412.61	2.5140 + 9	1.6413 − 7	28.964
8550	8562	9.7803	6826.1	1.0233	412.32	2.4973	1.6510	28.964
8600	8612	9.7801	6816.7	1.0172	412.03	2.4808	1.6609	28.964
8650	8662	9.7800	6807.3	1.0112	411.74	2.4643	1.6708	28.964
8700	8712	9.7798	6797.8	1.0051	411.45	2.4479	1.6808	28.964
8750	8762	9.7797	6788.4	9.9915 +24	411.16	2.4316	1.6909	28.964
8800	8812	9.7795	6779.0	9.9319	410.88	2.4154	1.7011	28.964
8850	8862	9.7794	6769.5	9.8725	410.59	2.3993	1.7113	28.964
8900	8912	9.7792	6760.1	9.8135	410.30	2.3833	1.7216	28.964
8950	8963	9.7791	6750.7	9.7547	410.01	2.3673	1.7320	28.964
9000	9013	9.7789	6741.2	9.6961 +24	409.72	2.3514 + 9	1.7424 − 7	28.964
9050	9063	9.7787	6731.8	9.6379	409.43	2.3357	1.7529	28.964
9100	9113	9.7786	6722.4	9.5799	409.14	2.3200	1.7636	28.964
9150	9163	9.7784	6712.9	9.5221	408.85	2.3043	1.7743	28.964
9200	9213	9.7783	6703.5	9.4647	408.56	2.2888	1.7850	28.964
9250	9263	9.7781	6694.0	9.4075	408.27	2.2733	1.7959	28.964
9300	9314	9.7780	6684.6	9.3505	407.97	2.2580	1.8068	28.964
9350	9364	9.7778	6675.2	9.2939	407.68	2.2427	1.8178	28.964
9400	9414	9.7777	6665.7	9.2375	407.39	2.2275	1.8289	28.964
9450	9464	9.7775	6656.3	9.1813	407.10	2.2124	1.8401	28.964
9500	9514	9.7774	6646.9	9.1254 +24	406.81	2.1973 + 9	1.8514 − 7	28.964
9550	9564	9.7772	6637.4	9.0698	406.52	2.1824	1.8627	28.964
9600	9615	9.7771	6628.0	9.0145	406.22	2.1675	1.8742	28.964
9650	9665	9.7769	6618.6	8.9594	405.93	2.1527	1.8857	28.964
9700	9715	9.7767	6609.1	8.9045	405.64	2.1380	1.8973	28.964
9750	9765	9.7766	6599.7	8.8499	405.35	2.1233	1.9090	28.964
9800	9815	9.7764	6590.2	8.7956	405.05	2.1088	1.9208	28.964
9850	9865	9.7763	6580.8	8.7415	404.76	2.0943	1.9327	28.964
9900	9915	9.7761	6571.4	8.6877	404.47	2.0799	1.9447	28.964
9950	9966	9.7760	6561.9	8.6341	404.17	2.0655	1.9567	28.964
10000	10016	9.7758	6552.5	8.5808 +24	403.88	2.0513 + 9	1.9689 − 7	28.964
10050	10066	9.7757	6543.0	8.5278	403.58	2.0371	1.9811	28.964
10100	10116	9.7755	6533.6	8.4750	403.29	2.0230	1.9935	28.964
10150	10166	9.7754	6524.2	8.4224	402.99	2.0090	2.0059	28.964
10200	10216	9.7752	6514.7	8.3701	402.70	1.9951	2.0185	28.964
10250	10267	9.7750	6505.3	8.3180	402.40	1.9812	2.0311	28.964
10300	10317	9.7749	6495.8	8.2662	402.11	1.9674	2.0438	28.964
10350	10367	9.7747	6486.4	8.2147	401.81	1.9537	2.0566	28.964
10400	10417	9.7746	6477.0	8.1633	401.52	1.9401	2.0696	28.964
10450	10467	9.7744	6467.5	8.1123	401.22	1.9265	2.0826	28.964
10500	10517	9.7743	6458.1	8.0614 +24	400.93	1.9131 + 9	2.0957 − 7	28.964
10550	10568	9.7741	6448.6	8.0109	400.63	1.8996	2.1090	28.964
10600	10618	9.7740	6439.2	7.9605	400.33	1.8863	2.1223	28.964
10650	10668	9.7738	6429.7	7.9104	400.04	1.8730	2.1357	28.964
10700	10718	9.7737	6420.3	7.8606	399.74	1.8599	2.1493	28.964
10750	10768	9.7735	6410.9	7.8109	399.44	1.8467	2.1629	28.964
10800	10818	9.7734	6401.4	7.7616	399.14	1.8337	2.1767	28.964
10850	10869	9.7732	6392.0	7.7124	398.85	1.8207	2.1906	28.964
10900	10919	9.7730	6382.5	7.6635	398.55	1.8078	2.2046	28.964
10950	10969	9.7729	6373.1	7.6149	398.25	1.7950	2.2186	28.964

Table II
Geometric Altitude, Metric Units

Altitude		Accel. due to gravity	Pressure scale height	Number density	Particle speed	Collision frequency	Mean free path	Molecular weight
H (m)	Z (m)	g (m/s^2)	H$_p$ (m)	n (m^{-3})	V (m/s)	ν (s^{-1})	L (m)	M (kg/kmol)
7000	6992	9.7851	7119.8	1.2267 +25	421.20	3.0584 + 9	1.3772 − 7	28.964
7050	7042	9.7849	7110.4	1.2198	420.92	3.0390	1.3851	28.964
7100	7092	9.7848	7101.0	1.2129	420.63	3.0197	1.3930	28.964
7150	7142	9.7846	7091.6	1.2060	420.35	3.0005	1.4009	28.964
7200	7192	9.7845	7082.2	1.1991	420.07	2.9814	1.4090	28.964
7250	7242	9.7843	7072.8	1.1922	419.79	2.9624	1.4170	28.964
7300	7292	9.7842	7063.4	1.1854	419.51	2.9435	1.4252	28.964
7350	7342	9.7840	7054.0	1.1787	419.22	2.9247	1.4334	28.964
7400	7391	9.7839	7044.6	1.1719	418.94	2.9060	1.4416	28.964
7450	7441	9.7837	7035.2	1.1652	418.66	2.8874	1.4500	28.964
7500	7491	9.7836	7025.8	1.1585 +25	418.37	2.8689 + 9	1.4583 − 7	28.964
7550	7541	9.7834	7016.4	1.1518	418.09	2.8504	1.4668	28.964
7600	7591	9.7832	7007.0	1.1452	417.81	2.8321	1.4753	28.964
7650	7641	9.7831	6997.6	1.1386	417.52	2.8139	1.4838	28.964
7700	7691	9.7829	6988.2	1.1320	417.24	2.7957	1.4924	28.964
7750	7741	9.7828	6978.8	1.1255	416.96	2.7777	1.5011	28.964
7800	7790	9.7826	6969.4	1.1190	416.67	2.7597	1.5098	28.964
7850	7840	9.7825	6959.9	1.1125	416.39	2.7418	1.5186	28.964
7900	7890	9.7823	6950.5	1.1060	416.10	2.7240	1.5275	28.964
7950	7940	9.7822	6941.1	1.0996	415.82	2.7064	1.5364	28.964
8000	7990	9.7820	6931.7	1.0932 +25	415.53	2.6888 + 9	1.5454 − 7	28.964
8050	8040	9.7819	6922.3	1.0868	415.25	2.6713	1.5545	28.964
8100	8090	9.7817	6912.9	1.0805	414.96	2.6538	1.5636	28.964
8150	8140	9.7816	6903.5	1.0742	414.68	2.6365	1.5728	28.964
8200	8189	9.7814	6894.1	1.0679	414.39	2.6193	1.5821	28.964
8250	8239	9.7812	6884.7	1.0616	414.10	2.6021	1.5914	28.964
8300	8289	9.7811	6875.3	1.0554	413.82	2.5851	1.6008	28.964
8350	8339	9.7809	6865.9	1.0492	413.53	2.5681	1.6102	28.964
8400	8389	9.7808	6856.5	1.0430	413.25	2.5512	1.6198	28.964
8450	8439	9.7806	6847.1	1.0369	412.96	2.5345	1.6294	28.964
8500	8489	9.7805	6837.7	1.0308 +25	412.67	2.5178 + 9	1.6390 − 7	28.964
8550	8539	9.7803	6828.3	1.0247	412.38	2.5011	1.6488	28.964
8600	8588	9.7802	6818.9	1.0186	412.10	2.4846	1.6586	28.964
8650	8638	9.7800	6809.5	1.0126	411.81	2.4682	1.6685	28.964
8700	8688	9.7799	6800.1	1.0066	411.52	2.4518	1.6784	28.964
8750	8738	9.7797	6790.7	1.0006	411.23	2.4355	1.6885	28.964
8800	8788	9.7796	6781.3	9.9464 +24	410.95	2.4194	1.6986	28.964
8850	8838	9.7794	6771.8	9.8871	410.66	2.4033	1.7088	28.964
8900	8888	9.7792	6762.4	9.8281	410.37	2.3872	1.7190	28.964
8950	8937	9.7791	6753.0	9.7694	410.08	2.3713	1.7293	28.964
9000	8987	9.7789	6743.6	9.7110 +24	409.79	2.3555 + 9	1.7397 − 7	28.964
9050	9037	9.7788	6734.2	9.6528	409.50	2.3397	1.7502	28.964
9100	9087	9.7786	6724.8	9.5949	409.21	2.3240	1.7608	28.964
9150	9137	9.7785	6715.4	9.5373	408.92	2.3084	1.7714	28.964
9200	9187	9.7783	6706.0	9.4799	408.63	2.2929	1.7822	28.964
9250	9237	9.7782	6696.6	9.4228	408.34	2.2775	1.7929	28.964
9300	9286	9.7780	6687.2	9.3660	408.05	2.2621	1.8038	28.964
9350	9336	9.7779	6677.8	9.3094	407.76	2.2469	1.8148	28.964
9400	9386	9.7777	6668.4	9.2531	407.47	2.2317	1.8258	28.964
9450	9436	9.7776	6659.0	9.1971	407.18	2.2166	1.8370	28.964
9500	9486	9.7774	6649.5	9.1413 +24	406.89	2.2016 + 9	1.8482 − 7	28.964
9550	9536	9.7773	6640.1	9.0857	406.60	2.1866	1.8595	28.964
9600	9586	9.7771	6630.7	9.0305	406.31	2.1718	1.8709	28.964
9650	9635	9.7769	6621.3	8.9755	406.02	2.1570	1.8823	28.964
9700	9685	9.7768	6611.9	8.9207	405.72	2.1423	1.8939	28.964
9750	9735	9.7766	6602.5	8.8662	405.43	2.1277	1.9055	28.964
9800	9785	9.7765	6593.1	8.8120	405.14	2.1131	1.9172	28.964
9850	9835	9.7763	6583.7	8.7580	404.85	2.0987	1.9291	28.964
9900	9885	9.7762	6574.3	8.7043	404.56	2.0843	1.9410	28.964
9950	9934	9.7760	6564.9	8.6508	404.26	2.0700	1.9530	28.964
10000	9984	9.7759	6555.4	8.5976 +24	403.97	2.0558 + 9	1.9651 − 7	28.964
10050	10034	9.7757	6546.0	8.5446	403.68	2.0416	1.9772	28.964
10100	10084	9.7756	6536.6	8.4919	403.38	2.0275	1.9895	28.964
10150	10134	9.7754	6527.2	8.4394	403.09	2.0136	2.0019	28.964
10200	10184	9.7753	6517.8	8.3872	402.80	1.9996	2.0143	28.964
10250	10233	9.7751	6508.4	8.3352	402.50	1.9858	2.0269	28.964
10300	10283	9.7749	6499.0	8.2835	402.21	1.9720	2.0396	28.964
10350	10333	9.7748	6489.6	8.2320	401.91	1.9583	2.0523	28.964
10400	10383	9.7746	6480.2	8.1807	401.62	1.9447	2.0652	28.964
10450	10433	9.7745	6470.8	8.1298	401.32	1.9312	2.0781	28.964
10500	10483	9.7743	6461.3	8.0790 +24	401.03	1.9177 + 9	2.0912 − 7	28.964
10550	10533	9.7742	6451.9	8.0285	400.73	1.9043	2.1043	28.964
10600	10582	9.7740	6442.5	7.9782	400.44	1.8910	2.1176	28.964
10650	10632	9.7739	6433.1	7.9282	400.14	1.8778	2.1309	28.964
10700	10682	9.7737	6423.7	7.8785	399.85	1.8646	2.1444	28.964
10750	10732	9.7736	6414.3	7.8289	399.55	1.8515	2.1580	28.964
10800	10782	9.7734	6404.9	7.7796	399.25	1.8385	2.1717	28.964
10850	10832	9.7733	6395.5	7.7306	398.96	1.8255	2.1854	28.964
10900	10881	9.7731	6386.0	7.6817	398.66	1.8126	2.1993	28.964
10950	10931	9.7730	6376.6	7.6332	398.36	1.7998	2.2133	28.964

Table II
Geopotential Altitude, Metric Units

Altitude		Accel. due to gravity	Pressure scale height	Number density	Particle speed	Collision frequency	Mean free path	Molecular weight
Z (m)	H (m)	g (m/s^2)	H$_p$ (m)	n (m^{-3})	V (m/s)	ν (s^{-1})	L (m)	M (kg/kmol)
11000	11019	9.7727	6363.6	7.5664 +24	397.95	1.7823 + 9	2.2328 - 7	28.964
11100	11119	9.7724	6363.8	7.4481	397.95	1.7544	2.2683	28.964
11200	11220	9.7721	6364.0	7.3315	397.95	1.7269	2.3044	28.964
11300	11320	9.7718	6364.2	7.2168	397.95	1.6999	2.3410	28.964
11400	11420	9.7715	6364.4	7.1039	397.95	1.6733	2.3782	28.964
11500	11521	9.7712	6364.6	6.9928	397.95	1.6471	2.4160	28.964
11600	11621	9.7709	6364.8	6.8834	397.95	1.6214	2.4544	28.964
11700	11722	9.7706	6365.0	6.7757	397.95	1.5960	2.4934	28.964
11800	11822	9.7703	6365.2	6.6697	397.95	1.5710	2.5331	28.964
11900	11922	9.7700	6365.4	6.5653	397.95	1.5465	2.5733	28.964
12000	12023	9.7697	6365.6	6.4626 +24	397.95	1.5223 + 9	2.6142 - 7	28.964
12100	12123	9.7694	6365.8	6.3615	397.95	1.4984	2.6558	28.964
12200	12223	9.7690	6366.0	6.2620	397.95	1.4750	2.6980	28.964
12300	12324	9.7687	6366.2	6.1640	397.95	1.4519	2.7409	28.964
12400	12424	9.7684	6366.4	6.0676	397.95	1.4292	2.7844	28.964
12500	12525	9.7681	6366.6	5.9726	397.95	1.4069	2.8287	28.964
12600	12625	9.7678	6366.8	5.8792	397.95	1.3848	2.8736	28.964
12700	12725	9.7675	6367.0	5.7872	397.95	1.3632	2.9193	28.964
12800	12826	9.7672	6367.2	5.6967	397.95	1.3418	2.9657	28.964
12900	12926	9.7669	6367.4	5.6076	397.95	1.3209	3.0128	28.964
13000	13027	9.7666	6367.6	5.5198 +24	397.95	1.3002 + 9	3.0607 - 7	28.964
13100	13127	9.7663	6367.8	5.4335	397.95	1.2798	3.1094	28.964
13200	13227	9.7660	6368.0	5.3485	397.95	1.2598	3.1588	28.964
13300	13328	9.7657	6368.2	5.2648	397.95	1.2401	3.2090	28.964
13400	13428	9.7653	6368.4	5.1824	397.95	1.2207	3.2600	28.964
13500	13529	9.7650	6368.6	5.1013	397.95	1.2016	3.3118	28.964
13600	13629	9.7647	6368.8	5.0215	397.95	1.1828	3.3645	28.964
13700	13730	9.7644	6369.0	4.9430	397.95	1.1643	3.4179	28.964
13800	13830	9.7641	6369.2	4.8656	397.95	1.1461	3.4722	28.964
13900	13930	9.7638	6369.4	4.7895	397.95	1.1282	3.5274	28.964
14000	14031	9.7635	6369.6	4.7146 +24	397.95	1.1105 + 9	3.5835 - 7	28.964
14100	14131	9.7632	6369.8	4.6408	397.95	1.0931	3.6405	28.964
14200	14232	9.7629	6370.0	4.5682	397.95	1.0760	3.6983	28.964
14300	14332	9.7626	6370.2	4.4967	397.95	1.0592	3.7571	28.964
14400	14433	9.7623	6370.4	4.4264	397.95	1.0426	3.8168	28.964
14500	14533	9.7620	6370.7	4.3571	397.95	1.0263	3.8775	28.964
14600	14634	9.7617	6370.9	4.2890	397.95	1.0103	3.9391	28.964
14700	14734	9.7613	6371.1	4.2219	397.95	9.9445 + 8	4.0017	28.964
14800	14835	9.7610	6371.3	4.1558	397.95	9.7890	4.0653	28.964
14900	14935	9.7607	6371.5	4.0908	397.95	9.6358	4.1299	28.964
15000	15035	9.7604	6371.7	4.0268 +24	397.95	9.4851 + 8	4.1956 - 7	28.964
15100	15136	9.7601	6371.9	3.9638	397.95	9.3367	4.2623	28.964
15200	15236	9.7598	6372.1	3.9018	397.95	9.1906	4.3300	28.964
15300	15337	9.7595	6372.3	3.8407	397.95	9.0468	4.3988	28.964
15400	15437	9.7592	6372.5	3.7806	397.95	8.9053	4.4687	28.964
15500	15538	9.7589	6372.7	3.7215	397.95	8.7659	4.5398	28.964
15600	15638	9.7586	6372.9	3.6633	397.95	8.6288	4.6119	28.964
15700	15739	9.7583	6373.1	3.6060	397.95	8.4938	4.6852	28.964
15800	15839	9.7580	6373.3	3.5495	397.95	8.3609	4.7597	28.964
15900	15940	9.7577	6373.5	3.4940	397.95	8.2301	4.8353	28.964
16000	16040	9.7573	6373.7	3.4393 +24	397.95	8.1013 + 8	4.9122 - 7	28.964
16100	16141	9.7570	6373.9	3.3855	397.95	7.9746	4.9902	28.964
16200	16241	9.7567	6374.1	3.3326	397.95	7.8498	5.0696	28.964
16300	16342	9.7564	6374.3	3.2804	397.95	7.7270	5.1501	28.964
16400	16442	9.7561	6374.5	3.2291	397.95	7.6061	5.2320	28.964
16500	16543	9.7558	6374.7	3.1786	397.95	7.4871	5.3152	28.964
16600	16643	9.7555	6374.9	3.1289	397.95	7.3700	5.3996	28.964
16700	16744	9.7552	6375.1	3.0799	397.95	7.2547	5.4854	28.964
16800	16845	9.7549	6375.3	3.0317	397.95	7.1412	5.5726	28.964
16900	16945	9.7546	6375.5	2.9843	397.95	7.0295	5.6612	28.964
17000	17046	9.7543	6375.7	2.9376 +24	397.95	6.9195 + 8	5.7512 - 7	28.964
17100	17146	9.7540	6375.9	2.8916	397.95	6.8112	5.8426	28.964
17200	17247	9.7537	6376.1	2.8464	397.95	6.7047	5.9355	28.964
17300	17347	9.7533	6376.3	2.8019	397.95	6.5998	6.0298	28.964
17400	17448	9.7530	6376.5	2.7580	397.95	6.4965	6.1256	28.964
17500	17548	9.7527	6376.7	2.7149	397.95	6.3949	6.2230	28.964
17600	17649	9.7524	6376.9	2.6724	397.95	6.2948	6.3219	28.964
17700	17749	9.7521	6377.1	2.6306	397.95	6.1963	6.4224	28.964
17800	17850	9.7518	6377.3	2.5894	397.95	6.0994	6.5244	28.964
17900	17951	9.7515	6377.5	2.5489	397.95	6.0040	6.6281	28.964
18000	18051	9.7512	6377.7	2.5090 +24	397.95	5.9100 + 8	6.7335 - 7	28.964
18100	18152	9.7509	6377.9	2.4698	397.95	5.8176	6.8405	28.964
18200	18252	9.7506	6378.1	2.4312	397.95	5.7266	6.9492	28.964
18300	18353	9.7503	6378.3	2.3931	397.95	5.6370	7.0597	28.964
18400	18453	9.7500	6378.5	2.3557	397.95	5.5488	7.1719	28.964
18500	18554	9.7497	6378.7	2.3188	397.95	5.4620	7.2859	28.964
18600	18655	9.7493	6378.9	2.2825	397.95	5.3765	7.4017	28.964
18700	18755	9.7490	6379.1	2.2468	397.95	5.2924	7.5193	28.964
18800	18856	9.7487	6379.3	2.2117	397.95	5.2096	7.6388	28.964
18900	18956	9.7484	6379.5	2.1771	397.95	5.1281	7.7602	28.964

Table II
Geometric Altitude, Metric Units

Altitude		Accel. due to gravity	Pressure scale height	Number density	Particle speed	Collision frequency	Mean free path	Molecular weight
H (m)	Z (m)	g (m/s^2)	H$_P$ (m)	n (m^{-3})	V (m/s)	ν (s^{-1})	L (m)	M (kg/kmol)
11000	10981	9.7728	6367.2	7.5848 +24	398.07	1.7871 + 9	2.2274 − 7	28.964
11100	11081	9.7725	6363.8	7.4708	397.95	1.7597	2.2614	28.964
11200	11180	9.7722	6364.0	7.3543	397.95	1.7323	2.2972	28.964
11300	11280	9.7719	6364.2	7.2397	397.95	1.7053	2.3336	28.964
11400	11380	9.7716	6364.4	7.1268	397.95	1.6787	2.3706	28.964
11500	11479	9.7713	6364.6	7.0157	397.95	1.6525	2.4081	28.964
11600	11579	9.7710	6364.8	6.9064	397.95	1.6268	2.4462	28.964
11700	11679	9.7706	6365.0	6.7987	397.95	1.6014	2.4850	28.964
11800	11778	9.7703	6365.2	6.6927	397.95	1.5765	2.5243	28.964
11900	11878	9.7700	6365.4	6.5884	397.95	1.5519	2.5643	28.964
12000	11977	9.7697	6365.6	6.4857 +24	397.95	1.5277 + 9	2.6049 − 7	28.964
12100	12077	9.7694	6365.8	6.3846	397.95	1.5039	2.6462	28.964
12200	12177	9.7691	6366.0	6.2851	397.95	1.4804	2.6880	28.964
12300	12276	9.7688	6366.2	6.1871	397.95	1.4574	2.7306	28.964
12400	12376	9.7685	6366.4	6.0907	397.95	1.4347	2.7738	28.964
12500	12475	9.7682	6366.6	5.9958	397.95	1.4123	2.8178	28.964
12600	12575	9.7679	6366.8	5.9024	397.95	1.3903	2.8624	28.964
12700	12675	9.7676	6367.0	5.8104	397.95	1.3686	2.9077	28.964
12800	12774	9.7673	6367.2	5.7198	397.95	1.3473	2.9537	28.964
12900	12874	9.7670	6367.4	5.6307	397.95	1.3263	3.0005	28.964
13000	12973	9.7667	6367.6	5.5430 +24	397.95	1.3056 + 9	3.0479 − 7	28.964
13100	13073	9.7664	6367.8	5.4566	397.95	1.2853	3.0962	28.964
13200	13173	9.7660	6368.0	5.3716	397.95	1.2653	3.1452	28.964
13300	13272	9.7657	6368.2	5.2879	397.95	1.2456	3.1950	28.964
13400	13372	9.7654	6368.4	5.2055	397.95	1.2261	3.2455	28.964
13500	13471	9.7651	6368.6	5.1244	397.95	1.2070	3.2969	28.964
13600	13571	9.7648	6368.8	5.0446	397.95	1.1882	3.3491	28.964
13700	13671	9.7645	6369.0	4.9660	397.95	1.1697	3.4021	28.964
13800	13770	9.7642	6369.2	4.8886	397.95	1.1515	3.4559	28.964
13900	13870	9.7639	6369.4	4.8125	397.95	1.1336	3.5106	28.964
14000	13969	9.7636	6369.6	4.7375 +24	397.95	1.1159 + 9	3.5662 − 7	28.964
14100	14069	9.7633	6369.8	4.6637	397.95	1.0985	3.6226	28.964
14200	14168	9.7630	6370.0	4.5911	397.95	1.0814	3.6799	28.964
14300	14268	9.7627	6370.2	4.5195	397.95	1.0646	3.7381	28.964
14400	14367	9.7624	6370.4	4.4492	397.95	1.0480	3.7973	28.964
14500	14467	9.7621	6370.6	4.3799	397.95	1.0317	3.8574	28.964
14600	14567	9.7618	6370.8	4.3116	397.95	1.0156	3.9184	28.964
14700	14666	9.7615	6371.0	4.2445	397.95	9.9979 + 8	3.9804	28.964
14800	14766	9.7611	6371.2	4.1784	397.95	9.8422	4.0433	28.964
14900	14865	9.7608	6371.4	4.1133	397.95	9.6889	4.1073	28.964
15000	14965	9.7605	6371.6	4.0493 +24	397.95	9.5380 + 8	4.1723 − 7	28.964
15100	15064	9.7602	6371.8	3.9862	397.95	9.3895	4.2383	28.964
15200	15164	9.7599	6372.0	3.9241	397.95	9.2433	4.3053	28.964
15300	15263	9.7596	6372.2	3.8630	397.95	9.0994	4.3734	28.964
15400	15363	9.7593	6372.4	3.8029	397.95	8.9577	4.4426	28.964
15500	15462	9.7590	6372.6	3.7437	397.95	8.8182	4.5128	28.964
15600	15562	9.7587	6372.8	3.6854	397.95	8.6809	4.5842	28.964
15700	15661	9.7584	6373.0	3.6280	397.95	8.5458	4.6567	28.964
15800	15761	9.7581	6373.2	3.5715	397.95	8.4127	4.7304	28.964
15900	15860	9.7578	6373.4	3.5159	397.95	8.2817	4.8052	28.964
16000	15960	9.7575	6373.6	3.4612 +24	397.95	8.1528 + 8	4.8812 − 7	28.964
16100	16059	9.7572	6373.8	3.4073	397.95	8.0259	4.9583	28.964
16200	16159	9.7569	6374.0	3.3543	397.95	7.9010	5.0367	28.964
16300	16258	9.7566	6374.2	3.3021	397.95	7.7780	5.1164	28.964
16400	16358	9.7562	6374.4	3.2507	397.95	7.6569	5.1973	28.964
16500	16457	9.7559	6374.6	3.2001	397.95	7.5377	5.2795	28.964
16600	16557	9.7556	6374.8	3.1503	397.95	7.4204	5.3629	28.964
16700	16656	9.7553	6375.0	3.1012	397.95	7.3049	5.4477	28.964
16800	16756	9.7550	6375.2	3.0530	397.95	7.1912	5.5339	28.964
16900	16855	9.7547	6375.4	3.0055	397.95	7.0793	5.6213	28.964
17000	16955	9.7544	6375.6	2.9587 +24	397.95	6.9691 + 8	5.7102 − 7	28.964
17100	17054	9.7541	6375.8	2.9126	397.95	6.8607	5.8005	28.964
17200	17154	9.7538	6376.0	2.8673	397.95	6.7539	5.8922	28.964
17300	17253	9.7535	6376.2	2.8227	397.95	6.6488	5.9853	28.964
17400	17352	9.7532	6376.4	2.7788	397.95	6.5454	6.0799	28.964
17500	17452	9.7529	6376.6	2.7355	397.95	6.4435	6.1760	28.964
17600	17551	9.7526	6376.8	2.6930	397.95	6.3432	6.2736	28.964
17700	17651	9.7523	6377.0	2.6511	397.95	6.2445	6.3728	28.964
17800	17750	9.7520	6377.2	2.6098	397.95	6.1474	6.4735	28.964
17900	17850	9.7517	6377.4	2.5692	397.95	6.0517	6.5758	28.964
18000	17949	9.7513	6377.6	2.5292 +24	397.95	5.9576 + 8	6.6797 − 7	28.964
18100	18049	9.7510	6377.8	2.4899	397.95	5.8649	6.7853	28.964
18200	18148	9.7507	6378.0	2.4512	397.95	5.7737	6.8925	28.964
18300	18247	9.7504	6378.2	2.4130	397.95	5.6839	7.0014	28.964
18400	18347	9.7501	6378.4	2.3755	397.95	5.5954	7.1121	28.964
18500	18446	9.7498	6378.6	2.3385	397.95	5.5084	7.2245	28.964
18600	18546	9.7495	6378.8	2.3022	397.95	5.4227	7.3386	28.964
18700	18645	9.7492	6379.0	2.2664	397.95	5.3384	7.4546	28.964
18800	18745	9.7489	6379.2	2.2311	397.95	5.2553	7.5723	28.964
18900	18844	9.7486	6379.4	2.1964	397.95	5.1736	7.6920	28.964

Table II
Geopotential Altitude, Metric Units

Altitude		Accel. due to gravity	Pressure scale height	Number density	Particle speed	Collision frequency	Mean free path	Molecular weight
Z (m)	H (m)	g (m/s^2)	H$_p$ (m)	n (m^{-3})	V (m/s)	ν (s^{-1})	L (m)	M (kg/kmol)
19000	19057	9.7481	6379.7	2.1430 +24	397.95	5.0479 + 8	7.8836 − 7	28.964
19100	19158	9.7478	6379.9	2.1095	397.95	4.9689	8.0089	28.964
19200	19258	9.7475	6380.1	2.0765	397.95	4.8911	8.1362	28.964
19300	19359	9.7472	6380.3	2.0440	397.95	4.8146	8.2655	28.964
19400	19459	9.7469	6380.5	2.0120	397.95	4.7393	8.3969	28.964
19500	19560	9.7466	6380.7	1.9805	397.95	4.6651	8.5303	28.964
19600	19661	9.7463	6380.9	1.9496	397.95	4.5922	8.6659	28.964
19700	19761	9.7460	6381.1	1.9191	397.95	4.5203	8.8036	28.964
19800	19862	9.7457	6381.3	1.8890	397.95	4.4496	8.9436	28.964
19900	19962	9.7453	6381.5	1.8595	397.95	4.3800	9.0857	28.964
20000	20063	9.7450	6381.7	1.8304 +24	397.95	4.3115 + 8	9.2301 − 7	28.964
20100	20164	9.7447	6384.9	1.8009	398.04	4.2430	9.3811	28.964
20200	20264	9.7444	6388.0	1.7720	398.14	4.1757	9.5345	28.964
20300	20365	9.7441	6391.2	1.7435	398.23	4.1095	9.6903	28.964
20400	20466	9.7438	6394.3	1.7154	398.32	4.0444	9.8486	28.964
20500	20566	9.7435	6397.5	1.6879	398.41	3.9803	1.0009 − 6	28.964
20600	20667	9.7432	6400.6	1.6608	398.50	3.9173	1.0173	28.964
20700	20768	9.7429	6403.7	1.6341	398.59	3.8553	1.0339	28.964
20800	20868	9.7426	6406.9	1.6079	398.69	3.7944	1.0507	28.964
20900	20969	9.7423	6410.0	1.5821	398.78	3.7344	1.0679	28.964
21000	21070	9.7420	6413.2	1.5567 +24	398.87	3.6753 + 8	1.0853 − 6	28.964
21100	21170	9.7417	6416.3	1.5318	398.96	3.6173	1.1029	28.964
21200	21271	9.7413	6419.5	1.5073	399.05	3.5602	1.1209	28.964
21300	21372	9.7410	6422.6	1.4831	399.14	3.5040	1.1391	28.964
21400	21472	9.7407	6425.8	1.4594	399.24	3.4487	1.1576	28.964
21500	21573	9.7404	6428.9	1.4361	399.33	3.3943	1.1765	28.964
21600	21674	9.7401	6432.1	1.4131	399.42	3.3408	1.1956	28.964
21700	21774	9.7398	6435.2	1.3905	399.51	3.2882	1.2150	28.964
21800	21875	9.7395	6438.4	1.3683	399.60	3.2364	1.2347	28.964
21900	21976	9.7392	6441.5	1.3465	399.69	3.1855	1.2547	28.964
22000	22076	9.7389	6444.7	1.3250 +24	399.78	3.1354 + 8	1.2751 − 6	28.964
22100	22177	9.7386	6447.8	1.3039	399.88	3.0861	1.2957	28.964
22200	22278	9.7383	6451.0	1.2831	399.97	3.0376	1.3167	28.964
22300	22379	9.7380	6454.1	1.2626	400.06	2.9898	1.3381	28.964
22400	22479	9.7377	6457.3	1.2425	400.15	2.9429	1.3597	28.964
22500	22580	9.7374	6460.5	1.2227	400.24	2.8967	1.3817	28.964
22600	22681	9.7370	6463.6	1.2033	400.33	2.8513	1.4041	28.964
22700	22781	9.7367	6466.8	1.1841	400.42	2.8065	1.4267	28.964
22800	22882	9.7364	6469.9	1.1653	400.52	2.7626	1.4498	28.964
22900	22983	9.7361	6473.1	1.1468	400.61	2.7193	1.4732	28.964
23000	23084	9.7358	6476.2	1.1286 +24	400.70	2.6767 + 8	1.4970 − 6	28.964
23100	23184	9.7355	6479.4	1.1107	400.79	2.6348	1.5211	28.964
23200	23285	9.7352	6482.5	1.0930	400.88	2.5936	1.5457	28.964
23300	23386	9.7349	6485.7	1.0757	400.97	2.5530	1.5706	28.964
23400	23486	9.7346	6488.8	1.0586	401.06	2.5131	1.5959	28.964
23500	23587	9.7343	6492.0	1.0419	401.15	2.4738	1.6216	28.964
23600	23688	9.7340	6495.1	1.0253	401.24	2.4352	1.6477	28.964
23700	23789	9.7337	6498.3	1.0091	401.34	2.3972	1.6742	28.964
23800	23889	9.7334	6501.4	9.9314 +23	401.43	2.3598	1.7011	28.964
23900	23990	9.7330	6504.6	9.7743	401.52	2.3230	1.7285	28.964
24000	24091	9.7327	6507.8	9.6197 +23	401.61	2.2867 + 8	1.7563 − 6	28.964
24100	24192	9.7324	6510.9	9.4677	401.70	2.2511	1.7845	28.964
24200	24292	9.7321	6514.1	9.3181	401.79	2.2160	1.8131	28.964
24300	24393	9.7318	6517.2	9.1709	401.88	2.1815	1.8422	28.964
24400	24494	9.7315	6520.4	9.0262	401.97	2.1476	1.8717	28.964
24500	24595	9.7312	6523.5	8.8838	402.06	2.1142	1.9017	28.964
24600	24696	9.7309	6526.7	8.7437	402.15	2.0813	1.9322	28.964
24700	24796	9.7306	6529.8	8.6058	402.25	2.0490	1.9632	28.964
24800	24897	9.7303	6533.0	8.4702	402.34	2.0171	1.9946	28.964
24900	24998	9.7300	6536.2	8.3368	402.43	1.9858	2.0265	28.964
25000	25099	9.7297	6539.3	8.2056 +23	402.52	1.9550 + 8	2.0589 − 6	28.964
25100	25200	9.7294	6542.5	8.0765	402.61	1.9247	2.0918	28.964
25200	25300	9.7291	6545.6	7.9494	402.70	1.8948	2.1253	28.964
25300	25401	9.7287	6548.8	7.8244	402.79	1.8654	2.1592	28.964
25400	25502	9.7284	6551.9	7.7015	402.88	1.8365	2.1937	28.964
25500	25603	9.7281	6555.1	7.5805	402.97	1.8081	2.2287	28.964
25600	25704	9.7278	6558.3	7.4615	403.06	1.7801	2.2642	28.964
25700	25804	9.7275	6561.4	7.3444	403.15	1.7526	2.3003	28.964
25800	25905	9.7272	6564.6	7.2292	403.24	1.7255	2.3370	28.964
25900	26006	9.7269	6567.7	7.1158	403.33	1.6988	2.3742	28.964
26000	26107	9.7266	6570.9	7.0043 +23	403.42	1.6726 + 8	2.4120 − 6	28.964
26100	26208	9.7263	6574.0	6.8946	403.52	1.6467	2.4504	28.964
26200	26308	9.7260	6577.2	6.7866	403.61	1.6213	2.4894	28.964
26300	26409	9.7257	6580.4	6.6804	403.70	1.5963	2.5290	28.964
26400	26510	9.7254	6583.5	6.5759	403.79	1.5717	2.5692	28.964
26500	26611	9.7251	6586.7	6.4731	403.88	1.5474	2.6100	28.964
26600	26712	9.7247	6589.8	6.3719	403.97	1.5236	2.6514	28.964
26700	26813	9.7244	6593.0	6.2723	404.06	1.5001	2.6935	28.964
26800	26913	9.7241	6596.2	6.1744	404.15	1.4770	2.7362	28.964
26900	27014	9.7238	6599.3	6.0780	404.24	1.4543	2.7796	28.964

Table II
Geometric Altitude, Metric Units

Altitude		Accel. due to gravity	Pressure scale height	Number density	Particle speed	Collision frequency	Mean free path	Molecular weight
H (m)	Z (m)	g (m/s²)	H_p (m)	n (m⁻³)	V (m/s)	ν (s⁻¹)	L (m)	M (kg/kmol)
19000	18943	9.7483	6379.6	2.1622 +24	397.95	5.0931 + 8	7.8135 - 7	28.964
19100	19043	9.7480	6379.8	2.1286	397.95	5.0139	7.9369	28.964
19200	19142	9.7477	6380.0	2.0955	397.95	4.9359	8.0623	28.964
19300	19242	9.7474	6380.2	2.0629	397.95	4.8592	8.1897	28.964
19400	19341	9.7471	6380.4	2.0308	397.95	4.7836	8.3191	28.964
19500	19440	9.7468	6380.6	1.9993	397.95	4.7092	8.4505	28.964
19600	19540	9.7465	6380.8	1.9682	397.95	4.6360	8.5840	28.964
19700	19639	9.7461	6381.0	1.9376	397.95	4.5639	8.7195	28.964
19800	19739	9.7458	6381.2	1.9074	397.95	4.4929	8.8573	28.964
19900	19838	9.7455	6381.4	1.8778	397.95	4.4231	8.9972	28.964
20000	19937	9.7452	6381.6	1.8486 +24	397.95	4.3543 + 8	9.1393 - 7	28.964
20100	20037	9.7449	6382.9	1.8195	397.99	4.2863	9.2852	28.964
20200	20136	9.7446	6386.0	1.7904	398.08	4.2187	9.4361	28.964
20300	20235	9.7443	6389.1	1.7618	398.17	4.1522	9.5893	28.964
20400	20335	9.7440	6392.2	1.7337	398.26	4.0868	9.7450	28.964
20500	20434	9.7437	6395.4	1.7060	398.35	4.0224	9.9032	28.964
20600	20533	9.7434	6398.5	1.6788	398.44	3.9591	1.0064 - 6	28.964
20700	20633	9.7431	6401.6	1.6520	398.53	3.8969	1.0227	28.964
20800	20732	9.7428	6404.8	1.6256	398.62	3.8356	1.0393	28.964
20900	20832	9.7425	6407.9	1.5997	398.71	3.7753	1.0561	28.964
21000	20931	9.7422	6411.0	1.5742 +24	398.81	3.7161 + 8	1.0732 - 6	28.964
21100	21030	9.7419	6414.1	1.5492	398.90	3.6577	1.0906	28.964
21200	21130	9.7416	6417.3	1.5245	398.99	3.6003	1.1082	28.964
21300	21229	9.7413	6420.4	1.5003	399.08	3.5439	1.1261	28.964
21400	21328	9.7410	6423.5	1.4764	399.17	3.4883	1.1443	28.964
21500	21428	9.7406	6426.7	1.4529	399.26	3.4337	1.1628	28.964
21600	21527	9.7403	6429.8	1.4299	399.35	3.3799	1.1816	28.964
21700	21626	9.7400	6432.9	1.4072	399.44	3.3270	1.2006	28.964
21800	21725	9.7397	6436.0	1.3848	399.53	3.2749	1.2200	28.964
21900	21825	9.7394	6439.2	1.3629	399.62	3.2237	1.2396	28.964
22000	21924	9.7391	6442.3	1.3413 +24	399.72	3.1733 + 8	1.2596 - 6	28.964
22100	22023	9.7388	6445.4	1.3200	399.81	3.1238	1.2799	28.964
22200	22123	9.7385	6448.6	1.2991	399.90	3.0750	1.3005	28.964
22300	22222	9.7382	6451.7	1.2785	399.99	3.0270	1.3214	28.964
22400	22321	9.7379	6454.8	1.2583	400.08	2.9798	1.3426	28.964
22500	22421	9.7376	6457.9	1.2384	400.17	2.9333	1.3642	28.964
22600	22520	9.7373	6461.1	1.2188	400.26	2.8876	1.3861	28.964
22700	22619	9.7370	6464.2	1.1996	400.35	2.8426	1.4084	28.964
22800	22719	9.7367	6467.3	1.1806	400.44	2.7983	1.4310	28.964
22900	22818	9.7364	6470.5	1.1620	400.53	2.7548	1.4539	28.964
23000	22917	9.7361	6473.6	1.1437 +24	400.62	2.7119 + 8	1.4772 - 6	28.964
23100	23016	9.7358	6476.7	1.1256	400.71	2.6698	1.5009	28.964
23200	23116	9.7355	6479.9	1.1079	400.80	2.6283	1.5250	28.964
23300	23215	9.7352	6483.0	1.0904	400.89	2.5875	1.5494	28.964
23400	23314	9.7348	6486.1	1.0733	400.98	2.5473	1.5742	28.964
23500	23413	9.7345	6489.3	1.0564	401.07	2.5078	1.5993	28.964
23600	23513	9.7342	6492.4	1.0397	401.16	2.4689	1.6249	28.964
23700	23612	9.7339	6495.5	1.0234	401.26	2.4306	1.6508	28.964
23800	23711	9.7336	6498.6	1.0073	401.35	2.3929	1.6772	28.964
23900	23810	9.7333	6501.8	9.9148 +23	401.44	2.3559	1.7040	28.964
24000	23910	9.7330	6504.9	9.7591 +23	401.53	2.3194 + 8	1.7312 - 6	28.964
24100	24009	9.7327	6508.0	9.6060	401.62	2.2835	1.7588	28.964
24200	24108	9.7324	6511.2	9.4553	401.71	2.2482	1.7868	28.964
24300	24207	9.7321	6514.3	9.3070	401.80	2.2134	1.8153	28.964
24400	24307	9.7318	6517.4	9.1612	401.89	2.1792	1.8442	28.964
24500	24406	9.7315	6520.6	9.0177	401.98	2.1456	1.8735	28.964
24600	24505	9.7312	6523.7	8.8765	402.07	2.1125	1.9033	28.964
24700	24604	9.7309	6526.8	8.7376	402.16	2.0799	1.9336	28.964
24800	24704	9.7306	6530.0	8.6009	402.25	2.0478	1.9643	28.964
24900	24803	9.7303	6533.1	8.4664	402.34	2.0162	1.9955	28.964
25000	24902	9.7300	6536.2	8.3341 +23	402.43	1.9852 + 8	2.0272 - 6	28.964
25100	25001	9.7297	6539.4	8.2039	402.52	1.9546	2.0593	28.964
25200	25100	9.7294	6542.5	8.0758	402.61	1.9245	2.0920	28.964
25300	25200	9.7291	6545.6	7.9498	402.70	1.8949	2.1252	28.964
25400	25299	9.7287	6548.7	7.8258	402.79	1.8658	2.1588	28.964
25500	25398	9.7284	6551.9	7.7038	402.88	1.8371	2.1930	28.964
25600	25497	9.7281	6555.0	7.5837	402.97	1.8089	2.2277	28.964
25700	25597	9.7278	6558.1	7.4656	403.06	1.7811	2.2630	28.964
25800	25696	9.7275	6561.3	7.3494	403.15	1.7538	2.2988	28.964
25900	25795	9.7272	6564.4	7.2350	403.24	1.7268	2.3351	28.964
26000	25894	9.7269	6567.5	7.1225 +23	403.33	1.7004 + 8	2.3720 - 6	28.964
26100	25993	9.7266	6570.7	7.0118	403.42	1.6743	2.4095	28.964
26200	26092	9.7263	6573.8	6.9028	403.51	1.6487	2.4475	28.964
26300	26192	9.7260	6576.9	6.7956	403.60	1.6234	2.4861	28.964
26400	26291	9.7257	6580.1	6.6901	403.69	1.5986	2.5253	28.964
26500	26390	9.7254	6583.2	6.5863	403.78	1.5741	2.5651	28.964
26600	26489	9.7251	6586.3	6.4842	403.87	1.5500	2.6055	28.964
26700	26588	9.7248	6589.5	6.3836	403.96	1.5263	2.6466	28.964
26800	26687	9.7245	6592.6	6.2847	404.05	1.5030	2.6882	28.964
26900	26787	9.7242	6595.7	6.1874	404.14	1.4801	2.7305	28.964

Table II
Geopotential Altitude, Metric Units

Altitude		Accel. due to gravity	Pressure scale height	Number density	Particle speed	Collision frequency	Mean free path	Molecular weight
Z (m)	H (m)	g (m/s^2)	H$_p$ (m)	n (m^{-3})	V (m/s)	ν (s^{-1})	L (m)	M (kg/kmol)
27000	27115	9.7235	6602.5	5.9832 +23	404.33	1.4319 + 8	2.8237 - 6	28.964
27100	27216	9.7232	6605.6	5.8899	404.42	1.4099	2.8684	28.964
27200	27317	9.7229	6608.8	5.7980	404.51	1.3882	2.9139	28.964
27300	27418	9.7226	6612.0	5.7077	404.60	1.3669	2.9600	28.964
27400	27519	9.7223	6615.1	5.6188	404.69	1.3459	3.0068	28.964
27500	27619	9.7220	6618.3	5.5313	404.78	1.3253	3.0544	28.964
27600	27720	9.7217	6621.5	5.4452	404.87	1.3049	3.1026	28.964
27700	27821	9.7214	6624.6	5.3605	404.96	1.2849	3.1517	28.964
27800	27922	9.7211	6627.8	5.2772	405.05	1.2652	3.2014	28.964
27900	28023	9.7208	6630.9	5.1952	405.14	1.2458	3.2520	28.964
28000	28124	9.7204	6634.1	5.1145 +23	405.23	1.2268 + 8	3.3033 - 6	28.964
28100	28225	9.7201	6637.3	5.0351	405.32	1.2080	3.3554	28.964
28200	28326	9.7198	6640.4	4.9569	405.41	1.1895	3.4083	28.964
28300	28427	9.7195	6643.6	4.8800	405.50	1.1713	3.4620	28.964
28400	28527	9.7192	6646.8	4.8044	405.59	1.1534	3.5165	28.964
28500	28628	9.7189	6649.9	4.7299	405.68	1.1358	3.5719	28.964
28600	28729	9.7186	6653.1	4.6566	405.77	1.1184	3.6281	28.964
28700	28830	9.7183	6656.2	4.5845	405.86	1.1013	3.6852	28.964
28800	28931	9.7180	6659.4	4.5135	405.95	1.0845	3.7431	28.964
28900	29032	9.7177	6662.6	4.4437	406.04	1.0680	3.8019	28.964
29000	29133	9.7174	6665.7	4.3750 +23	406.13	1.0517 + 8	3.8617 - 6	28.964
29100	29234	9.7171	6668.9	4.3073	406.22	1.0357	3.9223	28.964
29200	29335	9.7168	6672.1	4.2408	406.31	1.0199	3.9839	28.964
29300	29436	9.7165	6675.2	4.1753	406.40	1.0044	4.0464	28.964
29400	29537	9.7161	6678.4	4.1108	406.49	9.8908 + 7	4.1098	28.964
29500	29638	9.7158	6681.6	4.0474	406.58	9.7403	4.1742	28.964
29600	29738	9.7155	6684.7	3.9850	406.67	9.5922	4.2396	28.964
29700	29839	9.7152	6687.9	3.9235	406.76	9.4464	4.3060	28.964
29800	29940	9.7149	6691.1	3.8630	406.85	9.3029	4.3734	28.964
29900	30041	9.7146	6694.2	3.8035	406.94	9.1616	4.4418	28.964
30000	30142	9.7143	6697.4	3.7450 +23	407.03	9.0225 + 7	4.5113 - 6	28.964
30100	30243	9.7140	6700.6	3.6873	407.12	8.8856	4.5818	28.964
30200	30344	9.7137	6703.7	3.6306	407.21	8.7508	4.6534	28.964
30300	30445	9.7134	6706.9	3.5748	407.30	8.6182	4.7261	28.964
30400	30546	9.7131	6710.1	3.5198	407.39	8.4876	4.7999	28.964
30500	30647	9.7128	6713.2	3.4657	407.48	8.3590	4.8748	28.964
30600	30748	9.7125	6716.4	3.4125	407.57	8.2324	4.9508	28.964
30700	30849	9.7122	6719.6	3.3601	407.66	8.1078	5.0280	28.964
30800	30950	9.7118	6722.7	3.3086	407.75	7.9852	5.1063	28.964
30900	31051	9.7115	6725.9	3.2578	407.84	7.8645	5.1859	28.964
31000	31152	9.7112	6729.1	3.2079 +23	407.93	7.7456 + 7	5.2666 - 6	28.964
31100	31253	9.7109	6732.2	3.1587	408.02	7.6286	5.3486	28.964
31200	31354	9.7106	6735.4	3.1103	408.11	7.5134	5.4318	28.964
31300	31455	9.7103	6738.6	3.0627	408.20	7.4000	5.5162	28.964
31400	31556	9.7100	6741.8	3.0158	408.29	7.2883	5.6020	28.964
31500	31657	9.7097	6744.9	2.9697	408.38	7.1784	5.6890	28.964
31600	31758	9.7094	6748.1	2.9243	408.47	7.0702	5.7773	28.964
31700	31859	9.7091	6751.3	2.8796	408.56	6.9636	5.8670	28.964
31800	31960	9.7088	6754.4	2.8356	408.65	6.8587	5.9580	28.964
31900	32061	9.7085	6757.6	2.7923	408.73	6.7555	6.0504	28.964
32000	32162	9.7082	6760.8	2.7497 +23	408.82	6.6538 + 7	6.1442 - 6	28.964
32200	32364	9.7076	6777.8	2.6623	409.32	6.4503	6.3459	28.964
32400	32566	9.7069	6794.7	2.5779	409.82	6.2534	6.5536	28.964
32600	32768	9.7063	6811.7	2.4964	410.32	6.0630	6.7676	28.964
32800	32970	9.7057	6828.7	2.4176	410.82	5.8789	6.9881	28.964
33000	33172	9.7051	6845.7	2.3415	411.32	5.7008	7.2152	28.964
33200	33374	9.7045	6862.7	2.2680	411.82	5.5284	7.4491	28.964
33400	33576	9.7039	6879.7	2.1970	412.31	5.3617	7.6899	28.964
33600	33779	9.7033	6896.7	2.1283	412.81	5.2004	7.9380	28.964
33800	33981	9.7026	6913.7	2.0620	413.31	5.0443	8.1934	28.964
34000	34183	9.7020	6930.7	1.9978 +23	413.80	4.8933 + 7	8.4565 - 6	28.964
34200	34385	9.7014	6947.7	1.9358	414.29	4.7471	8.7273	28.964
34400	34587	9.7008	6964.8	1.8759	414.79	4.6057	9.0061	28.964
34600	34789	9.7002	6981.8	1.8180	415.28	4.4687	9.2931	28.964
34800	34992	9.6996	6998.8	1.7620	415.77	4.3362	9.5885	28.964
35000	35194	9.6990	7015.8	1.7078	416.27	4.2078	9.8926	28.964
35200	35396	9.6983	7032.8	1.6554	416.76	4.0836	1.0206 - 5	28.964
35400	35598	9.6977	7049.8	1.6048	417.25	3.9633	1.0528	28.964
35600	35801	9.6971	7066.9	1.5558	417.74	3.8468	1.0859	28.964
35800	36003	9.6965	7083.9	1.5084	418.23	3.7341	1.1200	28.964
36000	36205	9.6959	7100.9	1.4626 +23	418.72	3.6248 + 7	1.1551 - 5	28.964
36200	36407	9.6953	7117.9	1.4182	419.21	3.5190	1.1913	28.964
36400	36610	9.6947	7135.0	1.3753	419.69	3.4166	1.2284	28.964
36600	36812	9.6940	7152.0	1.3338	420.18	3.3173	1.2666	28.964
36800	37014	9.6934	7169.0	1.2937	420.67	3.2212	1.3060	28.964
37000	37217	9.6928	7186.1	1.2548	421.15	3.1280	1.3464	28.964
37200	37419	9.6922	7203.1	1.2172	421.64	3.0377	1.3880	28.964
37400	37621	9.6916	7220.2	1.1808	422.13	2.9503	1.4308	28.964
37600	37824	9.6910	7237.2	1.1456	422.61	2.8655	1.4748	28.964
37800	38026	9.6904	7254.3	1.1115	423.09	2.7834	1.5200	28.964

Table II
Geometric Altitude, Metric Units

Altitude		Accel. due to gravity	Pressure scale height	Number density	Particle speed	Collision frequency	Mean free path	Molecular weight
Z (m)	H (m)	g (m/s^2)	H$_p$ (m)	n (m^{-3})	V (m/s)	ν (s^{-1})	L (m)	M (kg/kmol)
27000	26886	9.7239	6598.9	6.0916 +23	404.23	1.4575 + 8	2.7734 − 6	28.964
27100	26985	9.7236	6602.0	5.9973	404.32	1.4353	2.8170	28.964
27200	27084	9.7233	6605.1	5.9046	404.41	1.4134	2.8613	28.964
27300	27183	9.7230	6608.3	5.8133	404.50	1.3918	2.9062	28.964
27400	27282	9.7227	6611.4	5.7235	404.58	1.3706	2.9518	28.964
27500	27382	9.7223	6614.5	5.6351	404.67	1.3498	2.9981	28.964
27600	27481	9.7220	6617.7	5.5481	404.76	1.3292	3.0451	28.964
27700	27580	9.7217	6620.8	5.4625	404.85	1.3090	3.0928	28.964
27800	27679	9.7214	6624.0	5.3783	404.94	1.2891	3.1413	28.964
27900	27778	9.7211	6627.1	5.2954	405.03	1.2695	3.1905	28.964
28000	27877	9.7208	6630.2	5.2138 +23	405.12	1.2502 + 8	3.2404 − 6	28.964
28100	27976	9.7205	6633.4	5.1335	405.21	1.2312	3.2911	28.964
28200	28075	9.7202	6636.5	5.0545	405.30	1.2126	3.3425	28.964
28300	28175	9.7199	6639.6	4.9767	405.39	1.1942	3.3948	28.964
28400	28274	9.7196	6642.8	4.9002	405.48	1.1761	3.4478	28.964
28500	28373	9.7193	6645.9	4.8248	405.57	1.1582	3.5016	28.964
28600	28472	9.7190	6649.0	4.7507	405.66	1.1407	3.5562	28.964
28700	28571	9.7187	6652.2	4.6777	405.75	1.1234	3.6117	28.964
28800	28670	9.7184	6655.3	4.6059	405.84	1.1064	3.6680	28.964
28900	28769	9.7181	6658.4	4.5353	405.93	1.0897	3.7252	28.964
29000	28868	9.7178	6661.6	4.4657 +23	406.01	1.0732 + 8	3.7832 − 6	28.964
29100	28967	9.7175	6664.7	4.3973	406.10	1.0570	3.8421	28.964
29200	29066	9.7172	6667.8	4.3299	406.19	1.0410	3.9019	28.964
29300	29166	9.7169	6671.0	4.2636	406.28	1.0253	3.9625	28.964
29400	29265	9.7166	6674.1	4.1983	406.37	1.0098	4.0241	28.964
29500	29364	9.7163	6677.3	4.1341	406.46	9.9460 + 7	4.0867	28.964
29600	29463	9.7160	6680.4	4.0709	406.55	9.7960	4.1501	28.964
29700	29562	9.7157	6683.5	4.0086	406.64	9.6484	4.2146	28.964
29800	29661	9.7153	6686.7	3.9474	406.73	9.5031	4.2800	28.964
29900	29760	9.7150	6689.8	3.8871	406.82	9.3600	4.3463	28.964
30000	29859	9.7147	6692.9	3.8278 +23	406.91	9.2192 + 7	4.4137 − 6	28.964
30100	29958	9.7144	6696.1	3.7694	406.99	9.0805	4.4821	28.964
30200	30057	9.7141	6699.2	3.7119	407.08	8.9440	4.5515	28.964
30300	30156	9.7138	6702.3	3.6553	407.17	8.8095	4.6219	28.964
30400	30255	9.7135	6705.5	3.5996	407.26	8.6772	4.6935	28.964
30500	30354	9.7132	6708.6	3.5448	407.35	8.5469	4.7660	28.964
30600	30453	9.7129	6711.8	3.4908	407.44	8.4187	4.8397	28.964
30700	30552	9.7126	6714.9	3.4377	407.53	8.2924	4.9145	28.964
30800	30651	9.7123	6718.0	3.3854	407.62	8.1681	4.9904	28.964
30900	30751	9.7120	6721.2	3.3340	407.71	8.0457	5.0674	28.964
31000	30850	9.7117	6724.3	3.2833 +23	407.79	7.9251 + 7	5.1456 − 6	28.964
31100	30949	9.7114	6727.4	3.2335	407.88	7.8065	5.2249	28.964
31200	31048	9.7111	6730.6	3.1844	407.97	7.6897	5.3055	28.964
31300	31147	9.7108	6733.7	3.1361	408.06	7.5746	5.3872	28.964
31400	31246	9.7105	6736.9	3.0885	408.15	7.4614	5.4702	28.964
31500	31345	9.7102	6740.0	3.0417	408.24	7.3499	5.5544	28.964
31600	31444	9.7099	6743.1	2.9956	408.33	7.2401	5.6398	28.964
31700	31543	9.7096	6746.3	2.9502	408.42	7.1320	5.7265	28.964
31800	31642	9.7093	6749.4	2.9056	408.50	7.0255	5.8146	28.964
31900	31741	9.7090	6752.6	2.8616	408.59	6.9207	5.9039	28.964
32000	31840	9.7087	6755.7	2.8183 +23	408.68	6.8175 + 7	5.9945 − 6	28.964
32200	32038	9.7080	6764.0	2.7330	408.92	6.6149	6.1818	28.964
32400	32236	9.7074	6780.8	2.6470	409.41	6.4147	6.3825	28.964
32600	32434	9.7068	6797.6	2.5640	409.91	6.2209	6.5892	28.964
32800	32632	9.7062	6814.4	2.4838	410.40	6.0335	6.8020	28.964
33000	32830	9.7056	6831.2	2.4062	410.90	5.8522	7.0212	28.964
33200	33027	9.7050	6848.1	2.3313	411.39	5.6767	7.2469	28.964
33400	33225	9.7044	6864.9	2.2589	411.88	5.5070	7.4793	28.964
33600	33423	9.7038	6881.7	2.1889	412.37	5.3426	7.7185	28.964
33800	33621	9.7032	6898.5	2.1212	412.86	5.1836	7.9647	28.964
34000	33819	9.7026	6915.4	2.0558 +23	413.35	5.0297 + 7	8.2182 − 6	28.964
34200	34017	9.7020	6932.2	1.9925	413.84	4.8807	8.4791	28.964
34400	34215	9.7014	6949.0	1.9313	414.33	4.7365	8.7477	28.964
34600	34413	9.7008	6965.8	1.8722	414.82	4.5968	9.0240	28.964
34800	34611	9.7002	6982.7	1.8150	415.31	4.4616	9.3084	28.964
35000	34808	9.6995	6999.5	1.7597	415.79	4.3307	9.6010	28.964
35200	35006	9.6989	7016.3	1.7062	416.28	4.2040	9.9021	28.964
35400	35204	9.6983	7033.2	1.6544	416.77	4.0812	1.0212 − 5	28.964
35600	35402	9.6977	7050.0	1.6043	417.25	3.9623	1.0531	28.964
35800	35599	9.6971	7066.8	1.5559	417.74	3.8471	1.0858	28.964
36000	35797	9.6965	7083.7	1.5090 +23	418.22	3.7356 + 7	1.1196 − 5	28.964
36200	35995	9.6959	7100.5	1.4637	418.71	3.6275	1.1542	28.964
36400	36193	9.6953	7117.3	1.4198	419.19	3.5228	1.1899	28.964
36600	36390	9.6947	7134.2	1.3773	419.67	3.4214	1.2266	28.964
36800	36588	9.6941	7151.0	1.3362	420.15	3.3231	1.2643	28.964
37000	36786	9.6935	7167.8	1.2965	420.63	3.2278	1.3031	28.964
37200	36984	9.6929	7184.7	1.2579	421.11	3.1355	1.3430	28.964
37400	37181	9.6923	7201.5	1.2207	421.59	3.0461	1.3841	28.964
37600	37379	9.6917	7218.4	1.1846	422.07	2.9594	1.4262	28.964
37800	37577	9.6911	7235.2	1.1496	422.55	2.8753	1.4696	28.964

Table II
Geopotential Altitude, Metric Units

Altitude		Accel. due to gravity	Pressure scale height	Number density	Particle speed	Collision frequency	Mean free path	Molecular weight
Z (m)	H (m)	g (m/s²)	H_P (m)	n (m⁻³)	V (m/s)	ν (s⁻¹)	L (m)	M (kg/kmol)
38000	38229	9.6898	7271.3	1.0784 +23	423.58	2.7038 + 7	1.5666 - 5	28.964
38200	38431	9.6891	7288.4	1.0465	424.06	2.6267	1.6144	28.964
38400	38633	9.6885	7305.4	1.0155	424.54	2.5519	1.6636	28.964
38600	38836	9.6879	7322.5	9.8557 +22	425.02	2.4794	1.7142	28.964
38800	39038	9.6873	7339.5	9.5656	425.51	2.4092	1.7662	28.964
39000	39241	9.6867	7356.6	9.2846	425.99	2.3411	1.8196	28.964
39200	39443	9.6861	7373.6	9.0125	426.47	2.2750	1.8746	28.964
39400	39646	9.6855	7390.7	8.7490	426.95	2.2110	1.9310	28.964
39600	39848	9.6848	7407.8	8.4937	427.43	2.1489	1.9891	28.964
39800	40051	9.6842	7424.8	8.2464	427.90	2.0886	2.0487	28.964
40000	40253	9.6836	7441.9	8.0069 +22	428.38	2.0302 + 7	2.1100 - 5	28.964
40200	40456	9.6830	7459.0	7.7748	428.86	1.9736	2.1730	28.964
40400	40658	9.6824	7476.1	7.5499	429.34	1.9186	2.2377	28.964
40600	40861	9.6818	7493.1	7.3320	429.81	1.8653	2.3042	28.964
40800	41064	9.6812	7510.2	7.1209	430.29	1.8136	2.3725	28.964
41000	41266	9.6806	7527.3	6.9163	430.76	1.7635	2.4427	28.964
41200	41469	9.6799	7544.4	6.7180	431.24	1.7148	2.5148	28.964
41400	41671	9.6793	7561.5	6.5258	431.71	1.6676	2.5889	28.964
41600	41874	9.6787	7578.6	6.3395	432.19	1.6217	2.6650	28.964
41800	42077	9.6781	7595.6	6.1589	432.66	1.5773	2.7431	28.964
42000	42279	9.6775	7612.7	5.9839 +22	433.13	1.5341 + 7	2.8234 - 5	28.964
42200	42482	9.6769	7629.8	5.8141	433.61	1.4922	2.9058	28.964
42400	42685	9.6763	7646.9	5.6496	434.08	1.4516	2.9904	28.964
42600	42887	9.6757	7664.0	5.4900	434.55	1.4121	3.0773	28.964
42800	43090	9.6750	7681.1	5.3353	435.02	1.3738	3.1666	28.964
43000	43293	9.6744	7698.2	5.1853	435.49	1.3366	3.2582	28.964
43200	43496	9.6738	7715.3	5.0398	435.96	1.3005	3.3523	28.964
43400	43698	9.6732	7732.4	4.8987	436.43	1.2654	3.4488	28.964
43600	43901	9.6726	7749.5	4.7618	436.90	1.2314	3.5480	28.964
43800	44104	9.6720	7766.7	4.6290	437.37	1.1983	3.6497	28.964
44000	44307	9.6714	7783.8	4.5002 +22	437.83	1.1662 + 7	3.7542 - 5	28.964
44200	44510	9.6707	7800.9	4.3752	438.30	1.1351	3.8614	28.964
44400	44712	9.6701	7818.0	4.2540	438.77	1.1048	3.9715	28.964
44600	44915	9.6695	7835.1	4.1364	439.23	1.0754	4.0844	28.964
44800	45118	9.6689	7852.2	4.0223	439.70	1.0468	4.2003	28.964
45000	45321	9.6683	7869.4	3.9115	440.16	1.0191	4.3192	28.964
45200	45524	9.6677	7886.5	3.8040	440.63	9.9213 + 6	4.4413	28.964
45400	45727	9.6671	7903.6	3.6997	441.09	9.6594	4.5665	28.964
45600	45929	9.6665	7920.8	3.5985	441.56	9.4049	4.6949	28.964
45800	46132	9.6658	7937.9	3.5002	442.02	9.1577	4.8268	28.964
46000	46335	9.6652	7955.0	3.4048 +22	442.48	8.9175 + 6	4.9620 - 5	28.964
46200	46538	9.6646	7972.2	3.3122	442.95	8.6841	5.1007	28.964
46400	46741	9.6640	7989.3	3.2223	443.41	8.4572	5.2430	28.964
46600	46944	9.6634	8006.4	3.1351	443.87	8.2367	5.3889	28.964
46800	47147	9.6628	8023.6	3.0503	444.33	8.0224	5.5386	28.964
47000	47350	9.6622	8040.7	2.9681	444.79	7.8141	5.6921	28.964
47200	47553	9.6616	8041.2	2.8941	444.79	7.6193	5.8377	28.964
47400	47756	9.6609	8041.7	2.8219	444.79	7.4294	5.9869	28.964
47600	47959	9.6603	8042.3	2.7516	444.79	7.2442	6.1400	28.964
47800	48162	9.6597	8042.8	2.6830	444.79	7.0636	6.2970	28.964
48000	48365	9.6591	8043.3	2.6161 +22	444.79	6.8875 + 6	6.4580 - 5	28.964
48200	48568	9.6585	8043.8	2.5509	444.79	6.7158	6.6231	28.964
48400	48771	9.6579	8044.3	2.4873	444.79	6.5484	6.7924	28.964
48600	48974	9.6573	8044.8	2.4253	444.79	6.3851	6.9661	28.964
48800	49178	9.6567	8045.3	2.3648	444.79	6.2259	7.1442	28.964
49000	49381	9.6560	8045.8	2.3059	444.79	6.0707	7.3268	28.964
49200	49584	9.6554	8046.3	2.2484	444.79	5.9194	7.5141	28.964
49400	49787	9.6548	8046.9	2.1923	444.79	5.7718	7.7062	28.964
49600	49990	9.6542	8047.4	2.1377	444.79	5.6279	7.9033	28.964
49800	50193	9.6536	8047.9	2.0844	444.79	5.4876	8.1053	28.964
50000	50396	9.6530	8048.4	2.0324 +22	444.79	5.3508 + 6	8.3125 - 5	28.964
50500	50904	9.6515	8049.7	1.9081	444.79	5.0236	8.8541	28.964
51000	51413	9.6499	8050.9	1.7914	444.79	4.7163	9.4309	28.964
51500	51921	9.6484	8010.6	1.6903	443.64	4.4386	9.9950	28.964
52000	52429	9.6469	7970.2	1.5944	442.48	4.1759	1.0596 - 4	28.964
52500	52937	9.6453	7929.8	1.5035	441.33	3.9276	1.1237	28.964
53000	53446	9.6438	7889.4	1.4174	440.16	3.6928	1.1920	28.964
53500	53954	9.6423	7848.9	1.3357	439.00	3.4709	1.2648	28.964
54000	54463	9.6407	7808.5	1.2584	437.83	3.2612	1.3425	28.964
54500	54971	9.6392	7768.0	1.1852	436.66	3.0632	1.4255	28.964
55000	55480	9.6377	7727.6	1.1159 +22	435.49	2.8763 + 6	1.5141 - 4	28.964
55500	55989	9.6362	7687.1	1.0502	434.31	2.6998	1.6087	28.964
56000	56498	9.6346	7646.6	9.8815 +21	433.13	2.5333	1.7097	28.964
56500	57007	9.6331	7606.1	9.2942	431.95	2.3763	1.8178	28.964
57000	57516	9.6316	7565.6	8.7389	430.76	2.2282	1.9333	28.964
57500	58025	9.6300	7525.1	8.2140	429.57	2.0886	2.0568	28.964
58000	58534	9.6285	7484.5	7.7180	428.38	1.9570	2.1890	28.964
58500	59043	9.6270	7444.0	7.2494	427.19	1.8330	2.3305	28.964
59000	59553	9.6255	7403.4	6.8068	425.99	1.7163	2.4820	28.964
59500	60062	9.6239	7362.8	6.3890	424.78	1.6064	2.6443	28.964

Table II
Geometric Altitude, Metric Units

Altitude		Accel. due to gravity	Pressure scale height	Number density		Particle speed	Collision frequency		Mean free path		Molecular weight
Z (m)	H (m)	g (m/s^2)	H$_p$ (m)	n (m^{-3})		V (m/s)	ν (s^{-1})		L (m)		M (kg/kmol)
38000	37774	9.6904	7252.1	1.1158	+23	423.03	2.7939	+ 7	1.5141	- 5	28.964
38200	37972	9.6898	7268.9	1.0830		423.51	2.7149		1.5599		28.964
38400	38169	9.6892	7285.7	1.0513		423.99	2.6383		1.6070		28.964
38600	38367	9.6886	7302.6	1.0206		424.46	2.5641		1.6554		28.964
38800	38565	9.6880	7319.4	9.9081	+22	424.94	2.4921		1.7051		28.964
39000	38762	9.6874	7336.3	9.6198		425.41	2.4223		1.7562		28.964
39200	38960	9.6868	7353.1	9.3405		425.89	2.3546		1.8088		28.964
39400	39157	9.6862	7370.0	9.0699		426.36	2.2889		1.8627		28.964
39600	39355	9.6856	7386.9	8.8078		426.84	2.2253		1.9182		28.964
39800	39552	9.6850	7403.7	8.5538		427.31	2.1635		1.9751		28.964
40000	39750	9.6844	7420.6	8.3077	+22	427.78	2.1036	+ 7	2.0336	- 5	28.964
40200	39947	9.6838	7437.4	8.0692		428.26	2.0454		2.0937		28.964
40400	40145	9.6832	7454.3	7.8380		428.73	1.9890		2.1555		28.964
40600	40342	9.6826	7471.1	7.6140		429.20	1.9343		2.2189		28.964
40800	40540	9.6820	7488.0	7.3969		429.67	1.8812		2.2840		28.964
41000	40737	9.6814	7504.9	7.1864		430.14	1.8297		2.3509		28.964
41200	40935	9.6808	7521.7	6.9824		430.61	1.7797		2.4196		28.964
41400	41132	9.6802	7538.6	6.7846		431.08	1.7311		2.4901		28.964
41600	41330	9.6795	7555.4	6.5928		431.55	1.6840		2.5626		28.964
41800	41527	9.6789	7572.3	6.4069		432.01	1.6383		2.6369		28.964
42000	41724	9.6783	7589.2	6.2266	+22	432.48	1.5939	+ 7	2.7133	- 5	28.964
42200	41922	9.6777	7606.0	6.0518		432.95	1.5508		2.7917		28.964
42400	42119	9.6771	7622.9	5.8822		433.41	1.5090		2.8722		28.964
42600	42316	9.6765	7639.8	5.7178		433.88	1.4684		2.9548		28.964
42800	42514	9.6759	7656.6	5.5582		434.35	1.4290		3.0396		28.964
43000	42711	9.6753	7673.5	5.4035		434.81	1.3907		3.1266		28.964
43200	42908	9.6747	7690.4	5.2534		435.27	1.3535		3.2159		28.964
43400	43106	9.6741	7707.3	5.1078		435.74	1.3174		3.3076		28.964
43600	43303	9.6735	7724.1	4.9666		436.20	1.2823		3.4017		28.964
43800	43500	9.6729	7741.0	4.8295		436.66	1.2482		3.4982		28.964
44000	43698	9.6723	7757.9	4.6965	+22	437.13	1.2152	+ 7	3.5973	- 5	28.964
44200	43895	9.6717	7774.8	4.5675		437.59	1.1830		3.6989		28.964
44400	44092	9.6711	7791.6	4.4422		438.05	1.1518		3.8032		28.964
44600	44289	9.6705	7808.5	4.3207		438.51	1.1215		3.9102		28.964
44800	44486	9.6699	7825.4	4.2027		438.97	1.0920		4.0199		28.964
45000	44684	9.6693	7842.3	4.0882		439.43	1.0633		4.1325		28.964
45200	44881	9.6687	7859.2	3.9771		439.89	1.0355		4.2480		28.964
45400	45078	9.6681	7876.1	3.8692		440.35	1.0085		4.3665		28.964
45600	45275	9.6675	7892.9	3.7644		440.80	9.8219	+ 6	4.4880		28.964
45800	45472	9.6669	7909.8	3.6627		441.26	9.5665		4.6126		28.964
46000	45669	9.6662	7926.7	3.5640	+22	441.72	9.3182	+ 6	4.7404	- 5	28.964
46200	45867	9.6656	7943.6	3.4681		442.17	9.0769		4.8714		28.964
46400	46064	9.6650	7960.5	3.3750		442.63	8.8424		5.0058		28.964
46600	46261	9.6644	7977.4	3.2846		443.09	8.6143		5.1436		28.964
46800	46458	9.6638	7994.3	3.1968		443.54	8.3927		5.2849		28.964
47000	46655	9.6632	8011.2	3.1115		444.00	8.1771		5.4297		28.964
47200	46852	9.6626	8028.1	3.0287		444.45	7.9676		5.5782		28.964
47400	47049	9.6620	8040.9	2.9497		444.79	7.7658		5.7276		28.964
47600	47246	9.6614	8041.4	2.8773		444.79	7.5750		5.8718		28.964
47800	47443	9.6608	8041.9	2.8066		444.79	7.3889		6.0197		28.964
48000	47640	9.6602	8042.4	2.7376	+22	444.79	7.2075	+ 6	6.1713	- 5	28.964
48200	47837	9.6596	8042.9	2.6704		444.79	7.0304		6.3266		28.964
48400	48034	9.6590	8043.4	2.6048		444.79	6.8578		6.4859		28.964
48600	48231	9.6584	8043.9	2.5408		444.79	6.6894		6.6492		28.964
48800	48428	9.6578	8044.4	2.4785		444.79	6.5251		6.8166		28.964
49000	48625	9.6572	8044.9	2.4176		444.79	6.3649		6.9882		28.964
49200	48822	9.6566	8045.4	2.3582		444.79	6.2086		7.1641		28.964
49400	49019	9.6560	8045.9	2.3003		444.79	6.0562		7.3444		28.964
49600	49216	9.6554	8046.4	2.2439		444.79	5.9075		7.5293		28.964
49800	49413	9.6548	8046.9	2.1888		444.79	5.7625		7.7188		28.964
50000	49610	9.6542	8047.4	2.1351	+22	444.79	5.6210	+ 6	7.9130	- 5	28.964
50500	50102	9.6527	8048.6	2.0064		444.79	5.2824		8.4202		28.964
51000	50594	9.6512	8049.9	1.8856		444.79	4.9643		8.9598		28.964
51500	51086	9.6497	8044.0	1.7736		444.59	4.6674		9.5255		28.964
52000	51578	9.6482	8004.3	1.6750		443.46	4.3966		1.0086	- 4	28.964
52500	52070	9.6467	7964.5	1.5814		442.32	4.1404		1.0683		28.964
53000	52562	9.6451	7924.8	1.4926		441.18	3.8979		1.1319		28.964
53500	53053	9.6436	7885.0	1.4084		440.04	3.6684		1.1995		28.964
54000	53545	9.6421	7845.3	1.3286		438.90	3.4515		1.2716		28.964
54500	54037	9.6406	7805.5	1.2529		437.75	3.2463		1.3484		28.964
55000	54528	9.6391	7765.8	1.1812	+22	436.60	3.0524	+ 6	1.4303	- 4	28.964
55500	55020	9.6376	7726.0	1.1132		435.44	2.8692		1.5177		28.964
56000	55511	9.6361	7686.2	1.0488		434.29	2.6961		1.6108		28.964
56500	56002	9.6346	7646.4	9.8788	+21	433.13	2.5326		1.7102		28.964
57000	56493	9.6331	7606.6	9.3018		431.97	2.3783		1.8163		28.964
57500	56985	9.6316	7566.8	8.7557		430.80	2.2326		1.9296		28.964
58000	57476	9.6301	7527.0	8.2390		429.63	2.0952		2.0506		28.964
58500	57967	9.6286	7487.2	7.7503		428.46	1.9655		2.1799		28.964
59000	58457	9.6271	7447.4	7.2883		427.29	1.8433		2.3181		28.964
59500	58948	9.6256	7407.6	6.8515		426.11	1.7281		2.4658		28.964

Table II
Geopotential Altitude, Metric Units

Altitude		Accel. due to gravity	Pressure scale height	Number density	Particle speed	Collision frequency	Mean free path	Molecular weight
Z (m)	H (m)	g (m/s^2)	H$_p$ (m)	n (m^{-3})	V (m/s)	ν (s^{-1})	L (m)	M (kg/kmol)
60000	60572	9.6224	7322.2	5.9946 +21	423.58	1.5030 + 6	2.8183 − 4	28.964
60500	61081	9.6209	7281.6	5.6226	422.37	1.4057	3.0048	28.964
61000	61591	9.6193	7241.0	5.2717	421.15	1.3141	3.2048	28.964
61500	62101	9.6178	7200.3	4.9409	419.94	1.2281	3.4194	28.964
62000	62611	9.6163	7159.7	4.6290	418.72	1.1473	3.6497	28.964
62500	63121	9.6148	7119.0	4.3352	417.49	1.0713	3.8971	28.964
63000	63631	9.6132	7078.4	4.0585	416.27	9.9998 + 5	4.1628	28.964
63500	64141	9.6117	7037.7	3.7980	415.04	9.3301	4.4483	28.964
64000	64651	9.6102	6997.0	3.5528	413.80	8.7018	4.7554	28.964
64500	65161	9.6086	6956.3	3.3220	412.56	8.1123	5.0856	28.964
65000	65672	9.6071	6915.5	3.1051 +21	411.32	7.5596 + 5	5.4410 − 4	28.964
65500	66182	9.6056	6874.8	2.9010	410.07	7.0415	5.8236	28.964
66000	66692	9.6041	6834.0	2.7093	408.82	6.5561	6.2358	28.964
66500	67203	9.6025	6793.3	2.5292	407.57	6.1015	6.6798	28.964
67000	67714	9.6010	6752.5	2.3601	406.31	5.6759	7.1586	28.964
67500	68224	9.5995	6711.7	2.2013	405.05	5.2776	7.6750	28.964
68000	68735	9.5980	6670.9	2.0523	403.79	4.9050	8.2322	28.964
68500	69246	9.5964	6630.1	1.9125	402.52	4.5566	8.8337	28.964
69000	69757	9.5949	6589.3	1.7815	401.24	4.2310	9.4835	28.964
69500	70268	9.5934	6548.4	1.6587	399.97	3.9268	1.0186 − 3	28.964
70000	70779	9.5919	6507.6	1.5436 +21	398.69	3.6427 + 5	1.0945 − 3	28.964
70500	71291	9.5903	6466.7	1.4359	397.40	3.3775	1.1766	28.964
71000	71802	9.5888	6425.8	1.3350	396.11	3.1301	1.2655	28.964
71500	72313	9.5873	6396.9	1.2385	395.19	2.8969	1.3642	28.964
72000	72825	9.5858	6368.0	1.1485	394.26	2.6801	1.4711	28.964
72500	73336	9.5842	6339.0	1.0646	393.33	2.4786	1.5869	28.964
73000	73848	9.5827	6310.1	9.8655 +20	392.40	2.2914	1.7125	28.964
73500	74360	9.5812	6281.1	9.1387	391.47	2.1176	1.8487	28.964
74000	74872	9.5797	6252.2	8.4624	390.54	1.9562	1.9964	28.964
74500	75384	9.5781	6223.2	7.8332	389.60	1.8064	2.1568	28.964
75000	75896	9.5766	6194.2	7.2481 +20	388.66	1.6674 + 5	2.3309 − 3	28.964
75500	76408	9.5751	6165.2	6.7042	387.72	1.5385	2.5200	28.964
76000	76920	9.5736	6136.2	6.1987	386.77	1.4191	2.7255	28.964
76500	77432	9.5720	6107.2	5.7291	385.83	1.3084	2.9489	28.964
77000	77944	9.5705	6078.2	5.2931	384.88	1.2058	3.1918	28.964
77500	78457	9.5690	6049.2	4.8883	383.93	1.1109	3.4561	28.964
78000	78969	9.5675	6020.1	4.5127	382.98	1.0230	3.7438	28.964
78500	79482	9.5659	5991.1	4.1643	382.02	9.4163 + 4	4.0570	28.964
79000	79994	9.5644	5962.0	3.8413	381.06	8.6640	4.3982	28.964
79500	80507	9.5629	5932.9	3.5418	380.10	7.9685	4.7700	28.964
80000	81020	9.5614	5903.9	3.2644 +20	379.14	7.3257 + 4	5.1754 − 3	28.964
80500	81533	9.5598	5874.8	3.0074	378.17	6.7319	5.6176	28.964
81000	82046	9.5583	5845.7	2.7695	377.21	6.1835	6.1002	28.964
81500	82559	9.5568	5816.6	2.5494	376.24	5.6773	6.6270	28.964
82000	83072	9.5553	5787.5	2.3457	375.26	5.2103	7.2024	28.964
82500	83585	9.5538	5758.3	2.1574	374.29	4.7795	7.8311	28.964
83000	84098	9.5522	5729.2	1.9833	373.31	4.3824	8.5184	28.964
83500	84611	9.5507	5700.1	1.8225	372.33	4.0164	9.2702	28.964
84000	85125	9.5492	5670.9	1.6739	371.35	3.6793	1.0093 − 2	28.964
84500	85638	9.5477	5641.7	1.5368	370.36	3.3689	1.0993	28.964

Table II
Geometric Altitude, Metric Units

Altitude		Accel. due to gravity	Pressure scale height	Number density	Particle speed	Collision frequency	Mean free path	Molecular weight
H (m)	Z (m)	g (m/s^2)	H$_p$ (m)	n (m^{-3})	V (m/s)	ν (s^{-1})	L (m)	M (kg/kmol)
60000	59439	9.6241	7367.8	6.4387 +21	424.93	1.6195 + 6	2.6239 − 4	28.964
60500	59930	9.6226	7327.9	6.0488	423.75	1.5171	2.7931	28.964
61000	60420	9.6211	7288.1	5.6806	422.56	1.4208	2.9741	28.964
61500	60911	9.6196	7248.2	5.3329	421.37	1.3301	3.1680	28.964
62000	61401	9.6181	7208.4	5.0048	420.18	1.2447	3.3757	28.964
62500	61891	9.6166	7168.5	4.6952	418.98	1.1644	3.5983	28.964
63000	62382	9.6151	7128.7	4.4032	417.78	1.0888	3.8369	28.964
63500	62872	9.6136	7088.8	4.1278	416.58	1.0178	4.0929	28.964
64000	63362	9.6121	7048.9	3.8683	415.38	9.5107 + 5	4.3675	28.964
64500	63852	9.6106	7009.0	3.6238	414.17	8.8835	4.6622	28.964
65000	64342	9.6091	6969.1	3.3934 +21	412.95	8.2945 + 5	4.9787 − 4	28.964
65500	64832	9.6076	6929.2	3.1765	411.74	7.7414	5.3186	28.964
66000	65322	9.6061	6889.3	2.9723	410.52	7.2224	5.6840	28.964
66500	65811	9.6046	6849.4	2.7802	409.30	6.7354	6.0768	28.964
67000	66301	9.6031	6809.5	2.5995	408.07	6.2787	6.4992	28.964
67500	66791	9.6017	6769.6	2.4296	406.84	5.8506	6.9538	28.964
68000	67280	9.6002	6729.6	2.2698	405.61	5.4494	7.4432	28.964
68500	67770	9.5987	6689.7	2.1197	404.37	5.0735	7.9702	28.964
69000	68259	9.5972	6649.8	1.9788	403.13	4.7216	8.5380	28.964
69500	68748	9.5957	6609.8	1.8464	401.89	4.3921	9.1501	28.964
70000	69238	9.5942	6569.9	1.7222 +21	400.64	4.0839 + 5	9.8102 − 4	28.964
70500	69727	9.5927	6529.9	1.6056	399.39	3.7956	1.0522 − 3	28.964
71000	70216	9.5912	6489.9	1.4963	398.13	3.5261	1.1291	28.964
71500	70705	9.5897	6450.0	1.3938	396.87	3.2742	1.2121	28.964
72000	71194	9.5882	6414.6	1.2968	395.75	3.0378	1.3027	28.964
72500	71682	9.5867	6386.3	1.2049	394.85	2.8160	1.4022	28.964
73000	72171	9.5852	6358.1	1.1191	393.94	2.6095	1.5097	28.964
73500	72660	9.5837	6329.8	1.0391	393.04	2.4173	1.6260	28.964
74000	73148	9.5823	6301.5	9.6443 +20	392.13	2.2384	1.7518	28.964
74500	73637	9.5808	6273.2	8.9486	391.21	2.0721	1.8880	28.964
75000	74125	9.5793	6244.9	8.3003 +20	390.30	1.9175 + 5	2.0354 − 3	28.964
75500	74614	9.5778	6216.6	7.6963	389.38	1.7738	2.1952	28.964
76000	75102	9.5763	6188.3	7.1338	388.47	1.6403	2.3682	28.964
76500	75590	9.5748	6160.0	6.6101	387.55	1.5163	2.5559	28.964
77000	76078	9.5733	6131.7	6.1228	386.63	1.4012	2.7593	28.964
77500	76566	9.5718	6103.3	5.6693	385.70	1.2943	2.9800	28.964
78000	77054	9.5703	6075.0	5.2475	384.78	1.1951	3.2195	28.964
78500	77542	9.5689	6046.7	4.8554	383.85	1.1032	3.4796	28.964
79000	78030	9.5674	6018.4	4.4909	382.92	1.0179	3.7620	28.964
79500	78518	9.5659	5990.0	4.1523	381.99	9.3883 + 4	4.0688	28.964
80000	79006	9.5644	5961.7	3.8378 +20	381.05	8.6559 + 4	4.4022 − 3	28.964
80500	79493	9.5629	5933.3	3.5457	380.11	7.9775	4.7648	28.964
81000	79981	9.5614	5905.0	3.2747	379.18	7.3495	5.1592	28.964
81500	80468	9.5599	5876.6	3.0232	378.23	6.7682	5.5884	28.964
82000	80956	9.5585	5848.3	2.7899	377.29	6.2304	6.0556	28.964
82500	81443	9.5570	5819.9	2.5736	376.35	5.7331	6.5645	28.964
83000	81930	9.5555	5791.5	2.3732	375.40	5.2733	7.1189	28.964
83500	82417	9.5540	5763.2	2.1875	374.45	4.8483	7.7232	28.964
84000	82904	9.5525	5734.8	2.0155	373.50	4.4558	8.3822	28.964
84500	83391	9.5510	5706.4	1.8563	372.54	4.0934	9.1012	28.964
85000	83878	9.5496	5678.0	1.7090 +20	371.59	3.7588 + 4	9.8858 − 3	28.964
85500	84365	9.5481	5649.6	1.5727	370.63	3.4501	1.0743 − 2	28.964

Table II
Geometric Altitude, Metric Units

Altitude		Accel. due to gravity	Pressure scale height	Number density	Particle speed	Collision frequency	Mean free path	Molecular weight
H (m)	Z (m)	g (m/s²)	H_P (m)	n (m⁻³)	V (m/s)	ν (s⁻¹)	L (m)	M (kg/kmol)
86000	84852	9.5466	5621.	1.447+ 20	369.7	3.17+ 4	1.17- 2	28.95
86500	85339	9.5451	5623.	1.324	369.7	2.90	1.28	28.95
87000	85825	9.5436	5624.	1.212	369.7	2.65	1.39	28.95
87500	86312	9.5421	5625.	1.109	369.7	2.43	1.52	28.94
88000	86798	9.5407	5627.	1.014	369.7	2.22	1.67	28.94
88500	87285	9.5392	5629.	9.284+ 19	369.8	2.03	1.82	28.93
89000	87771	9.5377	5631.	8.496	369.8	1.86	1.99	28.93
89500	88257	9.5362	5634.	7.775	369.9	1.70	2.17	28.92
90000	88744	9.5348	5636.	7.116+ 19	369.9	1.56+ 4	2.37- 2	28.91
90500	89230	9.5333	5639.	6.513	370.0	1.43	2.59	28.90
91000	89716	9.5318	5642.	5.962	370.1	1.31	2.83	28.89
91500	90202	9.5303	5647.	5.456	370.2	1.20	3.10	28.87
92000	90688	9.5288	5653.	4.993	370.4	1.09	3.38	28.86
92500	91173	9.5274	5661.	4.568	370.6	1.00	3.70	28.84
93000	91659	9.5259	5670.	4.178	370.9	9.17+ 3	4.04	28.82
93500	92145	9.5244	5682.	3.821	371.2	8.40	4.42	28.80
94000	92630	9.5229	5695.	3.494	371.6	7.69	4.84	28.78
94500	93116	9.5215	5710.	3.194	372.1	7.04	5.29	28.76
95000	93601	9.5200	5727.	2.920+ 19	372.6	6.44+ 3	5.79- 2	28.73
95500	94087	9.5185	5745.	2.669	373.2	5.90	6.33	28.71
96000	94572	9.5170	5766.	2.440	373.8	5.40	6.92	28.68
96500	95057	9.5156	5789.	2.230	374.5	4.94	7.58	28.65
97000	95542	9.5141	5814.	2.038	375.3	4.53	8.29	28.62
97500	96027	9.5126	5840.	1.862	376.1	4.15	9.07	28.59
98000	96512	9.5111	5870.	1.702	377.0	3.80	9.93	28.55
98500	96997	9.5097	5901.	1.556	378.0	3.48	1.09- 1	28.52
99000	97482	9.5082	5935.	1.422	379.1	3.19	1.19	28.48
99500	97967	9.5067	5971.	1.300	380.2	2.93	1.30	28.44
100000	98451	9.5052	6009.	1.189+ 19	381.4	2.68+ 3	1.42- 1	28.40
101000	99420	9.5023	6095.	9.990+ 18	384.0	2.27	1.69	28.30
102000	100389	9.4994	6191.	8.402	387.0	1.92	2.01	28.21
103000	101358	9.4964	6300.	7.071	390.3	1.63	2.39	28.10
104000	102326	9.4935	6423.	5.956	394.0	1.39	2.84	28.00
105000	103294	9.4905	6561.	5.021	398.2	1.18	3.36	27.88
106000	104261	9.4876	6719.	4.237	402.9	1.01	3.99	27.77
107000	105229	9.4847	6901.	3.578	408.3	8.65+ 2	4.72	27.64
108000	106196	9.4817	7115.	3.023	414.5	7.42	5.59	27.52
109000	107162	9.4788	7375.	2.552	421.9	6.37	6.62	27.39
110000	108129	9.4759	7723.	2.144+ 18	431.7	5.48+ 2	7.88- 1	27.27
111000	109095	9.4729	8149.	1.800	443.4	4.72	9.39	27.14
112000	110061	9.4700	8578.	1.524	454.8	4.10	1.11+ 0	27.02
113000	111026	9.4671	9010.	1.301	466.1	3.59	1.30	26.90
114000	111992	9.4642	9445.	1.118	477.1	3.16	1.51	26.79
115000	112957	9.4612	9882.	9.681+ 17	487.9	2.80	1.75	26.68
116000	113921	9.4583	10320.	8.430	498.6	2.49	2.00	26.58
117000	114885	9.4554	10760.	7.382	509.0	2.22	2.29	26.48
118000	115849	9.4525	11202.	6.498	519.3	2.00	2.60	26.38
119000	116813	9.4495	11646.	5.748	529.4	1.80	2.94	26.29
120000	117777	9.4466	12091.	5.107+ 17	539.3	1.63+ 2	3.31+ 0	26.20
121000	118740	9.4437	12535.	4.558	549.0	1.5	3.7	26.12
122000	119703	9.4408	12973.	4.086	558.5	1.4	4.1	26.04
123000	120665	9.4379	13405.	3.678	567.6	1.2	4.6	25.96
124000	121627	9.4350	13832.	3.323	576.5	1.1	5.1	25.88
125000	122589	9.4321	14254.	3.013	585.1	1.0	5.6	25.80
126000	123551	9.4291	14670.	2.740	593.5	9.6 + 1	6.2	25.73
127000	124512	9.4262	15082.	2.500	601.7	8.9	6.8	25.65
128000	125473	9.4233	15489.	2.288	609.6	8.3	7.4	25.58
129000	126434	9.4204	15891.	2.099	617.4	7.7	8.1	25.51
130000	127395	9.4175	16288.	1.930+ 17	625.0	7.1 + 1	8.8 + 0	25.44
131000	128355	9.4146	16681.	1.779	632.4	6.7	9.5	25.36
132000	129315	9.4117	17069.	1.644	639.6	6.2	1.0 + 1	25.29
133000	130274	9.4088	17453.	1.522	646.7	5.8	1.1	25.22
134000	131234	9.4059	17833.	1.412	653.5	5.5	1.2	25.16
135000	132193	9.4030	18208.	1.312	660.3	5.1	1.3	25.09
136000	133151	9.4001	18579.	1.221	666.9	4.8	1.4	25.02
137000	134110	9.3972	18947.	1.139	673.3	4.5	1.5	24.95
138000	135068	9.3943	19310.	1.064	679.7	4.3	1.6	24.88
139000	136026	9.3914	19669.	9.952+ 16	685.8	4.0	1.7	24.82
140000	136983	9.3886	20025.	9.322+ 16	691.9	3.8 + 1	1.8 + 1	24.75
141000	137940	9.3857	20376.	8.745	697.9	3.6	1.9	24.68
142000	138897	9.3828	20724.	8.214	703.7	3.4	2.1	24.62
143000	139854	9.3799	21068.	7.726	709.4	3.2	2.2	24.55
144000	140810	9.3770	21409.	7.275	715.0	3.1	2.3	24.49
145000	141766	9.3741	21746.	6.858	720.5	2.9	2.5	24.42
146000	142722	9.3712	22080.	6.472	725.9	2.8	2.6	24.36
147000	143677	9.3684	22410.	6.114	731.2	2.6	2.8	24.29
148000	144633	9.3655	22737.	5.782	736.4	2.5	2.9	24.23
149000	145587	9.3626	23060.	5.473	741.5	2.4	3.1	24.17

Table II
Geometric Altitude, Metric Units

Altitude		Accel. due to gravity	Pressure scale height	Number density	Particle speed	Collision frequency	Mean free path	Molecular weight
H (m)	Z (m)	g (m/s^2)	H$_p$ (m)	n (m^{-3})	V (m/s)	ν (s^{-1})	L (m)	M (kg/kmol)
150000	146542	9.3597	23380.	5.186+ 16	746.5	2.3 + 1	3.3 + 1	24.10
151000	147496	9.3568	23697.	4.918	751.4	2.2	3.4	24.04
152000	148450	9.3540	24011.	4.668	756.3	2.1	3.6	23.98
153000	149404	9.3511	24322.	4.435	761.0	2.0	3.8	23.92
154000	150357	9.3482	24630.	4.216	765.7	1.9	4.0	23.85
155000	151311	9.3453	24934.	4.012	770.3	1.8	4.2	23.79
156000	152263	9.3425	25236.	3.820	774.8	1.8	4.4	23.73
157000	153216	9.3396	25535.	3.640	779.3	1.7	4.6	23.67
158000	154168	9.3367	25831.	3.471	783.7	1.6	4.9	23.61
159000	155120	9.3339	26124.	3.311	788.0	1.5	5.1	23.55
160000	156072	9.3310	26414.	3.162+ 16	792.2	1.5 + 1	5.3 + 1	23.49
161000	157023	9.3282	26702.	3.021	796.4	1.4	5.6	23.43
162000	157974	9.3253	26987.	2.888	800.5	1.4	5.9	23.37
163000	158925	9.3224	27269.	2.762	804.6	1.3	6.1	23.31
164000	159875	9.3196	27549.	2.644	808.6	1.3	6.4	23.25
165000	160826	9.3167	27826.	2.532	812.5	1.2	6.7	23.19
166000	161775	9.3139	28101.	2.426	816.4	1.2	7.0	23.13
167000	162725	9.3110	28373.	2.326	820.2	1.1	7.3	23.07
168000	163674	9.3081	28643.	2.231	824.0	1.1	7.6	23.02
169000	164623	9.3053	28910.	2.141	827.7	1.0	7.9	22.96
170000	165572	9.3024	29175.	2.055+ 16	831.3	1.0 + 1	8.2 + 1	22.90
171000	166521	9.2996	29438.	1.974	834.9	9.8 + 0	8.6	22.84
172000	167469	9.2967	29698.	1.897	838.5	9.4	8.9	22.79
173000	168417	9.2939	29956.	1.824	842.0	9.1	9.3	22.73
174000	169364	9.2911	30212.	1.754	845.5	8.8	9.6	22.67
175000	170311	9.2882	30466.	1.688	848.9	8.5	1.0 + 2	22.62
176000	171258	9.2854	30717.	1.624	852.2	8.2	1.0	22.56
177000	172205	9.2825	30967.	1.564	855.6	7.9	1.1	22.51
178000	173151	9.2797	31214.	1.507	858.8	7.7	1.1	22.45
179000	174098	9.2768	31459.	1.452	862.1	7.4	1.2	22.40
180000	175043	9.2740	31703.	1.400+ 16	865.3	7.2 + 0	1.2 + 2	22.34
181000	175989	9.2712	31944.	1.350	868.4	6.9	1.3	22.29
182000	176934	9.2683	32183.	1.303	871.5	6.7	1.3	22.23
183000	177879	9.2655	32421.	1.257	874.6	6.5	1.3	22.18
184000	178824	9.2627	32656.	1.214	877.6	6.3	1.4	22.13
185000	179768	9.2598	32890.	1.172	880.6	6.1	1.4	22.07
186000	180712	9.2570	33121.	1.132	883.6	5.9	1.5	22.02
187000	181656	9.2542	33351.	1.094	886.5	5.7	1.5	21.97
188000	182600	9.2513	33579.	1.057	889.4	5.6	1.6	21.91
189000	183543	9.2485	33805.	1.022	892.3	5.4	1.7	21.86
190000	184486	9.2457	34030.	9.887+ 15	895.1	5.2 + 0	1.7 + 2	21.81
191000	185428	9.2429	34253.	9.565	897.9	5.1	1.8	21.76
192000	186371	9.2400	34474.	9.256	900.6	4.9	1.8	21.71
193000	187313	9.2372	34693.	8.959	903.4	4.8	1.9	21.65
194000	188255	9.2344	34911.	8.674	906.1	4.7	1.9	21.60
195000	189196	9.2316	35127.	8.400	908.7	4.5	2.0	21.55
196000	190137	9.2288	35341.	8.137	911.3	4.4	2.1	21.50
197000	191078	9.2260	35554.	7.884	913.9	4.3	2.1	21.45
198000	192019	9.2231	35765.	7.641	916.5	4.1	2.2	21.40
199000	192959	9.2203	35975.	7.407	919.1	4.0	2.3	21.35
200000	193899	9.2175	36183.	7.182+ 15	921.6	3.9 + 0	2.4 + 2	21.30
201000	194839	9.2147	36389.	6.965	924.1	3.8	2.4	21.25
202000	195779	9.2119	36594.	6.757	926.5	3.7	2.5	21.21
203000	196718	9.2091	36798.	6.556	928.9	3.6	2.6	21.16
204000	197657	9.2063	37000.	6.362	931.3	3.5	2.7	21.11
205000	198595	9.2035	37200.	6.175	933.7	3.4	2.7	21.06
206000	199534	9.2007	37399.	5.995	936.1	3.3	2.8	21.01
207000	200472	9.1979	37597.	5.822	938.4	3.2	2.9	20.97
208000	201410	9.1951	37793.	5.654	940.7	3.1	3.0	20.92
209000	202347	9.1923	37988.	5.493	943.0	3.1	3.1	20.87
210000	203284	9.1895	38182.	5.337+ 15	945.2	3.0 + 0	3.2 + 2	20.83
211000	204221	9.1867	38374.	5.186	947.5	2.9	3.3	20.78
212000	205158	9.1839	38564.	5.041	949.7	2.8	3.4	20.73
213000	206094	9.1811	38754.	4.901	951.9	2.8	3.4	20.69
214000	207030	9.1783	38942.	4.765	954.0	2.7	3.5	20.64
215000	207966	9.1755	39129.	4.634	956.2	2.6	3.6	20.60
216000	208902	9.1727	39314.	4.507	958.3	2.6	3.7	20.55
217000	209837	9.1699	39498.	4.385	960.4	2.5	3.9	20.51
218000	210772	9.1671	39681.	4.266	962.5	2.4	4.0	20.46
219000	211706	9.1643	39863.	4.151	964.5	2.4	4.1	20.42
220000	212641	9.1615	40043.	4.040+ 15	966.5	2.3 + 0	4.2 + 2	20.37
221000	213575	9.1588	40222.	3.933	968.6	2.3	4.3	20.33
222000	214509	9.1560	40400.	3.829	970.5	2.2	4.4	20.29
223000	215442	9.1532	40577.	3.728	972.5	2.1	4.5	20.25
224000	216375	9.1504	40753.	3.631	974.5	2.1	4.7	20.20
225000	217308	9.1476	40927.	3.537	976.4	2.0	4.8	20.16
226000	218241	9.1448	41100.	3.445	978.3	2.0	4.9	20.12
227000	219173	9.1421	41272.	3.356	980.2	1.9	5.0	20.08
228000	220105	9.1393	41443.	3.271	982.1	1.9	5.2	20.03
229000	221037	9.1365	41612.	3.187	983.9	1.9	5.3	19.99

94

Table II
Geometric Altitude, Metric Units

Altitude		Accel. due to gravity	Pressure scale height	Number density	Particle speed	Collision frequency	Mean free path	Molecular weight
H (m)	Z (m)	g (m/s²)	H_P (m)	n (m⁻³)	V (m/s)	ν (s⁻¹)	L (m)	M (kg/kmol)
230000	221969	9.1337	41781.	3.106+ 15	985.8	1.8 + 0	5.4 + 2	19.95
231000	222900	9.1310	41948.	3.028	987.6	1.8	5.6	19.91
232000	223831	9.1282	42114.	2.952	989.4	1.7	5.7	19.87
233000	224762	9.1254	42280.	2.878	991.2	1.7	5.9	19.83
234000	225692	9.1227	42444.	2.807	993.0	1.6	6.0	19.79
235000	226622	9.1199	42606.	2.738	994.7	1.6	6.2	19.75
236000	227552	9.1171	42768.	2.670	996.5	1.6	6.3	19.71
237000	228481	9.1144	42929.	2.605	998.2	1.5	6.5	19.67
238000	229411	9.1116	43089.	2.541	999.9	1.5	6.6	19.63
239000	230340	9.1088	43247.	2.480	1001.6	1.5	6.8	19.60
240000	231268	9.1061	43405.	2.420+ 15	1003.2	1.4 + 0	7.0 + 2	19.56
241000	232197	9.1033	43561.	2.361	1004.9	1.4	7.2	19.52
242000	233125	9.1006	43717.	2.305	1006.5	1.4	7.3	19.48
243000	234053	9.0978	43871.	2.250	1008.2	1.3	7.5	19.44
244000	234980	9.0950	44025.	2.197	1009.8	1.3	7.7	19.41
245000	235908	9.0923	44177.	2.145	1011.4	1.3	7.9	19.37
246000	236835	9.0895	44328.	2.094	1012.9	1.3	8.1	19.33
247000	237761	9.0868	44479.	2.045	1014.5	1.2	8.3	19.30
248000	238688	9.0840	44628.	1.997	1016.0	1.2	8.5	19.26
249000	239614	9.0813	44777.	1.951	1017.6	1.2	8.7	19.23
250000	240540	9.0785	44924.	1.906+ 15	1019.1	1.1 + 0	8.9 + 2	19.19
251000	241466	9.0758	45071.	1.862	1020.6	1.1	9.1	19.15
252000	242391	9.0730	45216.	1.819	1022.1	1.1	9.3	19.12
253000	243316	9.0703	45361.	1.777	1023.6	1.1	9.5	19.08
254000	244241	9.0675	45504.	1.737	1025.0	1.1	9.7	19.05
255000	245165	9.0648	45647.	1.697	1026.5	1.0	1.0 + 3	19.02
256000	246089	9.0621	45788.	1.659	1027.9	1.0	1.0	18.98
257000	247013	9.0593	45929.	1.622	1029.3	9.9 - 1	1.0	18.95
258000	247937	9.0566	46069.	1.585	1030.8	9.7	1.1	18.92
259000	248860	9.0538	46208.	1.550	1032.2	9.5	1.1	18.88
260000	249784	9.0511	46346.	1.515+ 15	1033.5	9.3 - 1	1.1 + 3	18.85
261000	250706	9.0484	46483.	1.482	1034.9	9.1	1.1	18.82
262000	251629	9.0456	46619.	1.449	1036.3	8.9	1.2	18.78
263000	252551	9.0429	46755.	1.417	1037.6	8.7	1.2	18.75
264000	253473	9.0402	46889.	1.386	1039.0	8.5	1.2	18.72
265000	254395	9.0374	47023.	1.355	1040.3	8.3	1.2	18.69
266000	255316	9.0347	47155.	1.326	1041.6	8.2	1.3	18.66
267000	256237	9.0320	47287.	1.297	1042.9	8.0	1.3	18.63
268000	257158	9.0293	47418.	1.269	1044.2	7.8	1.3	18.59
269000	258079	9.0265	47548.	1.241	1045.4	7.7	1.4	18.56
270000	258999	9.0238	47678.	1.215+ 15	1046.7	7.5 - 1	1.4 + 3	18.53
271000	259919	9.0211	47806.	1.189	1048.0	7.4	1.4	18.50
272000	260839	9.0184	47934.	1.163	1049.2	7.2	1.5	18.47
273000	261758	9.0156	48060.	1.138	1050.4	7.1	1.5	18.44
274000	262678	9.0129	48186.	1.114	1051.6	6.9	1.5	18.41
275000	263597	9.0102	48312.	1.090	1052.8	6.8	1.5	18.38
276000	264515	9.0075	48436.	1.067	1054.0	6.7	1.6	18.36
277000	265434	9.0048	48559.	1.045	1055.2	6.5	1.6	18.33
278000	266352	9.0021	48682.	1.023	1056.4	6.4	1.7	18.30
279000	267269	8.9993	48804.	1.002	1057.6	6.3	1.7	18.27
280000	268187	8.9966	48925.	9.807+ 14	1058.7	6.1 - 1	1.7 + 3	18.24
281000	269104	8.9939	49046.	9.603	1059.9	6.0	1.8	18.21
282000	270021	8.9912	49165.	9.403	1061.0	5.9	1.8	18.19
283000	270938	8.9885	49284.	9.209	1062.1	5.8	1.8	18.16
284000	271854	8.9858	49402.	9.018	1063.2	5.7	1.9	18.13
285000	272771	8.9831	49519.	8.833	1064.3	5.6	1.9	18.11
286000	273686	8.9804	49636.	8.652	1065.4	5.5	2.0	18.08
287000	274602	8.9777	49752.	8.474	1066.5	5.3	2.0	18.05
288000	275517	8.9750	49867.	8.301	1067.6	5.2	2.0	18.03
289000	276432	8.9723	49981.	8.132	1068.6	5.1	2.1	18.00
290000	277347	8.9696	50095.	7.967+ 14	1069.7	5.0 - 1	2.1 + 3	17.97
291000	278262	8.9669	50208.	7.806	1070.7	4.9	2.2	17.95
292000	279176	8.9642	50320.	7.648	1071.8	4.9	2.2	17.92
293000	280090	8.9615	50432.	7.494	1072.8	4.8	2.3	17.90
294000	281004	8.9588	50542.	7.344	1073.8	4.7	2.3	17.87
295000	281917	8.9561	50653.	7.197	1074.8	4.6	2.3	17.85
296000	282830	8.9534	50762.	7.053	1075.8	4.5	2.4	17.82
297000	283743	8.9507	50871.	6.912	1076.8	4.4	2.4	17.80
298000	284656	8.9480	50979.	6.775	1077.8	4.3	2.5	17.77
299000	285568	8.9453	51086.	6.640	1078.7	4.2	2.5	17.75
300000	286480	8.9427	51193.	6.509+ 14	1079.7	4.2 - 1	2.6 + 3	17.73
302000	288303	8.9373	51405.	6.254	1081.6	4.0	2.7	17.68
304000	290125	8.9319	51614.	6.011	1083.5	3.9	2.8	17.63
306000	291946	8.9266	51820.	5.779	1085.3	3.7	2.9	17.59
308000	293766	8.9212	52024.	5.556	1087.1	3.6	3.0	17.54
310000	295585	8.9158	52226.	5.343	1088.9	3.4	3.2	17.50
312000	297403	8.9105	52425.	5.139	1090.7	3.3	3.3	17.45
314000	299220	8.9052	52622.	4.944	1092.4	3.2	3.4	17.41
316000	301035	8.8998	52817.	4.756	1094.1	3.1	3.6	17.37
318000	302850	8.8945	53009.	4.577	1095.7	3.0	3.7	17.33

Table II
Geometric Altitude, Metric Units

Altitude		Accel. due to gravity	Pressure scale height	Number density	Particle speed	Collision frequency	Mean free path	Molecular weight
H (m)	Z (m)	g (m/s^2)	H$_p$ (m)	n (m^{-3})	V (m/s)	ν (s^{-1})	L (m)	M (kg/kmol)
320000	304663	8.8892	53199.	4.405+ 14	1097.4	2.9 − 1	3.8 + 3	17.29
322000	306476	8.8838	53388.	4.240	1099.0	2.8	4.0	17.25
324000	308287	8.8785	53574.	4.083	1100.6	2.7	4.1	17.21
326000	310097	8.8732	53758.	3.931	1102.1	2.6	4.3	17.17
328000	311906	8.8679	53940.	3.786	1103.7	2.5	4.5	17.13
330000	313714	8.8626	54121.	3.646	1105.2	2.4	4.6	17.09
332000	315521	8.8573	54299.	3.512	1106.7	2.3	4.8	17.05
334000	317327	8.8520	54476.	3.384	1108.1	2.2	5.0	17.01
336000	319132	8.8467	54651.	3.261	1109.6	2.1	5.2	16.98
338000	320935	8.8414	54824.	3.142	1111.0	2.1	5.4	16.94
340000	322738	8.8361	54996.	3.029+ 14	1112.4	2.0 − 1	5.6 + 3	16.91
342000	324539	8.8309	55166.	2.920	1113.8	1.9	5.8	16.87
344000	326340	8.8256	55335.	2.815	1115.2	1.9	6.0	16.84
346000	328139	8.8203	55502.	2.714	1116.5	1.8	6.2	16.80
348000	329938	8.8151	55668.	2.617	1117.9	1.7	6.5	16.77
350000	331735	8.8098	55832.	2.524	1119.2	1.7	6.7	16.74
352000	333531	8.8046	55996.	2.434	1120.5	1.6	6.9	16.70
354000	335326	8.7993	56158.	2.348	1121.8	1.6	7.2	16.67
356000	337120	8.7941	56319.	2.265	1123.0	1.5	7.5	16.64
358000	338913	8.7888	56478.	2.186	1124.3	1.5	7.7	16.61
360000	340705	8.7836	56637.	2.109+ 14	1125.5	1.4 − 1	8.0 + 3	16.57
362000	342496	8.7784	56795.	2.036	1126.8	1.4	8.3	16.54
364000	344286	8.7732	56951.	1.965	1128.0	1.3	8.6	16.51
366000	346074	8.7679	57107.	1.897	1129.2	1.3	8.9	16.48
368000	347862	8.7627	57262.	1.831	1130.4	1.2	9.2	16.45
370000	349648	8.7575	57417.	1.768	1131.6	1.2	9.6	16.42
372000	351434	8.7523	57570.	1.707	1132.7	1.1	9.9	16.39
374000	353218	8.7471	57723.	1.648	1133.9	1.1	1.0 + 4	16.36
376000	355002	8.7419	57875.	1.592	1135.1	1.1	1.1	16.33
378000	356784	8.7367	58027.	1.538	1136.2	1.0	1.1	16.30
380000	358565	8.7315	58178.	1.485+ 14	1137.4	1.0 − 1	1.1 + 4	16.27
382000	360346	8.7263	58329.	1.435	1138.5	9.7 − 2	1.2	16.24
384000	362125	8.7212	58480.	1.386	1139.6	9.4	1.2	16.21
386000	363903	8.7160	58630.	1.339	1140.7	9.0	1.3	16.18
388000	365680	8.7108	58780.	1.294	1141.9	8.7	1.3	16.15
390000	367456	8.7057	58930.	1.251	1143.0	8.5	1.4	16.13
392000	369231	8.7005	59079.	1.209	1144.1	8.2	1.4	16.10
394000	371005	8.6953	59229.	1.169	1145.2	7.9	1.4	16.07
396000	372778	8.6902	59378.	1.130	1146.3	7.7	1.5	16.04
398000	374549	8.6851	59528.	1.092	1147.4	7.4	1.5	16.01
400000	376320	8.6799	59678.	1.056+ 14	1148.5	7.2 − 2	1.6 + 4	15.98
402000	378090	8.6748	59828.	1.021	1149.6	6.9	1.7	15.96
404000	379858	8.6696	59978.	9.874+ 13	1150.7	6.7	1.7	15.93
406000	381626	8.6645	60128.	9.549	1151.8	6.5	1.8	15.90
408000	383392	8.6594	60279.	9.236	1152.9	6.3	1.8	15.87
410000	385158	8.6543	60430.	8.934	1154.0	6.1	1.9	15.84
412000	386922	8.6492	60582.	8.642	1155.1	5.9	2.0	15.81
414000	388686	8.6441	60734.	8.361	1156.2	5.7	2.0	15.79
416000	390448	8.6390	60887.	8.090	1157.3	5.5	2.1	15.76
418000	392210	8.6339	61041.	7.828	1158.5	5.4	2.2	15.73
420000	393970	8.6288	61195.	7.575+ 13	1159.6	5.2 − 2	2.2 + 4	15.70
422000	395729	8.6237	61350.	7.331	1160.7	5.0	2.3	15.67
424000	397487	8.6186	61506.	7.096	1161.8	4.9	2.4	15.64
426000	399245	8.6135	61663.	6.868	1163.0	4.7	2.5	15.61
428000	401001	8.6084	61821.	6.649	1164.1	4.6	2.5	15.58
430000	402756	8.6033	61980.	6.437	1165.3	4.4	2.6	15.55
432000	404510	8.5983	62140.	6.232	1166.4	4.3	2.7	15.52
434000	406263	8.5932	62302.	6.035	1167.6	4.2	2.8	15.49
436000	408015	8.5882	62464.	5.844	1168.8	4.0	2.9	15.46
438000	409766	8.5831	62628.	5.659	1170.0	3.9	3.0	15.43
440000	411516	8.5780	62794.	5.481+ 13	1171.2	3.8 − 2	3.1 + 4	15.40
442000	413265	8.5730	62961.	5.309	1172.4	3.7	3.2	15.37
444000	415013	8.5680	63129.	5.143	1173.6	3.6	3.3	15.34
446000	416760	8.5629	63299.	4.983	1174.8	3.5	3.4	15.31
448000	418505	8.5579	63471.	4.828	1176.1	3.4	3.5	15.28
450000	420250	8.5529	63644.	4.678	1177.4	3.3	3.6	15.25
452000	421994	8.5478	63820.	4.533	1178.6	3.2	3.7	15.21
454000	423737	8.5428	63997.	4.393	1179.9	3.1	3.8	15.18
456000	425478	8.5378	64176.	4.258	1181.2	3.0	4.0	15.15
458000	427219	8.5328	64357.	4.127	1182.5	2.9	4.1	15.12
460000	428959	8.5278	64541.	4.001+ 13	1183.9	2.8 − 2	4.2 + 4	15.08
462000	430698	8.5228	64727.	3.879	1185.2	2.7	4.4	15.05
464000	432435	8.5178	64915.	3.761	1186.6	2.6	4.5	15.02
466000	434172	8.5128	65105.	3.647	1188.0	2.6	4.6	14.98
468000	435907	8.5078	65298.	3.536	1189.4	2.5	4.8	14.95
470000	437642	8.5028	65493.	3.430	1190.8	2.4	4.9	14.91
472000	439376	8.4978	65691.	3.327	1192.3	2.3	5.1	14.88
474000	441108	8.4929	65892.	3.227	1193.7	2.3	5.2	14.84
476000	442840	8.4879	66095.	3.130	1195.2	2.2	5.4	14.80
478000	444570	8.4829	66301.	3.037	1196.8	2.2	5.6	14.77

Table II
Geometric Altitude, Metric Units

Altitude		Accel. due to gravity	Pressure scale height	Number density	Particle speed	Collision frequency	Mean free path	Molecular weight
H (m)	Z (m)	g (m/s²)	H_p (m)	n (m⁻³)	V (m/s)	ν (s⁻¹)	L (m)	M (kg/kmol)
480000	446300	8.4780	66511.	2.947+ 13	1198.3	2.1 − 2	5.7 + 4	14.73
482000	448028	8.4730	66723.	2.860	1199.8	2.0	5.9	14.69
484000	449756	8.4681	66938.	2.775	1201.4	2.0	6.1	14.65
486000	451482	8.4631	67157.	2.694	1203.0	1.9	6.3	14.61
488000	453208	8.4582	67379.	2.615	1204.7	1.9	6.5	14.58
490000	454932	8.4532	67604.	2.538	1206.3	1.8	6.7	14.54
492000	456656	8.4483	67833.	2.464	1208.0	1.8	6.9	14.50
494000	458378	8.4434	68065.	2.393	1209.7	1.7	7.1	14.46
496000	460100	8.4384	68301.	2.324	1211.5	1.7	7.3	14.41
498000	461820	8.4335	68541.	2.257	1213.2	1.6	7.5	14.37
500000	463540	8.4286	68785.	2.192+ 13	1215.0	1.6 − 2	7.7 + 4	14.33
505000	467834	8.4163	69411.	2.039	1219.7	1.5	8.3	14.22
510000	472122	8.4041	70064.	1.897	1224.5	1.4	8.9	14.11
515000	476404	8.3918	70745.	1.767	1229.5	1.3	9.6	14.00
520000	480679	8.3796	71455.	1.647	1234.8	1.2	1.0 + 5	13.88
525000	484949	8.3675	72196.	1.536	1240.3	1.1	1.1	13.76
530000	489212	8.3553	72970.	1.434	1246.0	1.1	1.2	13.63
535000	493469	8.3432	73778.	1.339	1252.0	9.9 − 3	1.3	13.50
540000	497719	8.3311	74622.	1.252	1258.2	9.3	1.3	13.37
545000	501964	8.3190	75504.	1.171	1264.7	8.8	1.4	13.23
550000	506202	8.3070	76427.	1.097+ 13	1271.5	8.3 − 3	1.5 + 5	13.09
555000	510435	8.2950	77390.	1.028	1278.6	7.8	1.6	12.95
560000	514661	8.2830	78397.	9.638+ 12	1285.9	7.3	1.8	12.80
565000	518881	8.2710	79450.	9.046	1293.6	6.9	1.9	12.65
570000	523095	8.2591	80550.	8.498	1301.6	6.5	2.0	12.49
575000	527303	8.2472	81699.	7.990	1309.9	6.2	2.1	12.34
580000	531505	8.2353	82898.	7.519	1318.5	5.9	2.2	12.18
585000	535701	8.2234	84151.	7.082	1327.5	5.6	2.4	12.01
590000	539890	8.2116	85458.	6.676	1336.8	5.3	2.5	11.85
595000	544074	8.1998	86822.	6.299	1346.4	5.0	2.7	11.68
600000	548252	8.1880	88244.	5.950+ 12	1356.4	4.8 − 3	2.8 + 5	11.51
605000	552424	8.1763	89726.	5.624	1366.8	4.6	3.0	11.33
610000	556589	8.1645	91269.	5.322	1377.5	4.3	3.2	11.16
615000	560749	8.1528	92875.	5.041	1388.6	4.1	3.4	10.98
620000	564903	8.1411	94546.	4.779	1400.0	4.0	3.5	10.80
625000	569051	8.1295	96283.	4.535	1411.8	3.8	3.7	10.62
630000	573193	8.1178	98087.	4.307	1424.0	3.6	3.9	10.44
635000	577329	8.1062	99959.	4.095	1436.4	3.5	4.1	10.26
640000	581459	8.0947	101900.	3.897	1449.3	3.3	4.3	10.08
645000	585583	8.0831	103911.	3.712	1462.5	3.2	4.6	9.90
650000	589701	8.0716	105992.	3.540+ 12	1476.0	3.1 − 3	4.8 + 5	9.72
655000	593814	8.0601	108144.	3.378	1489.8	3.0	5.0	9.54
660000	597920	8.0486	110366.	3.227	1504.0	2.9	5.2	9.36
665000	602021	8.0371	112660.	3.085	1518.5	2.8	5.5	9.18
670000	606116	8.0257	115023.	2.953	1533.2	2.7	5.7	9.01
675000	610205	8.0143	117457.	2.828	1548.2	2.6	6.0	8.83
680000	614288	8.0029	119959.	2.712	1563.5	2.5	6.2	8.66
685000	618365	7.9915	122529.	2.602	1579.1	2.4	6.5	8.49
690000	622437	7.9802	125165.	2.499	1594.8	2.4	6.8	8.32
695000	626503	7.9689	127866.	2.402	1610.8	2.3	7.0	8.16
700000	630563	7.9576	130630.	2.311+ 12	1627.0	2.2 − 3	7.3 + 5	8.00
705000	634617	7.9463	133453.	2.225	1643.3	2.2	7.6	7.84
710000	638666	7.9351	136335.	2.144	1659.8	2.1	7.9	7.69
715000	642709	7.9239	139271.	2.068	1676.4	2.1	8.2	7.53
720000	646746	7.9127	142259.	1.996	1693.1	2.0	8.5	7.39
725000	650778	7.9015	145296.	1.928	1709.8	2.0	8.8	7.24
730000	654803	7.8904	148378.	1.863	1726.6	1.9	9.1	7.10
735000	658824	7.8792	151500.	1.802	1743.5	1.9	9.4	6.96
740000	662838	7.8681	154660.	1.744	1760.3	1.8	9.7	6.83
745000	666847	7.8571	157853.	1.689	1777.2	1.8	1.0 + 6	6.70
750000	670850	7.8460	161074.	1.637+ 12	1793.9	1.7 − 3	1.0 + 6	6.58
755000	674848	7.8350	164320.	1.587	1810.6	1.7	1.1	6.46
760000	678840	7.8240	167585.	1.540	1827.3	1.7	1.1	6.34
765000	682826	7.8130	170865.	1.495	1843.8	1.6	1.1	6.23
770000	686807	7.8020	174156.	1.453	1860.1	1.6	1.2	6.12
775000	690782	7.7911	177452.	1.412	1876.3	1.6	1.2	6.01
780000	694751	7.7802	180750.	1.373	1892.4	1.5	1.2	5.91
785000	698715	7.7693	184044.	1.336	1908.2	1.5	1.3	5.81
790000	702674	7.7584	187331.	1.300	1923.8	1.5	1.3	5.72
795000	706627	7.7476	190605.	1.266	1939.2	1.5	1.3	5.63
800000	710574	7.7368	193862.	1.234+ 12	1954.3	1.4 − 3	1.4 + 6	5.54
805000	714516	7.7260	197100.	1.203	1969.2	1.4	1.4	5.46
810000	718452	7.7152	200312.	1.173	1983.8	1.4	1.4	5.38
815000	722383	7.7044	203497.	1.144	1998.1	1.4	1.5	5.30
820000	726309	7.6937	206650.	1.117	2012.1	1.3	1.5	5.23
825000	730229	7.6830	209768.	1.090	2025.8	1.3	1.5	5.16
830000	734143	7.6723	212848.	1.065	2039.2	1.3	1.6	5.09
835000	738052	7.6616	215887.	1.040	2052.3	1.3	1.6	5.03
840000	741956	7.6510	218883.	1.016	2065.1	1.2	1.7	4.96
845000	745854	7.6404	221834.	9.937+ 11	2077.5	1.2	1.7	4.91

Table II
Geometric Altitude, Metric Units

Altitude		Accel. due to gravity	Pressure scale height	Number density	Particle speed	Collision frequency		Mean free path		Molecular weight
H (m)	Z (m)	g (m/s^2)	H$_P$ (m)	n (m^{-3})	V (m/s)	ν (s^{-1})		L (m)		M (kg/kmol)
850000	749747	7.6298	224737.	9.717+ 11	2089.6	1.2 −	3	1.7 +	6	4.85
855000	753634	7.6192	227591.	9.504	2101.4	1.2		1.8		4.79
860000	757516	7.6087	230395.	9.299	2112.8	1.2		1.8		4.74
865000	761393	7.5981	233146.	9.100	2123.9	1.1		1.9		4.69
870000	765264	7.5876	235845.	8.908	2134.7	1.1		1.9		4.65
875000	769130	7.5771	238489.	8.723	2145.1	1.1		1.9		4.60
880000	772991	7.5667	241080.	8.543	2155.3	1.1		2.0		4.56
885000	776846	7.5562	243615.	8.368	2165.1	1.1		2.0		4.52
890000	780696	7.5458	246096.	8.199	2174.6	1.1		2.1		4.48
895000	784541	7.5354	248522.	8.035	2183.8	1.0		2.1		4.44
900000	788380	7.5250	250894.	7.876+ 11	2192.6	1.0 −	3	2.1 +	6	4.40
905000	792214	7.5146	253211.	7.721	2201.2	1.0		2.2		4.37
910000	796043	7.5043	255475.	7.571	2209.5	9.9 −	4	2.2		4.34
915000	799866	7.4940	257686.	7.425	2217.5	9.7		2.3		4.31
920000	803685	7.4837	259844.	7.282	2225.3	9.6		2.3		4.28
925000	807498	7.4734	261951.	7.144	2232.8	9.4		2.4		4.25
930000	811305	7.4632	264008.	7.010	2240.0	9.3		2.4		4.22
935000	815108	7.4529	266016.	6.879	2246.9	9.1		2.5		4.19
940000	818905	7.4427	267975.	6.751	2253.6	9.0		2.5		4.17
945000	822697	7.4325	269887.	6.627	2260.1	8.9		2.5		4.14
950000	826484	7.4224	271754.	6.505+ 11	2266.4	8.7 −	4	2.6 +	6	4.12
955000	830266	7.4122	273576.	6.387	2272.4	8.6		2.6		4.10
960000	834043	7.4021	275355.	6.272	2278.2	8.5		2.7		4.08
965000	837814	7.3920	277092.	6.159	2283.8	8.3		2.7		4.06
970000	841580	7.3819	278790.	6.050	2289.2	8.2		2.8		4.04
975000	845342	7.3718	280448.	5.942	2294.5	8.1		2.8		4.02
980000	849098	7.3618	282068.	5.838	2299.5	7.9		2.9		4.00
985000	852849	7.3518	283653.	5.735	2304.4	7.8		2.9		3.99
990000	856594	7.3418	285202.	5.636	2309.1	7.7		3.0		3.97
995000	860335	7.3318	286719.	5.538	2313.7	7.6		3.1		3.96
1000000	864071	7.3218	288203.	5.442+ 11	2318.1	7.5 −	4	3.1 +	6	3.94

Table III
Geopotential Altitude, Metric Units

Altitude		Sound speed	Dynamic viscosity		Kinematic viscosity		Thermal conductivity	
H (m)	Z (m)	C_s (m/s)	μ (N·s/m²)	μ/μ_0	η (m²/s)	η/η_0	κ (J/m·s·K)	κ/κ_0
-5000	-4996	358.97	1.9421 − 5	1.0853 + 0	1.0060 − 5	6.8872 − 1	2.7880 − 5	1.0992 + 0
-4950	-4946	358.79	1.9406	1.0845	1.0096	6.9117	2.7856	1.0983
-4900	-4896	358.61	1.9391	1.0836	1.0132	6.9363	2.7831	1.0973
-4850	-4846	358.43	1.9377	1.0828	1.0168	6.9610	2.7806	1.0963
-4800	-4796	358.24	1.9362	1.0820	1.0204	6.9858	2.7781	1.0953
-4750	-4746	358.06	1.9347	1.0811	1.0241	7.0108	2.7756	1.0943
-4700	-4697	357.88	1.9332	1.0803	1.0277	7.0358	2.7732	1.0934
-4650	-4647	357.70	1.9317	1.0795	1.0314	7.0610	2.7707	1.0924
-4600	-4597	357.51	1.9302	1.0786	1.0351	7.0863	2.7682	1.0914
-4550	-4547	357.33	1.9287	1.0778	1.0388	7.1116	2.7657	1.0904
-4500	-4497	357.15	1.9272 − 5	1.0770 + 0	1.0425 − 5	7.1371 − 1	2.7632 − 5	1.0894 + 0
-4450	-4447	356.97	1.9257	1.0761	1.0463	7.1628	2.7607	1.0885
-4400	-4397	356.78	1.9242	1.0753	1.0500	7.1885	2.7582	1.0875
-4350	-4347	356.60	1.9227	1.0745	1.0538	7.2144	2.7558	1.0865
-4300	-4297	356.42	1.9212	1.0736	1.0576	7.2403	2.7533	1.0855
-4250	-4247	356.23	1.9197	1.0728	1.0614	7.2664	2.7508	1.0845
-4200	-4197	356.05	1.9182	1.0719	1.0653	7.2926	2.7483	1.0836
-4150	-4147	355.87	1.9167	1.0711	1.0691	7.3190	2.7458	1.0826
-4100	-4097	355.68	1.9152	1.0703	1.0730	7.3454	2.7433	1.0816
-4050	-4047	355.50	1.9137	1.0694	1.0768	7.3720	2.7408	1.0806
-4000	-3997	355.31	1.9122 − 5	1.0686 + 0	1.0807 − 5	7.3987 − 1	2.7383 − 5	1.0796 + 0
-3950	-3948	355.13	1.9107	1.0678	1.0847	7.4255	2.7358	1.0786
-3900	-3898	354.95	1.9092	1.0669	1.0886	7.4525	2.7333	1.0777
-3850	-3848	354.76	1.9077	1.0661	1.0926	7.4795	2.7308	1.0767
-3800	-3798	354.58	1.9062	1.0652	1.0965	7.5067	2.7283	1.0757
-3750	-3748	354.39	1.9047	1.0644	1.1005	7.5340	2.7258	1.0747
-3700	-3698	354.21	1.9032	1.0635	1.1045	7.5615	2.7233	1.0737
-3650	-3648	354.03	1.9017	1.0627	1.1086	7.5890	2.7208	1.0727
-3600	-3598	353.84	1.9002	1.0619	1.1126	7.6167	2.7183	1.0718
-3550	-3548	353.66	1.8986	1.0610	1.1167	7.6446	2.7158	1.0708
-3500	-3498	353.47	1.8971 − 5	1.0602 + 0	1.1207 − 5	7.6725 − 1	2.7133 − 5	1.0698 + 0
-3450	-3448	353.29	1.8956	1.0593	1.1249	7.7006	2.7108	1.0688
-3400	-3398	353.10	1.8941	1.0585	1.1290	7.7288	2.7083	1.0678
-3350	-3348	352.92	1.8926	1.0576	1.1331	7.7572	2.7058	1.0668
-3300	-3298	352.73	1.8911	1.0568	1.1373	7.7857	2.7033	1.0658
-3250	-3248	352.55	1.8896	1.0559	1.1415	7.8143	2.7008	1.0648
-3200	-3198	352.36	1.8880	1.0551	1.1457	7.8430	2.6983	1.0639
-3150	-3148	352.18	1.8865	1.0542	1.1499	7.8719	2.6958	1.0629
-3100	-3098	351.99	1.8850	1.0534	1.1541	7.9009	2.6933	1.0619
-3050	-3049	351.81	1.8835	1.0525	1.1584	7.9301	2.6908	1.0609
-3000	-2999	351.62	1.8820 − 5	1.0517 + 0	1.1626 − 5	7.9594 − 1	2.6883 − 5	1.0599 + 0
-2950	-2949	351.43	1.8805	1.0508	1.1669	7.9888	2.6858	1.0589
-2900	-2899	351.25	1.8789	1.0500	1.1713	8.0184	2.6833	1.0579
-2850	-2849	351.06	1.8774	1.0491	1.1756	8.0481	2.6807	1.0569
-2800	-2799	350.88	1.8759	1.0483	1.1800	8.0779	2.6782	1.0559
-2750	-2749	350.69	1.8744	1.0474	1.1843	8.1079	2.6757	1.0549
-2700	-2699	350.50	1.8728	1.0466	1.1887	8.1380	2.6732	1.0540
-2650	-2649	350.32	1.8713	1.0457	1.1932	8.1683	2.6707	1.0530
-2600	-2599	350.13	1.8698	1.0449	1.1976	8.1987	2.6682	1.0520
-2550	-2549	349.94	1.8683	1.0440	1.2021	8.2293	2.6657	1.0510
-2500	-2499	349.76	1.8667 − 5	1.0432 + 0	1.2066 − 5	8.2600 − 1	2.6631 − 5	1.0500 + 0
-2450	-2449	349.57	1.8652	1.0423	1.2111	8.2908	2.6606	1.0490
-2400	-2399	349.38	1.8637	1.0415	1.2156	8.3218	2.6581	1.0480
-2350	-2349	349.20	1.8622	1.0406	1.2201	8.3530	2.6556	1.0470
-2300	-2299	349.01	1.8606	1.0398	1.2247	8.3843	2.6531	1.0460
-2250	-2249	348.82	1.8591	1.0389	1.2293	8.4157	2.6505	1.0450
-2200	-2199	348.64	1.8576	1.0381	1.2339	8.4473	2.6480	1.0440
-2150	-2149	348.45	1.8560	1.0372	1.2386	8.4790	2.6455	1.0430
-2100	-2099	348.26	1.8545	1.0363	1.2432	8.5109	2.6430	1.0420
-2050	-2049	348.07	1.8530	1.0355	1.2479	8.5430	2.6404	1.0410
-2000	-1999	347.89	1.8514 − 5	1.0346 + 0	1.2526 − 5	8.5752 − 1	2.6379 − 5	1.0400 + 0
-1950	-1949	347.70	1.8499	1.0338	1.2573	8.6075	2.6354	1.0390
-1900	-1899	347.51	1.8484	1.0329	1.2621	8.6400	2.6329	1.0381
-1850	-1849	347.32	1.8468	1.0321	1.2668	8.6727	2.6303	1.0371
-1800	-1799	347.13	1.8453	1.0312	1.2716	8.7055	2.6278	1.0361
-1750	-1750	346.95	1.8438	1.0303	1.2765	8.7385	2.6253	1.0351
-1700	-1700	346.76	1.8422	1.0295	1.2813	8.7716	2.6227	1.0341
-1650	-1650	346.57	1.8407	1.0286	1.2862	8.8049	2.6202	1.0331
-1600	-1600	346.38	1.8391	1.0278	1.2910	8.8384	2.6177	1.0321
-1550	-1550	346.19	1.8376	1.0269	1.2960	8.8720	2.6152	1.0311
-1500	-1500	346.00	1.8360 − 5	1.0260 + 0	1.3009 − 5	8.9058 − 1	2.6126 − 5	1.0301 + 0
-1450	-1450	345.81	1.8345	1.0252	1.3059	8.9398	2.6101	1.0291
-1400	-1400	345.63	1.8330	1.0243	1.3108	8.9739	2.6076	1.0281
-1350	-1350	345.44	1.8314	1.0234	1.3158	9.0081	2.6050	1.0271
-1300	-1300	345.25	1.8299	1.0226	1.3209	9.0426	2.6025	1.0261
-1250	-1250	345.06	1.8283	1.0217	1.3259	9.0772	2.5999	1.0251
-1200	-1200	344.87	1.8268	1.0208	1.3310	9.1120	2.5974	1.0241
-1150	-1150	344.68	1.8252	1.0200	1.3361	9.1469	2.5949	1.0231
-1100	-1100	344.49	1.8237	1.0191	1.3412	9.1820	2.5923	1.0221
-1050	-1050	344.30	1.8221	1.0182	1.3464	9.2173	2.5898	1.0211

Table III
Geometric Altitude, Metric Units

Altitude		Sound speed	Dynamic viscosity		Kinematic viscosity		Thermal conductivity	
Z (m)	H (m)	C_s (m/s)	μ (N $\cdot$ s/m^2)	μ/μ_0	η (m^2/s)	η/η_0	κ (J/m $\cdot$ s $\cdot$ K)	κ/κ_0
-5000	-5004	358.99	1.9422 − 5	1.0854 + 0	1.0058 − 5	6.8853 − 1	2.7882 − 5	1.0993 + 0
-4950	-4954	358.80	1.9407	1.0845	1.0093	6.9098	2.7858	1.0983
-4900	-4904	358.62	1.9393	1.0837	1.0129	6.9344	2.7833	1.0974
-4850	-4854	358.44	1.9378	1.0829	1.0165	6.9592	2.7808	1.0964
-4800	-4804	358.26	1.9363	1.0820	1.0202	6.9840	2.7783	1.0954
-4750	-4754	358.07	1.9348	1.0812	1.0238	7.0090	2.7758	1.0944
-4700	-4703	357.89	1.9333	1.0804	1.0275	7.0341	2.7733	1.0934
-4650	-4653	357.71	1.9318	1.0795	1.0312	7.0593	2.7708	1.0925
-4600	-4603	357.53	1.9303	1.0787	1.0349	7.0846	2.7684	1.0915
-4550	-4553	357.34	1.9288	1.0779	1.0386	7.1100	2.7659	1.0905
-4500	-4503	357.16	1.9273 − 5	1.0770 + 0	1.0423 − 5	7.1355 − 1	2.7634 − 5	1.0895 + 0
-4450	-4453	356.98	1.9258	1.0762	1.0461	7.1612	2.7609	1.0885
-4400	-4403	356.79	1.9243	1.0753	1.0498	7.1869	2.7584	1.0875
-4350	-4353	356.61	1.9228	1.0745	1.0536	7.2128	2.7559	1.0866
-4300	-4303	356.43	1.9213	1.0737	1.0574	7.2388	2.7534	1.0856
-4250	-4253	356.24	1.9198	1.0728	1.0612	7.2649	2.7509	1.0846
-4200	-4203	356.06	1.9183	1.0720	1.0650	7.2912	2.7484	1.0836
-4150	-4153	355.88	1.9168	1.0712	1.0689	7.3175	2.7459	1.0826
-4100	-4103	355.69	1.9153	1.0703	1.0728	7.3440	2.7434	1.0816
-4050	-4053	355.51	1.9138	1.0695	1.0766	7.3706	2.7409	1.0807
-4000	-4003	355.32	1.9123 − 5	1.0686 + 0	1.0806 − 5	7.3973 − 1	2.7384 − 5	1.0797 + 0
-3950	-3952	355.14	1.9108	1.0678	1.0845	7.4242	2.7359	1.0787
-3900	-3902	354.96	1.9093	1.0669	1.0884	7.4512	2.7334	1.0777
-3850	-3852	354.77	1.9078	1.0661	1.0924	7.4783	2.7309	1.0767
-3800	-3802	354.59	1.9063	1.0653	1.0963	7.5055	2.7284	1.0757
-3750	-3752	354.40	1.9047	1.0644	1.1003	7.5328	2.7259	1.0748
-3700	-3702	354.22	1.9032	1.0636	1.1044	7.5603	2.7234	1.0738
-3650	-3652	354.03	1.9017	1.0627	1.1084	7.5879	2.7209	1.0728
-3600	-3602	353.85	1.9002	1.0619	1.1124	7.6156	2.7184	1.0718
-3550	-3552	353.66	1.8987	1.0610	1.1165	7.6435	2.7159	1.0708
-3500	-3502	353.48	1.8972 − 5	1.0602 + 0	1.1206 − 5	7.6715 − 1	2.7134 − 5	1.0698 + 0
-3450	-3452	353.29	1.8957	1.0594	1.1247	7.6996	2.7109	1.0688
-3400	-3402	353.11	1.8942	1.0585	1.1288	7.7278	2.7084	1.0678
-3350	-3352	352.92	1.8926	1.0577	1.1330	7.7562	2.7059	1.0669
-3300	-3302	352.74	1.8911	1.0568	1.1371	7.7847	2.7034	1.0659
-3250	-3252	352.55	1.8896	1.0560	1.1413	7.8133	2.7009	1.0649
-3200	-3202	352.37	1.8881	1.0551	1.1455	7.8421	2.6984	1.0639
-3150	-3152	352.18	1.8866	1.0543	1.1497	7.8710	2.6959	1.0629
-3100	-3102	352.00	1.8851	1.0534	1.1540	7.9001	2.6934	1.0619
-3050	-3051	351.81	1.8835	1.0526	1.1582	7.9292	2.6909	1.0609
-3000	-3001	351.63	1.8820 − 5	1.0517 + 0	1.1625 − 5	7.9586 − 1	2.6884 − 5	1.0599 + 0
-2950	-2951	351.44	1.8805	1.0509	1.1668	7.9880	2.6858	1.0589
-2900	-2901	351.25	1.8790	1.0500	1.1712	8.0176	2.6833	1.0579
-2850	-2851	351.07	1.8775	1.0492	1.1755	8.0473	2.6808	1.0570
-2800	-2801	350.88	1.8759	1.0483	1.1799	8.0772	2.6783	1.0560
-2750	-2751	350.69	1.8744	1.0475	1.1842	8.1072	2.6758	1.0550
-2700	-2701	350.51	1.8729	1.0466	1.1886	8.1374	2.6733	1.0540
-2650	-2651	350.32	1.8714	1.0458	1.1931	8.1676	2.6707	1.0530
-2600	-2601	350.13	1.8698	1.0449	1.1975	8.1981	2.6682	1.0520
-2550	-2551	349.95	1.8683	1.0441	1.2020	8.2287	2.6657	1.0510
-2500	-2501	349.76	1.8668 − 5	1.0432 + 0	1.2065 − 5	8.2594 − 1	2.6632 − 5	1.0500 + 0
-2450	-2451	349.57	1.8652	1.0423	1.2110	8.2903	2.6607	1.0490
-2400	-2401	349.39	1.8637	1.0415	1.2155	8.3213	2.6581	1.0480
-2350	-2351	349.20	1.8622	1.0406	1.2201	8.3524	2.6556	1.0470
-2300	-2301	349.01	1.8607	1.0398	1.2246	8.3838	2.6531	1.0460
-2250	-2251	348.83	1.8591	1.0389	1.2292	8.4152	2.6506	1.0450
-2200	-2201	348.64	1.8576	1.0381	1.2339	8.4468	2.6481	1.0440
-2150	-2151	348.45	1.8561	1.0372	1.2385	8.4786	2.6455	1.0430
-2100	-2101	348.26	1.8545	1.0364	1.2432	8.5105	2.6430	1.0420
-2050	-2051	348.08	1.8530	1.0355	1.2478	8.5426	2.6405	1.0411
-2000	-2001	347.89	1.8515 − 5	1.0346 + 0	1.2525 − 5	8.5748 − 1	2.6380 − 5	1.0401 + 0
-1950	-1951	347.70	1.8499	1.0338	1.2573	8.6071	2.6354	1.0391
-1900	-1901	347.51	1.8484	1.0329	1.2620	8.6397	2.6329	1.0381
-1850	-1851	347.32	1.8468	1.0321	1.2668	8.6724	2.6304	1.0371
-1800	-1801	347.14	1.8453	1.0312	1.2716	8.7052	2.6278	1.0361
-1750	-1750	346.95	1.8438	1.0303	1.2764	8.7382	2.6253	1.0351
-1700	-1700	346.76	1.8422	1.0295	1.2813	8.7713	2.6228	1.0341
-1650	-1650	346.57	1.8407	1.0286	1.2861	8.8047	2.6202	1.0331
-1600	-1600	346.38	1.8391	1.0278	1.2910	8.8381	2.6177	1.0321
-1550	-1550	346.19	1.8376	1.0269	1.2959	8.8718	2.6152	1.0311
-1500	-1500	346.00	1.8361 − 5	1.0260 + 0	1.3009 − 5	8.9056 − 1	2.6126 − 5	1.0301 + 0
-1450	-1450	345.82	1.8345	1.0252	1.3058	8.9395	2.6101	1.0291
-1400	-1400	345.63	1.8330	1.0243	1.3108	8.9737	2.6076	1.0281
-1350	-1350	345.44	1.8314	1.0234	1.3158	9.0079	2.6050	1.0271
-1300	-1300	345.25	1.8299	1.0226	1.3208	9.0424	2.6025	1.0261
-1250	-1250	345.06	1.8283	1.0217	1.3259	9.0770	2.6000	1.0251
-1200	-1200	344.87	1.8268	1.0209	1.3310	9.1118	2.5974	1.0241
-1150	-1150	344.68	1.8252	1.0200	1.3361	9.1468	2.5949	1.0231
-1100	-1100	344.49	1.8237	1.0191	1.3412	9.1819	2.5923	1.0221
-1050	-1050	344.30	1.8221	1.0183	1.3464	9.2172	2.5898	1.0211

Table III
Geopotential Altitude, Metric Units

Altitude		Sound speed	Dynamic viscosity		Kinematic viscosity		Thermal conductivity	
H (m)	Z (m)	C_s (m/s)	μ (N·s/m²)	μ/μ_0	η (m²/s)	η/η_0	κ (J/m·s·K)	κ/κ_0
−1000	−1000	344.11	1.8206 − 5	1.0174 + 0	1.3516 − 5	9.2528 − 1	2.5872 − 5	1.0201 + 0
−950	−950	343.92	1.8190	1.0165	1.3568	9.2884	2.5847	1.0191
−900	−900	343.73	1.8175	1.0156	1.3620	9.3243	2.5822	1.0181
−850	−850	343.54	1.8159	1.0148	1.3673	9.3602	2.5796	1.0171
−800	−800	343.35	1.8144	1.0139	1.3726	9.3964	2.5771	1.0160
−750	−750	343.16	1.8128	1.0130	1.3779	9.4327	2.5745	1.0150
−700	−700	342.97	1.8113	1.0122	1.3832	9.4693	2.5720	1.0140
−650	−650	342.78	1.8097	1.0113	1.3886	9.5060	2.5694	1.0130
−600	−600	342.59	1.8081	1.0104	1.3939	9.5429	2.5669	1.0120
−550	−550	342.40	1.8066	1.0096	1.3994	9.5799	2.5643	1.0110
−500	−500	342.21	1.8050 − 5	1.0087 + 0	1.4048 − 5	9.6172 − 1	2.5618 − 5	1.0100 + 0
−450	−450	342.02	1.8035	1.0078	1.4103	9.6546	2.5592	1.0090
−400	−400	341.83	1.8019	1.0069	1.4158	9.6922	2.5567	1.0080
−350	−350	341.63	1.8003	1.0061	1.4213	9.7300	2.5541	1.0070
−300	−300	341.44	1.7988	1.0052	1.4268	9.7680	2.5516	1.0060
−250	−250	341.25	1.7972	1.0043	1.4324	9.8062	2.5490	1.0050
−200	−200	341.06	1.7956	1.0035	1.4380	9.8446	2.5465	1.0040
−150	−150	340.87	1.7941	1.0026	1.4437	9.8831	2.5439	1.0030
−100	−100	340.68	1.7925	1.0017	1.4493	9.9219	2.5413	1.0020
−50	−50	340.49	1.7909	1.0008	1.4550	9.9608	2.5388	1.0010
0	0	340.29	1.7894 − 5	1.0000 + 0	1.4607 − 5	1.0000 + 0	2.5362 − 5	1.0000 + 0
50	50	340.10	1.7878	9.9912 − 1	1.4665	1.0039	2.5337	9.9899 − 1
100	100	339.91	1.7862	9.9824	1.4722	1.0078	2.5311	9.9798
150	150	339.72	1.7847	9.9736	1.4780	1.0118	2.5286	9.9697
200	200	339.53	1.7831	9.9649	1.4839	1.0158	2.5260	9.9596
250	250	339.33	1.7815	9.9561	1.4897	1.0198	2.5234	9.9495
300	300	339.14	1.7800	9.9473	1.4956	1.0238	2.5209	9.9394
350	350	338.95	1.7784	9.9385	1.5015	1.0279	2.5183	9.9293
400	400	338.76	1.7768	9.9297	1.5075	1.0320	2.5157	9.9191
450	450	338.56	1.7752	9.9209	1.5135	1.0361	2.5132	9.9090
500	500	338.37	1.7737 − 5	9.9121 − 1	1.5195 − 5	1.0402 + 0	2.5106 − 5	9.8989 − 1
550	550	338.18	1.7721	9.9033	1.5255	1.0443	2.5080	9.8888
600	600	337.98	1.7705	9.8944	1.5316	1.0485	2.5055	9.8787
650	650	337.79	1.7689	9.8856	1.5377	1.0527	2.5029	9.8685
700	700	337.60	1.7673	9.8768	1.5438	1.0569	2.5003	9.8584
750	750	337.40	1.7658	9.8680	1.5500	1.0611	2.4978	9.8483
800	800	337.21	1.7642	9.8591	1.5562	1.0653	2.4952	9.8381
850	850	337.02	1.7626	9.8503	1.5624	1.0696	2.4926	9.8280
900	900	336.82	1.7610	9.8414	1.5687	1.0739	2.4900	9.8178
950	950	336.63	1.7594	9.8326	1.5750	1.0782	2.4875	9.8077
1000	1000	336.43	1.7578 − 5	9.8237 − 1	1.5813 − 5	1.0825 + 0	2.4849 − 5	9.7975 − 1
1050	1050	336.24	1.7563	9.8149	1.5877	1.0869	2.4823	9.7874
1100	1100	336.05	1.7547	9.8060	1.5940	1.0912	2.4797	9.7772
1150	1150	335.85	1.7531	9.7971	1.6005	1.0956	2.4772	9.7671
1200	1200	335.66	1.7515	9.7882	1.6069	1.1000	2.4746	9.7569
1250	1250	335.46	1.7499	9.7794	1.6134	1.1045	2.4720	9.7467
1300	1300	335.27	1.7483	9.7705	1.6199	1.1089	2.4694	9.7366
1350	1350	335.07	1.7467	9.7616	1.6265	1.1134	2.4669	9.7264
1400	1400	334.88	1.7451	9.7527	1.6331	1.1179	2.4643	9.7162
1450	1450	334.68	1.7435	9.7438	1.6397	1.1225	2.4617	9.7060
1500	1500	334.49	1.7419 − 5	9.7349 − 1	1.6463 − 5	1.1270 + 0	2.4591 − 5	9.6959 − 1
1550	1550	334.29	1.7404	9.7260	1.6530	1.1316	2.4565	9.6857
1600	1600	334.10	1.7388	9.7170	1.6598	1.1362	2.4539	9.6755
1650	1650	333.90	1.7372	9.7081	1.6665	1.1408	2.4514	9.6653
1700	1700	333.71	1.7356	9.6992	1.6733	1.1455	2.4488	9.6551
1750	1750	333.51	1.7340	9.6903	1.6801	1.1502	2.4462	9.6449
1800	1801	333.31	1.7324	9.6813	1.6870	1.1549	2.4436	9.6347
1850	1851	333.12	1.7308	9.6724	1.6939	1.1596	2.4410	9.6245
1900	1901	332.92	1.7292	9.6634	1.7008	1.1643	2.4384	9.6143
1950	1951	332.73	1.7276	9.6545	1.7078	1.1691	2.4358	9.6041
2000	2001	332.53	1.7260 − 5	9.6455 − 1	1.7148 − 5	1.1739 + 0	2.4332 − 5	9.5938 − 1
2050	2051	332.33	1.7244	9.6366	1.7219	1.1787	2.4306	9.5836
2100	2101	332.14	1.7228	9.6276	1.7290	1.1836	2.4281	9.5734
2150	2151	331.94	1.7211	9.6186	1.7361	1.1885	2.4255	9.5632
2200	2201	331.74	1.7195	9.6097	1.7432	1.1934	2.4229	9.5530
2250	2251	331.55	1.7179	9.6007	1.7504	1.1983	2.4203	9.5427
2300	2301	331.35	1.7163	9.5917	1.7577	1.2032	2.4177	9.5325
2350	2351	331.15	1.7147	9.5827	1.7649	1.2082	2.4151	9.5222
2400	2401	330.95	1.7131	9.5737	1.7722	1.2132	2.4125	9.5120
2450	2451	330.76	1.7115	9.5647	1.7796	1.2182	2.4099	9.5018
2500	2501	330.56	1.7099 − 5	9.5557 − 1	1.7870 − 5	1.2233 + 0	2.4073 − 5	9.4915 − 1
2550	2551	330.36	1.7083	9.5467	1.7944	1.2284	2.4047	9.4813
2600	2601	330.16	1.7067	9.5377	1.8019	1.2335	2.4021	9.4710
2650	2651	329.97	1.7050	9.5286	1.8094	1.2386	2.3995	9.4607
2700	2701	329.77	1.7034	9.5196	1.8169	1.2438	2.3969	9.4505
2750	2751	329.57	1.7018	9.5106	1.8245	1.2490	2.3943	9.4402
2800	2801	329.37	1.7002	9.5015	1.8321	1.2542	2.3917	9.4299
2850	2851	329.17	1.6986	9.4925	1.8398	1.2595	2.3891	9.4197
2900	2901	328.98	1.6970	9.4835	1.8475	1.2647	2.3865	9.4094
2950	2951	328.78	1.6953	9.4744	1.8552	1.2700	2.3838	9.3991

Table III
Geometric Altitude, Metric Units

Altitude		Sound speed	Dynamic viscosity		Kinematic viscosity		Thermal conductivity	
Z (m)	H (m)	C_s (m/s)	$(N \cdot \frac{\mu}{s}/m^2)$	μ/μ_0	$(m^2 \frac{\eta}{/s})$	η/η_0	$(J/m \frac{\kappa}{s} \cdot K)$	κ/κ_0
-1000	-1000	344.11	1.8206 - 5	1.0174 + 0	1.3516 - 5	9.2527 - 1	2.5872 - 5	1.0201 + 0
-950	-950	343.92	1.8190	1.0165	1.3568	9.2883	2.5847	1.0191
-900	-900	343.73	1.8175	1.0157	1.3620	9.3242	2.5822	1.0181
-850	-850	343.54	1.8159	1.0148	1.3673	9.3602	2.5796	1.0171
-800	-800	343.35	1.8144	1.0139	1.3725	9.3963	2.5771	1.0161
-750	-750	343.16	1.8128	1.0130	1.3779	9.4327	2.5745	1.0150
-700	-700	342.97	1.8113	1.0122	1.3832	9.4692	2.5720	1.0140
-650	-650	342.78	1.8097	1.0113	1.3886	9.5059	2.5694	1.0130
-600	-600	342.59	1.8081	1.0104	1.3939	9.5428	2.5669	1.0120
-550	-550	342.40	1.8066	1.0096	1.3994	9.5799	2.5643	1.0110
-500	-500	342.21	1.8050 - 5	1.0087 + 0	1.4048 - 5	9.6171 - 1	2.5618 - 5	1.0100 + 0
-450	-450	342.02	1.8035	1.0078	1.4103	9.6546	2.5592	1.0090
-400	-400	341.83	1.8019	1.0069	1.4158	9.6922	2.5567	1.0080
-350	-350	341.63	1.8003	1.0061	1.4213	9.7300	2.5541	1.0070
-300	-300	341.44	1.7988	1.0052	1.4268	9.7680	2.5516	1.0060
-250	-250	341.25	1.7972	1.0043	1.4324	9.8062	2.5490	1.0050
-200	-200	341.06	1.7956	1.0035	1.4380	9.8445	2.5465	1.0040
-150	-150	340.87	1.7941	1.0026	1.4437	9.8831	2.5439	1.0030
-100	-100	340.68	1.7925	1.0017	1.4493	9.9219	2.5413	1.0020
-50	-50	340.49	1.7909	1.0008	1.4550	9.9608	2.5388	1.0010
0	0	340.29	1.7894 - 5	1.0000 + 0	1.4607 - 5	1.0000 + 0	2.5362 - 5	1.0000 + 0
50	50	340.10	1.7878	9.9912 - 1	1.4665	1.0039	2.5337	9.9899 - 1
100	100	339.91	1.7862	9.9824	1.4722	1.0078	2.5311	9.9798
150	150	339.72	1.7847	9.9736	1.4780	1.0118	2.5286	9.9697
200	200	339.53	1.7831	9.9649	1.4839	1.0158	2.5260	9.9596
250	250	339.33	1.7815	9.9561	1.4897	1.0198	2.5234	9.9495
300	300	339.14	1.7800	9.9473	1.4956	1.0238	2.5209	9.9394
350	350	338.95	1.7784	9.9385	1.5015	1.0279	2.5183	9.9293
400	400	338.76	1.7768	9.9297	1.5075	1.0320	2.5157	9.9191
450	450	338.56	1.7752	9.9209	1.5135	1.0361	2.5132	9.9090
500	500	338.37	1.7737 - 5	9.9121 - 1	1.5195 - 5	1.0402 + 0	2.5106 - 5	9.8989 - 1
550	550	338.18	1.7721	9.9033	1.5255	1.0443	2.5080	9.8888
600	600	337.98	1.7705	9.8945	1.5316	1.0485	2.5055	9.8787
650	650	337.79	1.7689	9.8856	1.5377	1.0527	2.5029	9.8685
700	700	337.60	1.7673	9.8768	1.5438	1.0568	2.5003	9.8584
750	750	337.40	1.7658	9.8680	1.5500	1.0611	2.4978	9.8483
800	800	337.21	1.7642	9.8591	1.5562	1.0653	2.4952	9.8382
850	850	337.02	1.7626	9.8503	1.5624	1.0696	2.4926	9.8280
900	900	336.82	1.7610	9.8414	1.5687	1.0739	2.4901	9.8179
950	950	336.63	1.7594	9.8326	1.5750	1.0782	2.4875	9.8077
1000	1000	336.43	1.7579 - 5	9.8237 - 1	1.5813 - 5	1.0825 + 0	2.4849 - 5	9.7976 - 1
1050	1050	336.24	1.7563	9.8149	1.5876	1.0868	2.4823	9.7874
1100	1100	336.05	1.7547	9.8060	1.5940	1.0912	2.4798	9.7773
1150	1150	335.85	1.7531	9.7972	1.6004	1.0956	2.4772	9.7671
1200	1200	335.66	1.7515	9.7883	1.6069	1.1000	2.4746	9.7570
1250	1250	335.46	1.7499	9.7794	1.6134	1.1045	2.4720	9.7468
1300	1300	335.27	1.7483	9.7705	1.6199	1.1089	2.4694	9.7366
1350	1350	335.07	1.7467	9.7616	1.6264	1.1134	2.4669	9.7265
1400	1400	334.88	1.7451	9.7527	1.6330	1.1179	2.4643	9.7163
1450	1450	334.68	1.7436	9.7438	1.6396	1.1224	2.4617	9.7061
1500	1500	334.49	1.7420 - 5	9.7349 - 1	1.6463 - 5	1.1270 + 0	2.4591 - 5	9.6959 - 1
1550	1550	334.29	1.7404	9.7260	1.6530	1.1316	2.4565	9.6858
1600	1600	334.10	1.7388	9.7171	1.6597	1.1362	2.4540	9.6756
1650	1650	333.90	1.7372	9.7082	1.6665	1.1408	2.4514	9.6654
1700	1700	333.71	1.7356	9.6993	1.6733	1.1455	2.4488	9.6552
1750	1750	333.51	1.7340	9.6904	1.6801	1.1501	2.4462	9.6450
1800	1799	333.32	1.7324	9.6814	1.6869	1.1548	2.4436	9.6348
1850	1849	333.12	1.7308	9.6725	1.6938	1.1595	2.4410	9.6246
1900	1899	332.92	1.7292	9.6635	1.7008	1.1643	2.4384	9.6144
1950	1949	332.73	1.7276	9.6546	1.7077	1.1691	2.4359	9.6042
2000	1999	332.53	1.7260 - 5	9.6456 - 1	1.7147 - 5	1.1739 + 0	2.4333 - 5	9.5940 - 1
2050	2049	332.34	1.7244	9.6367	1.7218	1.1787	2.4307	9.5838
2100	2099	332.14	1.7228	9.6277	1.7289	1.1835	2.4281	9.5735
2150	2149	331.94	1.7212	9.6188	1.7360	1.1884	2.4255	9.5633
2200	2199	331.75	1.7196	9.6098	1.7431	1.1933	2.4229	9.5531
2250	2249	331.55	1.7180	9.6008	1.7503	1.1982	2.4203	9.5429
2300	2299	331.35	1.7164	9.5918	1.7575	1.2032	2.4177	9.5327
2350	2349	331.16	1.7147	9.5829	1.7648	1.2081	2.4151	9.5224
2400	2399	330.96	1.7131	9.5739	1.7721	1.2131	2.4125	9.5122
2450	2449	330.76	1.7115	9.5649	1.7795	1.2182	2.4099	9.5019
2500	2499	330.56	1.7099 - 5	9.5559 - 1	1.7868 - 5	1.2232 + 0	2.4073 - 5	9.4917 - 1
2550	2549	330.37	1.7083	9.5469	1.7943	1.2283	2.4047	9.4815
2600	2599	330.17	1.7067	9.5379	1.8017	1.2334	2.4021	9.4712
2650	2649	329.97	1.7051	9.5288	1.8092	1.2385	2.3995	9.4610
2700	2699	329.77	1.7035	9.5198	1.8167	1.2437	2.3969	9.4507
2750	2749	329.57	1.7019	9.5108	1.8243	1.2489	2.3943	9.4405
2800	2799	329.38	1.7002	9.5018	1.8319	1.2541	2.3917	9.4302
2850	2849	329.18	1.6986	9.4927	1.8396	1.2593	2.3891	9.4199
2900	2899	328.98	1.6970	9.4837	1.8473	1.2646	2.3865	9.4097
2950	2949	328.78	1.6954	9.4746	1.8550	1.2699	2.3839	9.3994

Table III
Geopotential Altitude, Metric Units

Altitude		Sound speed	Dynamic viscosity		Kinematic viscosity		Thermal conductivity	
H (m)	Z (m)	C_s (m/s)	μ (N $\cdot$ s/m^2)	μ/μ_0	η (m^2/s)	η/η_0	κ (J/m $\cdot$ s $\cdot$ K)	κ/κ_0
3000	3001	328.58	1.6937 − 5	9.4653 − 1	1.8630 − 5	1.2754 + 0	2.3812 − 5	9.3888 − 1
3050	3051	328.38	1.6921	9.4563	1.8709	1.2807	2.3786	9.3786
3100	3102	328.18	1.6905	9.4472	1.8787	1.2861	2.3760	9.3683
3150	3152	327.98	1.6889	9.4381	1.8866	1.2915	2.3734	9.3580
3200	3202	327.78	1.6872	9.4291	1.8946	1.2970	2.3708	9.3477
3250	3252	327.58	1.6856	9.4200	1.9026	1.3025	2.3682	9.3374
3300	3302	327.38	1.6840	9.4109	1.9106	1.3080	2.3656	9.3271
3350	3352	327.18	1.6823	9.4018	1.9187	1.3135	2.3630	9.3168
3400	3402	326.98	1.6807	9.3927	1.9268	1.3191	2.3604	9.3065
3450	3452	326.78	1.6791	9.3836	1.9350	1.3247	2.3577	9.2962
3500	3502	326.58	1.6775 − 5	9.3745 − 1	1.9432 − 5	1.3303 + 0	2.3551 − 5	9.2858 − 1
3550	3552	326.38	1.6758	9.3654	1.9515	1.3359	2.3525	9.2755
3600	3602	326.18	1.6742	9.3562	1.9598	1.3416	2.3499	9.2652
3650	3652	325.98	1.6726	9.3471	1.9682	1.3473	2.3473	9.2549
3700	3702	325.78	1.6709	9.3380	1.9766	1.3531	2.3446	9.2446
3750	3752	325.58	1.6693	9.3289	1.9850	1.3589	2.3420	9.2342
3800	3802	325.38	1.6677	9.3197	1.9935	1.3647	2.3394	9.2239
3850	3852	325.18	1.6660	9.3106	2.0020	1.3705	2.3368	9.2136
3900	3902	324.98	1.6644	9.3014	2.0106	1.3764	2.3342	9.2032
3950	3952	324.78	1.6627	9.2923	2.0192	1.3823	2.3315	9.1929
4000	4003	324.58	1.6611 − 5	9.2831 − 1	2.0279 − 5	1.3882 + 0	2.3289 − 5	9.1825 − 1
4050	4053	324.38	1.6595	9.2739	2.0366	1.3942	2.3263	9.1722
4100	4103	324.18	1.6578	9.2648	2.0454	1.4002	2.3237	9.1618
4150	4153	323.97	1.6562	9.2556	2.0542	1.4062	2.3210	9.1515
4200	4203	323.77	1.6545	9.2464	2.0631	1.4123	2.3184	9.1411
4250	4253	323.57	1.6529	9.2372	2.0720	1.4184	2.3158	9.1307
4300	4303	323.37	1.6513	9.2280	2.0809	1.4246	2.3132	9.1204
4350	4353	323.17	1.6496	9.2188	2.0900	1.4307	2.3105	9.1100
4400	4403	322.97	1.6480	9.2096	2.0990	1.4369	2.3079	9.0996
4450	4453	322.76	1.6463	9.2004	2.1081	1.4432	2.3053	9.0893
4500	4503	322.56	1.6447 − 5	9.1912 − 1	2.1173 − 5	1.4494 + 0	2.3026 − 5	9.0789 − 1
4550	4553	322.36	1.6430	9.1820	2.1265	1.4557	2.3000	9.0685
4600	4603	322.16	1.6414	9.1727	2.1358	1.4621	2.2974	9.0581
4650	4653	321.95	1.6397	9.1635	2.1451	1.4685	2.2947	9.0477
4700	4703	321.75	1.6381	9.1543	2.1545	1.4749	2.2921	9.0373
4750	4754	321.55	1.6364	9.1450	2.1639	1.4813	2.2894	9.0269
4800	4804	321.34	1.6347	9.1358	2.1733	1.4878	2.2868	9.0165
4850	4854	321.14	1.6331	9.1265	2.1829	1.4943	2.2842	9.0061
4900	4904	320.94	1.6314	9.1173	2.1925	1.5009	2.2815	8.9957
4950	4954	320.73	1.6298	9.1080	2.2021	1.5075	2.2789	8.9853
5000	5004	320.53	1.6281 − 5	9.0987 − 1	2.2118 − 5	1.5141 + 0	2.2763 − 5	8.9749 − 1
5050	5054	320.33	1.6265	9.0895	2.2215	1.5208	2.2736	8.9645
5100	5104	320.12	1.6248	9.0802	2.2313	1.5275	2.2710	8.9541
5150	5154	319.92	1.6231	9.0709	2.2412	1.5342	2.2683	8.9436
5200	5204	319.71	1.6215	9.0616	2.2511	1.5410	2.2657	8.9332
5250	5254	319.51	1.6198	9.0523	2.2610	1.5478	2.2630	8.9228
5300	5304	319.30	1.6181	9.0430	2.2710	1.5547	2.2604	8.9123
5350	5355	319.10	1.6165	9.0337	2.2811	1.5616	2.2577	8.9019
5400	5405	318.90	1.6148	9.0244	2.2912	1.5685	2.2551	8.8915
5450	5455	318.69	1.6131	9.0151	2.3014	1.5755	2.2524	8.8810
5500	5505	318.49	1.6115 − 5	9.0057 − 1	2.3117 − 5	1.5825 + 0	2.2498 − 5	8.8706 − 1
5550	5555	318.28	1.6098	8.9964	2.3220	1.5896	2.2471	8.8601
5600	5605	318.08	1.6081	8.9871	2.3323	1.5967	2.2445	8.8497
5650	5655	317.87	1.6065	8.9777	2.3428	1.6038	2.2418	8.8392
5700	5705	317.66	1.6048	8.9684	2.3532	1.6110	2.2392	8.8288
5750	5755	317.46	1.6031	8.9590	2.3638	1.6182	2.2365	8.8183
5800	5805	317.25	1.6014	8.9497	2.3744	1.6254	2.2339	8.8078
5850	5855	317.05	1.5998	8.9403	2.3850	1.6327	2.2312	8.7974
5900	5905	316.84	1.5981	8.9309	2.3958	1.6401	2.2286	8.7869
5950	5956	316.63	1.5964	8.9216	2.4065	1.6475	2.2259	8.7764
6000	6006	316.43	1.5947 − 5	8.9122 − 1	2.4174 − 5	1.6549 + 0	2.2233 − 5	8.7659 − 1
6050	6056	316.22	1.5931	8.9028	2.4283	1.6623	2.2206	8.7555
6100	6106	316.02	1.5914	8.8934	2.4393	1.6699	2.2179	8.7450
6150	6156	315.81	1.5897	8.8840	2.4503	1.6774	2.2153	8.7345
6200	6206	315.60	1.5880	8.8746	2.4614	1.6850	2.2126	8.7240
6250	6256	315.39	1.5863	8.8652	2.4725	1.6926	2.2100	8.7135
6300	6306	315.19	1.5846	8.8558	2.4838	1.7003	2.2073	8.7030
6350	6356	314.98	1.5830	8.8464	2.4951	1.7081	2.2046	8.6925
6400	6406	314.77	1.5813	8.8370	2.5064	1.7158	2.2020	8.6820
6450	6457	314.57	1.5796	8.8275	2.5178	1.7236	2.1993	8.6715
6500	6507	314.36	1.5779 − 5	8.8181 − 1	2.5293 − 5	1.7315 + 0	2.1966 − 5	8.6610 − 1
6550	6557	314.15	1.5762	8.8086	2.5409	1.7394	2.1940	8.6505
6600	6607	313.94	1.5745	8.7992	2.5525	1.7474	2.1913	8.6399
6650	6657	313.73	1.5728	8.7897	2.5642	1.7554	2.1886	8.6294
6700	6707	313.53	1.5711	8.7803	2.5759	1.7634	2.1860	8.6189
6750	6757	313.32	1.5694	8.7708	2.5878	1.7715	2.1833	8.6084
6800	6807	313.11	1.5677	8.7614	2.5997	1.7797	2.1806	8.5978
6850	6857	312.90	1.5661	8.7519	2.6116	1.7879	2.1779	8.5873
6900	6907	312.69	1.5644	8.7424	2.6237	1.7961	2.1753	8.5768
6950	6958	312.48	1.5627	8.7329	2.6358	1.8044	2.1726	8.5662

Table III
Geometric Altitude, Metric Units

Altitude		Sound speed	Dynamic viscosity		Kinematic viscosity		Thermal conductivity	
Z (m)	H (m)	C_s (m/s)	$(N \cdot \frac{\mu \cdot s}{m^2})$	μ/μ_0	$(m^2 \frac{\eta}{/s})$	η/η_0	$(J/m \cdot \overset{\kappa}{s} \cdot K)$	κ/κ_0
3000	2999	328.58	1.6938 − 5	9.4656 − 1	1.8628 − 5	1.2752 + 0	2.3813 − 5	9.3891 − 1
3050	3049	328.38	1.6921	9.4565	1.8706	1.2806	2.3787	9.3789
3100	3098	328.19	1.6905	9.4475	1.8785	1.2860	2.3761	9.3686
3150	3148	327.99	1.6889	9.4384	1.8864	1.2914	2.3735	9.3583
3200	3198	327.79	1.6873	9.4294	1.8943	1.2968	2.3709	9.3480
3250	3248	327.59	1.6857	9.4203	1.9023	1.3023	2.3683	9.3377
3300	3298	327.39	1.6840	9.4112	1.9104	1.3078	2.3657	9.3274
3350	3348	327.19	1.6824	9.4021	1.9184	1.3133	2.3631	9.3171
3400	3398	326.99	1.6808	9.3930	1.9266	1.3189	2.3604	9.3068
3450	3448	326.79	1.6792	9.3839	1.9347	1.3244	2.3578	9.2965
3500	3498	326.59	1.6775 − 5	9.3748 − 1	1.9429 − 5	1.3301 + 0	2.3552 − 5	9.2862 − 1
3550	3548	326.39	1.6759	9.3657	1.9512	1.3357	2.3526	9.2759
3600	3598	326.19	1.6743	9.3566	1.9595	1.3414	2.3500	9.2656
3650	3648	325.99	1.6726	9.3475	1.9678	1.3471	2.3474	9.2553
3700	3698	325.79	1.6710	9.3384	1.9762	1.3528	2.3448	9.2450
3750	3748	325.59	1.6694	9.3293	1.9846	1.3586	2.3421	9.2347
3800	3798	325.39	1.6677	9.3201	1.9931	1.3644	2.3395	9.2244
3850	3848	325.19	1.6661	9.3110	2.0016	1.3702	2.3369	9.2140
3900	3898	324.99	1.6645	9.3019	2.0102	1.3761	2.3343	9.2037
3950	3948	324.79	1.6628	9.2927	2.0188	1.3820	2.3317	9.1934
4000	3997	324.59	1.6612 − 5	9.2836 − 1	2.0275 − 5	1.3879 + 0	2.3290 − 5	9.1830 − 1
4050	4047	324.39	1.6596	9.2744	2.0362	1.3939	2.3264	9.1727
4100	4097	324.19	1.6579	9.2652	2.0449	1.3999	2.3238	9.1624
4150	4147	323.99	1.6563	9.2561	2.0537	1.4059	2.3212	9.1520
4200	4197	323.78	1.6546	9.2469	2.0626	1.4120	2.3186	9.1417
4250	4247	323.58	1.6530	9.2377	2.0715	1.4181	2.3159	9.1313
4300	4297	323.38	1.6513	9.2285	2.0804	1.4242	2.3133	9.1210
4350	4347	323.18	1.6497	9.2194	2.0894	1.4304	2.3107	9.1106
4400	4397	322.98	1.6481	9.2102	2.0985	1.4365	2.3081	9.1003
4450	4447	322.78	1.6464	9.2010	2.1076	1.4428	2.3054	9.0899
4500	4497	322.57	1.6448 − 5	9.1918 − 1	2.1167 − 5	1.4490 + 0	2.3028 − 5	9.0795 − 1
4550	4547	322.37	1.6431	9.1826	2.1259	1.4553	2.3002	9.0692
4600	4597	322.17	1.6415	9.1733	2.1352	1.4617	2.2975	9.0588
4650	4647	321.97	1.6398	9.1641	2.1445	1.4680	2.2949	9.0484
4700	4697	321.76	1.6382	9.1549	2.1538	1.4744	2.2923	9.0380
4750	4746	321.56	1.6365	9.1457	2.1632	1.4809	2.2896	9.0277
4800	4796	321.36	1.6349	9.1364	2.1727	1.4873	2.2870	9.0173
4850	4846	321.16	1.6332	9.1272	2.1822	1.4938	2.2844	9.0069
4900	4896	320.95	1.6316	9.1180	2.1917	1.5004	2.2817	8.9965
4950	4946	320.75	1.6299	9.1087	2.2013	1.5070	2.2791	8.9861
5000	4996	320.55	1.6282 − 5	9.0995 − 1	2.2110 − 5	1.5136 + 0	2.2765 − 5	8.9757 − 1
5050	5046	320.34	1.6266	9.0902	2.2207	1.5202	2.2738	8.9653
5100	5096	320.14	1.6249	9.0809	2.2305	1.5269	2.2712	8.9549
5150	5146	319.93	1.6233	9.0717	2.2403	1.5337	2.2685	8.9445
5200	5196	319.73	1.6216	9.0624	2.2502	1.5404	2.2659	8.9341
5250	5246	319.53	1.6200	9.0531	2.2602	1.5472	2.2633	8.9237
5300	5296	319.32	1.6183	9.0438	2.2701	1.5541	2.2606	8.9133
5350	5346	319.12	1.6166	9.0345	2.2802	1.5610	2.2580	8.9028
5400	5395	318.91	1.6150	9.0252	2.2903	1.5679	2.2553	8.8924
5450	5445	318.71	1.6133	9.0159	2.3005	1.5748	2.2527	8.8820
5500	5495	318.50	1.6116 − 5	9.0066 − 1	2.3107 − 5	1.5818 + 0	2.2500 − 5	8.8716 − 1
5550	5545	318.30	1.6100	8.9973	2.3210	1.5889	2.2474	8.8611
5600	5595	318.10	1.6083	8.9880	2.3313	1.5960	2.2448	8.8507
5650	5645	317.89	1.6066	8.9787	2.3417	1.6031	2.2421	8.8403
5700	5695	317.69	1.6050	8.9693	2.3522	1.6102	2.2395	8.8298
5750	5745	317.48	1.6033	8.9600	2.3627	1.6174	2.2368	8.8194
5800	5795	317.27	1.6016	8.9507	2.3732	1.6247	2.2342	8.8089
5850	5845	317.07	1.6000	8.9413	2.3839	1.6319	2.2315	8.7985
5900	5895	316.86	1.5983	8.9320	2.3946	1.6393	2.2289	8.7880
5950	5944	316.66	1.5966	8.9226	2.4053	1.6466	2.2262	8.7776
6000	5994	316.45	1.5949 − 5	8.9133 − 1	2.4161 − 5	1.6540 + 0	2.2236 − 5	8.7671 − 1
6050	6044	316.25	1.5933	8.9039	2.4270	1.6615	2.2209	8.7567
6100	6094	316.04	1.5916	8.8945	2.4380	1.6690	2.2183	8.7462
6150	6144	315.83	1.5899	8.8851	2.4490	1.6765	2.2156	8.7357
6200	6194	315.63	1.5882	8.8758	2.4600	1.6841	2.2129	8.7253
6250	6244	315.42	1.5865	8.8664	2.4712	1.6917	2.2103	8.7148
6300	6294	315.21	1.5849	8.8570	2.4824	1.6994	2.2076	8.7043
6350	6344	315.01	1.5832	8.8476	2.4936	1.7071	2.2050	8.6938
6400	6394	314.80	1.5815	8.8382	2.5049	1.7148	2.2023	8.6833
6450	6443	314.59	1.5798	8.8288	2.5163	1.7226	2.1996	8.6729
6500	6493	314.39	1.5781 − 5	8.8193 − 1	2.5278 − 5	1.7305 + 0	2.1970 − 5	8.6624 − 1
6550	6543	314.18	1.5764	8.8099	2.5393	1.7383	2.1943	8.6519
6600	6593	313.97	1.5748	8.8005	2.5509	1.7463	2.1917	8.6414
6650	6643	313.76	1.5731	8.7911	2.5626	1.7543	2.1890	8.6309
6700	6693	313.56	1.5714	8.7816	2.5743	1.7623	2.1863	8.6204
6750	6743	313.35	1.5697	8.7722	2.5861	1.7704	2.1837	8.6099
6800	6793	313.14	1.5680	8.7627	2.5979	1.7785	2.1810	8.5994
6850	6843	312.93	1.5663	8.7533	2.6099	1.7866	2.1783	8.5888
6900	6893	312.72	1.5646	8.7438	2.6218	1.7949	2.1757	8.5783
6950	6942	312.51	1.5629	8.7344	2.6339	1.8031	2.1730	8.5678

Table III
Geopotential Altitude, Metric Units

Altitude		Sound speed	Dynamic viscosity		Kinematic viscosity		Thermal conductivity	
H(m)	Z(m)	C_s(m/s)	μ (N·s/m²)	μ/μ_0	η (m²/s)	η/η_0	κ (J/m·s·K)	κ/κ_0
7000	7008	312.27	1.5610 − 5	8.7234 − 1	2.6479 − 5	1.8127 + 0	2.1699 − 5	8.5557 − 1
7050	7058	312.06	1.5593	8.7139	2.6602	1.8211	2.1673	8.5451
7100	7108	311.85	1.5576	8.7044	2.6725	1.8295	2.1646	8.5346
7150	7158	311.65	1.5559	8.6949	2.6849	1.8380	2.1619	8.5240
7200	7208	311.44	1.5542	8.6854	2.6974	1.8465	2.1592	8.5135
7250	7258	311.23	1.5525	8.6759	2.7099	1.8551	2.1565	8.5029
7300	7308	311.02	1.5507	8.6663	2.7225	1.8638	2.1539	8.4923
7350	7359	310.81	1.5490	8.6568	2.7352	1.8725	2.1512	8.4818
7400	7409	310.60	1.5473	8.6473	2.7480	1.8812	2.1485	8.4712
7450	7459	310.39	1.5456	8.6377	2.7608	1.8900	2.1458	8.4606
7500	7509	310.18	1.5439 − 5	8.6282 − 1	2.7737 − 5	1.8988 + 0	2.1431 − 5	8.4500 − 1
7550	7559	309.96	1.5422	8.6186	2.7867	1.9077	2.1405	8.4395
7600	7609	309.75	1.5405	8.6091	2.7998	1.9167	2.1378	8.4289
7650	7659	309.54	1.5388	8.5995	2.8129	1.9257	2.1351	8.4183
7700	7709	309.33	1.5371	8.5899	2.8262	1.9347	2.1324	8.4077
7750	7759	309.12	1.5354	8.5803	2.8395	1.9438	2.1297	8.3971
7800	7810	308.91	1.5336	8.5707	2.8528	1.9530	2.1270	8.3865
7850	7860	308.70	1.5319	8.5612	2.8663	1.9622	2.1243	8.3759
7900	7910	308.49	1.5302	8.5516	2.8799	1.9715	2.1216	8.3653
7950	7960	308.27	1.5285	8.5420	2.8935	1.9808	2.1190	8.3547
8000	8010	308.06	1.5268 − 5	8.5323 − 1	2.9072 − 5	1.9902 + 0	2.1163 − 5	8.3441 − 1
8050	8060	307.85	1.5250	8.5227	2.9210	1.9997	2.1136	8.3335
8100	8110	307.64	1.5233	8.5131	2.9349	2.0092	2.1109	8.3228
8150	8160	307.43	1.5216	8.5035	2.9488	2.0187	2.1082	8.3122
8200	8211	307.21	1.5199	8.4938	2.9629	2.0283	2.1055	8.3016
8250	8261	307.00	1.5182	8.4842	2.9770	2.0380	2.1028	8.2910
8300	8311	306.79	1.5164	8.4746	2.9912	2.0477	2.1001	8.2803
8350	8361	306.58	1.5147	8.4649	3.0055	2.0575	2.0974	8.2697
8400	8411	306.36	1.5130	8.4553	3.0199	2.0674	2.0947	8.2591
8450	8461	306.15	1.5112	8.4456	3.0344	2.0773	2.0920	8.2484
8500	8511	305.94	1.5095 − 5	8.4359 − 1	3.0490 − 5	2.0873 + 0	2.0893 − 5	8.2378 − 1
8550	8562	305.72	1.5078	8.4263	3.0636	2.0973	2.0866	8.2271
8600	8612	305.51	1.5061	8.4166	3.0784	2.1074	2.0839	8.2165
8650	8662	305.29	1.5043	8.4069	3.0932	2.1175	2.0812	8.2058
8700	8712	305.08	1.5026	8.3972	3.1081	2.1278	2.0785	8.1952
8750	8762	304.87	1.5009	8.3875	3.1232	2.1381	2.0758	8.1845
8800	8812	304.65	1.4991	8.3778	3.1383	2.1484	2.0731	8.1738
8850	8862	304.44	1.4974	8.3681	3.1535	2.1588	2.0704	8.1632
8900	8912	304.22	1.4956	8.3584	3.1688	2.1693	2.0677	8.1525
8950	8963	304.01	1.4939	8.3486	3.1842	2.1798	2.0650	8.1418
9000	9013	303.79	1.4922 − 5	8.3389 − 1	3.1997 − 5	2.1904 + 0	2.0623 − 5	8.1312 − 1
9050	9063	303.58	1.4904	8.3292	3.2152	2.2011	2.0596	8.1205
9100	9113	303.36	1.4887	8.3194	3.2309	2.2118	2.0568	8.1098
9150	9163	303.15	1.4869	8.3097	3.2467	2.2226	2.0541	8.0991
9200	9213	302.93	1.4852	8.2999	3.2626	2.2335	2.0514	8.0884
9250	9263	302.72	1.4834	8.2902	3.2786	2.2444	2.0487	8.0777
9300	9314	302.50	1.4817	8.2804	3.2946	2.2554	2.0460	8.0670
9350	9364	302.28	1.4799	8.2706	3.3108	2.2665	2.0433	8.0563
9400	9414	302.07	1.4782	8.2609	3.3271	2.2777	2.0406	8.0456
9450	9464	301.85	1.4764	8.2511	3.3435	2.2889	2.0379	8.0349
9500	9514	301.64	1.4747 − 5	8.2413 − 1	3.3600 − 5	2.3002 + 0	2.0351 − 5	8.0242 − 1
9550	9564	301.42	1.4729	8.2315	3.3765	2.3115	2.0324	8.0135
9600	9615	301.20	1.4712	8.2217	3.3932	2.3229	2.0297	8.0028
9650	9665	300.99	1.4694	8.2119	3.4100	2.3344	2.0270	7.9921
9700	9715	300.77	1.4677	8.2021	3.4269	2.3460	2.0243	7.9813
9750	9765	300.55	1.4659	8.1922	3.4439	2.3577	2.0215	7.9706
9800	9815	300.33	1.4642	8.1824	3.4611	2.3694	2.0188	7.9599
9850	9865	300.12	1.4624	8.1726	3.4783	2.3812	2.0161	7.9492
9900	9915	299.90	1.4606	8.1627	3.4956	2.3930	2.0134	7.9384
9950	9966	299.68	1.4589	8.1529	3.5131	2.4050	2.0107	7.9277
10000	10016	299.46	1.4571 − 5	8.1430 − 1	3.5306 − 5	2.4170 + 0	2.0079 − 5	7.9169 − 1
10050	10066	299.25	1.4553	8.1332	3.5483	2.4291	2.0052	7.9062
10100	10116	299.03	1.4536	8.1233	3.5661	2.4413	2.0025	7.8954
10150	10166	298.81	1.4518	8.1134	3.5840	2.4535	1.9998	7.8847
10200	10216	298.59	1.4500	8.1036	3.6020	2.4658	1.9970	7.8739
10250	10267	298.37	1.4483	8.0937	3.6201	2.4782	1.9943	7.8632
10300	10317	298.15	1.4465	8.0838	3.6383	2.4907	1.9916	7.8524
10350	10367	297.93	1.4447	8.0739	3.6567	2.5033	1.9888	7.8417
10400	10417	297.71	1.4430	8.0640	3.6752	2.5159	1.9861	7.8309
10450	10467	297.49	1.4412	8.0541	3.6938	2.5287	1.9834	7.8201
10500	10517	297.27	1.4394 − 5	8.0442 − 1	3.7125 − 5	2.5415 + 0	1.9806 − 5	7.8093 − 1
10550	10568	297.05	1.4376	8.0343	3.7313	2.5544	1.9779	7.7986
10600	10618	296.83	1.4359	8.0243	3.7503	2.5674	1.9752	7.7878
10650	10668	296.61	1.4341	8.0144	3.7693	2.5804	1.9724	7.7770
10700	10718	296.39	1.4323	8.0045	3.7885	2.5936	1.9697	7.7662
10750	10768	296.17	1.4305	7.9945	3.8079	2.6068	1.9670	7.7554
10800	10818	295.95	1.4287	7.9846	3.8273	2.6201	1.9642	7.7446
10850	10869	295.73	1.4270	7.9746	3.8469	2.6335	1.9615	7.7338
10900	10919	295.51	1.4252	7.9646	3.8666	2.6470	1.9587	7.7230
10950	10969	295.29	1.4234	7.9547	3.8864	2.6606	1.9560	7.7122

Table III
Geometric Altitude, Metric Units

Altitude		Sound speed	Dynamic viscosity		Kinematic viscosity		Thermal conductivity	
Z (m)	H (m)	C_s (m/s)	$(N \cdot s/m^2)$ μ	μ/μ_0	(m^2/s) η	η/η_0	$(J/m \cdot s \cdot K)$ κ	κ/κ_0
7000	6992	312.31	1.5612 − 5	8.7249 − 1	2.6461 − 5	1.8114 + 0	2.1703 − 5	8.5573 − 1
7050	7042	312.10	1.5595	8.7154	2.6583	1.8198	2.1677	8.5468
7100	7092	311.89	1.5578	8.7059	2.6705	1.8282	2.1650	8.5362
7150	7142	311.68	1.5561	8.6964	2.6829	1.8366	2.1623	8.5257
7200	7192	311.47	1.5544	8.6869	2.6953	1.8452	2.1597	8.5152
7250	7242	311.26	1.5527	8.6774	2.7078	1.8537	2.1570	8.5046
7300	7292	311.05	1.5510	8.6679	2.7204	1.8623	2.1543	8.4941
7350	7342	310.84	1.5493	8.6584	2.7330	1.8710	2.1516	8.4836
7400	7391	310.63	1.5476	8.6489	2.7458	1.8797	2.1490	8.4730
7450	7441	310.42	1.5459	8.6394	2.7586	1.8884	2.1463	8.4625
7500	7491	310.21	1.5442 − 5	8.6299 − 1	2.7714 − 5	1.8973 + 0	2.1436 − 5	8.4519 − 1
7550	7541	310.00	1.5425	8.6203	2.7844	1.9061	2.1409	8.4413
7600	7591	309.79	1.5408	8.6108	2.7974	1.9150	2.1383	8.4308
7650	7641	309.58	1.5391	8.6012	2.8105	1.9240	2.1356	8.4202
7700	7691	309.37	1.5374	8.5917	2.8237	1.9330	2.1329	8.4097
7750	7741	309.16	1.5357	8.5821	2.8369	1.9421	2.1302	8.3991
7800	7790	308.95	1.5340	8.5726	2.8503	1.9512	2.1275	8.3885
7850	7840	308.74	1.5323	8.5630	2.8637	1.9604	2.1249	8.3779
7900	7890	308.53	1.5305	8.5534	2.8772	1.9697	2.1222	8.3674
7950	7940	308.32	1.5288	8.5439	2.8908	1.9790	2.1195	8.3568
8000	7990	308.11	1.5271 − 5	8.5343 − 1	2.9044 − 5	1.9883 + 0	2.1168 − 5	8.3462 − 1
8050	8040	307.89	1.5254	8.5247	2.9182	1.9977	2.1141	8.3356
8100	8090	307.68	1.5237	8.5151	2.9320	2.0072	2.1114	8.3250
8150	8140	307.47	1.5220	8.5055	2.9459	2.0167	2.1087	8.3144
8200	8189	307.26	1.5202	8.4959	2.9599	2.0263	2.1061	8.3038
8250	8239	307.05	1.5185	8.4863	2.9740	2.0359	2.1034	8.2932
8300	8289	306.83	1.5168	8.4767	2.9881	2.0456	2.1007	8.2826
8350	8339	306.62	1.5151	8.4670	3.0024	2.0554	2.0980	8.2720
8400	8389	306.41	1.5134	8.4574	3.0167	2.0652	2.0953	8.2614
8450	8439	306.20	1.5116	8.4478	3.0312	2.0751	2.0926	8.2508
8500	8489	305.98	1.5099 − 5	8.4381 − 1	3.0457 − 5	2.0850 + 0	2.0899 − 5	8.2402 − 1
8550	8539	305.77	1.5082	8.4285	3.0603	2.0950	2.0872	8.2296
8600	8588	305.56	1.5065	8.4188	3.0749	2.1050	2.0845	8.2190
8650	8638	305.34	1.5047	8.4092	3.0897	2.1152	2.0818	8.2083
8700	8688	305.13	1.5030	8.3995	3.1046	2.1253	2.0791	8.1977
8750	8738	304.92	1.5013	8.3898	3.1195	2.1356	2.0764	8.1871
8800	8788	304.70	1.4995	8.3801	3.1346	2.1459	2.0737	8.1764
8850	8838	304.49	1.4978	8.3705	3.1497	2.1562	2.0711	8.1658
8900	8888	304.28	1.4961	8.3608	3.1650	2.1667	2.0684	8.1552
8950	8937	304.06	1.4943	8.3511	3.1803	2.1772	2.0657	8.1445
9000	8987	303.85	1.4926 − 5	8.3414 − 1	3.1957 − 5	2.1877 + 0	2.0630 − 5	8.1339 − 1
9050	9037	303.63	1.4909	8.3317	3.2112	2.1983	2.0603	8.1232
9100	9087	303.42	1.4891	8.3220	3.2268	2.2090	2.0576	8.1126
9150	9137	303.20	1.4874	8.3122	3.2425	2.2198	2.0548	8.1019
9200	9187	302.99	1.4856	8.3025	3.2584	2.2306	2.0521	8.0913
9250	9237	302.77	1.4839	8.2928	3.2743	2.2415	2.0494	8.0806
9300	9286	302.56	1.4822	8.2831	3.2903	2.2524	2.0467	8.0699
9350	9336	302.34	1.4804	8.2733	3.3064	2.2635	2.0440	8.0593
9400	9386	302.13	1.4787	8.2636	3.3226	2.2746	2.0413	8.0486
9450	9436	301.91	1.4769	8.2538	3.3389	2.2857	2.0386	8.0379
9500	9486	301.70	1.4752 − 5	8.2441 − 1	3.3553 − 5	2.2970 + 0	2.0359 − 5	8.0273 − 1
9550	9536	301.48	1.4734	8.2343	3.3718	2.3083	2.0332	8.0166
9600	9586	301.27	1.4717	8.2245	3.3884	2.3196	2.0305	8.0059
9650	9635	301.05	1.4699	8.2147	3.4051	2.3311	2.0278	7.9952
9700	9685	300.83	1.4682	8.2050	3.4219	2.3426	2.0251	7.9845
9750	9735	300.62	1.4664	8.1952	3.4389	2.3542	2.0224	7.9738
9800	9785	300.40	1.4647	8.1854	3.4559	2.3658	2.0196	7.9631
9850	9835	300.18	1.4629	8.1756	3.4730	2.3776	2.0169	7.9524
9900	9885	299.97	1.4612	8.1658	3.4903	2.3894	2.0142	7.9417
9950	9934	299.75	1.4594	8.1560	3.5076	2.4013	2.0115	7.9310
10000	9984	299.53	1.4577 − 5	8.1461 − 1	3.5251 − 5	2.4132 + 0	2.0088 − 5	7.9203 − 1
10050	10034	299.31	1.4559	8.1363	3.5427	2.4252	2.0061	7.9096
10100	10084	299.10	1.4541	8.1265	3.5604	2.4373	2.0034	7.8989
10150	10134	298.88	1.4524	8.1166	3.5782	2.4495	2.0006	7.8882
10200	10184	298.66	1.4506	8.1068	3.5961	2.4618	1.9979	7.8775
10250	10233	298.44	1.4489	8.0969	3.6141	2.4741	1.9952	7.8667
10300	10283	298.22	1.4471	8.0871	3.6322	2.4866	1.9925	7.8560
10350	10333	298.01	1.4453	8.0772	3.6505	2.4991	1.9898	7.8453
10400	10383	297.79	1.4436	8.0674	3.6689	2.5116	1.9870	7.8345
10450	10433	297.57	1.4418	8.0575	3.6874	2.5243	1.9843	7.8238
10500	10483	297.35	1.4400 − 5	8.0476 − 1	3.7060 − 5	2.5370 + 0	1.9816 − 5	7.8131 − 1
10550	10533	297.13	1.4383	8.0377	3.7247	2.5499	1.9789	7.8023
10600	10582	296.91	1.4365	8.0278	3.7436	2.5628	1.9761	7.7916
10650	10632	296.69	1.4347	8.0179	3.7625	2.5758	1.9734	7.7808
10700	10682	296.47	1.4329	8.0080	3.7816	2.5888	1.9707	7.7701
10750	10732	296.25	1.4312	7.9981	3.8008	2.6020	1.9680	7.7593
10800	10782	296.03	1.4294	7.9882	3.8202	2.6152	1.9652	7.7486
10850	10832	295.81	1.4276	7.9783	3.8396	2.6286	1.9625	7.7378
10900	10881	295.59	1.4258	7.9683	3.8592	2.6420	1.9598	7.7271
10950	10931	295.37	1.4241	7.9584	3.8790	2.6555	1.9570	7.7163

Table III
Geopotential Altitude, Metric Units

Altitude		Sound speed	Dynamic viscosity		Kinematic viscosity		Thermal conductivity	
H (m)	Z (m)	C_s (m/s)	μ (N·s/m²)	μ/μ_0	η (m²/s)	η/η_0	κ (J/m·s·K)	κ/κ_0
11000	11019	295.07	1.4216 − 5	7.9447 − 1	3.9064 − 5	2.6743 + 0	1.9533 − 5	7.7014 − 1
11100	11119	295.07	1.4216	7.9447	3.9685	2.7168	1.9533	7.7014
11200	11220	295.07	1.4216	7.9447	4.0316	2.7599	1.9533	7.7014
11300	11320	295.07	1.4216	7.9447	4.0956	2.8038	1.9533	7.7014
11400	11420	295.07	1.4216	7.9447	4.1607	2.8484	1.9533	7.7014
11500	11521	295.07	1.4216	7.9447	4.2269	2.8936	1.9533	7.7014
11600	11621	295.07	1.4216	7.9447	4.2941	2.9396	1.9533	7.7014
11700	11722	295.07	1.4216	7.9447	4.3623	2.9864	1.9533	7.7014
11800	11822	295.07	1.4216	7.9447	4.4316	3.0338	1.9533	7.7014
11900	11922	295.07	1.4216	7.9447	4.5021	3.0820	1.9533	7.7014
12000	12023	295.07	1.4216 − 5	7.9447 − 1	4.5736 − 5	3.1310 + 0	1.9533 − 5	7.7014 − 1
12100	12123	295.07	1.4216	7.9447	4.6463	3.1808	1.9533	7.7014
12200	12223	295.07	1.4216	7.9447	4.7202	3.2314	1.9533	7.7014
12300	12324	295.07	1.4216	7.9447	4.7952	3.2827	1.9533	7.7014
12400	12424	295.07	1.4216	7.9447	4.8714	3.3349	1.9533	7.7014
12500	12525	295.07	1.4216	7.9447	4.9488	3.3879	1.9533	7.7014
12600	12625	295.07	1.4216	7.9447	5.0275	3.4417	1.9533	7.7014
12700	12725	295.07	1.4216	7.9447	5.1074	3.4964	1.9533	7.7014
12800	12826	295.07	1.4216	7.9447	5.1886	3.5520	1.9533	7.7014
12900	12926	295.07	1.4216	7.9447	5.2710	3.6085	1.9533	7.7014
13000	13027	295.07	1.4216 − 5	7.9447 − 1	5.3548 − 5	3.6658 + 0	1.9533 − 5	7.7014 − 1
13100	13127	295.07	1.4216	7.9447	5.4399	3.7241	1.9533	7.7014
13200	13227	295.07	1.4216	7.9447	5.5264	3.7833	1.9533	7.7014
13300	13328	295.07	1.4216	7.9447	5.6142	3.8434	1.9533	7.7014
13400	13428	295.07	1.4216	7.9447	5.7034	3.9045	1.9533	7.7014
13500	13529	295.07	1.4216	7.9447	5.7941	3.9666	1.9533	7.7014
13600	13629	295.07	1.4216	7.9447	5.8862	4.0296	1.9533	7.7014
13700	13730	295.07	1.4216	7.9447	5.9797	4.0937	1.9533	7.7014
13800	13830	295.07	1.4216	7.9447	6.0748	4.1587	1.9533	7.7014
13900	13930	295.07	1.4216	7.9447	6.1713	4.2248	1.9533	7.7014
14000	14031	295.07	1.4216 − 5	7.9447 − 1	6.2694 − 5	4.2920 + 0	1.9533 − 5	7.7014 − 1
14100	14131	295.07	1.4216	7.9447	6.3691	4.3602	1.9533	7.7014
14200	14232	295.07	1.4216	7.9447	6.4703	4.4295	1.9533	7.7014
14300	14332	295.07	1.4216	7.9447	6.5731	4.4999	1.9533	7.7014
14400	14433	295.07	1.4216	7.9447	6.6776	4.5714	1.9533	7.7014
14500	14533	295.07	1.4216	7.9447	6.7837	4.6441	1.9533	7.7014
14600	14634	295.07	1.4216	7.9447	6.8916	4.7179	1.9533	7.7014
14700	14734	295.07	1.4216	7.9447	7.0011	4.7929	1.9533	7.7014
14800	14835	295.07	1.4216	7.9447	7.1124	4.8690	1.9533	7.7014
14900	14935	295.07	1.4216	7.9447	7.2254	4.9464	1.9533	7.7014
15000	15035	295.07	1.4216 − 5	7.9447 − 1	7.3402 − 5	5.0250 + 0	1.9533 − 5	7.7014 − 1
15100	15136	295.07	1.4216	7.9447	7.4569	5.1049	1.9533	7.7014
15200	15236	295.07	1.4216	7.9447	7.5754	5.1861	1.9533	7.7014
15300	15337	295.07	1.4216	7.9447	7.6958	5.2685	1.9533	7.7014
15400	15437	295.07	1.4216	7.9447	7.8182	5.3522	1.9533	7.7014
15500	15538	295.07	1.4216	7.9447	7.9424	5.4373	1.9533	7.7014
15600	15638	295.07	1.4216	7.9447	8.0686	5.5237	1.9533	7.7014
15700	15739	295.07	1.4216	7.9447	8.1969	5.6115	1.9533	7.7014
15800	15839	295.07	1.4216	7.9447	8.3272	5.7007	1.9533	7.7014
15900	15940	295.07	1.4216	7.9447	8.4595	5.7913	1.9533	7.7014
16000	16040	295.07	1.4216 − 5	7.9447 − 1	8.5940 − 5	5.8833 + 0	1.9533 − 5	7.7014 − 1
16100	16141	295.07	1.4216	7.9447	8.7306	5.9768	1.9533	7.7014
16200	16241	295.07	1.4216	7.9447	8.8693	6.0718	1.9533	7.7014
16300	16342	295.07	1.4216	7.9447	9.0103	6.1683	1.9533	7.7014
16400	16442	295.07	1.4216	7.9447	9.1535	6.2664	1.9533	7.7014
16500	16543	295.07	1.4216	7.9447	9.2990	6.3660	1.9533	7.7014
16600	16643	295.07	1.4216	7.9447	9.4468	6.4672	1.9533	7.7014
16700	16744	295.07	1.4216	7.9447	9.5969	6.5700	1.9533	7.7014
16800	16845	295.07	1.4216	7.9447	9.7495	6.6744	1.9533	7.7014
16900	16945	295.07	1.4216	7.9447	9.9044	6.7805	1.9533	7.7014
17000	17046	295.07	1.4216 − 5	7.9447 − 1	1.0062 − 4	6.8882 + 0	1.9533 − 5	7.7014 − 1
17100	17146	295.07	1.4216	7.9447	1.0222	6.9977	1.9533	7.7014
17200	17247	295.07	1.4216	7.9447	1.0384	7.1089	1.9533	7.7014
17300	17347	295.07	1.4216	7.9447	1.0549	7.2219	1.9533	7.7014
17400	17448	295.07	1.4216	7.9447	1.0717	7.3367	1.9533	7.7014
17500	17548	295.07	1.4216	7.9447	1.0887	7.4533	1.9533	7.7014
17600	17649	295.07	1.4216	7.9447	1.1060	7.5718	1.9533	7.7014
17700	17749	295.07	1.4216	7.9447	1.1236	7.6921	1.9533	7.7014
17800	17850	295.07	1.4216	7.9447	1.1415	7.8144	1.9533	7.7014
17900	17951	295.07	1.4216	7.9447	1.1596	7.9386	1.9533	7.7014
18000	18051	295.07	1.4216 − 5	7.9447 − 1	1.1780 − 4	8.0648 + 0	1.9533 − 5	7.7014 − 1
18100	18152	295.07	1.4216	7.9447	1.1968	8.1929	1.9533	7.7014
18200	18252	295.07	1.4216	7.9447	1.2158	8.3232	1.9533	7.7014
18300	18353	295.07	1.4216	7.9447	1.2351	8.4554	1.9533	7.7014
18400	18453	295.07	1.4216	7.9447	1.2547	8.5898	1.9533	7.7014
18500	18554	295.07	1.4216	7.9447	1.2747	8.7264	1.9533	7.7014
18600	18655	295.07	1.4216	7.9447	1.2949	8.8651	1.9533	7.7014
18700	18755	295.07	1.4216	7.9447	1.3155	9.0060	1.9533	7.7014
18800	18856	295.07	1.4216	7.9447	1.3364	9.1491	1.9533	7.7014
18900	18956	295.07	1.4216	7.9447	1.3577	9.2945	1.9533	7.7014

Table III
Geometric Altitude, Metric Units

Altitude		Sound speed	Dynamic viscosity		Kinematic viscosity		Thermal conductivity	
Z (m)	H (m)	C_s (m/s)	$(N \cdot \frac{\mu}{s}/m^2)$	μ/μ_0	$(m^2 \frac{\eta}{/s})$	η/η_0	$(J/m \cdot \frac{\kappa}{s} \cdot K)$	κ/κ_0
11000	10981	295.15	1.4223 − 5	7.9485 − 1	3.8988 − 5	2.6691 + 0	1.9543 − 5	7.7055 − 1
11100	11081	295.07	1.4216	7.9447	3.9564	2.7085	1.9533	7.7014
11200	11180	295.07	1.4216	7.9447	4.0191	2.7514	1.9533	7.7014
11300	11280	295.07	1.4216	7.9447	4.0827	2.7950	1.9533	7.7014
11400	11380	295.07	1.4216	7.9447	4.1474	2.8392	1.9533	7.7014
11500	11479	295.07	1.4216	7.9447	4.2131	2.8842	1.9533	7.7014
11600	11579	295.07	1.4216	7.9447	4.2798	2.9299	1.9533	7.7014
11700	11679	295.07	1.4216	7.9447	4.3475	2.9763	1.9533	7.7014
11800	11778	295.07	1.4216	7.9447	4.4164	3.0234	1.9533	7.7014
11900	11878	295.07	1.4216	7.9447	4.4863	3.0713	1.9533	7.7014
12000	11977	295.07	1.4216 − 5	7.9447 − 1	4.5574 − 5	3.1199 + 0	1.9533 − 5	7.7014 − 1
12100	12077	295.07	1.4216	7.9447	4.6295	3.1693	1.9533	7.7014
12200	12177	295.07	1.4216	7.9447	4.7028	3.2195	1.9533	7.7014
12300	12276	295.07	1.4216	7.9447	4.7773	3.2704	1.9533	7.7014
12400	12376	295.07	1.4216	7.9447	4.8529	3.3222	1.9533	7.7014
12500	12475	295.07	1.4216	7.9447	4.9297	3.3748	1.9533	7.7014
12600	12575	295.07	1.4216	7.9447	5.0078	3.4282	1.9533	7.7014
12700	12675	295.07	1.4216	7.9447	5.0870	3.4825	1.9533	7.7014
12800	12774	295.07	1.4216	7.9447	5.1676	3.5376	1.9533	7.7014
12900	12874	295.07	1.4216	7.9447	5.2494	3.5936	1.9533	7.7014
13000	12973	295.07	1.4216 − 5	7.9447 − 1	5.3325 − 5	3.6505 + 0	1.9533 − 5	7.7014 − 1
13100	13073	295.07	1.4216	7.9447	5.4169	3.7083	1.9533	7.7014
13200	13173	295.07	1.4216	7.9447	5.5026	3.7670	1.9533	7.7014
13300	13272	295.07	1.4216	7.9447	5.5897	3.8266	1.9533	7.7014
13400	13372	295.07	1.4216	7.9447	5.6782	3.8872	1.9533	7.7014
13500	13471	295.07	1.4216	7.9447	5.7680	3.9487	1.9533	7.7014
13600	13571	295.07	1.4216	7.9447	5.8593	4.0112	1.9533	7.7014
13700	13671	295.07	1.4216	7.9447	5.9520	4.0747	1.9533	7.7014
13800	13770	295.07	1.4216	7.9447	6.0462	4.1392	1.9533	7.7014
13900	13870	295.07	1.4216	7.9447	6.1419	4.2047	1.9533	7.7014
14000	13969	295.07	1.4216 − 5	7.9447 − 1	6.2391 − 5	4.2712 + 0	1.9533 − 5	7.7014 − 1
14100	14069	295.07	1.4216	7.9447	6.3378	4.3388	1.9533	7.7014
14200	14168	295.07	1.4216	7.9447	6.4381	4.4074	1.9533	7.7014
14300	14268	295.07	1.4216	7.9447	6.5399	4.4772	1.9533	7.7014
14400	14367	295.07	1.4216	7.9447	6.6434	4.5480	1.9533	7.7014
14500	14467	295.07	1.4216	7.9447	6.7485	4.6200	1.9533	7.7014
14600	14567	295.07	1.4216	7.9447	6.8553	4.6930	1.9533	7.7014
14700	14666	295.07	1.4216	7.9447	6.9637	4.7673	1.9533	7.7014
14800	14766	295.07	1.4216	7.9447	7.0739	4.8427	1.9533	7.7014
14900	14865	295.07	1.4216	7.9447	7.1858	4.9193	1.9533	7.7014
15000	14965	295.07	1.4216 − 5	7.9447 − 1	7.2995 − 5	4.9971 + 0	1.9533 − 5	7.7014 − 1
15100	15064	295.07	1.4216	7.9447	7.4150	5.0762	1.9533	7.7014
15200	15164	295.07	1.4216	7.9447	7.5322	5.1565	1.9533	7.7014
15300	15263	295.07	1.4216	7.9447	7.6514	5.2380	1.9533	7.7014
15400	15363	295.07	1.4216	7.9447	7.7724	5.3209	1.9533	7.7014
15500	15462	295.07	1.4216	7.9447	7.8953	5.4051	1.9533	7.7014
15600	15562	295.07	1.4216	7.9447	8.0202	5.4905	1.9533	7.7014
15700	15661	295.07	1.4216	7.9447	8.1470	5.5774	1.9533	7.7014
15800	15761	295.07	1.4216	7.9447	8.2759	5.6656	1.9533	7.7014
15900	15860	295.07	1.4216	7.9447	8.4068	5.7552	1.9533	7.7014
16000	15960	295.07	1.4216 − 5	7.9447 − 1	8.5397 − 5	5.8462 + 0	1.9533 − 5	7.7014 − 1
16100	16059	295.07	1.4216	7.9447	8.6747	5.9386	1.9533	7.7014
16200	16159	295.07	1.4216	7.9447	8.8119	6.0325	1.9533	7.7014
16300	16258	295.07	1.4216	7.9447	8.9512	6.1279	1.9533	7.7014
16400	16358	295.07	1.4216	7.9447	9.0928	6.2248	1.9533	7.7014
16500	16457	295.07	1.4216	7.9447	9.2366	6.3232	1.9533	7.7014
16600	16557	295.07	1.4216	7.9447	9.3826	6.4232	1.9533	7.7014
16700	16656	295.07	1.4216	7.9447	9.5309	6.5248	1.9533	7.7014
16800	16756	295.07	1.4216	7.9447	9.6816	6.6279	1.9533	7.7014
16900	16855	295.07	1.4216	7.9447	9.8347	6.7327	1.9533	7.7014
17000	16955	295.07	1.4216 − 5	7.9447 − 1	9.9901 − 5	6.8392 + 0	1.9533 − 5	7.7014 − 1
17100	17054	295.07	1.4216	7.9447	1.0148 − 4	6.9473	1.9533	7.7014
17200	17154	295.07	1.4216	7.9447	1.0308	7.0571	1.9533	7.7014
17300	17253	295.07	1.4216	7.9447	1.0471	7.1686	1.9533	7.7014
17400	17352	295.07	1.4216	7.9447	1.0637	7.2820	1.9533	7.7014
17500	17452	295.07	1.4216	7.9447	1.0805	7.3971	1.9533	7.7014
17600	17551	295.07	1.4216	7.9447	1.0976	7.5140	1.9533	7.7014
17700	17651	295.07	1.4216	7.9447	1.1149	7.6327	1.9533	7.7014
17800	17750	295.07	1.4216	7.9447	1.1326	7.7534	1.9533	7.7014
17900	17850	295.07	1.4216	7.9447	1.1505	7.8759	1.9533	7.7014
18000	17949	295.07	1.4216 − 5	7.9447 − 1	1.1686 − 4	8.0004 + 0	1.9533 − 5	7.7014 − 1
18100	18049	295.07	1.4216	7.9447	1.1871	8.1268	1.9533	7.7014
18200	18148	295.07	1.4216	7.9447	1.2059	8.2552	1.9533	7.7014
18300	18247	295.07	1.4216	7.9447	1.2249	8.3857	1.9533	7.7014
18400	18347	295.07	1.4216	7.9447	1.2443	8.5182	1.9533	7.7014
18500	18446	295.07	1.4216	7.9447	1.2639	8.6528	1.9533	7.7014
18600	18546	295.07	1.4216	7.9447	1.2839	8.7895	1.9533	7.7014
18700	18645	295.07	1.4216	7.9447	1.3042	8.9284	1.9533	7.7014
18800	18745	295.07	1.4216	7.9447	1.3248	9.0695	1.9533	7.7014
18900	18844	295.07	1.4216	7.9447	1.3457	9.2128	1.9533	7.7014

Table III
Geopotential Altitude, Metric Units

Altitude		Sound speed	Dynamic viscosity		Kinematic viscosity		Thermal conductivity	
H (m)	Z (m)	C_s (m/s)	μ (N·s/m²)	μ/μ_0	η (m²/s)	η/η_0	κ (J/m·s·K)	κ/κ_0
19000	19057	295.07	1.4216 − 5	7.9447 − 1	1.3793 − 4	9.4422 + 0	1.9533 − 5	7.7014 − 1
19100	19158	295.07	1.4216	7.9447	1.4012	9.5923	1.9533	7.7014
19200	19258	295.07	1.4216	7.9447	1.4234	9.7448	1.9533	7.7014
19300	19359	295.07	1.4216	7.9447	1.4461	9.8997	1.9533	7.7014
19400	19459	295.07	1.4216	7.9447	1.4691	1.0057 + 1	1.9533	7.7014
19500	19560	295.07	1.4216	7.9447	1.4924	1.0216	1.9533	7.7014
19600	19661	295.07	1.4216	7.9447	1.5161	1.0379	1.9533	7.7014
19700	19761	295.07	1.4216	7.9447	1.5402	1.0544	1.9533	7.7014
19800	19862	295.07	1.4216	7.9447	1.5647	1.0711	1.9533	7.7014
19900	19962	295.07	1.4216	7.9447	1.5896	1.0882	1.9533	7.7014
20000	20063	295.07	1.4216 − 5	7.9447 − 1	1.6148 − 4	1.1055 + 1	1.9533 − 5	7.7014 − 1
20100	20164	295.14	1.4222	7.9477	1.6419	1.1240	1.9541	7.7047
20200	20264	295.21	1.4227	7.9508	1.6694	1.1428	1.9550	7.7081
20300	20365	295.27	1.4233	7.9539	1.6973	1.1619	1.9558	7.7114
20400	20466	295.34	1.4238	7.9570	1.7257	1.1814	1.9566	7.7147
20500	20566	295.41	1.4244	7.9600	1.7546	1.2011	1.9575	7.7180
20600	20667	295.48	1.4249	7.9631	1.7839	1.2212	1.9583	7.7214
20700	20768	295.55	1.4255	7.9662	1.8137	1.2416	1.9592	7.7247
20800	20868	295.61	1.4260	7.9692	1.8440	1.2623	1.9600	7.7280
20900	20969	295.68	1.4266	7.9723	1.8747	1.2834	1.9609	7.7313
21000	21070	295.75	1.4271 − 5	7.9754 − 1	1.9060 − 4	1.3048 + 1	1.9617 − 5	7.7347 − 1
21100	21170	295.82	1.4277	7.9784	1.9378	1.3266	1.9625	7.7380
21200	21271	295.89	1.4282	7.9815	1.9701	1.3487	1.9634	7.7413
21300	21372	295.95	1.4287	7.9846	2.0029	1.3711	1.9642	7.7446
21400	21472	296.02	1.4293	7.9876	2.0363	1.3940	1.9651	7.7479
21500	21573	296.09	1.4298	7.9907	2.0701	1.4172	1.9659	7.7513
21600	21674	296.16	1.4304	7.9937	2.1046	1.4407	1.9668	7.7546
21700	21774	296.22	1.4309	7.9968	2.1396	1.4647	1.9676	7.7579
21800	21875	296.29	1.4315	7.9999	2.1751	1.4890	1.9684	7.7612
21900	21976	296.36	1.4320	8.0029	2.2113	1.5138	1.9693	7.7645
22000	22076	296.43	1.4326 − 5	8.0060 − 1	2.2480 − 4	1.5389 + 1	1.9701 − 5	7.7679 − 1
22100	22177	296.50	1.4331	8.0090	2.2853	1.5645	1.9710	7.7712
22200	22278	296.56	1.4337	8.0121	2.3232	1.5904	1.9718	7.7745
22300	22379	296.63	1.4342	8.0152	2.3617	1.6168	1.9726	7.7778
22400	22479	296.70	1.4348	8.0182	2.4009	1.6436	1.9735	7.7811
22500	22580	296.77	1.4353	8.0213	2.4406	1.6708	1.9743	7.7845
22600	22681	296.83	1.4359	8.0243	2.4811	1.6985	1.9752	7.7878
22700	22781	296.90	1.4364	8.0274	2.5221	1.7266	1.9760	7.7911
22800	22882	296.97	1.4370	8.0304	2.5638	1.7551	1.9769	7.7944
22900	22983	297.04	1.4375	8.0335	2.6062	1.7842	1.9777	7.7977
23000	23084	297.11	1.4381 − 5	8.0365 − 1	2.6493 − 4	1.8137 + 1	1.9785 − 5	7.8010 − 1
23100	23184	297.17	1.4386	8.0396	2.6931	1.8436	1.9794	7.8044
23200	23285	297.24	1.4391	8.0426	2.7375	1.8741	1.9802	7.8077
23300	23386	297.31	1.4397	8.0457	2.7827	1.9050	1.9811	7.8110
23400	23486	297.38	1.4402	8.0488	2.8286	1.9364	1.9819	7.8143
23500	23587	297.44	1.4408	8.0518	2.8753	1.9683	1.9827	7.8176
23600	23688	297.51	1.4413	8.0549	2.9227	2.0008	1.9836	7.8209
23700	23789	297.58	1.4419	8.0579	2.9708	2.0338	1.9844	7.8243
23800	23889	297.65	1.4424	8.0609	3.0197	2.0672	1.9853	7.8276
23900	23990	297.71	1.4430	8.0640	3.0694	2.1013	1.9861	7.8309
24000	24091	297.78	1.4435 − 5	8.0670 − 1	3.1199 − 4	2.1358 + 1	1.9869 − 5	7.8342 − 1
24100	24192	297.85	1.4441	8.0701	3.1712	2.1710	1.9878	7.8375
24200	24292	297.92	1.4446	8.0731	3.2234	2.2066	1.9886	7.8408
24300	24393	297.98	1.4451	8.0762	3.2763	2.2429	1.9895	7.8441
24400	24494	298.05	1.4457	8.0792	3.3301	2.2797	1.9903	7.8474
24500	24595	298.12	1.4462	8.0823	3.3848	2.3172	1.9911	7.8508
24600	24696	298.19	1.4468	8.0853	3.4403	2.3552	1.9920	7.8541
24700	24796	298.25	1.4473	8.0884	3.4967	2.3938	1.9928	7.8574
24800	24897	298.32	1.4479	8.0914	3.5540	2.4330	1.9937	7.8607
24900	24998	298.39	1.4484	8.0944	3.6123	2.4729	1.9945	7.8640
25000	25099	298.45	1.4490 − 5	8.0975 − 1	3.6714 − 4	2.5134 + 1	1.9953 − 5	7.8673 − 1
25100	25200	298.52	1.4495	8.1005	3.7315	2.5545	1.9962	7.8706
25200	25300	298.59	1.4500	8.1036	3.7926	2.5963	1.9970	7.8739
25300	25401	298.66	1.4506	8.1066	3.8546	2.6388	1.9979	7.8772
25400	25502	298.72	1.4511	8.1096	3.9176	2.6819	1.9987	7.8806
25500	25603	298.79	1.4517	8.1127	3.9816	2.7257	1.9995	7.8839
25600	25704	298.86	1.4522	8.1157	4.0466	2.7703	2.0004	7.8872
25700	25804	298.93	1.4528	8.1188	4.1127	2.8155	2.0012	7.8905
25800	25905	298.99	1.4533	8.1218	4.1798	2.8614	2.0021	7.8938
25900	26006	299.06	1.4539	8.1248	4.2480	2.9081	2.0029	7.8971
26000	26107	299.13	1.4544 − 5	8.1279 − 1	4.3172 − 4	2.9555 + 1	2.0037 − 5	7.9004 − 1
26100	26208	299.19	1.4549	8.1309	4.3876	3.0037	2.0046	7.9037
26200	26308	299.26	1.4555	8.1339	4.4590	3.0526	2.0054	7.9070
26300	26409	299.33	1.4560	8.1370	4.5316	3.1023	2.0063	7.9103
26400	26510	299.40	1.4566	8.1400	4.6054	3.1527	2.0071	7.9136
26500	26611	299.46	1.4571	8.1430	4.6803	3.2040	2.0079	7.9169
26600	26712	299.53	1.4577	8.1461	4.7563	3.2561	2.0088	7.9202
26700	26813	299.60	1.4582	8.1491	4.8336	3.3090	2.0096	7.9235
26800	26913	299.66	1.4587	8.1521	4.9121	3.3628	2.0104	7.9269
26900	27014	299.73	1.4593	8.1552	4.9919	3.4174	2.0113	7.9302

Table III
Geometric Altitude, Metric Units

Altitude		Sound speed	Dynamic viscosity		Kinematic viscosity		Thermal conductivity	
Z (m)	H (m)	C_s (m/s)	μ (N·s/m²)	μ/μ_0	η (m²/s)	η/η_0	κ (J/m·s·K)	κ/κ_0
19000	18943	295.07	1.4216 − 5	7.9447 − 1	1.3670 − 4	9.3583 + 0	1.9533 − 5	7.7014 − 1
19100	19043	295.07	1.4216	7.9447	1.3886	9.5061	1.9533	7.7014
19200	19142	295.07	1.4216	7.9447	1.4105	9.6563	1.9533	7.7014
19300	19242	295.07	1.4216	7.9447	1.4328	9.8089	1.9533	7.7014
19400	19341	295.07	1.4216	7.9447	1.4554	9.9638	1.9533	7.7014
19500	19440	295.07	1.4216	7.9447	1.4784	1.0121 + 1	1.9533	7.7014
19600	19540	295.07	1.4216	7.9447	1.5018	1.0281	1.9533	7.7014
19700	19639	295.07	1.4216	7.9447	1.5255	1.0443	1.9533	7.7014
19800	19739	295.07	1.4216	7.9447	1.5496	1.0608	1.9533	7.7014
19900	19838	295.07	1.4216	7.9447	1.5741	1.0776	1.9533	7.7014
20000	19937	295.07	1.4216 − 5	7.9447 − 1	1.5989 − 4	1.0946 + 1	1.9533 − 5	7.7014 − 1
20100	20037	295.09	1.4218	7.9458	1.6247	1.1122	1.9536	7.7026
20200	20136	295.16	1.4224	7.9488	1.6517	1.1307	1.9544	7.7059
20300	20235	295.23	1.4229	7.9519	1.6792	1.1495	1.9553	7.7092
20400	20335	295.30	1.4235	7.9550	1.7071	1.1686	1.9561	7.7125
20500	20434	295.36	1.4240	7.9580	1.7355	1.1881	1.9569	7.7158
20600	20533	295.43	1.4245	7.9610	1.7643	1.2078	1.9578	7.7191
20700	20633	295.50	1.4251	7.9641	1.7936	1.2278	1.9586	7.7224
20800	20732	295.57	1.4256	7.9671	1.8234	1.2482	1.9594	7.7258
20900	20832	295.64	1.4262	7.9702	1.8536	1.2689	1.9603	7.7291
21000	20931	295.70	1.4267 − 5	7.9732 − 1	1.8843 − 4	1.2900 + 1	1.9611 − 5	7.7324 − 1
21100	21030	295.77	1.4273	7.9763	1.9156	1.3113	1.9620	7.7357
21200	21130	295.84	1.4278	7.9793	1.9473	1.3330	1.9628	7.7390
21300	21229	295.91	1.4284	7.9824	1.9795	1.3551	1.9636	7.7423
21400	21328	295.97	1.4289	7.9854	2.0123	1.3775	1.9645	7.7456
21500	21428	296.04	1.4294	7.9885	2.0455	1.4003	1.9653	7.7489
21600	21527	296.11	1.4300	7.9915	2.0793	1.4235	1.9661	7.7522
21700	21626	296.17	1.4305	7.9945	2.1137	1.4470	1.9670	7.7555
21800	21725	296.24	1.4311	7.9976	2.1486	1.4709	1.9678	7.7587
21900	21825	296.31	1.4316	8.0006	2.1840	1.4951	1.9686	7.7620
22000	21924	296.38	1.4322 − 5	8.0037 − 1	2.2201 − 4	1.5198 + 1	1.9695 − 5	7.7653 − 1
22100	22023	296.44	1.4327	8.0067	2.2567	1.5449	1.9703	7.7686
22200	22123	296.51	1.4333	8.0097	2.2939	1.5703	1.9712	7.7719
22300	22222	296.58	1.4338	8.0128	2.3316	1.5962	1.9720	7.7752
22400	22321	296.65	1.4343	8.0158	2.3700	1.6225	1.9728	7.7785
22500	22421	296.71	1.4349	8.0188	2.4090	1.6492	1.9737	7.7818
22600	22520	296.78	1.4354	8.0219	2.4486	1.6763	1.9745	7.7851
22700	22619	296.85	1.4360	8.0249	2.4889	1.7038	1.9753	7.7884
22800	22719	296.91	1.4365	8.0279	2.5298	1.7318	1.9762	7.7917
22900	22818	296.98	1.4371	8.0310	2.5713	1.7603	1.9770	7.7950
23000	22917	297.05	1.4376 − 5	8.0340 − 1	2.6135 − 4	1.7892 + 1	1.9778 − 5	7.7983 − 1
23100	23016	297.12	1.4381	8.0370	2.6564	1.8185	1.9787	7.8016
23200	23116	297.18	1.4387	8.0401	2.7000	1.8483	1.9795	7.8049
23300	23215	297.25	1.4392	8.0431	2.7442	1.8786	1.9803	7.8082
23400	23314	297.32	1.4398	8.0461	2.7892	1.9094	1.9812	7.8115
23500	23413	297.38	1.4403	8.0492	2.8349	1.9407	1.9820	7.8148
23600	23513	297.45	1.4409	8.0522	2.8813	1.9724	1.9829	7.8180
23700	23612	297.52	1.4414	8.0552	2.9284	2.0047	1.9837	7.8213
23800	23711	297.59	1.4419	8.0582	2.9763	2.0375	1.9845	7.8246
23900	23810	297.65	1.4425	8.0613	3.0249	2.0708	1.9854	7.8279
24000	23910	297.72	1.4430 − 5	8.0643 − 1	3.0743 − 4	2.1046 + 1	1.9862 − 5	7.8312 − 1
24100	24009	297.79	1.4436	8.0673	3.1245	2.1390	1.9870	7.8345
24200	24108	297.85	1.4441	8.0703	3.1755	2.1739	1.9879	7.8378
24300	24207	297.92	1.4446	8.0734	3.2273	2.2093	1.9887	7.8411
24400	24307	297.99	1.4452	8.0764	3.2799	2.2453	1.9895	7.8444
24500	24406	298.05	1.4457	8.0794	3.3333	2.2819	1.9904	7.8476
24600	24505	298.12	1.4463	8.0824	3.3876	2.3191	1.9912	7.8509
24700	24604	298.19	1.4468	8.0855	3.4428	2.3569	1.9920	7.8542
24800	24704	298.26	1.4473	8.0885	3.4988	2.3952	1.9929	7.8575
24900	24803	298.32	1.4479	8.0915	3.5557	2.4342	1.9937	7.8608
25000	24902	298.39	1.4484 − 5	8.0945 − 1	3.6135 − 4	2.4737 + 1	1.9945 − 5	7.8641 − 1
25001	25001	298.46	1.4490	8.0975	3.6722	2.5139	1.9954	7.8674
25200	25100	298.52	1.4495	8.1005	3.7318	2.5547	1.9962	7.8706
25300	25200	298.59	1.4500	8.1036	3.7924	2.5962	1.9970	7.8739
25400	25299	298.66	1.4506	8.1066	3.8539	2.6383	1.9979	7.8772
25500	25398	298.72	1.4511	8.1096	3.9164	2.6811	1.9987	7.8805
25600	25497	298.79	1.4517	8.1126	3.9799	2.7246	1.9995	7.8838
25700	25597	298.86	1.4522	8.1156	4.0444	2.7687	2.0004	7.8871
25800	25696	298.92	1.4527	8.1186	4.1098	2.8135	2.0012	7.8903
25900	25795	298.99	1.4533	8.1216	4.1763	2.8591	2.0020	7.8936
26000	25894	299.06	1.4538 − 5	8.1247 − 1	4.2439 − 4	2.9053 + 1	2.0029 − 5	7.8969 − 1
26100	25993	299.12	1.4544	8.1277	4.3125	2.9523	2.0037	7.9002
26200	26092	299.19	1.4549	8.1307	4.3822	3.0000	2.0045	7.9035
26300	26192	299.26	1.4554	8.1337	4.4530	3.0484	2.0053	7.9067
26400	26291	299.32	1.4560	8.1367	4.5249	3.0977	2.0062	7.9100
26500	26390	299.39	1.4565	8.1397	4.5979	3.1477	2.0070	7.9133
26600	26489	299.46	1.4570	8.1427	4.6721	3.1984	2.0078	7.9166
26700	26588	299.52	1.4576	8.1457	4.7474	3.2500	2.0087	7.9199
26800	26687	299.59	1.4581	8.1487	4.8239	3.3024	2.0095	7.9231
26900	26787	299.66	1.4587	8.1517	4.9016	3.3555	2.0103	7.9264

Table III
Geopotential Altitude, Metric Units

Altitude		Sound speed	Dynamic viscosity		Kinematic viscosity		Thermal conductivity	
H (m)	Z (m)	C_s (m/s)	μ (N·s/m²)	μ/μ_0	η (m²/s)	η/η_0	κ (J/m·s·K)	κ/κ_0
27000	27115	299.80	1.4598 − 5	8.1582 − 1	5.0729 − 4	3.4728 + 1	2.0121 − 5	7.9335 − 1
27100	27216	299.87	1.4604	8.1612	5.1552	3.5292	2.0130	7.9368
27200	27317	299.93	1.4609	8.1643	5.2388	3.5864	2.0138	7.9401
27300	27418	300.00	1.4614	8.1673	5.3237	3.6445	2.0146	7.9434
27400	27519	300.07	1.4620	8.1703	5.4099	3.7035	2.0155	7.9467
27500	27619	300.13	1.4625	8.1733	5.4975	3.7635	2.0163	7.9500
27600	27720	300.20	1.4631	8.1764	5.5865	3.8244	2.0172	7.9533
27700	27821	300.27	1.4636	8.1794	5.6768	3.8863	2.0180	7.9566
27800	27922	300.33	1.4642	8.1824	5.7686	3.9491	2.0188	7.9599
27900	28023	300.40	1.4647	8.1854	5.8618	4.0129	2.0197	7.9632
28000	28124	300.47	1.4652 − 5	8.1885 − 1	5.9565 − 4	4.0778 + 1	2.0205 − 5	7.9665 − 1
28100	28225	300.53	1.4658	8.1915	6.0527	4.1436	2.0213	7.9698
28200	28326	300.60	1.4663	8.1945	6.1504	4.2105	2.0222	7.9731
28300	28427	300.67	1.4669	8.1975	6.2496	4.2784	2.0230	7.9764
28400	28527	300.74	1.4674	8.2005	6.3504	4.3474	2.0238	7.9797
28500	28628	300.80	1.4679	8.2036	6.4528	4.4175	2.0247	7.9830
28600	28729	300.87	1.4685	8.2066	6.5567	4.4886	2.0255	7.9863
28700	28830	300.94	1.4690	8.2096	6.6623	4.5609	2.0264	7.9896
28800	28931	301.00	1.4696	8.2126	6.7695	4.6343	2.0272	7.9929
28900	29032	301.07	1.4701	8.2156	6.8785	4.7089	2.0280	7.9962
29000	29133	301.14	1.4706 − 5	8.2187 − 1	6.9891 − 4	4.7846 + 1	2.0289 − 5	7.9995 − 1
29100	29234	301.20	1.4712	8.2217	7.1014	4.8615	2.0297	8.0028
29200	29335	301.27	1.4717	8.2247	7.2155	4.9397	2.0305	8.0061
29300	29436	301.34	1.4723	8.2277	7.3314	5.0190	2.0314	8.0094
29400	29537	301.40	1.4728	8.2307	7.4491	5.0996	2.0322	8.0127
29500	29638	301.47	1.4733	8.2337	7.5686	5.1814	2.0330	8.0160
29600	29738	301.54	1.4739	8.2368	7.6900	5.2645	2.0339	8.0193
29700	29839	301.60	1.4744	8.2398	7.8133	5.3489	2.0347	8.0226
29800	29940	301.67	1.4750	8.2428	7.9385	5.4346	2.0356	8.0259
29900	30041	301.74	1.4755	8.2458	8.0656	5.5216	2.0364	8.0292
30000	30142	301.80	1.4760 − 5	8.2488 − 1	8.1948 − 4	5.6100 + 1	2.0372 − 5	8.0325 − 1
30100	30243	301.87	1.4766	8.2518	8.3259	5.6998	2.0381	8.0357
30200	30344	301.94	1.4771	8.2548	8.4591	5.7910	2.0389	8.0390
30300	30445	302.00	1.4777	8.2578	8.5943	5.8836	2.0397	8.0423
30400	30546	302.07	1.4782	8.2609	8.7317	5.9776	2.0406	8.0456
30500	30647	302.14	1.4787	8.2639	8.8712	6.0731	2.0414	8.0489
30600	30748	302.20	1.4793	8.2669	9.0128	6.1701	2.0422	8.0522
30700	30849	302.27	1.4798	8.2699	9.1566	6.2685	2.0431	8.0555
30800	30950	302.33	1.4803	8.2729	9.3027	6.3685	2.0439	8.0588
30900	31051	302.40	1.4809	8.2759	9.4510	6.4701	2.0447	8.0621
31000	31152	302.47	1.4814 − 5	8.2789 − 1	9.6017 − 4	6.5732 + 1	2.0456 − 5	8.0654 − 1
31100	31253	302.53	1.4820	8.2819	9.7547	6.6779	2.0464	8.0687
31200	31354	302.60	1.4825	8.2849	9.9100	6.7843	2.0473	8.0720
31300	31455	302.67	1.4830	8.2879	1.0068 − 3	6.8923	2.0481	8.0753
31400	31556	302.73	1.4836	8.2909	1.0228	7.0019	2.0489	8.0786
31500	31657	302.80	1.4841	8.2939	1.0391	7.1133	2.0498	8.0818
31600	31758	302.87	1.4846	8.2969	1.0556	7.2263	2.0506	8.0851
31700	31859	302.93	1.4852	8.2999	1.0723	7.3412	2.0514	8.0884
31800	31960	303.00	1.4857	8.3029	1.0894	7.4578	2.0523	8.0917
31900	32061	303.06	1.4863	8.3059	1.1067	7.5761	2.0531	8.0950
32000	32162	303.13	1.4868 − 5	8.3089 − 1	1.1242 − 3	7.6964 + 1	2.0539 − 5	8.0983 − 1
32200	32364	303.50	1.4898	8.3257	1.1635	7.9650	2.0586	8.1167
32400	32566	303.87	1.4928	8.3425	1.2040	8.2424	2.0633	8.1351
32600	32768	304.24	1.4958	8.3593	1.2458	8.5286	2.0679	8.1535
32800	32970	304.61	1.4988	8.3760	1.2890	8.8241	2.0726	8.1719
33000	33172	304.98	1.5018	8.3927	1.3335	9.1290	2.0773	8.1903
33200	33374	305.35	1.5048	8.4094	1.3795	9.4437	2.0819	8.2086
33400	33576	305.72	1.5078	8.4261	1.4269	9.7684	2.0866	8.2270
33600	33779	306.09	1.5107	8.4428	1.4758	1.0103 + 2	2.0912	8.2453
33800	33981	306.45	1.5137	8.4594	1.5263	1.0449	2.0959	8.2636
34000	34183	306.82	1.5167 − 5	8.4760 − 1	1.5784 − 3	1.0805 + 2	2.1005 − 5	8.2820 − 1
34200	34385	307.19	1.5197	8.4927	1.6322	1.1173	2.1052	8.3003
34400	34587	307.55	1.5226	8.5093	1.6876	1.1553	2.1098	8.3186
34600	34789	307.92	1.5256	8.5258	1.7448	1.1944	2.1144	8.3369
34800	34992	308.28	1.5286	8.5424	1.8037	1.2348	2.1191	8.3552
35000	35194	308.65	1.5315	8.5589	1.8646	1.2764	2.1237	8.3734
35200	35396	309.01	1.5345	8.5755	1.9273	1.3193	2.1283	8.3917
35400	35598	309.38	1.5374	8.5920	1.9919	1.3636	2.1330	8.4100
35600	35801	309.74	1.5404	8.6085	2.0586	1.4092	2.1376	8.4282
35800	36003	310.10	1.5433	8.6249	2.1273	1.4563	2.1422	8.4465
36000	36205	310.47	1.5463 − 5	8.6414 − 1	2.1982 − 3	1.5048 + 2	2.1469 − 5	8.4647 − 1
36200	36407	310.83	1.5492	8.6578	2.2712	1.5548	2.1515	8.4829
36400	36610	311.19	1.5522	8.6743	2.3465	1.6063	2.1561	8.5011
36600	36812	311.55	1.5551	8.6907	2.4241	1.6595	2.1607	8.5193
36800	37014	311.91	1.5580	8.7070	2.5041	1.7142	2.1653	8.5375
37000	37217	312.27	1.5610	8.7234	2.5865	1.7706	2.1699	8.5557
37200	37419	312.63	1.5639	8.7398	2.6714	1.8288	2.1745	8.5738
37400	37621	312.99	1.5668	8.7561	2.7589	1.8887	2.1791	8.5920
37600	37824	313.35	1.5697	8.7724	2.8490	1.9504	2.1837	8.6101
37800	38026	313.71	1.5726	8.7887	2.9419	2.0140	2.1883	8.6283

Table III
Geometric Altitude, Metric Units

Altitude		Sound speed	Dynamic viscosity		Kinematic viscosity		Thermal conductivity	
Z (m)	H (m)	C_s (m/s)	$(N \cdot \mu\,s/m^2)$	μ/μ_0	$(m^2\, \eta/s)$	η/η_0	$(J/m \cdot \kappa\, s \cdot K)$	κ/κ_0
27000	26886	299.72	1.4592 − 5	8.1547 − 1	4.9805 − 4	3.4096 + 1	2.0112 − 5	7.9297 − 1
27100	26985	299.79	1.4597	8.1577	5.0606	3.4644	2.0120	7.9330
27200	27084	299.85	1.4603	8.1607	5.1420	3.5201	2.0128	7.9362
27300	27183	299.92	1.4608	8.1637	5.2247	3.5767	2.0137	7.9395
27400	27282	299.99	1.4614	8.1667	5.3086	3.6342	2.0145	7.9428
27500	27382	300.05	1.4619	8.1697	5.3939	3.6926	2.0153	7.9461
27600	27481	300.12	1.4624	8.1728	5.4804	3.7518	2.0162	7.9493
27700	27580	300.19	1.4630	8.1758	5.5684	3.8120	2.0170	7.9526
27800	27679	300.25	1.4635	8.1787	5.6577	3.8732	2.0178	7.9559
27900	27778	300.32	1.4640	8.1817	5.7484	3.9352	2.0186	7.9592
28000	27877	300.39	1.4646 − 5	8.1847 − 1	5.8405 − 4	3.9983 + 1	2.0195 − 5	7.9624 − 1
28100	27976	300.45	1.4651	8.1877	5.9340	4.0623	2.0203	7.9657
28200	28075	300.52	1.4656	8.1907	6.0290	4.1273	2.0211	7.9690
28300	28175	300.58	1.4662	8.1937	6.1254	4.1934	2.0220	7.9723
28400	28274	300.65	1.4667	8.1967	6.2234	4.2604	2.0228	7.9755
28500	28373	300.72	1.4673	8.1997	6.3228	4.3285	2.0236	7.9788
28600	28472	300.78	1.4678	8.2027	6.4238	4.3977	2.0244	7.9821
28700	28571	300.85	1.4683	8.2057	6.5264	4.4679	2.0253	7.9853
28800	28670	300.92	1.4689	8.2087	6.6306	4.5392	2.0261	7.9886
28900	28769	300.98	1.4694	8.2117	6.7363	4.6116	2.0269	7.9919
29000	28868	301.05	1.4699 − 5	8.2147 − 1	6.8437 − 4	4.6851 + 1	2.0278 − 5	7.9951 − 1
29100	28967	301.11	1.4705	8.2177	6.9528	4.7598	2.0286	7.9984
29200	29066	301.18	1.4710	8.2207	7.0636	4.8356	2.0294	8.0017
29300	29166	301.25	1.4715	8.2237	7.1760	4.9126	2.0303	8.0049
29400	29265	301.31	1.4721	8.2267	7.2902	4.9908	2.0311	8.0082
29500	29364	301.38	1.4726	8.2296	7.4062	5.0702	2.0319	8.0115
29600	29463	301.44	1.4731	8.2326	7.5239	5.1508	2.0327	8.0147
29700	29562	301.51	1.4737	8.2356	7.6435	5.2326	2.0336	8.0180
29800	29661	301.58	1.4742	8.2386	7.7649	5.3158	2.0344	8.0213
29900	29760	301.64	1.4747	8.2416	7.8882	5.4002	2.0352	8.0245
30000	29859	301.71	1.4753 − 5	8.2446 − 1	8.0134 − 4	5.4859 + 1	2.0361 − 5	8.0278 − 1
30100	29958	301.77	1.4758	8.2476	8.1405	5.5729	2.0369	8.0311
30200	30057	301.84	1.4763	8.2505	8.2695	5.6612	2.0377	8.0343
30300	30156	301.91	1.4769	8.2535	8.4006	5.7509	2.0385	8.0376
30400	30255	301.97	1.4774	8.2565	8.5336	5.8420	2.0394	8.0409
30500	30354	302.04	1.4779	8.2595	8.6687	5.9345	2.0402	8.0441
30600	30453	302.10	1.4785	8.2625	8.8059	6.0284	2.0410	8.0474
30700	30552	302.17	1.4790	8.2654	8.9452	6.1238	2.0418	8.0507
30800	30651	302.24	1.4795	8.2684	9.0866	6.2206	2.0427	8.0539
30900	30751	302.30	1.4801	8.2714	9.2301	6.3189	2.0435	8.0572
31000	30850	302.37	1.4806 − 5	8.2744 − 1	9.3759 − 4	6.4187 + 1	2.0443 − 5	8.0604 − 1
31100	30949	302.43	1.4811	8.2774	9.5239	6.5200	2.0452	8.0637
31200	31048	302.50	1.4817	8.2803	9.6742	6.6229	2.0460	8.0670
31300	31147	302.56	1.4822	8.2833	9.8268	6.7273	2.0468	8.0702
31400	31246	302.63	1.4827	8.2863	9.9817	6.8334	2.0476	8.0735
31500	31345	302.70	1.4833	8.2893	1.0139 − 3	6.9410	2.0485	8.0767
31600	31444	302.76	1.4838	8.2922	1.0299	7.0503	2.0493	8.0800
31700	31543	302.83	1.4843	8.2952	1.0461	7.1613	2.0501	8.0832
31800	31642	302.89	1.4849	8.2982	1.0625	7.2740	2.0509	8.0865
31900	31741	302.96	1.4854	8.3012	1.0792	7.3884	2.0518	8.0898
32000	31840	303.02	1.4859 − 5	8.3041 − 1	1.0962 − 3	7.5046 + 1	2.0526 − 5	8.0930 − 1
32200	32038	303.20	1.4874	8.3121	1.1315	7.7464	2.0548	8.1018
32400	32236	303.57	1.4903	8.3287	1.1706	8.0139	2.0594	8.1200
32600	32434	303.93	1.4933	8.3453	1.2109	8.2899	2.0640	8.1382
32800	32632	304.30	1.4963	8.3619	1.2525	8.5747	2.0687	8.1564
33000	32830	304.67	1.4992	8.3785	1.2955	8.8685	2.0733	8.1746
33200	33027	305.03	1.5022	8.3950	1.3397	9.1717	2.0779	8.1928
33400	33225	305.40	1.5052	8.4115	1.3854	9.4844	2.0825	8.2109
33600	33423	305.76	1.5081	8.4280	1.4325	9.8070	2.0871	8.2291
33800	33621	306.13	1.5111	8.4445	1.4811	1.0139 + 2	2.0917	8.2473
34000	33819	306.49	1.5140 − 5	8.4610 − 1	1.5312 − 3	1.0482 + 2	2.0963 − 5	8.2654 − 1
34200	34017	306.85	1.5169	8.4775	1.5829	1.0836	2.1009	8.2835
34400	34215	307.21	1.5199	8.4939	1.6362	1.1201	2.1055	8.3016
34600	34413	307.58	1.5228	8.5103	1.6912	1.1577	2.1101	8.3198
34800	34611	307.94	1.5258	8.5267	1.7478	1.1965	2.1147	8.3378
35000	34808	308.30	1.5287	8.5431	1.8062	1.2365	2.1193	8.3559
35200	35006	308.66	1.5316	8.5594	1.8665	1.2777	2.1239	8.3740
35400	35204	309.02	1.5345	8.5758	1.9285	1.3202	2.1284	8.3921
35600	35402	309.38	1.5375	8.5921	1.9925	1.3640	2.1330	8.4101
35800	35599	309.74	1.5404	8.6084	2.0584	1.4091	2.1376	8.4282
36000	35797	310.10	1.5433 − 5	8.6247 − 1	2.1264 − 3	1.4556 + 2	2.1422 − 5	8.4462 − 1
36200	35995	310.46	1.5462	8.6410	2.1964	1.5036	2.1467	8.4642
36400	36193	310.82	1.5491	8.6572	2.2685	1.5530	2.1513	8.4822
36600	36390	311.17	1.5520	8.6735	2.3428	1.6039	2.1559	8.5002
36800	36588	311.53	1.5549	8.6897	2.4194	1.6563	2.1604	8.5182
37000	36786	311.89	1.5578	8.7059	2.4983	1.7103	2.1650	8.5362
37200	36984	312.24	1.5607	8.7221	2.5796	1.7659	2.1695	8.5542
37400	37181	312.60	1.5636	8.7382	2.6633	1.8232	2.1741	8.5721
37600	37379	312.96	1.5665	8.7544	2.7495	1.8823	2.1787	8.5901
37800	37577	313.31	1.5694	8.7705	2.8383	1.9430	2.1832	8.6080

Table III
Geopotential Altitude, Metric Units

Altitude		Sound speed	Dynamic viscosity		Kinematic viscosity		Thermal conductivity	
H (m)	Z (m)	C_s (m/s)	μ (N·s/m²)	μ/μ_0	η (m²/s)	η/η_0	κ (J/m·s·K)	κ/κ_0
38000	38229	314.07	1.5756 − 5	8.8050 − 1	3.0376 − 3	2.0795 + 2	2.1929 − 5	8.6464 − 1
38200	38431	314.43	1.5785	8.8213	3.1361	2.1469	2.1975	8.6645
38400	38633	314.79	1.5814	8.8375	3.2376	2.2164	2.2021	8.6826
38600	38836	315.14	1.5843	8.8538	3.3422	2.2880	2.2067	8.7007
38800	39038	315.50	1.5872	8.8700	3.4499	2.3617	2.2113	8.7188
39000	39241	315.86	1.5901	8.8862	3.5608	2.4376	2.2159	8.7369
39200	39443	316.21	1.5930	8.9024	3.6750	2.5158	2.2205	8.7550
39400	39646	316.57	1.5959	8.9185	3.7925	2.5963	2.2251	8.7730
39600	39848	316.92	1.5988	8.9347	3.9136	2.6792	2.2296	8.7911
39800	40051	317.28	1.6017	8.9508	4.0382	2.7645	2.2342	8.8091
40000	40253	317.63	1.6045 − 5	8.9669 − 1	4.1665 − 3	2.8523 + 2	2.2388 − 5	8.8272 − 1
40200	40456	317.99	1.6074	8.9830	4.2986	2.9428	2.2434	8.8452
40400	40658	318.34	1.6103	8.9991	4.4346	3.0358	2.2479	8.8632
40600	40861	318.69	1.6132	9.0152	4.5745	3.1316	2.2525	8.8812
40800	41064	319.05	1.6160	9.0313	4.7185	3.2302	2.2571	8.8992
41000	41266	319.40	1.6189	9.0473	4.8667	3.3317	2.2616	8.9172
41200	41469	319.75	1.6218	9.0633	5.0193	3.4361	2.2662	8.9351
41400	41671	320.10	1.6246	9.0793	5.1762	3.5436	2.2707	8.9531
41600	41874	320.45	1.6275	9.0953	5.3377	3.6541	2.2753	8.9710
41800	42077	320.81	1.6304	9.1113	5.5039	3.7679	2.2798	8.9890
42000	42279	321.16	1.6332 − 5	9.1272 − 1	5.6748 − 3	3.8849 + 2	2.2844 − 5	9.0069 − 1
42200	42482	321.51	1.6361	9.1432	5.8507	4.0053	2.2889	9.0248
42400	42685	321.86	1.6389	9.1591	6.0315	4.1291	2.2935	9.0428
42600	42887	322.21	1.6418	9.1750	6.2176	4.2565	2.2980	9.0607
42800	43090	322.55	1.6446	9.1909	6.4090	4.3875	2.3025	9.0786
43000	43293	322.90	1.6475	9.2068	6.6058	4.5223	2.3071	9.0964
43200	43496	323.25	1.6503	9.2226	6.8083	4.6609	2.3116	9.1143
43400	43698	323.60	1.6531	9.2385	7.0164	4.8034	2.3161	9.1322
43600	43901	323.95	1.6560	9.2543	7.2305	4.9499	2.3207	9.1500
43800	44104	324.29	1.6588	9.2701	7.4506	5.1006	2.3252	9.1679
44000	44307	324.64	1.6616 − 5	9.2859 − 1	7.6769 − 3	5.2555 + 2	2.3297 − 5	9.1857 − 1
44200	44510	324.99	1.6644	9.3017	7.9096	5.4148	2.3342	9.2035
44400	44712	325.33	1.6673	9.3175	8.1488	5.5786	2.3388	9.2213
44600	44915	325.68	1.6701	9.3332	8.3947	5.7469	2.3433	9.2392
44800	45118	326.02	1.6729	9.3489	8.6474	5.9199	2.3478	9.2569
45000	45321	326.37	1.6757	9.3647	8.9072	6.0978	2.3523	9.2747
45200	45524	326.71	1.6785	9.3804	9.1742	6.2806	2.3568	9.2925
45400	45727	327.06	1.6813	9.3961	9.4487	6.4685	2.3613	9.3103
45600	45929	327.40	1.6841	9.4117	9.7307	6.6615	2.3658	9.3280
45800	46132	327.75	1.6869	9.4274	1.0021 − 2	6.8599	2.3703	9.3458
46000	46335	328.09	1.6897 − 5	9.4430 − 1	1.0318 − 2	7.0638 + 2	2.3748 − 5	9.3635 − 1
46200	46538	328.43	1.6925	9.4587	1.0624	7.2733	2.3793	9.3812
46400	46741	328.77	1.6953	9.4743	1.0939	7.4885	2.3838	9.3990
46600	46944	329.12	1.6981	9.4899	1.1262	7.7097	2.3883	9.4167
46800	47147	329.46	1.7009	9.5054	1.1594	7.9368	2.3928	9.4344
47000	47350	329.80	1.7037	9.5210	1.1934	8.1702	2.3973	9.4521
47200	47553	329.80	1.7037	9.5210	1.2240	8.3791	2.3973	9.4521
47400	47756	329.80	1.7037	9.5210	1.2552	8.5933	2.3973	9.4521
47600	47959	329.80	1.7037	9.5210	1.2873	8.8130	2.3973	9.4521
47800	48162	329.80	1.7037	9.5210	1.3203	9.0383	2.3973	9.4521
48000	48365	329.80	1.7037 − 5	9.5210 − 1	1.3540 − 2	9.2694 + 2	2.3973 − 5	9.4521 − 1
48200	48568	329.80	1.7037	9.5210	1.3886	9.5064	2.3973	9.4521
48400	48771	329.80	1.7037	9.5210	1.4241	9.7495	2.3973	9.4521
48600	48974	329.80	1.7037	9.5210	1.4605	9.9987	2.3973	9.4521
48800	49178	329.80	1.7037	9.5210	1.4979	1.0254 + 3	2.3973	9.4521
49000	49381	329.80	1.7037	9.5210	1.5362	1.0516	2.3973	9.4521
49200	49584	329.80	1.7037	9.5210	1.5754	1.0785	2.3973	9.4521
49400	49787	329.80	1.7037	9.5210	1.6157	1.1061	2.3973	9.4521
49600	49990	329.80	1.7037	9.5210	1.6570	1.1343	2.3973	9.4521
49800	50193	329.80	1.7037	9.5210	1.6994	1.1634	2.3973	9.4521
50000	50396	329.80	1.7037 − 5	9.5210 − 1	1.7429 − 2	1.1931 + 3	2.3973 − 5	9.4521 − 1
50500	50904	329.80	1.7037	9.5210	1.8564	1.2708	2.3973	9.4521
51000	51413	329.80	1.7037	9.5210	1.9773	1.3536	2.3973	9.4521
51500	51921	328.94	1.6967	9.4821	2.0870	1.4287	2.3861	9.4078
52000	52429	328.09	1.6897	9.4430	2.2034	1.5084	2.3748	9.3635
52500	52937	327.23	1.6827	9.4039	2.3269	1.5930	2.3636	9.3192
53000	53446	326.37	1.6757	9.3647	2.4581	1.6827	2.3523	9.2747
53500	53954	325.51	1.6687	9.3253	2.5974	1.7781	2.3410	9.2303
54000	54463	324.64	1.6616	9.2859	2.7453	1.8794	2.3297	9.1857
54500	54971	323.77	1.6545	9.2464	2.9026	1.9870	2.3184	9.1411
55000	55480	322.90	1.6475 − 5	9.2068 − 1	3.0697 − 2	2.1014 + 3	2.3071 − 5	9.0964 − 1
55500	55989	322.03	1.6403	9.1671	3.2474	2.2231	2.2957	9.0517
56000	56498	321.16	1.6332	9.1272	3.4365	2.3525	2.2844	9.0069
56500	57007	320.28	1.6261	9.0873	3.6376	2.4902	2.2730	8.9621
57000	57516	319.40	1.6189	9.0473	3.8517	2.6368	2.2616	8.9172
57500	58025	318.52	1.6117	9.0072	4.0797	2.7929	2.2502	8.8722
58000	58534	317.63	1.6045	8.9669	4.3225	2.9591	2.2388	8.8272
58500	59043	316.75	1.5973	8.9266	4.5812	3.1362	2.2273	8.7821
59000	59553	315.86	1.5901	8.8862	4.8570	3.3250	2.2159	8.7369
59500	60062	314.96	1.5828	8.8457	5.1510	3.5263	2.2044	8.6917

Table III
Geometric Altitude, Metric Units

Altitude		Sound speed	Dynamic viscosity		Kinematic viscosity		Thermal conductivity	
Z (m)	H (m)	C_s (m/s)	$(N \cdot \frac{\mu}{s}/m^2)$	μ/μ_0	$(m^2 \frac{\eta}{/s})$	η/η_0	$(J/m \cdot \frac{\kappa}{s} \cdot K)$	κ/κ_0
38000	37774	313.67	1.5723 − 5	8.7866 − 1	2.9297 − 3	2.0056 + 2	2.1878 − 5	8.6259 − 1
38200	37972	314.02	1.5751	8.8027	3.0239	2.0701	2.1923	8.6439
38400	38169	314.37	1.5780	8.8188	3.1209	2.1365	2.1968	8.6618
38600	38367	314.73	1.5809	8.8349	3.2207	2.2048	2.2014	8.6796
38800	38565	315.08	1.5838	8.8509	3.3235	2.2752	2.2059	8.6975
39000	38762	315.43	1.5866	8.8669	3.4293	2.3476	2.2104	8.7154
39200	38960	315.78	1.5895	8.8829	3.5382	2.4222	2.2150	8.7333
39400	39157	316.14	1.5924	8.8989	3.6503	2.4989	2.2195	8.7511
39600	39355	316.49	1.5952	8.9149	3.7657	2.5779	2.2240	8.7690
39800	39552	316.84	1.5981	8.9308	3.8844	2.6592	2.2285	8.7868
40000	39750	317.19	1.6009 − 5	8.9468 − 1	4.0066 − 3	2.7429 + 2	2.2331 − 5	8.8046 − 1
40200	39947	317.54	1.6038	8.9627	4.1324	2.8290	2.2376	8.8224
40400	40145	317.89	1.6066	8.9786	4.2618	2.9176	2.2421	8.8402
40600	40342	318.24	1.6095	8.9945	4.3950	3.0087	2.2466	8.8580
40800	40540	318.59	1.6123	9.0104	4.5320	3.1025	2.2511	8.8758
41000	40737	318.94	1.6151	9.0262	4.6729	3.1990	2.2556	8.8935
41200	40935	319.28	1.6180	9.0421	4.8179	3.2982	2.2601	8.9113
41400	41132	319.63	1.6208	9.0579	4.9670	3.4003	2.2646	8.9290
41600	41330	319.98	1.6236	9.0737	5.1204	3.5053	2.2691	8.9468
41800	41527	320.33	1.6265	9.0895	5.2782	3.6134	2.2736	8.9645
42000	41724	320.67	1.6293 − 5	9.1052 − 1	5.4404 − 3	3.7244 + 2	2.2781 − 5	8.9822 − 1
42200	41922	321.02	1.6321	9.1210	5.6073	3.8387	2.2826	8.9999
42400	42119	321.36	1.6349	9.1367	5.7789	3.9561	2.2871	9.0176
42600	42316	321.71	1.6377	9.1524	5.9553	4.0769	2.2916	9.0353
42800	42514	322.05	1.6405	9.1681	6.1367	4.2011	2.2960	9.0529
43000	42711	322.40	1.6433	9.1838	6.3232	4.3288	2.3005	9.0706
43200	42908	322.74	1.6461	9.1995	6.5150	4.4601	2.3050	9.0882
43400	43106	323.09	1.6490	9.2152	6.7121	4.5950	2.3095	9.1059
43600	43303	323.43	1.6517	9.2308	6.9147	4.7337	2.3139	9.1235
43800	43500	323.77	1.6545	9.2464	7.1230	4.8763	2.3184	9.1411
44000	43698	324.12	1.6573 − 5	9.2620 − 1	7.3371 − 3	5.0229 + 2	2.3229 − 5	9.1587 − 1
44200	43895	324.46	1.6601	9.2776	7.5571	5.1735	2.3273	9.1763
44400	44092	324.80	1.6629	9.2932	7.7832	5.3283	2.3318	9.1939
44600	44289	325.14	1.6657	9.3087	8.0155	5.4873	2.3363	9.2115
44800	44486	325.48	1.6685	9.3243	8.2542	5.6508	2.3407	9.2290
45000	44684	325.82	1.6713	9.3398	8.4995	5.8187	2.3452	9.2466
45200	44881	326.16	1.6740	9.3553	8.7516	5.9912	2.3496	9.2641
45400	45078	326.50	1.6768	9.3708	9.0105	6.1685	2.3541	9.2817
45600	45275	326.84	1.6796	9.3863	9.2765	6.3506	2.3585	9.2992
45800	45472	327.18	1.6823	9.4017	9.5498	6.5377	2.3629	9.3167
46000	45669	327.52	1.6851 − 5	9.4172 − 1	9.8305 − 3	6.7299 + 2	2.3674 − 5	9.3342 − 1
46200	45867	327.86	1.6879	9.4326	1.0119 − 2	6.9272	2.3718	9.3517
46400	46064	328.20	1.6906	9.4480	1.0415	7.1300	2.3763	9.3692
46600	46261	328.54	1.6934	9.4634	1.0719	7.3382	2.3807	9.3866
46800	46458	328.87	1.6961	9.4788	1.1031	7.5520	2.3851	9.4041
47000	46655	329.21	1.6989	9.4941	1.1352	7.7716	2.3895	9.4215
47200	46852	329.55	1.7016	9.5095	1.1681	7.9970	2.3940	9.4390
47400	47049	329.80	1.7037	9.5210	1.2009	8.2210	2.3973	9.4521
47600	47246	329.80	1.7037	9.5210	1.2311	8.4281	2.3973	9.4521
47800	47443	329.80	1.7037	9.5210	1.2621	8.6403	2.3973	9.4521
48000	47640	329.80	1.7037 − 5	9.5210 − 1	1.2939 − 2	8.8579 + 2	2.3973 − 5	9.4521 − 1
48200	47837	329.80	1.7037	9.5210	1.3265	9.0809	2.3973	9.4521
48400	48034	329.80	1.7037	9.5210	1.3599	9.3096	2.3973	9.4521
48600	48231	329.80	1.7037	9.5210	1.3941	9.5440	2.3973	9.4521
48800	48428	329.80	1.7037	9.5210	1.4292	9.7842	2.3973	9.4521
49000	48625	329.80	1.7037	9.5210	1.4652	1.0030 + 3	2.3973	9.4521
49200	48822	329.80	1.7037	9.5210	1.5021	1.0283	2.3973	9.4521
49400	49019	329.80	1.7037	9.5210	1.5399	1.0541	2.3973	9.4521
49600	49216	329.80	1.7037	9.5210	1.5786	1.0807	2.3973	9.4521
49800	49413	329.80	1.7037	9.5210	1.6184	1.1079	2.3973	9.4521
50000	49610	329.80	1.7037 − 5	9.5210 − 1	1.6591 − 2	1.1357 + 3	2.3973 − 5	9.4521 − 1
50500	50102	329.80	1.7037	9.5210	1.7654	1.2085	2.3973	9.4521
51000	50594	329.80	1.7037	9.5210	1.8786	1.2860	2.3973	9.4521
51500	51086	329.65	1.7025	9.5143	1.9958	1.3662	2.3953	9.4444
52000	51578	328.81	1.6956	9.4760	2.1047	1.4408	2.3843	9.4009
52500	52070	327.97	1.6887	9.4376	2.2203	1.5199	2.3732	9.3573
53000	52562	327.12	1.6819	9.3991	2.3427	1.6038	2.3622	9.3137
53500	53053	326.28	1.6750	9.3605	2.4726	1.6927	2.3511	9.2700
54000	53545	325.43	1.6680	9.3218	2.6104	1.7870	2.3400	9.2262
54500	54037	324.58	1.6611	9.2830	2.7565	1.8871	2.3289	9.1824
55000	54528	323.72	1.6541 − 5	9.2442 − 1	2.9117 − 2	1.9933 + 3	2.3178 − 5	9.1386 − 1
55500	55020	322.87	1.6472	9.2052	3.0765	2.1061	2.3066	9.0947
56000	55511	322.01	1.6402	9.1662	3.2514	2.2259	2.2955	9.0507
56500	56002	321.15	1.6332	9.1271	3.4373	2.3531	2.2843	9.0067
57000	56493	320.29	1.6262	9.0878	3.6349	2.4884	2.2732	8.9627
57500	56985	319.42	1.6191	9.0485	3.8449	2.6321	2.2620	8.9186
58000	57476	318.56	1.6121	9.0091	4.0682	2.7850	2.2508	8.8744
58500	57967	317.69	1.6050	8.9696	4.3057	2.9476	2.2395	8.8302
59000	58457	316.82	1.5979	8.9301	4.5585	3.1207	2.2283	8.7859
59500	58948	315.95	1.5908	8.8904	4.8276	3.3049	2.2171	8.7416

Table III
Geopotential Altitude, Metric Units

Altitude		Sound speed	Dynamic viscosity		Kinematic viscosity		Thermal conductivity	
H (m)	Z (m)	C_s (m/s)	μ (N·s/m²)	μ/μ_0	η (m²/s)	η/η_0	κ (J/m·s·K)	κ/κ_0
60000	60572	314.07	1.5756 − 5	8.8050 − 1	5.4646 − 2	3.7410 + 3	2.1929 − 5	8.6464 − 1
60500	61081	313.17	1.5683	8.7643	5.7992	3.9701	2.1814	8.6011
61000	61591	312.27	1.5610	8.7234	6.1564	4.2146	2.1699	8.5557
61500	62101	311.37	1.5536	8.6825	6.5378	4.4757	2.1584	8.5102
62000	62611	310.47	1.5463	8.6414	6.9452	4.7546	2.1469	8.4647
62500	63121	309.56	1.5389	8.6002	7.3806	5.0526	2.1353	8.4191
63000	63631	308.65	1.5315	8.5589	7.8459	5.3712	2.1237	8.3734
63500	64141	307.74	1.5241	8.5175	8.3436	5.7120	2.1121	8.3277
64000	64651	306.82	1.5167	8.4760	8.8761	6.0765	2.1005	8.2820
64500	65161	305.90	1.5093	8.4344	9.4459	6.4666	2.0889	8.2361
65000	65672	304.98	1.5018 − 5	8.3927 − 1	1.0056 − 1	6.8843 + 3	2.0773 − 5	8.1903 − 1
65500	66182	304.06	1.4943	8.3509	1.0710	7.3316	2.0656	8.1443
66000	66692	303.13	1.4868	8.3089	1.1410	7.8111	2.0539	8.0983
66500	67203	302.20	1.4793	8.2669	1.2161	8.3250	2.0422	8.0522
67000	67714	301.27	1.4717	8.2247	1.2966	8.8761	2.0305	8.0061
67500	68224	300.33	1.4642	8.1824	1.3829	9.4675	2.0188	7.9599
68000	68735	299.40	1.4566	8.1400	1.4756	1.0102 + 4	2.0071	7.9136
68500	69246	298.45	1.4490	8.0975	1.5752	1.0784	1.9953	7.8673
69000	69757	297.51	1.4413	8.0549	1.6822	1.1516	1.9836	7.8209
69500	70268	296.56	1.4337	8.0121	1.7971	1.2303	1.9718	7.7745
70000	70779	295.61	1.4260 − 5	7.9692 − 1	1.9207 − 1	1.3149 + 4	1.9600 − 5	7.7280 − 1
70500	71291	294.66	1.4183	7.9262	2.0537	1.4059	1.9482	7.6814
71000	71802	293.70	1.4106	7.8831	2.1968	1.5039	1.9364	7.6348
71500	72313	293.02	1.4051	7.8523	2.3589	1.6149	1.9279	7.6015
72000	72825	292.33	1.3995	7.8213	2.5337	1.7346	1.9195	7.5681
72500	73336	291.64	1.3940	7.7903	2.7224	1.8637	1.9110	7.5347
73000	73848	290.95	1.3884	7.7593	2.9261	2.0032	1.9025	7.5013
73500	74360	290.26	1.3829	7.7282	3.1462	2.1539	1.8940	7.4679
74000	74872	289.57	1.3773	7.6970	3.3839	2.3166	1.8855	7.4344
74500	75384	288.88	1.3717	7.6657	3.6409	2.4925	1.8770	7.4008
75000	75896	288.18	1.3661 − 5	7.6344 − 1	3.9188 − 1	2.6827 + 4	1.8685 − 5	7.3673 − 1
75500	76408	287.48	1.3605	7.6031	4.2193	2.8885	1.8600	7.3337
76000	76920	286.78	1.3549	7.5716	4.5445	3.1111	1.8515	7.3001
76500	77432	286.08	1.3492	7.5401	4.8965	3.3521	1.8430	7.2665
77000	77944	285.38	1.3436	7.5086	5.2777	3.6131	1.8344	7.2328
77500	78457	284.67	1.3379	7.4770	5.6906	3.8957	1.8259	7.1991
78000	78969	283.96	1.3323	7.4453	6.1381	4.2021	1.8173	7.1654
78500	79482	283.26	1.3266	7.4135	6.6233	4.5343	1.8088	7.1316
79000	79994	282.55	1.3209	7.3817	7.1495	4.8945	1.8002	7.0978
79500	80507	281.83	1.3152	7.3498	7.7204	5.2854	1.7916	7.0640
80000	81020	281.12	1.3095 − 5	7.3179 − 1	8.3402 − 1	5.7096 + 4	1.7830 − 5	7.0302 − 1
80500	81533	280.40	1.3037	7.2858	9.0132	6.1704	1.7744	6.9963
81000	82046	279.69	1.2980	7.2537	9.7443	6.6709	1.7658	6.9624
81500	82559	278.97	1.2922	7.2216	1.0539 + 0	7.2148	1.7572	6.9285
82000	83072	278.25	1.2865	7.1894	1.1403	7.8063	1.7486	6.8945
82500	83585	277.52	1.2807	7.1571	1.2342	8.4496	1.7400	6.8605
83000	84098	276.80	1.2749	7.1247	1.3365	9.1497	1.7314	6.8265
83500	84611	276.07	1.2691	7.0923	1.4478	9.9118	1.7227	6.7924
84000	85125	275.34	1.2633	7.0598	1.5691	1.0742 + 5	1.7141	6.7584
84500	85638	274.61	1.2575	7.0273	1.7012	1.1647	1.7054	6.7243

Table III
Geometric Altitude, Metric Units

Altitude		Sound speed	Dynamic viscosity		Kinematic viscosity		Thermal conductivity	
Z (m)	H (m)	C_s (m/s)	$(N \cdot s/m^2)$ μ	μ/μ_0	(m^2/s) η	η/η_0	$(J/m \cdot s \cdot K)$ κ	κ/κ_0
60000	59439	315.07	1.5837 − 5	8.8506 − 1	5.1141 − 2	3.5010 + 3	2.2058 − 5	8.6972 − 1
60500	59930	314.20	1.5766	8.8107	5.4192	3.7099	2.1946	8.6528
61000	60420	313.32	1.5694	8.7708	5.7443	3.9325	2.1833	8.6083
61500	60911	312.43	1.5623	8.7307	6.0909	4.1697	2.1720	8.5638
62000	61401	311.55	1.5551	8.6906	6.4604	4.4227	2.1607	8.5192
62500	61891	310.66	1.5479	8.6503	6.8545	4.6925	2.1494	8.4746
63000	62382	309.77	1.5407	8.6100	7.2749	4.9803	2.1380	8.4299
63500	62872	308.88	1.5334	8.5695	7.7237	5.2876	2.1267	8.3851
64000	63362	307.99	1.5262	8.5290	8.2029	5.6156	2.1153	8.3404
64500	63852	307.09	1.5189	8.4883	8.7148	5.9660	2.1039	8.2955
65000	64342	306.19	1.5116 − 5	8.4476 − 1	9.2617 − 2	6.3404 + 3	2.0926 − 5	8.2506 − 1
65500	64832	305.29	1.5043	8.4068	9.8463	6.7407	2.0812	8.2057
66000	65322	304.39	1.4970	8.3658	1.0471 − 1	7.1686	2.0698	8.1607
66500	65811	303.48	1.4896	8.3248	1.1140	7.6264	2.0583	8.1156
67000	66301	302.57	1.4823	8.2836	1.1856	8.1163	2.0469	8.0705
67500	66791	301.66	1.4749	8.2424	1.2622	8.6407	2.0354	8.0254
68000	67280	300.75	1.4675	8.2010	1.3442	9.2024	2.0240	7.9802
68500	67770	299.83	1.4601	8.1596	1.4321	9.8042	2.0125	7.9349
69000	68259	298.91	1.4526	8.1180	1.5263	1.0449 + 4	2.0010	7.8896
69500	68748	297.99	1.4452	8.0763	1.6274	1.1141	1.9895	7.8443
70000	69238	297.06	1.4377 − 5	8.0346 − 1	1.7357 − 1	1.1883 + 4	1.9780 − 5	7.7989 − 1
70500	69727	296.13	1.4302	7.9927	1.8520	1.2679	1.9665	7.7534
71000	70216	295.20	1.4227	7.9507	1.9769	1.3534	1.9549	7.7079
71500	70705	294.27	1.4152	7.9086	2.1110	1.4452	1.9434	7.6624
72000	71194	293.44	1.4085	7.8712	2.2581	1.5459	1.9331	7.6219
72500	71682	292.77	1.4031	7.8410	2.4211	1.6575	1.9248	7.5893
73000	72171	292.10	1.3976	7.8107	2.5967	1.7777	1.9166	7.5567
73500	72660	291.42	1.3922	7.7804	2.7858	1.9072	1.9083	7.5241
74000	73148	290.75	1.3868	7.7501	2.9897	2.0467	1.9000	7.4914
74500	73637	290.07	1.3813	7.7196	3.2095	2.1972	1.8917	7.4587
75000	74125	289.40	1.3759 − 5	7.6892 − 1	3.4465 − 1	2.3594 + 4	1.8834 − 5	7.4260 − 1
75500	74614	288.72	1.3704	7.6586	3.7022	2.5345	1.8751	7.3932
76000	75102	288.04	1.3650	7.6280	3.9782	2.7234	1.8668	7.3604
76500	75590	287.35	1.3595	7.5974	4.2761	2.9274	1.8585	7.3277
77000	76078	286.67	1.3540	7.5667	4.5978	3.1476	1.8502	7.2948
77500	76566	285.99	1.3485	7.5360	4.9454	3.3856	1.8418	7.2620
78000	77054	285.30	1.3430	7.5051	5.3210	3.6428	1.8335	7.2291
78500	77542	284.61	1.3374	7.4743	5.7271	3.9208	1.8252	7.1963
79000	78030	283.92	1.3319	7.4434	6.1663	4.2214	1.8168	7.1633
79500	78518	283.23	1.3264	7.4124	6.6415	4.5467	1.8085	7.1304
80000	79006	282.54	1.3208 − 5	7.3813 − 1	7.1557 − 1	4.8987 + 4	1.8001 − 5	7.0975 − 1
80500	79493	281.84	1.3152	7.3502	7.7124	5.2799	1.7917	7.0645
81000	79981	281.15	1.3097	7.3191	8.3154	5.6927	1.7834	7.0315
81500	80468	280.45	1.3041	7.2879	8.9688	6.1400	1.7750	6.9985
82000	80956	279.75	1.2985	7.2566	9.6769	6.6247	1.7666	6.9654
82500	81443	279.05	1.2929	7.2253	1.0445 + 0	7.1504	1.7582	6.9323
83000	81930	278.35	1.2873	7.1939	1.1278	7.7206	1.7498	6.8993
83500	82417	277.64	1.2816	7.1624	1.2182	8.3394	1.7414	6.8661
84000	82904	276.94	1.2760	7.1309	1.3163	9.0112	1.7330	6.8330
84500	83391	276.23	1.2704	7.0994	1.4229	9.7408	1.7246	6.7998
85000	83878	275.52	1.2647 − 5	7.0677 − 1	1.5386 + 0	1.0533 + 5	1.7162 − 5	6.7667 − 1
85500	84365	274.81	1.2590	7.0360	1.6645	1.1395	1.7078	6.7335

Table IV
Geopotential Altitude, English Altitudes

Altitude		Temperature		Pressure				Density			
H (ft)	Z (ft)	T (K)	t (°C)	P (mb)		P/P$_0$		ρ (kg/m^3)		ρ/ρ$_0$	
-16500	-16487	320.840	47.500	1.7824	◆ 3	1.7590	◆ 0	1.9353	◆ 0	1.5799	◆ 0
-16400	-16387	320.642	47.492	1.7766		1.7533		1.9303		1.5757	
-16300	-16287	320.444	47.294	1.7708		1.7477		1.9252		1.5716	
-16200	-16187	320.246	47.096	1.7651		1.7420		1.9201		1.5674	
-16100	-16088	320.048	46.898	1.7593		1.7363		1.9151		1.5633	
-16000	-15988	319.849	46.699	1.7536	◆ 3	1.7307	◆ 0	1.9100	◆ 0	1.5592	◆ 0
-15900	-15888	319.651	46.501	1.7479		1.7251		1.9050		1.5551	
-15800	-15788	319.453	46.303	1.7422		1.7194		1.9000		1.5510	
-15700	-15688	319.255	46.105	1.7366		1.7139		1.8950		1.5469	
-15600	-15588	319.057	45.907	1.7309		1.7083		1.8900		1.5428	
-15500	-15488	318.859	45.709	1.7253		1.7027		1.8850		1.5388	
-15400	-15389	318.661	45.511	1.7196		1.6971		1.8800		1.5347	
-15300	-15289	318.463	45.313	1.7140		1.6916		1.8750		1.5306	
-15200	-15189	318.264	45.114	1.7084		1.6861		1.8701		1.5266	
-15100	-15089	318.066	44.916	1.7028		1.6806		1.8651		1.5226	
-15000	-14989	317.868	44.718	1.6973	◆ 3	1.6751	◆ 0	1.8602	◆ 0	1.5185	◆ 0
-14900	-14889	317.670	44.520	1.6917		1.6696		1.8553		1.5145	
-14800	-14790	317.472	44.322	1.6862		1.6641		1.8503		1.5105	
-14700	-14690	317.274	44.124	1.6807		1.6587		1.8454		1.5065	
-14600	-14590	317.076	43.926	1.6752		1.6532		1.8405		1.5025	
-14500	-14490	316.878	43.728	1.6697		1.6478		1.8356		1.4985	
-14400	-14390	316.679	43.529	1.6642		1.6424		1.8308		1.4945	
-14300	-14290	316.481	43.331	1.6587		1.6370		1.8259		1.4905	
-14200	-14190	316.283	43.133	1.6533		1.6316		1.8210		1.4866	
-14100	-14090	316.085	42.935	1.6478		1.6263		1.8162		1.4826	
-14000	-13991	315.887	42.737	1.6424	◆ 3	1.6209	◆ 0	1.8113	◆ 0	1.4786	◆ 0
-13900	-13891	315.689	42.539	1.6370		1.6156		1.8065		1.4747	
-13800	-13791	315.491	42.341	1.6316		1.6103		1.8017		1.4708	
-13700	-13691	315.293	42.143	1.6262		1.6050		1.7969		1.4668	
-13600	-13591	315.095	41.945	1.6209		1.5997		1.7921		1.4629	
-13500	-13491	314.896	41.746	1.6155		1.5944		1.7873		1.4590	
-13400	-13391	314.698	41.548	1.6102		1.5891		1.7825		1.4551	
-13300	-13292	314.500	41.350	1.6049		1.5839		1.7777		1.4512	
-13200	-13192	314.302	41.152	1.5996		1.5786		1.7730		1.4473	
-13100	-13092	314.104	40.954	1.5943		1.5734		1.7682		1.4434	
-13000	-12992	313.906	40.756	1.5890	◆ 3	1.5682	◆ 0	1.7635	◆ 0	1.4396	◆ 0
-12900	-12892	313.708	40.558	1.5837		1.5630		1.7588		1.4357	
-12800	-12792	313.510	40.360	1.5785		1.5578		1.7540		1.4319	
-12700	-12692	313.311	40.161	1.5732		1.5527		1.7493		1.4280	
-12600	-12592	313.113	39.963	1.5680		1.5475		1.7446		1.4242	
-12500	-12493	312.915	39.765	1.5628		1.5424		1.7399		1.4203	
-12400	-12393	312.717	39.567	1.5576		1.5372		1.7352		1.4165	
-12300	-12293	312.519	39.369	1.5524		1.5321		1.7306		1.4127	
-12200	-12193	312.321	39.171	1.5473		1.5270		1.7259		1.4089	
-12100	-12093	312.123	38.973	1.5421		1.5219		1.7212		1.4051	
-12000	-11993	311.925	38.775	1.5370	◆ 3	1.5169	◆ 0	1.7166	◆ 0	1.4013	◆ 0
-11900	-11893	311.726	38.576	1.5318		1.5118		1.7120		1.3975	
-11800	-11793	311.528	38.378	1.5267		1.5068		1.7073		1.3937	
-11700	-11693	311.330	38.180	1.5216		1.5017		1.7027		1.3900	
-11600	-11594	311.132	37.982	1.5166		1.4967		1.6981		1.3862	
-11500	-11494	310.934	37.784	1.5115		1.4917		1.6935		1.3825	
-11400	-11394	310.736	37.586	1.5064		1.4867		1.6889		1.3787	
-11300	-11294	310.538	37.388	1.5014		1.4818		1.6844		1.3750	
-11200	-11194	310.340	37.190	1.4964		1.4768		1.6798		1.3713	
-11100	-11094	310.142	36.992	1.4914		1.4718		1.6752		1.3675	
-11000	-10994	309.943	36.793	1.4864	◆ 3	1.4669	◆ 0	1.6707	◆ 0	1.3638	◆ 0
-10900	-10894	309.745	36.595	1.4814		1.4620		1.6661		1.3601	
-10800	-10794	309.547	36.397	1.4764		1.4571		1.6616		1.3564	
-10700	-10695	309.349	36.199	1.4714		1.4522		1.6571		1.3527	
-10600	-10595	309.151	36.001	1.4665		1.4473		1.6526		1.3490	
-10500	-10495	308.953	35.803	1.4616		1.4424		1.6481		1.3454	
-10400	-10395	308.755	35.605	1.4566		1.4376		1.6436		1.3417	
-10300	-10295	308.557	35.407	1.4517		1.4327		1.6391		1.3380	
-10200	-10195	308.358	35.208	1.4468		1.4279		1.6346		1.3344	
-10100	-10095	308.160	35.010	1.4420		1.4231		1.6302		1.3307	
-10000	-9995	307.962	34.812	1.4371	◆ 3	1.4183	◆ 0	1.6257	◆ 0	1.3271	◆ 0
-9900	-9895	307.764	34.614	1.4322		1.4135		1.6213		1.3235	
-9800	-9795	307.566	34.416	1.4274		1.4087		1.6168		1.3198	
-9700	-9695	307.368	34.218	1.4226		1.4040		1.6124		1.3162	
-9600	-9596	307.170	34.020	1.4178		1.3992		1.6080		1.3126	
-9500	-9496	306.972	33.822	1.4130		1.3945		1.6036		1.3090	
-9400	-9396	306.773	33.623	1.4082		1.3898		1.5992		1.3054	
-9300	-9296	306.575	33.425	1.4034		1.3850		1.5948		1.3019	
-9200	-9196	306.377	33.227	1.3986		1.3803		1.5904		1.2983	
-9100	-9096	306.179	33.029	1.3939		1.3757		1.5860		1.2947	

Table IV
Geometric Altitude, English Altitudes

Altitude		Temperature		Pressure				Density			
Z (ft)	H (ft)	T (K)	t (°C)	P (mb)		P/P$_0$		ρ (kg/m^3)		ρ/ρ_0	
-16500	-16513	320.866	47.500	1.7831	+ 3	1.7598	+ 0	1.9360	+ 0	1.5804	+ 0
-16400	-16413	320.667	47.517	1.7773		1.7541		1.9309		1.5763	
-16300	-16313	320.469	47.319	1.7716		1.7484		1.9258		1.5721	
-16200	-16213	320.270	47.120	1.7658		1.7427		1.9208		1.5680	
-16100	-16112	320.072	46.922	1.7601		1.7370		1.9157		1.5638	
-16000	-16012	319.873	46.723	1.7543	+ 3	1.7314	+ 0	1.9107	+ 0	1.5597	+ 0
-15900	-15912	319.675	46.525	1.7486		1.7257		1.9056		1.5556	
-15800	-15812	319.477	46.327	1.7429		1.7201		1.9006		1.5515	
-15700	-15712	319.278	46.128	1.7372		1.7145		1.8956		1.5474	
-15600	-15612	319.080	45.930	1.7316		1.7089		1.8906		1.5433	
-15500	-15512	318.881	45.731	1.7259		1.7033		1.8856		1.5392	
-15400	-15411	318.683	45.533	1.7203		1.6978		1.8806		1.5352	
-15300	-15311	318.484	45.334	1.7147		1.6922		1.8756		1.5311	
-15200	-15211	318.286	45.136	1.7090		1.6867		1.8706		1.5270	
-15100	-15111	318.088	44.938	1.7035		1.6812		1.8657		1.5230	
-15000	-15011	317.889	44.739	1.6979	+ 3	1.6757	+ 0	1.8607	+ 0	1.5190	+ 0
-14900	-14911	317.691	44.541	1.6923		1.6702		1.8558		1.5149	
-14800	-14811	317.492	44.342	1.6868		1.6647		1.8509		1.5109	
-14700	-14710	317.294	44.144	1.6812		1.6592		1.8459		1.5069	
-14600	-14610	317.096	43.946	1.6757		1.6538		1.8410		1.5029	
-14500	-14510	316.897	43.747	1.6702		1.6484		1.8361		1.4989	
-14400	-14410	316.699	43.549	1.6647		1.6430		1.8312		1.4949	
-14300	-14310	316.500	43.350	1.6593		1.6376		1.8264		1.4909	
-14200	-14210	316.302	43.152	1.6538		1.6322		1.8215		1.4869	
-14100	-14110	316.104	42.954	1.6483		1.6268		1.8166		1.4830	
-14000	-14009	315.905	42.755	1.6429	+ 3	1.6214	+ 0	1.8118	+ 0	1.4790	+ 0
-13900	-13909	315.707	42.557	1.6375		1.6161		1.8070		1.4751	
-13800	-13809	315.509	42.359	1.6321		1.6108		1.8021		1.4711	
-13700	-13709	315.310	42.160	1.6267		1.6054		1.7973		1.4672	
-13600	-13609	315.112	41.962	1.6213		1.6001		1.7925		1.4633	
-13500	-13509	314.913	41.763	1.6160		1.5948		1.7877		1.4594	
-13400	-13409	314.715	41.565	1.6106		1.5896		1.7829		1.4554	
-13300	-13308	314.517	41.367	1.6053		1.5843		1.7781		1.4515	
-13200	-13208	314.318	41.168	1.6000		1.5791		1.7734		1.4477	
-13100	-13108	314.120	40.970	1.5947		1.5738		1.7686		1.4438	
-13000	-13008	313.922	40.772	1.5894	+ 3	1.5686	+ 0	1.7639	+ 0	1.4399	+ 0
-12900	-12908	313.723	40.573	1.5841		1.5634		1.7591		1.4360	
-12800	-12808	313.525	40.375	1.5789		1.5582		1.7544		1.4322	
-12700	-12708	313.326	40.176	1.5736		1.5531		1.7497		1.4283	
-12600	-12608	313.128	39.978	1.5684		1.5479		1.7450		1.4245	
-12500	-12507	312.930	39.780	1.5632		1.5427		1.7403		1.4206	
-12400	-12407	312.731	39.581	1.5580		1.5376		1.7356		1.4168	
-12300	-12307	312.533	39.383	1.5528		1.5325		1.7309		1.4130	
-12200	-12207	312.335	39.185	1.5476		1.5274		1.7262		1.4092	
-12100	-12107	312.136	38.986	1.5425		1.5223		1.7216		1.4054	
-12000	-12007	311.938	38.788	1.5373	+ 3	1.5172	+ 0	1.7169	+ 0	1.4016	+ 0
-11900	-11907	311.740	38.590	1.5322		1.5122		1.7123		1.3978	
-11800	-11807	311.541	38.391	1.5271		1.5071		1.7076		1.3940	
-11700	-11707	311.343	38.193	1.5220		1.5021		1.7030		1.3902	
-11600	-11606	311.145	37.995	1.5169		1.4971		1.6984		1.3865	
-11500	-11506	310.946	37.796	1.5118		1.4920		1.6938		1.3827	
-11400	-11406	310.748	37.598	1.5068		1.4870		1.6892		1.3790	
-11300	-11306	310.550	37.400	1.5017		1.4821		1.6846		1.3752	
-11200	-11206	310.351	37.201	1.4967		1.4771		1.6801		1.3715	
-11100	-11106	310.153	37.003	1.4916		1.4721		1.6755		1.3678	
-11000	-11006	309.955	36.805	1.4866	+ 3	1.4672	+ 0	1.6709	+ 0	1.3640	+ 0
-10900	-10906	309.756	36.606	1.4816		1.4623		1.6664		1.3603	
-10800	-10806	309.558	36.408	1.4767		1.4574		1.6619		1.3566	
-10700	-10705	309.360	36.210	1.4717		1.4525		1.6573		1.3529	
-10600	-10605	309.161	36.011	1.4668		1.4476		1.6528		1.3492	
-10500	-10505	308.963	35.813	1.4618		1.4427		1.6483		1.3456	
-10400	-10405	308.765	35.615	1.4569		1.4378		1.6438		1.3419	
-10300	-10305	308.566	35.416	1.4520		1.4330		1.6393		1.3382	
-10200	-10205	308.368	35.218	1.4471		1.4282		1.6348		1.3346	
-10100	-10105	308.170	35.020	1.4422		1.4233		1.6304		1.3309	
-10000	-10005	307.971	34.821	1.4373	+ 3	1.4185	+ 0	1.6259	+ 0	1.3273	+ 0
-9900	-9905	307.773	34.623	1.4325		1.4137		1.6215		1.3236	
-9800	-9805	307.575	34.425	1.4276		1.4089		1.6170		1.3200	
-9700	-9705	307.376	34.226	1.4228		1.4042		1.6126		1.3164	
-9600	-9604	307.178	34.028	1.4180		1.3994		1.6082		1.3128	
-9500	-9504	306.980	33.830	1.4132		1.3947		1.6038		1.3092	
-9400	-9404	306.782	33.632	1.4084		1.3900		1.5993		1.3056	
-9300	-9304	306.583	33.433	1.4036		1.3852		1.5950		1.3020	
-9200	-9204	306.385	33.235	1.3988		1.3805		1.5906		1.2984	
-9100	-9104	306.187	33.037	1.3941		1.3758		1.5862		1.2948	

Table IV
Geopotential Altitude, English Altitudes

Altitude		Temperature		Pressure		Density	
H (ft)	Z (ft)	T (K)	t (°C)	P (mb)	P/P$_0$	ρ (kg/m^3)	ρ/ρ_0
-9000	-8996	305.981	32.831	1.3892 ◆ 3	1.3710 ◆ 0	1.5817 ◆ 0	1.2911 ◆ 0
-8900	-8896	305.783	32.633	1.3844	1.3663	1.5773	1.2876
-8800	-8796	305.585	32.435	1.3797	1.3617	1.5730	1.2840
-8700	-8696	305.387	32.237	1.3750	1.3570	1.5686	1.2805
-8600	-8596	305.189	32.039	1.3703	1.3524	1.5643	1.2770
-8500	-8497	304.990	31.840	1.3657	1.3478	1.5600	1.2734
-8400	-8397	304.792	31.642	1.3610	1.3432	1.5557	1.2699
-8300	-8297	304.594	31.444	1.3564	1.3386	1.5514	1.2664
-8200	-8197	304.396	31.246	1.3517	1.3341	1.5471	1.2629
-8100	-8097	304.198	31.048	1.3471	1.3295	1.5428	1.2594
-8000	-7997	304.000	30.850	1.3425 ◆ 3	1.3250 ◆ 0	1.5385 ◆ 0	1.2559 ◆ 0
-7900	-7897	303.802	30.652	1.3379	1.3204	1.5343	1.2525
-7800	-7797	303.604	30.454	1.3334	1.3159	1.5300	1.2490
-7700	-7697	303.405	30.255	1.3288	1.3114	1.5258	1.2455
-7600	-7597	303.207	30.057	1.3242	1.3069	1.5215	1.2421
-7500	-7497	303.009	29.859	1.3197	1.3024	1.5173	1.2386
-7400	-7397	302.811	29.661	1.3152	1.2980	1.5131	1.2352
-7300	-7297	302.613	29.463	1.3106	1.2935	1.5089	1.2317
-7200	-7198	302.415	29.265	1.3061	1.2891	1.5047	1.2283
-7100	-7098	302.217	29.067	1.3017	1.2846	1.5005	1.2249
-7000	-6998	302.019	28.869	1.2972 ◆ 3	1.2802 ◆ 0	1.4963 ◆ 0	1.2215 ◆ 0
-6900	-6898	301.820	28.670	1.2927	1.2758	1.4921	1.2181
-6800	-6798	301.622	28.472	1.2883	1.2714	1.4880	1.2147
-6700	-6698	301.424	28.274	1.2838	1.2670	1.4838	1.2113
-6600	-6598	301.226	28.076	1.2794	1.2627	1.4797	1.2079
-6500	-6498	301.028	27.878	1.2750	1.2583	1.4755	1.2045
-6400	-6398	300.830	27.680	1.2706	1.2539	1.4714	1.2011
-6300	-6298	300.632	27.482	1.2662	1.2496	1.4673	1.1978
-6200	-6198	300.434	27.284	1.2618	1.2453	1.4632	1.1944
-6100	-6098	300.236	27.086	1.2574	1.2410	1.4591	1.1911
-6000	-5998	300.037	26.887	1.2531 ◆ 3	1.2367 ◆ 0	1.4550 ◆ 0	1.1877 ◆ 0
-5900	-5898	299.839	26.689	1.2487	1.2324	1.4509	1.1844
-5800	-5798	299.641	26.491	1.2444	1.2281	1.4468	1.1811
-5700	-5698	299.443	26.293	1.2401	1.2239	1.4427	1.1778
-5600	-5598	299.245	26.095	1.2358	1.2196	1.4387	1.1744
-5500	-5499	299.047	25.897	1.2315	1.2154	1.4346	1.1711
-5400	-5399	298.849	25.699	1.2272	1.2111	1.4306	1.1678
-5300	-5299	298.651	25.501	1.2229	1.2069	1.4266	1.1645
-5200	-5199	298.452	25.302	1.2187	1.2027	1.4225	1.1613
-5100	-5099	298.254	25.104	1.2144	1.1985	1.4185	1.1580
-5000	-4999	298.056	24.906	1.2102 ◆ 3	1.1944 ◆ 0	1.4145 ◆ 0	1.1547 ◆ 0
-4900	-4899	297.858	24.708	1.2060	1.1902	1.4105	1.1514
-4800	-4799	297.660	24.510	1.2018	1.1860	1.4065	1.1482
-4700	-4699	297.462	24.312	1.1976	1.1819	1.4026	1.1449
-4600	-4599	297.264	24.114	1.1934	1.1778	1.3986	1.1417
-4500	-4499	297.066	23.916	1.1892	1.1736	1.3946	1.1385
-4400	-4399	296.867	23.717	1.1850	1.1695	1.3907	1.1352
-4300	-4299	296.669	23.519	1.1809	1.1654	1.3867	1.1320
-4200	-4199	296.471	23.321	1.1767	1.1613	1.3828	1.1288
-4100	-4099	296.273	23.123	1.1726	1.1573	1.3789	1.1256
-4000	-3999	296.075	22.925	1.1685 ◆ 3	1.1532 ◆ 0	1.3749 ◆ 0	1.1224 ◆ 0
-3900	-3899	295.877	22.727	1.1644	1.1492	1.3710	1.1192
-3800	-3799	295.679	22.529	1.1603	1.1451	1.3671	1.1160
-3700	-3699	295.481	22.331	1.1562	1.1411	1.3632	1.1128
-3600	-3599	295.283	22.133	1.1522	1.1371	1.3593	1.1097
-3500	-3499	295.084	21.934	1.1481	1.1331	1.3555	1.1065
-3400	-3399	294.886	21.736	1.1440	1.1291	1.3516	1.1033
-3300	-3299	294.688	21.538	1.1400	1.1251	1.3477	1.1002
-3200	-3200	294.490	21.340	1.1360	1.1211	1.3439	1.0970
-3100	-3100	294.292	21.142	1.1320	1.1172	1.3400	1.0939
-3000	-3000	294.094	20.944	1.1280 ◆ 3	1.1132 ◆ 0	1.3362 ◆ 0	1.0908 ◆ 0
-2900	-2900	293.896	20.746	1.1240	1.1093	1.3324	1.0877
-2800	-2800	293.698	20.548	1.1200	1.1054	1.3286	1.0845
-2700	-2700	293.499	20.349	1.1160	1.1015	1.3247	1.0814
-2600	-2600	293.301	20.151	1.1121	1.0976	1.3209	1.0783
-2500	-2500	293.103	19.953	1.1082	1.0937	1.3172	1.0752
-2400	-2400	292.905	19.755	1.1042	1.0898	1.3134	1.0721
-2300	-2300	292.707	19.557	1.1003	1.0859	1.3096	1.0691
-2200	-2200	292.509	19.359	1.0964	1.0821	1.3058	1.0660
-2100	-2100	292.311	19.161	1.0925	1.0782	1.3021	1.0629
-2000	-2000	292.113	18.963	1.0886 ◆ 3	1.0744 ◆ 0	1.2983 ◆ 0	1.0598 ◆ 0
-1900	-1900	291.914	18.764	1.0847	1.0705	1.2946	1.0568
-1800	-1800	291.716	18.566	1.0809	1.0667	1.2908	1.0537
-1700	-1700	291.518	18.368	1.0770	1.0629	1.2871	1.0507
-1600	-1600	291.320	18.170	1.0732	1.0591	1.2834	1.0477
-1500	-1500	291.122	17.972	1.0693	1.0554	1.2797	1.0446
-1400	-1400	290.924	17.774	1.0655	1.0516	1.2760	1.0416
-1300	-1300	290.726	17.576	1.0617	1.0478	1.2723	1.0386
-1200	-1200	290.528	17.378	1.0579	1.0441	1.2686	1.0356
-1100	-1100	290.330	17.180	1.0541	1.0403	1.2649	1.0326

Table IV
Geometric Altitude, English Altitudes

Altitude		Temperature		Pressure		Density	
Z (ft)	H (ft)	T (K)	t (°C)	P (mb)	P/P$_0$	ρ (kg/m^3)	ρ/ρ$_0$
-9000	-9004	305.988	32.838	1.3893 + 3	1.3712 + 0	1.5818 + 0	1.2913 + 0
-8900	-8904	305.790	32.640	1.3846	1.3665	1.5775	1.2877
-8800	-8804	305.592	32.442	1.3799	1.3619	1.5731	1.2842
-8700	-8704	305.394	32.244	1.3752	1.3572	1.5688	1.2806
-8600	-8604	305.195	32.045	1.3705	1.3526	1.5644	1.2771
-8500	-8503	304.997	31.847	1.3658	1.3480	1.5601	1.2736
-8400	-8403	304.799	31.649	1.3612	1.3434	1.5558	1.2700
-8300	-8303	304.600	31.450	1.3565	1.3388	1.5515	1.2665
-8200	-8203	304.402	31.252	1.3519	1.3342	1.5472	1.2630
-8100	-8103	304.204	31.054	1.3473	1.3297	1.5429	1.2595
-8000	-8003	304.006	30.856	1.3427 + 3	1.3251 + 0	1.5387 + 0	1.2560 + 0
-7900	-7903	303.807	30.657	1.3381	1.3206	1.5344	1.2526
-7800	-7803	303.609	30.459	1.3335	1.3160	1.5301	1.2491
-7700	-7703	303.411	30.261	1.3289	1.3115	1.5259	1.2456
-7600	-7603	303.212	30.062	1.3244	1.3070	1.5216	1.2422
-7500	-7503	303.014	29.864	1.3198	1.3026	1.5174	1.2387
-7400	-7403	302.816	29.666	1.3153	1.2981	1.5132	1.2353
-7300	-7303	302.618	29.468	1.3108	1.2936	1.5090	1.2318
-7200	-7202	302.419	29.269	1.3063	1.2892	1.5048	1.2284
-7100	-7102	302.221	29.071	1.3018	1.2847	1.5006	1.2250
-7000	-7002	302.023	28.873	1.2973 + 3	1.2803 + 0	1.4964 + 0	1.2216 + 0
-6900	-6902	301.825	28.675	1.2928	1.2759	1.4922	1.2181
-6800	-6802	301.626	28.476	1.2884	1.2715	1.4881	1.2147
-6700	-6702	301.428	28.278	1.2839	1.2671	1.4839	1.2113
-6600	-6602	301.230	28.080	1.2795	1.2627	1.4798	1.2080
-6500	-6502	301.032	27.882	1.2751	1.2584	1.4756	1.2046
-6400	-6402	300.833	27.683	1.2706	1.2540	1.4715	1.2012
-6300	-6302	300.635	27.485	1.2663	1.2497	1.4674	1.1978
-6200	-6202	300.437	27.287	1.2619	1.2454	1.4632	1.1945
-6100	-6102	300.239	27.089	1.2575	1.2411	1.4591	1.1911
-6000	-6002	300.040	26.890	1.2531 + 3	1.2368 + 0	1.4550 + 0	1.1878 + 0
-5900	-5902	299.842	26.692	1.2488	1.2325	1.4510	1.1845
-5800	-5802	299.644	26.494	1.2445	1.2282	1.4469	1.1811
-5700	-5702	299.446	26.296	1.2401	1.2239	1.4428	1.1778
-5600	-5602	299.248	26.098	1.2358	1.2197	1.4387	1.1745
-5500	-5501	299.049	25.899	1.2315	1.2154	1.4347	1.1712
-5400	-5401	298.851	25.701	1.2273	1.2112	1.4307	1.1679
-5300	-5301	298.653	25.503	1.2230	1.2070	1.4266	1.1646
-5200	-5201	298.455	25.305	1.2187	1.2028	1.4226	1.1613
-5100	-5101	298.256	25.106	1.2145	1.1986	1.4186	1.1580
-5000	-5001	298.058	24.908	1.2102 + 3	1.1944 + 0	1.4146 + 0	1.1547 + 0
-4900	-4901	297.860	24.710	1.2060	1.1902	1.4106	1.1515
-4800	-4801	297.662	24.512	1.2018	1.1861	1.4066	1.1482
-4700	-4701	297.464	24.314	1.1976	1.1819	1.4026	1.1450
-4600	-4601	297.265	24.115	1.1934	1.1778	1.3986	1.1417
-4500	-4501	297.067	23.917	1.1892	1.1737	1.3947	1.1385
-4400	-4401	296.869	23.719	1.1851	1.1696	1.3907	1.1353
-4300	-4301	296.671	23.521	1.1809	1.1655	1.3868	1.1320
-4200	-4201	296.473	23.323	1.1768	1.1614	1.3828	1.1288
-4100	-4101	296.274	23.124	1.1726	1.1573	1.3789	1.1256
-4000	-4001	296.076	22.926	1.1685 + 3	1.1532 + 0	1.3750 + 0	1.1224 + 0
-3900	-3901	295.878	22.728	1.1644	1.1492	1.3711	1.1192
-3800	-3801	295.680	22.530	1.1603	1.1452	1.3672	1.1160
-3700	-3701	295.482	22.332	1.1562	1.1411	1.3633	1.1129
-3600	-3601	295.283	22.133	1.1522	1.1371	1.3594	1.1097
-3500	-3501	295.085	21.935	1.1481	1.1331	1.3555	1.1065
-3400	-3401	294.887	21.737	1.1441	1.1291	1.3516	1.1034
-3300	-3301	294.689	21.539	1.1400	1.1251	1.3478	1.1002
-3200	-3200	294.491	21.341	1.1360	1.1212	1.3439	1.0971
-3100	-3100	294.293	21.143	1.1320	1.1172	1.3401	1.0939
-3000	-3000	294.094	20.944	1.1280 + 3	1.1132 + 0	1.3362 + 0	1.0908 + 0
-2900	-2900	293.896	20.746	1.1240	1.1093	1.3324	1.0877
-2800	-2800	293.698	20.548	1.1200	1.1054	1.3286	1.0845
-2700	-2700	293.500	20.350	1.1161	1.1015	1.3248	1.0814
-2600	-2600	293.302	20.152	1.1121	1.0976	1.3210	1.0783
-2500	-2500	293.103	19.953	1.1082	1.0937	1.3172	1.0752
-2400	-2400	292.905	19.755	1.1042	1.0898	1.3134	1.0721
-2300	-2300	292.707	19.557	1.1003	1.0859	1.3096	1.0691
-2200	-2200	292.509	19.359	1.0964	1.0821	1.3058	1.0660
-2100	-2100	292.311	19.161	1.0925	1.0782	1.3021	1.0629
-2000	-2000	292.113	18.963	1.0886 + 3	1.0744 + 0	1.2983 + 0	1.0599 + 0
-1900	-1900	291.914	18.764	1.0847	1.0706	1.2946	1.0568
-1800	-1800	291.716	18.566	1.0809	1.0667	1.2908	1.0537
-1700	-1700	291.518	18.368	1.0770	1.0629	1.2871	1.0507
-1600	-1600	291.320	18.170	1.0732	1.0591	1.2834	1.0477
-1500	-1500	291.122	17.972	1.0693	1.0554	1.2797	1.0446
-1400	-1400	290.924	17.774	1.0655	1.0516	1.2760	1.0416
-1300	-1300	290.726	17.576	1.0617	1.0478	1.2723	1.0386
-1200	-1200	290.527	17.377	1.0579	1.0441	1.2686	1.0356
-1100	-1100	290.329	17.179	1.0541	1.0403	1.2649	1.0326

Table IV
Geopotential Altitude, English Altitudes

Altitude		Temperature		Pressure		Density	
H (ft)	Z (ft)	T (K)	t (°C)	P (mb)	P/P$_0$	ρ (kg/m^3)	ρ/ρ_0
-1000	-1000	290.131	16.981	1.0504 + 3	1.0366 + 0	1.2612 + 0	1.0296 + 0
-900	-900	289.933	16.783	1.0466	1.0329	1.2576	1.0266
-800	-800	289.735	16.585	1.0428	1.0292	1.2539	1.0236
-700	-700	289.537	16.387	1.0391	1.0255	1.2503	1.0206
-600	-600	289.339	16.189	1.0354	1.0218	1.2467	1.0177
-500	-500	289.141	15.991	1.0316	1.0182	1.2430	1.0147
-400	-400	288.943	15.793	1.0279	1.0145	1.2394	1.0118
-300	-300	288.745	15.595	1.0242	1.0108	1.2358	1.0088
-200	-200	288.546	15.396	1.0205	1.0072	1.2322	1.0059
-100	-100	288.348	15.198	1.0169	1.0036	1.2286	1.0029
0	0	288.150	15.000	1.01325 + 3	1.00000 + 0	1.2250 + 0	1.0000 + 0
100	100	287.952	14.802	1.0095	9.9639 - 1	1.2214	9.9708 - 1
200	200	287.754	14.604	1.0059	9.9279	1.2178	9.9416
300	300	287.556	14.406	1.0023	9.8920	1.2143	9.9125
400	400	287.358	14.208	9.9868 + 2	9.8562	1.2107	9.8835
500	500	287.160	14.010	9.9507	9.8206	1.2072	9.8545
600	600	286.961	13.811	9.9147	9.7850	1.2036	9.8256
700	700	286.763	13.613	9.8788	9.7496	1.2001	9.7968
800	800	286.565	13.415	9.8429	9.7142	1.1966	9.7680
900	900	286.367	13.217	9.8072	9.6790	1.1931	9.7393
1000	1000	286.169	13.019	9.7716 + 2	9.6438 - 1	1.1896 + 0	9.7106 - 1
1100	1100	285.971	12.821	9.7361	9.6088	1.1861	9.6821
1200	1200	285.773	12.623	9.7007	9.5738	1.1826	9.6535
1300	1300	285.575	12.425	9.6654	9.5390	1.1791	9.6251
1400	1400	285.377	12.227	9.6302	9.5043	1.1756	9.5967
1500	1500	285.178	12.028	9.5951	9.4697	1.1721	9.5684
1600	1600	284.980	11.830	9.5602	9.4351	1.1687	9.5401
1700	1700	284.782	11.632	9.5253	9.4007	1.1652	9.5119
1800	1800	284.584	11.434	9.4905	9.3664	1.1618	9.4838
1900	1900	284.386	11.236	9.4558	9.3322	1.1583	9.4557
2000	2000	284.188	11.038	9.4212 + 2	9.2980 - 1	1.1549 + 0	9.4277 - 1
2100	2100	283.990	10.840	9.3868	9.2640	1.1515	9.3998
2200	2200	283.792	10.642	9.3524	9.2301	1.1481	9.3719
2300	2300	283.593	10.443	9.3181	9.1963	1.1447	9.3441
2400	2400	283.395	10.245	9.2840	9.1626	1.1413	9.3164
2500	2500	283.197	10.047	9.2499	9.1290	1.1379	9.2887
2600	2600	282.999	9.849	9.2160	9.0954	1.1345	9.2610
2700	2700	282.801	9.651	9.1821	9.0620	1.1311	9.2335
2800	2800	282.603	9.453	9.1483	9.0287	1.1277	9.2060
2900	2900	282.405	9.255	9.1147	8.9955	1.1244	9.1785
3000	3000	282.207	9.057	9.0811 + 2	8.9624 - 1	1.1210 + 0	9.1512 - 1
3100	3100	282.008	8.858	9.0477	8.9293	1.1177	9.1239
3200	3200	281.810	8.660	9.0143	8.8964	1.1143	9.0966
3300	3301	281.612	8.462	8.9810	8.8636	1.1110	9.0694
3400	3401	281.414	8.264	8.9479	8.8309	1.1077	9.0423
3500	3501	281.216	8.066	8.9148	8.7982	1.1044	9.0152
3600	3601	281.018	7.868	8.8819	8.7657	1.1011	8.9882
3700	3701	280.820	7.670	8.8490	8.7333	1.0978	8.9613
3800	3801	280.622	7.472	8.8162	8.7009	1.0945	8.9344
3900	3901	280.424	7.274	8.7836	8.6687	1.0912	8.9076
4000	4001	280.225	7.075	8.7510 + 2	8.6366 - 1	1.0879 + 0	8.8809 - 1
4100	4101	280.027	6.877	8.7185	8.6045	1.0846	8.8542
4200	4201	279.829	6.679	8.6862	8.5726	1.0814	8.8275
4300	4301	279.631	6.481	8.6539	8.5407	1.0781	8.8010
4400	4401	279.433	6.283	8.6217	8.5090	1.0749	8.7745
4500	4501	279.235	6.085	8.5896	8.4773	1.0716	8.7480
4600	4601	279.037	5.887	8.5577	8.4457	1.0684	8.7216
4700	4701	278.839	5.689	8.5258	8.4143	1.0652	8.6953
4800	4801	278.640	5.490	8.4940	8.3829	1.0620	8.6691
4900	4901	278.442	5.292	8.4623	8.3516	1.0587	8.6428
5000	5001	278.244	5.094	8.4307 + 2	8.3204 - 1	1.0555 + 0	8.6167 - 1
5100	5101	278.046	4.896	8.3992	8.2893	1.0524	8.5906
5200	5201	277.848	4.698	8.3678	8.2583	1.0492	8.5646
5300	5301	277.650	4.500	8.3365	8.2274	1.0460	8.5386
5400	5401	277.452	4.302	8.3052	8.1966	1.0428	8.5127
5500	5501	277.254	4.104	8.2741	8.1659	1.0396	8.4869
5600	5602	277.055	3.905	8.2431	8.1353	1.0365	8.4611
5700	5702	276.857	3.707	8.2122	8.1048	1.0333	8.4354
5800	5802	276.659	3.509	8.1813	8.0743	1.0302	8.4097
5900	5902	276.461	3.311	8.1506	8.0440	1.0271	8.3841
6000	6002	276.263	3.113	8.1199 + 2	8.0137 - 1	1.0239 + 0	8.3586 - 1
6100	6102	276.065	2.915	8.0894	7.9836	1.0208	8.3331
6200	6202	275.867	2.717	8.0589	7.9535	1.0177	8.3077
6300	6302	275.669	2.519	8.0285	7.9235	1.0146	8.2823
6400	6402	275.471	2.321	7.9982	7.8936	1.0115	8.2570
6500	6502	275.272	2.122	7.9681	7.8638	1.0084	8.2318
6600	6602	275.074	1.924	7.9380	7.8341	1.0053	8.2066
6700	6702	274.876	1.726	7.9080	7.8045	1.0022	8.1815
6800	6802	274.678	1.528	7.8780	7.7750	9.9916 - 1	8.1565
6900	6902	274.480	1.330	7.8482	7.7456	9.9610	8.1314

Table IV
Geometric Altitude, English Altitudes

Altitude		Temperature		Pressure		Density	
Z (ft)	H (ft)	T (K)	t (°C)	P (mb)	P/P_0	ρ (kg/m³)	ρ/ρ_0
-1000	-1000	290.131	16.981	1.0504 + 3	1.0366 + 0	1.2613 + 0	1.0296 + 0
-900	-900	289.933	16.783	1.0466	1.0329	1.2576	1.0266
-800	-800	289.735	16.585	1.0428	1.0292	1.2539	1.0236
-700	-700	289.537	16.387	1.0391	1.0255	1.2503	1.0206
-600	-600	289.339	16.189	1.0354	1.0218	1.2467	1.0177
-500	-500	289.140	15.990	1.0316	1.0182	1.2430	1.0147
-400	-400	288.942	15.792	1.0279	1.0145	1.2394	1.0118
-300	-300	288.744	15.594	1.0242	1.0108	1.2358	1.0088
-200	-200	288.546	15.396	1.0205	1.0072	1.2322	1.0059
-100	-100	288.348	15.198	1.0169	1.0036	1.2286	1.0029
0	0	288.150	15.000	1.01325 + 3	1.00000 + 0	1.2250 + 0	1.0000 + 0
100	100	287.952	14.802	1.0095	9.9639 - 1	1.2214	9.9708 - 1
200	200	287.754	14.604	1.0059	9.9279	1.2178	9.9416
300	300	287.556	14.406	1.0023	9.8920	1.2143	9.9125
400	400	287.357	14.207	9.9868 + 2	9.8562	1.2107	9.8835
500	500	287.159	14.009	9.9507	9.8206	1.2072	9.8545
600	600	286.961	13.811	9.9147	9.7850	1.2036	9.8256
700	700	286.763	13.613	9.8788	9.7496	1.2001	9.7968
800	800	286.565	13.415	9.8429	9.7142	1.1966	9.7680
900	900	286.367	13.217	9.8072	9.6790	1.1931	9.7393
1000	1000	286.169	13.019	9.7716 + 2	9.6438 - 1	1.1896 + 0	9.7107 - 1
1100	1100	285.971	12.821	9.7361	9.6088	1.1861	9.6821
1200	1200	285.773	12.623	9.7007	9.5739	1.1826	9.6536
1300	1300	285.574	12.424	9.6654	9.5390	1.1791	9.6251
1400	1400	285.376	12.226	9.6303	9.5043	1.1756	9.5967
1500	1500	285.178	12.028	9.5952	9.4697	1.1721	9.5684
1600	1600	284.980	11.830	9.5602	9.4352	1.1687	9.5402
1700	1700	284.782	11.632	9.5253	9.4008	1.1652	9.5120
1800	1800	284.584	11.434	9.4905	9.3664	1.1618	9.4838
1900	1900	284.386	11.236	9.4559	9.3322	1.1583	9.4558
2000	2000	284.188	11.038	9.4213 + 2	9.2981 - 1	1.1549 + 0	9.4278 - 1
2100	2100	283.990	10.840	9.3868	9.2641	1.1515	9.3999
2200	2200	283.792	10.642	9.3525	9.2302	1.1481	9.3720
2300	2300	283.594	10.444	9.3182	9.1964	1.1447	9.3442
2400	2400	283.396	10.246	9.2841	9.1627	1.1413	9.3164
2500	2500	283.197	10.047	9.2500	9.1291	1.1379	9.2887
2600	2600	282.999	9.849	9.2161	9.0955	1.1345	9.2611
2700	2700	282.801	9.651	9.1822	9.0621	1.1311	9.2336
2800	2800	282.603	9.453	9.1485	9.0288	1.1277	9.2061
2900	2900	282.405	9.255	9.1148	8.9956	1.1244	9.1787
3000	3000	282.207	9.057	9.0813 + 2	8.9625 - 1	1.1210 + 0	9.1513 - 1
3100	3100	282.009	8.859	9.0478	8.9295	1.1177	9.1240
3200	3200	281.811	8.661	9.0145	8.8966	1.1144	9.0967
3300	3299	281.613	8.463	8.9812	8.8638	1.1110	9.0696
3400	3399	281.415	8.265	8.9481	8.8311	1.1077	9.0425
3500	3499	281.217	8.067	8.9150	8.7984	1.1044	9.0154
3600	3559	281.019	7.869	8.8821	8.7659	1.1011	8.9884
3700	3699	280.821	7.671	8.8492	8.7335	1.0978	8.9615
3800	3799	280.623	7.473	8.8165	8.7012	1.0945	8.9346
3900	3899	280.425	7.275	8.7838	8.6689	1.0912	8.9078
4000	3999	280.227	7.077	8.7513 + 2	8.6368 - 1	1.0879 + 0	8.8811 - 1
4100	4099	280.029	6.879	8.7188	8.6048	1.0847	8.8544
4200	4199	279.831	6.681	8.6864	8.5728	1.0814	8.8278
4300	4299	279.632	6.482	8.6542	8.5410	1.0781	8.8012
4400	4399	279.434	6.284	8.6220	8.5093	1.0749	8.7747
4500	4499	279.236	6.086	8.5899	8.4776	1.0717	8.7483
4600	4599	279.038	5.888	8.5580	8.4461	1.0684	8.7219
4700	4699	278.840	5.690	8.5261	8.4146	1.0652	8.6956
4800	4799	278.642	5.492	8.4943	8.3832	1.0620	8.6693
4900	4899	278.444	5.294	8.4626	8.3520	1.0588	8.6431
5000	4999	278.246	5.096	8.4311 + 2	8.3208 - 1	1.0556 + 0	8.6170 - 1
5100	5099	278.048	4.898	8.3996	8.2897	1.0524	8.5909
5200	5199	277.850	4.700	8.3682	8.2587	1.0492	8.5649
5300	5299	277.652	4.502	8.3369	8.2279	1.0460	8.5390
5400	5399	277.454	4.304	8.3057	8.1971	1.0429	8.5131
5500	5499	277.256	4.106	8.2746	8.1664	1.0397	8.4873
5600	5598	277.058	3.908	8.2436	8.1358	1.0365	8.4615
5700	5698	276.860	3.710	8.2126	8.1052	1.0334	8.4358
5800	5798	276.662	3.512	8.1818	8.0748	1.0302	8.4102
5900	5898	276.464	3.314	8.1511	8.0445	1.0271	8.3846
6000	5998	276.266	3.116	8.1204 + 2	8.0142 - 1	1.0240 + 0	8.3590 - 1
6100	6098	276.068	2.918	8.0899	7.9841	1.0209	8.3336
6200	6198	275.870	2.720	8.0594	7.9541	1.0178	8.3082
6300	6298	275.672	2.522	8.0291	7.9241	1.0146	8.2828
6400	6398	275.474	2.324	7.9988	7.8942	1.0115	8.2575
6500	6498	275.276	2.126	7.9687	7.8644	1.0085	8.2323
6600	6598	275.078	1.928	7.9386	7.8348	1.0054	8.2071
6700	6698	274.880	1.730	7.9086	7.8052	1.0023	8.1820
6800	6798	274.682	1.532	7.8787	7.7757	9.9923 - 1	8.1570
6900	6898	274.484	1.334	7.8489	7.7463	9.9617	8.1320

Table IV
Geopotential Altitude, English Altitudes

Altitude		Temperature		Pressure		Density	
H (ft)	Z (ft)	T (K)	t (°C)	P (mb)	P/P$_0$	ρ (kg/m³)	ρ/ρ_0
7000	7002	274.282	1.132	7.8185 + 2	7.7162 - 1	9.9304 - 1	8.1065 - 1
7100	7102	274.084	.934	7.7889	7.6870	9.8999	8.0816
7200	7202	273.886	.736	7.7593	7.6578	9.8695	8.0567
7300	7303	273.687	.537	7.7299	7.6288	9.8391	8.0320
7400	7403	273.489	.339	7.7005	7.5998	9.8089	8.0072
7500	7503	273.291	.141	7.6712	7.5709	9.7787	7.9826
7600	7603	273.093	-.057	7.6420	7.5421	9.7485	7.9580
7700	7703	272.895	-.255	7.6129	7.5134	9.7185	7.9334
7800	7803	272.697	-.453	7.5839	7.4848	9.6885	7.9090
7900	7903	272.499	-.651	7.5550	7.4562	9.6586	7.8845
8000	8003	272.301	-.849	7.5262 + 2	7.4278 - 1	9.6287 - 1	7.8602 - 1
8100	8103	272.102	-1.048	7.4975	7.3994	9.5989	7.8359
8200	8203	271.904	-1.246	7.4688	7.3711	9.5692	7.8116
8300	8303	271.706	-1.444	7.4403	7.3430	9.5396	7.7874
8400	8403	271.508	-1.642	7.4118	7.3149	9.5100	7.7633
8500	8503	271.310	-1.840	7.3834	7.2868	9.4805	7.7392
8600	8604	271.112	-2.038	7.3551	7.2589	9.4511	7.7152
8700	8704	270.914	-2.236	7.3269	7.2311	9.4217	7.6912
8800	8804	270.716	-2.434	7.2988	7.2033	9.3924	7.6673
8900	8904	270.518	-2.632	7.2707	7.1757	9.3632	7.6434
9000	9004	270.319	-2.831	7.2428 + 2	7.1481 - 1	9.3341 - 1	7.6196 - 1
9100	9104	270.121	-3.029	7.2149	7.1206	9.3050	7.5959
9200	9204	269.923	-3.227	7.1872	7.0932	9.2760	7.5722
9300	9304	269.725	-3.425	7.1595	7.0659	9.2470	7.5486
9400	9404	269.527	-3.623	7.1319	7.0386	9.2182	7.5250
9500	9504	269.329	-3.821	7.1044	7.0115	9.1894	7.5015
9600	9604	269.131	-4.019	7.0770	6.9844	9.1606	7.4781
9700	9705	268.933	-4.217	7.0496	6.9574	9.1320	7.4547
9800	9805	268.734	-4.416	7.0224	6.9305	9.1034	7.4313
9900	9905	268.536	-4.614	6.9952	6.9037	9.0748	7.4080
10000	10005	268.338	-4.812	6.9681 + 2	6.8770 - 1	9.0464 - 1	7.3848 - 1
10100	10105	268.140	-5.010	6.9411	6.8504	9.0180	7.3616
10200	10205	267.942	-5.208	6.9142	6.8238	8.9897	7.3385
10300	10305	267.744	-5.406	6.8874	6.7973	8.9614	7.3154
10400	10405	267.546	-5.604	6.8606	6.7709	8.9332	7.2924
10500	10505	267.348	-5.802	6.8340	6.7446	8.9051	7.2695
10600	10605	267.149	-6.001	6.8074	6.7184	8.8770	7.2466
10700	10705	266.951	-6.199	6.7809	6.6922	8.8491	7.2237
10800	10806	266.753	-6.397	6.7545	6.6662	8.8211	7.2009
10900	10906	266.555	-6.595	6.7282	6.6402	8.7933	7.1782
11000	11006	266.357	-6.793	6.7019 + 2	6.6143 - 1	8.7655 - 1	7.1555 - 1
11100	11106	266.159	-6.991	6.6758	6.5885	8.7378	7.1329
11200	11206	265.961	-7.189	6.6497	6.5627	8.7102	7.1103
11300	11306	265.763	-7.387	6.6237	6.5371	8.6826	7.0878
11400	11406	265.565	-7.585	6.5978	6.5115	8.6551	7.0654
11500	11506	265.366	-7.784	6.5720	6.4860	8.6276	7.0429
11600	11606	265.168	-7.982	6.5462	6.4606	8.6002	7.0206
11700	11707	264.970	-8.180	6.5205	6.4353	8.5729	6.9983
11800	11807	264.772	-8.378	6.4950	6.4100	8.5457	6.9761
11900	11907	264.574	-8.576	6.4695	6.3849	8.5185	6.9539
12000	12007	264.376	-8.774	6.4440 + 2	6.3598 - 1	8.4914 - 1	6.9317 - 1
12100	12107	264.178	-8.972	6.4187	6.3348	8.4643	6.9097
12200	12207	263.980	-9.170	6.3934	6.3098	8.4373	6.8876
12300	12307	263.781	-9.369	6.3683	6.2850	8.4104	6.8657
12400	12407	263.583	-9.567	6.3432	6.2602	8.3836	6.8437
12500	12507	263.385	-9.765	6.3181	6.2355	8.3568	6.8219
12600	12608	263.187	-9.963	6.2932	6.2109	8.3301	6.8001
12700	12708	262.989	-10.161	6.2683	6.1864	8.3034	6.7783
12800	12808	262.791	-10.359	6.2436	6.1619	8.2768	6.7566
12900	12908	262.593	-10.557	6.2189	6.1375	8.2503	6.7349
13000	13008	262.395	-10.755	6.1942 + 2	6.1132 - 1	8.2238 - 1	6.7133 - 1
13100	13108	262.196	-10.954	6.1697	6.0890	8.1975	6.6918
13200	13208	261.998	-11.152	6.1452	6.0649	8.1711	6.6703
13300	13308	261.800	-11.350	6.1209	6.0408	8.1449	6.6489
13400	13409	261.602	-11.548	6.0965	6.0168	8.1187	6.6275
13500	13509	261.404	-11.746	6.0723	5.9929	8.0925	6.6061
13600	13609	261.206	-11.944	6.0482	5.9691	8.0665	6.5849
13700	13709	261.008	-12.142	6.0241	5.9453	8.0404	6.5636
13800	13809	260.810	-12.340	6.0001	5.9216	8.0145	6.5425
13900	13909	260.612	-12.538	5.9762	5.8980	7.9886	6.5213
14000	14009	260.413	-12.737	5.9523 + 2	5.8745 - 1	7.9628 - 1	6.5003 - 1
14100	14110	260.215	-12.935	5.9286	5.8511	7.9371	6.4792
14200	14210	260.017	-13.133	5.9049	5.8277	7.9114	6.4583
14300	14310	259.819	-13.331	5.8813	5.8044	7.8858	6.4373
14400	14410	259.621	-13.529	5.8578	5.7811	7.8602	6.4165
14500	14510	259.423	-13.727	5.8343	5.7580	7.8347	6.3957
14600	14610	259.225	-13.925	5.8109	5.7349	7.8093	6.3749
14700	14710	259.027	-14.123	5.7876	5.7119	7.7839	6.3542
14800	14811	258.828	-14.322	5.7644	5.6890	7.7586	6.3335
14900	14911	258.630	-14.520	5.7412	5.6661	7.7333	6.3129

Table IV
Geometric Altitude, English Altitudes

Altitude		Temperature		Pressure		Density	
Z (ft)	H (ft)	T (K)	t (°C)	P (mb)	P/P$_0$	ρ (kg/m^3)	ρ/ρ_0
7000	6998	274.286	1.136	7.8192 + 2	7.7169 - 1	9.9311 - 1	8.1070 - 1
7100	7098	274.088	.938	7.7896	7.6877	9.9007	8.0822
7200	7198	273.890	.740	7.7600	7.6586	9.8703	8.0573
7300	7297	273.692	.542	7.7306	7.6295	9.8399	8.0326
7400	7397	273.494	.344	7.7013	7.6005	9.8097	8.0079
7500	7497	273.296	.146	7.6720	7.5717	9.7795	7.9832
7600	7597	273.098	-.052	7.6428	7.5429	9.7494	7.9587
7700	7697	272.900	-.250	7.6138	7.5142	9.7193	7.9341
7800	7797	272.702	-.448	7.5848	7.4856	9.6894	7.9097
7900	7897	272.504	-.646	7.5559	7.4571	9.6595	7.8853
8000	7997	272.306	-.844	7.5271 + 2	7.4286 - 1	9.6296 - 1	7.8609 - 1
8100	8097	272.108	-1.042	7.4984	7.4003	9.5999	7.8366
8200	8197	271.910	-1.240	7.4697	7.3720	9.5702	7.8124
8300	8297	271.712	-1.438	7.4412	7.3439	9.5406	7.7882
8400	8397	271.514	-1.636	7.4127	7.3158	9.5110	7.7641
8500	8497	271.317	-1.833	7.3844	7.2878	9.4815	7.7400
8600	8596	271.119	-2.031	7.3561	7.2599	9.4521	7.7160
8700	8696	270.921	-2.229	7.3279	7.2321	9.4228	7.6921
8800	8796	270.723	-2.427	7.2998	7.2044	9.3935	7.6682
8900	8896	270.525	-2.625	7.2718	7.1767	9.3643	7.6443
9000	8996	270.327	-2.823	7.2439 + 2	7.1492 - 1	9.3352 - 1	7.6206 - 1
9100	9096	270.129	-3.021	7.2160	7.1217	9.3061	7.5968
9200	9196	269.931	-3.219	7.1883	7.0943	9.2772	7.5732
9300	9296	269.733	-3.417	7.1606	7.0670	9.2482	7.5496
9400	9396	269.535	-3.615	7.1331	7.0398	9.2194	7.5260
9500	9496	269.337	-3.813	7.1056	7.0127	9.1906	7.5025
9600	9596	269.139	-4.011	7.0782	6.9856	9.1619	7.4791
9700	9695	268.941	-4.209	7.0509	6.9586	9.1333	7.4557
9800	9795	268.743	-4.407	7.0236	6.9318	9.1047	7.4324
9900	9895	268.545	-4.605	6.9965	6.9050	9.0762	7.4091
10000	9995	268.347	-4.803	6.9694 + 2	6.8783 - 1	9.0477 - 1	7.3859 - 1
10100	10095	268.149	-5.001	6.9424	6.8516	9.0194	7.3627
10200	10195	267.952	-5.198	6.9155	6.8251	8.9911	7.3396
10300	10295	267.754	-5.396	6.8887	6.7987	8.9628	7.3166
10400	10395	267.556	-5.594	6.8620	6.7723	8.9347	7.2936
10500	10495	267.358	-5.792	6.8354	6.7460	8.9066	7.2707
10600	10595	267.160	-5.990	6.8088	6.7198	8.8786	7.2478
10700	10695	266.962	-6.188	6.7824	6.6937	8.8506	7.2250
10800	10794	266.764	-6.386	6.7560	6.6676	8.8227	7.2022
10900	10894	266.566	-6.584	6.7297	6.6417	8.7949	7.1795
11000	10994	266.368	-6.782	6.7034 + 2	6.6158 - 1	8.7671 - 1	7.1568 - 1
11100	11094	266.170	-6.980	6.6773	6.5900	8.7394	7.1342
11200	11194	265.972	-7.178	6.6513	6.5643	8.7118	7.1117
11300	11294	265.774	-7.376	6.6253	6.5386	8.6843	7.0892
11400	11394	265.577	-7.573	6.5994	6.5131	8.6568	7.0667
11500	11494	265.379	-7.771	6.5736	6.4876	8.6294	7.0444
11600	11594	265.181	-7.969	6.5479	6.4622	8.6020	7.0220
11700	11693	264.983	-8.167	6.5222	6.4369	8.5747	6.9998
11800	11793	264.785	-8.365	6.4967	6.4117	8.5475	6.9775
11900	11893	264.587	-8.563	6.4712	6.3866	8.5203	6.9554
12000	11993	264.389	-8.761	6.4458 + 2	6.3615 - 1	8.4933 - 1	6.9333 - 1
12100	12093	264.191	-8.959	6.4205	6.3365	8.4662	6.9112
12200	12193	263.993	-9.157	6.3952	6.3116	8.4393	6.8892
12300	12293	263.795	-9.355	6.3701	6.2868	8.4124	6.8672
12400	12393	263.598	-9.552	6.3450	6.2620	8.3856	6.8453
12500	12493	263.400	-9.750	6.3200	6.2374	8.3588	6.8235
12600	12592	263.202	-9.948	6.2951	6.2128	8.3321	6.8017
12700	12692	263.004	-10.146	6.2703	6.1883	8.3055	6.7800
12800	12792	262.806	-10.344	6.2455	6.1638	8.2789	6.7583
12900	12892	262.608	-10.542	6.2208	6.1395	8.2524	6.7367
13000	12992	262.410	-10.740	6.1962 + 2	6.1152 - 1	8.2260 - 1	6.7151 - 1
13100	13092	262.212	-10.938	6.1717	6.0910	8.1996	6.6936
13200	13192	262.015	-11.135	6.1473	6.0669	8.1733	6.6721
13300	13292	261.817	-11.333	6.1229	6.0428	8.1471	6.6507
13400	13391	261.619	-11.531	6.0986	6.0189	8.1209	6.6293
13500	13491	261.421	-11.729	6.0744	5.9950	8.0948	6.6080
13600	13591	261.223	-11.927	6.0503	5.9712	8.0688	6.5867
13700	13691	261.025	-12.125	6.0263	5.9474	8.0428	6.5665
13800	13791	260.827	-12.323	6.0023	5.9238	8.0169	6.5444
13900	13891	260.630	-12.520	5.9784	5.9002	7.9910	6.5233
14000	13991	260.432	-12.718	5.9546 + 2	5.8767 - 1	7.9652 - 1	6.5022 - 1
14100	14090	260.234	-12.916	5.9308	5.8533	7.9395	6.4812
14200	14190	260.036	-13.114	5.9072	5.8299	7.9139	6.4603
14300	14290	259.838	-13.312	5.8836	5.8066	7.8883	6.4394
14400	14390	259.640	-13.510	5.8601	5.7834	7.8627	6.4186
14500	14490	259.442	-13.708	5.8367	5.7603	7.8373	6.3978
14600	14590	259.245	-13.905	5.8133	5.7373	7.8119	6.3770
14700	14690	259.047	-14.103	5.7900	5.7143	7.7865	6.3563
14800	14790	258.849	-14.301	5.7668	5.6914	7.7612	6.3357
14900	14889	258.651	-14.499	5.7437	5.6686	7.7360	6.3151

Table IV
Geopotential Altitude, English Altitudes

Altitude		Temperature		Pressure			Density		
H (ft)	Z (ft)	T (K)	t (°C)	P (mb)		P/P$_0$	ρ (kg/m^3)		ρ/ρ$_0$
15000	15011	258.432	-14.718	5.7182	+ 2	5.6434 − 1	7.7082 − 1		6.2924 − 1
15100	15111	258.234	-14.916	5.6951		5.6207	7.6830		6.2719
15200	15211	258.036	-15.114	5.6722		5.5980	7.6580		6.2514
15300	15311	257.838	-15.312	5.6494		5.5755	7.6330		6.2310
15400	15411	257.640	-15.510	5.6266		5.5530	7.6081		6.2107
15500	15512	257.442	-15.708	5.6039		5.5306	7.5832		6.1904
15600	15612	257.243	-15.907	5.5813		5.5083	7.5584		6.1701
15700	15712	257.045	-16.105	5.5587		5.4860	7.5337		6.1499
15800	15812	256.847	-16.303	5.5362		5.4638	7.5090		6.1298
15900	15912	256.649	-16.501	5.5138		5.4417	7.4844		6.1097
16000	16012	256.451	-16.699	5.4915	+ 2	5.4197 − 1	7.4598 − 1		6.0896 − 1
16100	16112	256.253	-16.897	5.4692		5.3977	7.4353		6.0696
16200	16213	256.055	-17.095	5.4470		5.3758	7.4109		6.0497
16300	16313	255.857	-17.293	5.4249		5.3540	7.3865		6.0298
16400	16413	255.659	-17.491	5.4029		5.3322	7.3622		6.0099
16500	16513	255.460	-17.690	5.3809		5.3105	7.3379		5.9901
16600	16613	255.262	-17.888	5.3590		5.2889	7.3137		5.9704
16700	16713	255.064	-18.086	5.3372		5.2674	7.2896		5.9507
16800	16814	254.866	-18.284	5.3154		5.2459	7.2655		5.9311
16900	16914	254.668	-18.482	5.2937		5.2245	7.2415		5.9115
17000	17014	254.470	-18.680	5.2721	+ 2	5.2032 − 1	7.2176 − 1		5.8919 − 1
17100	17114	254.272	-18.878	5.2506		5.1819	7.1937		5.8724
17200	17214	254.074	-19.076	5.2291		5.1607	7.1699		5.8530
17300	17314	253.875	-19.275	5.2077		5.1396	7.1461		5.8336
17400	17415	253.677	-19.473	5.1864		5.1186	7.1224		5.8142
17500	17515	253.479	-19.671	5.1652		5.0976	7.0988		5.7949
17600	17615	253.281	-19.869	5.1440		5.0767	7.0752		5.7757
17700	17715	253.083	-20.067	5.1229		5.0559	7.0517		5.7565
17800	17815	252.885	-20.265	5.1018		5.0351	7.0282		5.7373
17900	17915	252.687	-20.463	5.0808		5.0144	7.0048		5.7182
18000	18016	252.489	-20.661	5.0599	+ 2	4.9938 − 1	6.9815 − 1		5.6991 − 1
18100	18116	252.290	-20.860	5.0391		4.9732	6.9582		5.6801
18200	18216	252.092	-21.058	5.0183		4.9527	6.9349		5.6612
18300	18316	251.894	-21.256	4.9976		4.9323	6.9118		5.6423
18400	18416	251.696	-21.454	4.9770		4.9119	6.8887		5.6234
18500	18516	251.498	-21.652	4.9565		4.8916	6.8656		5.6046
18600	18617	251.300	-21.850	4.9360		4.8714	6.8426		5.5858
18700	18717	251.102	-22.048	4.9156		4.8513	6.8197		5.5671
18800	18817	250.904	-22.246	4.8952		4.8312	6.7968		5.5484
18900	18917	250.706	-22.444	4.8749		4.8112	6.7740		5.5298
19000	19017	250.507	-22.643	4.8547	+ 2	4.7912 − 1	6.7513 − 1		5.5112 − 1
19100	19118	250.309	-22.841	4.8346		4.7713	6.7286		5.4927
19200	19218	250.111	-23.039	4.8145		4.7515	6.7059		5.4742
19300	19318	249.913	-23.237	4.7945		4.7318	6.6834		5.4558
19400	19418	249.715	-23.435	4.7745		4.7121	6.6608		5.4374
19500	19518	249.517	-23.633	4.7547		4.6925	6.6384		5.4191
19600	19618	249.319	-23.831	4.7349		4.6729	6.6160		5.4008
19700	19719	249.121	-24.029	4.7151		4.6534	6.5936		5.3826
19800	19819	248.922	-24.228	4.6954		4.6340	6.5713		5.3644
19900	19919	248.724	-24.426	4.6758		4.6147	6.5491		5.3462
20000	20019	248.526	-24.624	4.6563	+ 2	4.5954 − 1	6.5269 − 1		5.3281 − 1
20100	20119	248.328	-24.822	4.6368		4.5762	6.5048		5.3101
20200	20220	248.130	-25.020	4.6174		4.5570	6.4828		5.2921
20300	20320	247.932	-25.218	4.5980		4.5379	6.4608		5.2741
20400	20420	247.734	-25.416	4.5788		4.5189	6.4388		5.2562
20500	20520	247.536	-25.614	4.5596		4.4999	6.4169		5.2383
20600	20620	247.337	-25.813	4.5404		4.4810	6.3951		5.2205
20700	20721	247.139	-26.011	4.5213		4.4622	6.3733		5.2027
20800	20821	246.941	-26.209	4.5023		4.4434	6.3516		5.1850
20900	20921	246.743	-26.407	4.4834		4.4247	6.3300		5.1673
21000	21021	246.545	-26.605	4.4645	+ 2	4.4061 − 1	6.3084 − 1		5.1497 − 1
21100	21121	246.347	-26.803	4.4456		4.3875	6.2868		5.1321
21200	21222	246.149	-27.001	4.4269		4.3690	6.2653		5.1146
21300	21322	245.951	-27.199	4.4082		4.3505	6.2439		5.0971
21400	21422	245.753	-27.397	4.3896		4.3322	6.2225		5.0796
21500	21522	245.554	-27.596	4.3710		4.3138	6.2012		5.0622
21600	21622	245.356	-27.794	4.3525		4.2956	6.1799		5.0448
21700	21723	245.158	-27.992	4.3340		4.2774	6.1587		5.0275
21800	21823	244.960	-28.190	4.3157		4.2592	6.1376		5.0103
21900	21923	244.762	-28.388	4.2974		4.2412	6.1165		4.9930
22000	22023	244.564	-28.586	4.2791	+ 2	4.2231 − 1	6.0954 − 1		4.9759 − 1
22100	22123	244.366	-28.784	4.2609		4.2052	6.0744		4.9587
22200	22224	244.168	-28.982	4.2428		4.1873	6.0535		4.9416
22300	22324	243.969	-29.181	4.2247		4.1695	6.0326		4.9246
22400	22424	243.771	-29.379	4.2067		4.1517	6.0118		4.9076
22500	22524	243.573	-29.577	4.1888		4.1340	5.9910		4.8906
22600	22625	243.375	-29.775	4.1709		4.1164	5.9703		4.8737
22700	22725	243.177	-29.973	4.1531		4.0988	5.9497		4.8569
22800	22825	242.979	-30.171	4.1353		4.0813	5.9291		4.8401
22900	22925	242.781	-30.369	4.1177		4.0638	5.9085		4.8233

Table IV
Geometric Altitude, English Altitudes

Altitude		Temperature		Pressure		Density	
Z (ft)	H (ft)	T (K)	t (°C)	P (mb)	P/P$_0$	ρ (kg/m³)	ρ/ρ$_0$
15000	14989	258.453	-14.697	5.7206 + 2	5.6458 - 1	7.7109 - 1	6.2946 - 1
15100	15089	258.255	-14.895	5.6977	5.6231	7.6858	6.2741
15200	15189	258.058	-15.092	5.6748	5.6005	7.6608	6.2537
15300	15289	257.860	-15.290	5.6519	5.5780	7.6358	6.2333
15400	15389	257.662	-15.488	5.6292	5.5556	7.6109	6.2130
15500	15488	257.464	-15.686	5.6065	5.5332	7.5861	6.1927
15600	15588	257.266	-15.884	5.5839	5.5109	7.5613	6.1725
15700	15688	257.068	-16.082	5.5614	5.4886	7.5366	6.1523
15800	15788	256.871	-16.279	5.5389	5.4665	7.5119	6.1322
15900	15888	256.673	-16.477	5.5165	5.4444	7.4873	6.1121
16000	15988	256.475	-16.675	5.4942 + 2	5.4224 - 1	7.4628 - 1	6.0921 - 1
16100	16088	256.277	-16.873	5.4720	5.4004	7.4383	6.0721
16200	16187	256.079	-17.071	5.4498	5.3785	7.4139	6.0522
16300	16287	255.882	-17.268	5.4277	5.3567	7.3896	6.0323
16400	16387	255.684	-17.466	5.4057	5.3350	7.3653	6.0125
16500	16487	255.486	-17.664	5.3838	5.3134	7.3411	5.9927
16600	16587	255.288	-17.862	5.3619	5.2918	7.3169	5.9730
16700	16687	255.090	-18.060	5.3401	5.2703	7.2928	5.9533
16800	16786	254.893	-18.257	5.3184	5.2488	7.2688	5.9337
16900	16886	254.695	-18.455	5.2967	5.2274	7.2448	5.9141
17000	16986	254.497	-18.653	5.2751 + 2	5.2061 - 1	7.2209 - 1	5.8946 - 1
17100	17086	254.299	-18.851	5.2536	5.1849	7.1971	5.8751
17200	17186	254.101	-19.049	5.2322	5.1637	7.1733	5.8557
17300	17286	253.904	-19.246	5.2108	5.1426	7.1495	5.8363
17400	17385	253.706	-19.444	5.1895	5.1216	7.1259	5.8170
17500	17485	253.508	-19.642	5.1683	5.1007	7.1022	5.7977
17600	17585	253.310	-19.840	5.1471	5.0798	7.0787	5.7785
17700	17685	253.112	-20.038	5.1260	5.0590	7.0552	5.7593
17800	17785	252.915	-20.235	5.1050	5.0382	7.0318	5.7402
17900	17885	252.717	-20.433	5.0841	5.0176	7.0084	5.7211
18000	17984	252.519	-20.631	5.0632 + 2	4.9970 - 1	6.9851 - 1	5.7021 - 1
18100	18084	252.321	-20.829	5.0424	4.9764	6.9618	5.6831
18200	18184	252.123	-21.027	5.0216	4.9560	6.9386	5.6642
18300	18284	251.926	-21.224	5.0010	4.9356	6.9155	5.6453
18400	18384	251.728	-21.422	4.9804	4.9152	6.8924	5.6265
18500	18484	251.530	-21.620	4.9598	4.8950	6.8694	5.6077
18600	18583	251.332	-21.818	4.9394	4.8748	6.8464	5.5889
18700	18683	251.135	-22.015	4.9190	4.8546	6.8236	5.5702
18800	18783	250.937	-22.213	4.8986	4.8346	6.8007	5.5516
18900	18883	250.739	-22.411	4.8784	4.8146	6.7779	5.5330
19000	18983	250.541	-22.609	4.8582 + 2	4.7947 - 1	6.7552 - 1	5.5144 - 1
19100	19083	250.344	-22.806	4.8381	4.7748	6.7325	5.4959
19200	19182	250.146	-23.004	4.8180	4.7550	6.7099	5.4775
19300	19282	249.948	-23.202	4.7980	4.7353	6.6874	5.4591
19400	19382	249.750	-23.400	4.7781	4.7156	6.6649	5.4407
19500	19482	249.553	-23.597	4.7583	4.6960	6.6425	5.4224
19600	19582	249.355	-23.795	4.7385	4.6765	6.6201	5.4042
19700	19681	249.157	-23.993	4.7188	4.6571	6.5978	5.3859
19800	19781	248.959	-24.191	4.6991	4.6377	6.5755	5.3678
19900	19881	248.762	-24.388	4.6795	4.6183	6.5533	5.3497
20000	19981	248.564	-24.586	4.6600 + 2	4.5991 - 1	6.5312 - 1	5.3316 - 1
20100	20081	248.366	-24.784	4.6406	4.5799	6.5091	5.3136
20200	20180	248.168	-24.982	4.6212	4.5607	6.4871	5.2956
20300	20280	247.971	-25.179	4.6019	4.5417	6.4651	5.2776
20400	20380	247.773	-25.377	4.5826	4.5227	6.4432	5.2597
20500	20480	247.575	-25.575	4.5634	4.5037	6.4213	5.2419
20600	20580	247.377	-25.773	4.5443	4.4849	6.3995	5.2241
20700	20679	247.180	-25.970	4.5252	4.4661	6.3778	5.2064
20800	20779	246.982	-26.168	4.5062	4.4473	6.3561	5.1887
20900	20879	246.784	-26.366	4.4873	4.4286	6.3345	5.1710
21000	20979	246.587	-26.563	4.4684 + 2	4.4100 - 1	6.3129 - 1	5.1534 - 1
21100	21079	246.389	-26.761	4.4496	4.3915	6.2914	5.1358
21200	21178	246.191	-26.959	4.4309	4.3730	6.2699	5.1183
21300	21278	245.993	-27.157	4.4122	4.3545	6.2485	5.1008
21400	21378	245.796	-27.354	4.3936	4.3362	6.2272	5.0834
21500	21478	245.598	-27.552	4.3751	4.3179	6.2059	5.0660
21600	21578	245.400	-27.750	4.3566	4.2996	6.1847	5.0487
21700	21677	245.203	-27.947	4.3382	4.2815	6.1635	5.0314
21800	21777	245.005	-28.145	4.3198	4.2633	6.1424	5.0142
21900	21877	244.807	-28.343	4.3016	4.2453	6.1213	4.9970
22000	21977	244.609	-28.541	4.2833 + 2	4.2273 - 1	6.1003 - 1	4.9798 - 1
22100	22077	244.412	-28.738	4.2652	4.2094	6.0793	4.9627
22200	22176	244.214	-28.936	4.2471	4.1915	6.0584	4.9457
22300	22276	244.016	-29.134	4.2290	4.1737	6.0376	4.9286
22400	22376	243.819	-29.331	4.2110	4.1560	6.0168	4.9117
22500	22476	243.621	-29.529	4.1931	4.1383	5.9961	4.8947
22600	22576	243.423	-29.727	4.1753	4.1207	5.9754	4.8779
22700	22675	243.226	-29.924	4.1575	4.1031	5.9548	4.8610
22800	22775	243.028	-30.122	4.1398	4.0856	5.9342	4.8442
22900	22875	242.830	-30.320	4.1221	4.0682	5.9137	4.8275

Table IV
Geopotential Altitude, English Altitudes

Altitude		Temperature		Pressure				Density			
H (ft)	Z (ft)	T (K)	t (°C)	P (mb)		P/P$_0$		ρ (kg/m³)		ρ/ρ$_0$	
23000	23025	242.583	−30.567	4.1000	+ 2	4.0464	− 1	5.8880	− 1	4.8066	− 1
23100	23126	242.384	−30.766	4.0825		4.0291		5.8676		4.7899	
23200	23226	242.186	−30.964	4.0649		4.0118		5.8472		4.7732	
23300	23326	241.988	−31.162	4.0475		3.9946		5.8269		4.7566	
23400	23426	241.790	−31.360	4.0301		3.9774		5.8066		4.7401	
23500	23527	241.592	−31.558	4.0128		3.9603		5.7864		4.7236	
23600	23627	241.394	−31.756	3.9955		3.9433		5.7662		4.7071	
23700	23727	241.196	−31.954	3.9783		3.9263		5.7461		4.6907	
23800	23827	240.998	−32.152	3.9612		3.9094		5.7260		4.6743	
23900	23927	240.800	−32.350	3.9441		3.8925		5.7060		4.6580	
24000	24028	240.601	−32.549	3.9271	+ 2	3.8757	− 1	5.6861	− 1	4.6417	− 1
24100	24128	240.403	−32.747	3.9101		3.8590		5.6662		4.6254	
24200	24228	240.205	−32.945	3.8932		3.8423		5.6463		4.6092	
24300	24328	240.007	−33.143	3.8763		3.8256		5.6265		4.5931	
24400	24429	239.809	−33.341	3.8595		3.8091		5.6068		4.5770	
24500	24529	239.611	−33.539	3.8428		3.7926		5.5871		4.5609	
24600	24629	239.413	−33.737	3.8261		3.7761		5.5675		4.5449	
24700	24729	239.215	−33.935	3.8095		3.7597		5.5479		4.5289	
24800	24830	239.016	−34.134	3.7930		3.7434		5.5284		4.5129	
24900	24930	238.818	−34.332	3.7765		3.7271		5.5089		4.4971	
25000	25030	238.620	−34.530	3.7600	+ 2	3.7109	− 1	5.4895	− 1	4.4812	− 1
25100	25130	238.422	−34.728	3.7437		3.6947		5.4701		4.4654	
25200	25230	238.224	−34.926	3.7273		3.6786		5.4508		4.4496	
25300	25331	238.026	−35.124	3.7111		3.6625		5.4315		4.4339	
25400	25431	237.828	−35.322	3.6949		3.6466		5.4123		4.4182	
25500	25531	237.630	−35.520	3.6787		3.6306		5.3931		4.4026	
25600	25631	237.431	−35.719	3.6626		3.6147		5.3740		4.3870	
25700	25732	237.233	−35.917	3.6466		3.5989		5.3550		4.3714	
25800	25832	237.035	−36.115	3.6306		3.5831		5.3360		4.3559	
25900	25932	236.837	−36.313	3.6147		3.5674		5.3170		4.3404	
26000	26032	236.639	−36.511	3.5988	+ 2	3.5518	− 1	5.2981	− 1	4.3250	− 1
26100	26133	236.441	−36.709	3.5830		3.5362		5.2792		4.3096	
26200	26233	236.243	−36.907	3.5673		3.5206		5.2604		4.2942	
26300	26333	236.045	−37.105	3.5516		3.5051		5.2417		4.2789	
26400	26433	235.847	−37.303	3.5359		3.4897		5.2230		4.2637	
26500	26534	235.648	−37.502	3.5204		3.4743		5.2043		4.2484	
26600	26634	235.450	−37.700	3.5048		3.4590		5.1858		4.2333	
26700	26734	235.252	−37.898	3.4894		3.4437		5.1672		4.2181	
26800	26834	235.054	−38.096	3.4739		3.4285		5.1487		4.2030	
26900	26935	234.856	−38.294	3.4586		3.4133		5.1303		4.1880	
27000	27035	234.658	−38.492	3.4433	+ 2	3.3982	− 1	5.1119	− 1	4.1730	− 1
27100	27135	234.460	−38.690	3.4280		3.3832		5.0935		4.1580	
27200	27236	234.262	−38.888	3.4128		3.3682		5.0752		4.1431	
27300	27336	234.063	−39.087	3.3977		3.3532		5.0570		4.1282	
27400	27436	233.865	−39.285	3.3826		3.3384		5.0388		4.1133	
27500	27536	233.667	−39.483	3.3676		3.3235		5.0207		4.0985	
27600	27637	233.469	−39.681	3.3526		3.3087		5.0026		4.0837	
27700	27737	233.271	−39.879	3.3376		3.2940		4.9845		4.0690	
27800	27837	233.073	−40.077	3.3228		3.2793		4.9665		4.0543	
27900	27937	232.875	−40.275	3.3080		3.2647		4.9486		4.0397	
28000	28038	232.677	−40.473	3.2932	+ 2	3.2501	− 1	4.9307	− 1	4.0251	− 1
28100	28138	232.478	−40.672	3.2785		3.2356		4.9129		4.0105	
28200	28238	232.280	−40.870	3.2638		3.2211		4.8951		3.9960	
28300	28338	232.082	−41.068	3.2492		3.2067		4.8773		3.9815	
28400	28439	231.884	−41.266	3.2347		3.1924		4.8596		3.9670	
28500	28539	231.686	−41.464	3.2202		3.1781		4.8420		3.9526	
28600	28639	231.488	−41.662	3.2057		3.1638		4.8244		3.9383	
28700	28740	231.290	−41.860	3.1913		3.1496		4.8068		3.9239	
28800	28840	231.092	−42.058	3.1770		3.1354		4.7893		3.9097	
28900	28940	230.894	−42.256	3.1627		3.1213		4.7719		3.8954	
29000	29040	230.695	−42.455	3.1485	+ 2	3.1073	− 1	4.7545	− 1	3.8812	− 1
29100	29141	230.497	−42.653	3.1343		3.0933		4.7371		3.8670	
29200	29241	230.299	−42.851	3.1201		3.0793		4.7198		3.8529	
29300	29341	230.101	−43.049	3.1061		3.0654		4.7026		3.8388	
29400	29442	229.903	−43.247	3.0920		3.0516		4.6854		3.8248	
29500	29542	229.705	−43.445	3.0780		3.0378		4.6682		3.8108	
29600	29642	229.507	−43.643	3.0641		3.0240		4.6511		3.7968	
29700	29742	229.309	−43.841	3.0502		3.0103		4.6340		3.7829	
29800	29843	229.110	−44.040	3.0364		2.9967		4.6170		3.7690	
29900	29943	228.912	−44.238	3.0226		2.9831		4.6000		3.7551	
30000	30043	228.714	−44.436	3.0089	+ 2	2.9696	− 1	4.5831	− 1	3.7413	− 1
30100	30144	228.516	−44.634	2.9952		2.9561		4.5663		3.7276	
30200	30244	228.318	−44.832	2.9816		2.9426		4.5494		3.7138	
30300	30344	228.120	−45.030	2.9680		2.9292		4.5327		3.7001	
30400	30444	227.922	−45.228	2.9545		2.9159		4.5159		3.6865	
30500	30545	227.724	−45.426	2.9410		2.9026		4.4992		3.6728	
30600	30645	227.525	−45.625	2.9276		2.8893		4.4826		3.6593	
30700	30745	227.327	−45.823	2.9142		2.8761		4.4660		3.6457	
30800	30846	227.129	−46.021	2.9009		2.8630		4.4493		3.6303	
30900	30946	226.931	−46.219	2.8876		2.8499		4.4330		3.6188	

Table IV
Geometric Altitude, English Altitudes

Altitude		Temperature		Pressure				Density			
Z (ft)	H (ft)	T (K)	t (°C)	P (mb)			P/P$_0$	ρ (kg/m³)		ρ/ρ$_0$	
23000	22975	242.632	-30.518	4.1045	+ 2	4.0508	- 1	5.8932	- 1	4.8108	- 1
23100	23074	242.435	-30.715	4.0869		4.0335		5.8728		4.7941	
23200	23174	242.237	-30.913	4.0694		4.0162		5.8525		4.7775	
23300	23274	242.039	-31.111	4.0520		3.9990		5.8322		4.7609	
23400	23374	241.842	-31.308	4.0347		3.9819		5.8119		4.7444	
23500	23474	241.644	-31.506	4.0174		3.9648		5.7917		4.7279	
23600	23573	241.446	-31.704	4.0001		3.9478		5.7716		4.7115	
23700	23673	241.249	-31.901	3.9829		3.9308		5.7515		4.6951	
23800	23773	241.051	-32.099	3.9658		3.9139		5.7315		4.6787	
23900	23873	240.853	-32.297	3.9487		3.8971		5.7115		4.6624	
24000	23972	240.656	-32.494	3.9317	+ 2	3.8803	- 1	5.6916	- 1	4.6462	- 1
24100	24072	240.458	-32.692	3.9148		3.8636		5.6717		4.6300	
24200	24172	240.260	-32.890	3.8979		3.8469		5.6519		4.6138	
24300	24272	240.063	-33.087	3.8811		3.8303		5.6321		4.5977	
24400	24371	239.865	-33.285	3.8643		3.8138		5.6124		4.5816	
24500	24471	239.667	-33.483	3.8476		3.7973		5.5928		4.5655	
24600	24571	239.470	-33.680	3.8310		3.7809		5.5732		4.5495	
24700	24671	239.272	-33.878	3.8144		3.7645		5.5536		4.5336	
24800	24771	239.074	-34.076	3.7978		3.7482		5.5341		4.5176	
24900	24870	238.877	-34.273	3.7814		3.7319		5.5147		4.5018	
25000	24970	238.679	-34.471	3.7650	+ 2	3.7157	- 1	5.4953	- 1	4.4859	- 1
25100	25070	238.482	-34.668	3.7486		3.6996		5.4759		4.4701	
25200	25170	238.284	-34.866	3.7323		3.6835		5.4566		4.4544	
25300	25269	238.086	-35.064	3.7161		3.6675		5.4374		4.4387	
25400	25369	237.889	-35.261	3.6999		3.6515		5.4182		4.4230	
25500	25469	237.691	-35.459	3.6837		3.6356		5.3991		4.4074	
25600	25569	237.493	-35.657	3.6677		3.6197		5.3800		4.3918	
25700	25668	237.296	-35.854	3.6517		3.6039		5.3610		4.3763	
25800	25768	237.098	-36.052	3.6357		3.5882		5.3420		4.3608	
25900	25868	236.900	-36.250	3.6198		3.5725		5.3231		4.3454	
26000	25968	236.703	-36.447	3.6040	+ 2	3.5568	- 1	5.3042	- 1	4.3300	- 1
26100	26067	236.505	-36.645	3.5882		3.5412		5.2854		4.3146	
26200	26167	236.308	-36.842	3.5724		3.5257		5.2666		4.2993	
26300	26267	236.110	-37.040	3.5568		3.5103		5.2479		4.2840	
26400	26367	235.912	-37.238	3.5411		3.4948		5.2292		4.2688	
26500	26466	235.715	-37.435	3.5256		3.4795		5.2106		4.2536	
26600	26566	235.517	-37.633	3.5101		3.4642		5.1920		4.2384	
26700	26666	235.319	-37.831	3.4946		3.4489		5.1735		4.2233	
26800	26766	235.122	-38.028	3.4792		3.4337		5.1551		4.2082	
26900	26865	234.924	-38.226	3.4639		3.4186		5.1367		4.1932	
27000	26965	234.727	-38.423	3.4486	+ 2	3.4035	- 1	5.1183	- 1	4.1782	- 1
27100	27065	234.529	-38.621	3.4334		3.3885		5.1000		4.1632	
27200	27165	234.331	-38.819	3.4182		3.3735		5.0817		4.1483	
27300	27264	234.134	-39.016	3.4031		3.3586		5.0635		4.1335	
27400	27364	233.936	-39.214	3.3880		3.3437		5.0453		4.1186	
27500	27464	233.739	-39.411	3.3730		3.3289		5.0272		4.1039	
27600	27564	233.541	-39.609	3.3580		3.3141		5.0092		4.0891	
27700	27663	233.343	-39.807	3.3431		3.2994		4.9912		4.0744	
27800	27763	233.146	-40.004	3.3283		3.2847		4.9732		4.0597	
27900	27863	232.948	-40.202	3.3135		3.2701		4.9553		4.0451	
28000	27962	232.751	-40.399	3.2987	+ 2	3.2556	- 1	4.9374	- 1	4.0305	- 1
28100	28062	232.553	-40.597	3.2840		3.2411		4.9196		4.0160	
28200	28162	232.355	-40.795	3.2694		3.2266		4.9018		4.0015	
28300	28262	232.158	-40.992	3.2548		3.2122		4.8841		3.9870	
28400	28361	231.960	-41.190	3.2403		3.1979		4.8665		3.9726	
28500	28461	231.763	-41.387	3.2258		3.1836		4.8488		3.9582	
28600	28561	231.565	-41.585	3.2114		3.1694		4.8313		3.9439	
28700	28661	231.368	-41.782	3.1970		3.1552		4.8138		3.9296	
28800	28760	231.170	-41.980	3.1827		3.1410		4.7963		3.9153	
28900	28860	230.972	-42.178	3.1684		3.1270		4.7789		3.9011	
29000	28960	230.775	-42.375	3.1542	+ 2	3.1129	- 1	4.7615	- 1	3.8869	- 1
29100	29059	230.577	-42.573	3.1400		3.0989		4.7442		3.8728	
29200	29159	230.380	-42.770	3.1259		3.0850		4.7269		3.8587	
29300	29259	230.182	-42.968	3.1118		3.0711		4.7097		3.8446	
29400	29359	229.985	-43.165	3.0978		3.0573		4.6925		3.8306	
29500	29458	229.787	-43.363	3.0839		3.0435		4.6753		3.8166	
29600	29558	229.589	-43.561	3.0699		3.0298		4.6583		3.8027	
29700	29658	229.392	-43.758	3.0561		3.0161		4.6412		3.7888	
29800	29757	229.194	-43.956	3.0423		3.0025		4.6242		3.7749	
29900	29857	228.997	-44.153	3.0285		2.9889		4.6073		3.7611	
30000	29957	228.799	-44.351	3.0148	+ 2	2.9754	- 1	4.5904	- 1	3.7473	- 1
30100	30057	228.602	-44.548	3.0012		2.9619		4.5736		3.7335	
30200	30156	228.404	-44.746	2.9876		2.9485		4.5568		3.7198	
30300	30256	228.207	-44.943	2.9740		2.9351		4.5400		3.7061	
30400	30356	228.009	-45.141	2.9605		2.9218		4.5233		3.6925	
30500	30455	227.812	-45.338	2.9470		2.9085		4.5067		3.6789	
30600	30555	227.614	-45.536	2.9336		2.8953		4.4901		3.6653	
30700	30655	227.416	-45.734	2.9203		2.8821		4.4735		3.6518	
30800	30755	227.219	-45.931	2.9070		2.8689		4.4570		3.6383	
30900	30854	227.021	-46.129	2.8937		2.8559		4.4405		3.6249	

Table IV
Geopotential Altitude, English Altitudes

Altitude		Temperature		Pressure		Density	
H (ft)	Z (ft)	T (K)	t (°C)	P (mb)	P/P$_0$	ρ (kg/m^3)	ρ/ρ_0
31000	31046	226.733	−46.417	2.8744 + 2	2.8368 − 1	4.4165 − 1	3.6053 − 1
31100	31146	226.535	−46.615	2.8612	2.8238	4.4001	3.5919
31200	31247	226.337	−46.813	2.8481	2.8109	4.3838	3.5786
31300	31347	226.139	−47.011	2.8350	2.7980	4.3675	3.5653
31400	31447	225.941	−47.209	2.8220	2.7851	4.3512	3.5520
31500	31548	225.742	−47.408	2.8090	2.7723	4.3350	3.5388
31600	31648	225.544	−47.606	2.7961	2.7595	4.3188	3.5256
31700	31748	225.346	−47.804	2.7832	2.7468	4.3027	3.5124
31800	31849	225.148	−48.002	2.7704	2.7341	4.2866	3.4993
31900	31949	224.950	−48.200	2.7576	2.7215	4.2706	3.4862
32000	32049	224.752	−48.398	2.7448 + 2	2.7089 − 1	4.2546 − 1	3.4732 − 1
32100	32149	224.554	−48.596	2.7321	2.6964	4.2387	3.4601
32200	32250	224.356	−48.794	2.7195	2.6839	4.2228	3.4472
32300	32350	224.157	−48.993	2.7069	2.6715	4.2069	3.4342
32400	32450	223.959	−49.191	2.6944	2.6591	4.1911	3.4213
32500	32551	223.761	−49.389	2.6818	2.6468	4.1754	3.4085
32600	32651	223.563	−49.587	2.6694	2.6345	4.1597	3.3956
32700	32751	223.365	−49.785	2.6570	2.6222	4.1440	3.3829
32800	32852	223.167	−49.983	2.6446	2.6100	4.1284	3.3701
32900	32952	222.969	−50.181	2.6323	2.5979	4.1128	3.3574
33000	33052	222.771	−50.379	2.6200 + 2	2.5858 − 1	4.0973 − 1	3.3447 − 1
33100	33153	222.572	−50.578	2.6078	2.5737	4.0818	3.3321
33200	33253	222.374	−50.776	2.5956	2.5617	4.0663	3.3195
33300	33353	222.176	−50.974	2.5835	2.5497	4.0510	3.3069
33400	33454	221.978	−51.172	2.5714	2.5378	4.0356	3.2944
33500	33554	221.780	−51.370	2.5594	2.5259	4.0203	3.2819
33600	33654	221.582	−51.568	2.5474	2.5141	4.0050	3.2694
33700	33755	221.384	−51.766	2.5354	2.5023	3.9898	3.2570
33800	33855	221.186	−51.964	2.5235	2.4905	3.9746	3.2446
33900	33955	220.988	−52.162	2.5117	2.4788	3.9595	3.2323
34000	34056	220.789	−52.361	2.4999 + 2	2.4672 − 1	3.9444 − 1	3.2199 − 1
34100	34156	220.591	−52.559	2.4881	2.4555	3.9294	3.2077
34200	34256	220.393	−52.757	2.4764	2.4440	3.9144	3.1954
34300	34357	220.195	−52.955	2.4647	2.4325	3.8994	3.1832
34400	34457	219.997	−53.153	2.4531	2.4210	3.8845	3.1710
34500	34557	219.799	−53.351	2.4415	2.4095	3.8697	3.1589
34600	34658	219.601	−53.549	2.4299	2.3981	3.8548	3.1468
34700	34758	219.403	−53.747	2.4184	2.3868	3.8401	3.1347
34800	34858	219.204	−53.946	2.4070	2.3755	3.8253	3.1227
34900	34959	219.006	−54.144	2.3956	2.3642	3.8106	3.1107
35000	35059	218.808	−54.342	2.3842 + 2	2.3530 − 1	3.7960 − 1	3.0988 − 1
35200	35260	218.412	−54.738	2.3616	2.3307	3.7668	3.0749
35400	35460	218.016	−55.134	2.3391	2.3086	3.7378	3.0513
35600	35661	217.619	−55.531	2.3169	2.2866	3.7090	3.0277
35800	35862	217.223	−55.927	2.2948	2.2648	3.6803	3.0043
36000	36062	216.827	−56.323	2.2729	2.2432	3.6518	2.9811
36200	36263	216.650	−56.500	2.2511	2.2217	3.6199	2.9550
36400	36464	216.650	−56.500	2.2296	2.2004	3.5852	2.9267
36600	36664	216.650	−56.500	2.2083	2.1794	3.5509	2.8987
36800	36865	216.650	−56.500	2.1872	2.1585	3.5170	2.8710
37000	37066	216.650	−56.500	2.1662 + 2	2.1379 − 1	3.4833 − 1	2.8435 − 1
37200	37266	216.650	−56.500	2.1455	2.1174	3.4500	2.8163
37400	37467	216.650	−56.500	2.1250	2.0972	3.4170	2.7894
37600	37668	216.650	−56.500	2.1046	2.0771	3.3843	2.7627
37800	37869	216.650	−56.500	2.0845	2.0573	3.3519	2.7363
38000	38069	216.650	−56.500	2.0646	2.0376	3.3199	2.7101
38200	38270	216.650	−56.500	2.0448	2.0181	3.2881	2.6842
38400	38471	216.650	−56.500	2.0253	1.9988	3.2566	2.6585
38600	38672	216.650	−56.500	2.0059	1.9796	3.2255	2.6330
38800	38872	216.650	−56.500	1.9867	1.9607	3.1946	2.6079
39000	39073	216.650	−56.500	1.9677 + 2	1.9420 − 1	3.1641 − 1	2.5829 − 1
39200	39274	216.650	−56.500	1.9489	1.9234	3.1338	2.5582
39400	39475	216.650	−56.500	1.9302	1.9050	3.1038	2.5337
39600	39675	216.650	−56.500	1.9117	1.8867	3.0741	2.5095
39800	39876	216.650	−56.500	1.8935	1.8687	3.0447	2.4855
40000	40077	216.650	−56.500	1.8753	1.8508	3.0156	2.4617
40200	40278	216.650	−56.500	1.8574	1.8331	2.9867	2.4382
40400	40478	216.650	−56.500	1.8396	1.8156	2.9582	2.4148
40600	40679	216.650	−56.500	1.8220	1.7982	2.9299	2.3917
40800	40880	216.650	−56.500	1.8046	1.7810	2.9018	2.3688
41000	41081	216.650	−56.500	1.7873 + 2	1.7640 − 1	2.8741 − 1	2.3462 − 1
41200	41282	216.650	−56.500	1.7702	1.7471	2.8466	2.3237
41400	41482	216.650	−56.500	1.7533	1.7304	2.8193	2.3015
41600	41683	216.650	−56.500	1.7365	1.7138	2.7924	2.2795
41800	41884	216.650	−56.500	1.7199	1.6974	2.7657	2.2577
42000	42085	216.650	−56.500	1.7035	1.6812	2.7392	2.2361
42200	42286	216.650	−56.500	1.6872	1.6651	2.7130	2.2147
42400	42486	216.650	−56.500	1.6710	1.6492	2.6870	2.1935
42600	42687	216.650	−56.500	1.6550	1.6334	2.6613	2.1725
42800	42888	216.650	−56.500	1.6392	1.6178	2.6359	2.1517

Table IV
Geometric Altitude, English Altitudes

Altitude		Temperature		Pressure		Density	
Z (ft)	H (ft)	T (K)	t (°C)	P (mb)	P/P$_0$	ρ (kg/m^3)	ρ/ρ_0
31000	30954	226.824	−46.326	2.8805　+ 2	2.8428　− 1	4.4241　− 1	3.6115　− 1
31100	31054	226.626	−46.524	2.8673	2.8298	4.4077	3.5981
31200	31153	226.429	−46.721	2.8542	2.8169	4.3914	3.5848
31300	31253	226.231	−46.919	2.8412	2.8040	4.3751	3.5715
31400	31353	226.034	−47.116	2.8281	2.7912	4.3589	3.5583
31500	31452	225.836	−47.314	2.8152	2.7784	4.3427	3.5450
31600	31552	225.639	−47.511	2.8023	2.7656	4.3265	3.5319
31700	31652	225.441	−47.709	2.7894	2.7529	4.3105	3.5187
31800	31752	225.244	−47.906	2.7766	2.7403	4.2944	3.5056
31900	31851	225.046	−48.104	2.7638	2.7277	4.2784	3.4926
32000	31951	224.849	−48.301	2.7511　+ 2	2.7151　− 1	4.2624　− 1	3.4795　− 1
32100	32051	224.651	−48.499	2.7384	2.7026	4.2465	3.4666
32200	32150	224.454	−48.696	2.7258	2.6901	4.2307	3.4536
32300	32250	224.256	−48.894	2.7132	2.6777	4.2148	3.4407
32400	32350	224.059	−49.091	2.7006	2.6653	4.1991	3.4278
32500	32449	223.861	−49.289	2.6882	2.6530	4.1833	3.4150
32600	32549	223.664	−49.486	2.6757	2.6407	4.1677	3.4022
32700	32649	223.466	−49.684	2.6633	2.6285	4.1520	3.3894
32800	32748	223.269	−49.881	2.6510	2.6163	4.1364	3.3767
32900	32848	223.071	−50.079	2.6387	2.6042	4.1209	3.3640
33000	32948	222.874	−50.276	2.6264　+ 2	2.5921　− 1	4.1054　− 1	3.3513　− 1
33100	33048	222.676	−50.474	2.6142	2.5800	4.0899	3.3387
33200	33147	222.479	−50.671	2.6020	2.5680	4.0745	3.3261
33300	33247	222.281	−50.869	2.5899	2.5561	4.0591	3.3136
33400	33347	222.084	−51.066	2.5779	2.5441	4.0438	3.3010
33500	33446	221.886	−51.264	2.5658	2.5323	4.0285	3.2886
33600	33546	221.689	−51.461	2.5538	2.5205	4.0133	3.2761
33700	33646	221.491	−51.659	2.5419	2.5087	3.9981	3.2637
33800	33745	221.294	−51.856	2.5300	2.4969	3.9829	3.2514
33900	33845	221.096	−52.054	2.5182	2.4852	3.9678	3.2390
34000	33945	220.899	−52.251	2.5064　+ 2	2.4736　− 1	3.9528　− 1	3.2267　− 1
34100	34044	220.701	−52.449	2.4946	2.4620	3.9377	3.2145
34200	34144	220.504	−52.646	2.4829	2.4504	3.9228	3.2023
34300	34244	220.306	−52.844	2.4713	2.4389	3.9078	3.1901
34400	34343	220.109	−53.041	2.4596	2.4275	3.8930	3.1779
34500	34443	219.911	−53.239	2.4481	2.4160	3.8781	3.1658
34600	34543	219.714	−53.436	2.4365	2.4047	3.8633	3.1537
34700	34642	219.516	−53.634	2.4250	2.3933	3.8486	3.1417
34800	34742	219.319	−53.831	2.4136	2.3820	3.8339	3.1297
34900	34842	219.122	−54.028	2.4022	2.3708	3.8192	3.1177
35000	34941	218.924	−54.226	2.3908　+ 2	2.3596　− 1	3.8046　− 1	3.1058　− 1
35200	35141	218.529	−54.621	2.3683	2.3373	3.7754	3.0820
35400	35340	218.134	−55.016	2.3459	2.3152	3.7465	3.0584
35600	35539	217.739	−55.411	2.3236	2.2932	3.7177	3.0349
35800	35739	217.344	−55.806	2.3016	2.2715	3.6891	3.0115
36000	35938	216.950	−56.200	2.2797	2.2498	3.6607	2.9883
36200	36137	216.650	−56.500	2.2579	2.2284	3.6308	2.9639
36400	36337	216.650	−56.500	2.2364	2.2072	3.5962	2.9356
36600	36536	216.650	−56.500	2.2151	2.1861	3.5619	2.9077
36800	36735	216.650	−56.500	2.1940	2.1653	3.5279	2.8799
37000	36934	216.650	−56.500	2.1731　+ 2	2.1446　− 1	3.4943　− 1	2.8525　− 1
37200	37134	216.650	−56.500	2.1523	2.1242	3.4610	2.8253
37400	37333	216.650	−56.500	2.1318	2.1039	3.4280	2.7984
37600	37532	216.650	−56.500	2.1115	2.0839	3.3953	2.7717
37800	37732	216.650	−56.500	2.0914	2.0640	3.3630	2.7453
38000	37931	216.650	−56.500	2.0714	2.0443	3.3309	2.7191
38200	38130	216.650	−56.500	2.0517	2.0249	3.2992	2.6932
38400	38329	216.650	−56.500	2.0321	2.0056	3.2677	2.6675
38600	38529	216.650	−56.500	2.0128	1.9864	3.2366	2.6421
38800	38728	216.650	−56.500	1.9936	1.9675	3.2057	2.6169
39000	38927	216.650	−56.500	1.9746　+ 2	1.9488　− 1	3.1752　− 1	2.5920　− 1
39200	39126	216.650	−56.500	1.9558	1.9302	3.1449	2.5673
39400	39326	216.650	−56.500	1.9371	1.9118	3.1149	2.5428
39600	39525	216.650	−56.500	1.9187	1.8936	3.0852	2.5186
39800	39724	216.650	−56.500	1.9004	1.8755	3.0558	2.4946
40000	39923	216.650	−56.500	1.8823	1.8576	3.0267	2.4708
40200	40123	216.650	−56.500	1.8643	1.8399	2.9979	2.4472
40400	40322	216.650	−56.500	1.8466	1.8224	2.9693	2.4239
40600	40521	216.650	−56.500	1.8290	1.8050	2.9410	2.4008
40800	40720	216.650	−56.500	1.8115	1.7878	2.9130	2.3779
41000	40920	216.650	−56.500	1.7943　+ 2	1.7708　− 1	2.8852　− 1	2.3553　− 1
41200	41119	216.650	−56.500	1.7772	1.7539	2.8577	2.3328
41400	41318	216.650	−56.500	1.7602	1.7372	2.8305	2.3106
41600	41517	216.650	−56.500	1.7435	1.7207	2.8035	2.2886
41800	41716	216.650	−56.500	1.7268	1.7043	2.7768	2.2668
42000	41916	216.650	−56.500	1.7104	1.6880	2.7503	2.2452
42200	42115	216.650	−56.500	1.6941	1.6719	2.7241	2.2238
42400	42314	216.650	−56.500	1.6779	1.6560	2.6982	2.2026
42600	42513	216.650	−56.500	1.6620	1.6402	2.6725	2.1816
42800	42712	216.650	−56.500	1.6461	1.6246	2.6470	2.1608

Table IV
Geopotential Altitude, English Altitudes

Altitude		Temperature		Pressure		Density	
H (ft)	Z (ft)	T (K)	t (°C)	P (mb)	P/P$_0$	ρ (kg/m³)	ρ/ρ$_0$
43000	43089	216.650	−56.500	1.6235 + 2	1.6023 − 1	2.6107 − 1	2.1312 − 1
43200	43290	216.650	−56.500	1.6080	1.5870	2.5857	2.1108
43400	43491	216.650	−56.500	1.5926	1.5718	2.5610	2.0906
43600	43691	216.650	−56.500	1.5774	1.5567	2.5365	2.0706
43800	43892	216.650	−56.500	1.5623	1.5418	2.5122	2.0508
44000	44093	216.650	−56.500	1.5473	1.5271	2.4882	2.0311
44200	44294	216.650	−56.500	1.5325	1.5125	2.4644	2.0117
44400	44495	216.650	−56.500	1.5179	1.4980	2.4408	1.9925
44600	44696	216.650	−56.500	1.5033	1.4837	2.4174	1.9734
44800	44896	216.650	−56.500	1.4890	1.4695	2.3943	1.9545
45000	45097	216.650	−56.500	1.4747 + 2	1.4554 − 1	2.3714 − 1	1.9358 − 1
45200	45298	216.650	−56.500	1.4606	1.4415	2.3487	1.9173
45400	45499	216.650	−56.500	1.4466	1.4277	2.3262	1.8990
45600	45700	216.650	−56.500	1.4328	1.4141	2.3040	1.8808
45800	45901	216.650	−56.500	1.4191	1.4005	2.2819	1.8628
46000	46102	216.650	−56.500	1.4055	1.3871	2.2601	1.8450
46200	46303	216.650	−56.500	1.3921	1.3739	2.2385	1.8273
46400	46503	216.650	−56.500	1.3788	1.3607	2.2171	1.8099
46600	46704	216.650	−56.500	1.3656	1.3477	2.1959	1.7925
46800	46905	216.650	−56.500	1.3525	1.3348	2.1749	1.7754
47000	47106	216.650	−56.500	1.3396 + 2	1.3220 − 1	2.1541 − 1	1.7584 −
47200	47307	216.650	−56.500	1.3267	1.3094	2.1334	1.7416
47400	47508	216.650	−56.500	1.3140	1.2969	2.1130	1.7249
47600	47709	216.650	−56.500	1.3015	1.2845	2.0928	1.7084
47800	47910	216.650	−56.500	1.2890	1.2722	2.0728	1.6921
48000	48111	216.650	−56.500	1.2767	1.2600	2.0530	1.6759
48200	48312	216.650	−56.500	1.2645	1.2479	2.0333	1.6599
48400	48513	216.650	−56.500	1.2524	1.2360	2.0139	1.6440
48600	48714	216.650	−56.500	1.2404	1.2242	1.9946	1.6283
48800	48914	216.650	−56.500	1.2285	1.2125	1.9755	1.6127
49000	49115	216.650	−56.500	1.2168 + 2	1.2009 − 1	1.9566 − 1	1.5972 − 1
49200	49316	216.650	−56.500	1.2051	1.1894	1.9379	1.5820
49400	49517	216.650	−56.500	1.1936	1.1780	1.9194	1.5668
49600	49718	216.650	−56.500	1.1822	1.1667	1.9010	1.5518
49800	49919	216.650	−56.500	1.1709	1.1556	1.8828	1.5370
50000	50120	216.650	−56.500	1.1597	1.1445	1.8648	1.5223
50200	50321	216.650	−56.500	1.1486	1.1336	1.8470	1.5077
50400	50522	216.650	−56.500	1.1376	1.1227	1.8293	1.4933
50600	50723	216.650	−56.500	1.1267	1.1120	1.8118	1.4790
50800	50924	216.650	−56.500	1.1159	1.1013	1.7945	1.4649
51000	51125	216.650	−56.500	1.1053 + 2	1.0908 − 1	1.7773 − 1	1.4509 − 1
51200	51326	216.650	−56.500	1.0947	1.0804	1.7603	1.4370
51400	51527	216.650	−56.500	1.0842	1.0700	1.7435	1.4232
51600	51728	216.650	−56.500	1.0738	1.0598	1.7268	1.4096
51800	51929	216.650	−56.500	1.0636	1.0497	1.7103	1.3961
52000	52130	216.650	−56.500	1.0534	1.0396	1.6939	1.3828
52200	52331	216.650	−56.500	1.0433	1.0297	1.6777	1.3695
52400	52532	216.650	−56.500	1.0333	1.0198	1.6616	1.3564
52600	52733	216.650	−56.500	1.0234	1.0101	1.6457	1.3435
52800	52934	216.650	−56.500	1.0137	1.0004	1.6300	1.3306
53000	53135	216.650	−56.500	1.0040 + 2	9.9087 − 2	1.6144 − 1	1.3179 − 1
53200	53336	216.650	−56.500	9.9439 + 1	9.8139	1.5990	1.3053
53400	53537	216.650	−56.500	9.8488	9.7200	1.5837	1.2928
53600	53738	216.650	−56.500	9.7546	9.6270	1.5685	1.2804
53800	53939	216.650	−56.500	9.6613	9.5349	1.5535	1.2682
54000	54140	216.650	−56.500	9.5688	9.4437	1.5387	1.2560
54200	54341	216.650	−56.500	9.4773	9.3534	1.5239	1.2440
54400	54542	216.650	−56.500	9.3866	9.2639	1.5094	1.2321
54600	54743	216.650	−56.500	9.2968	9.1753	1.4949	1.2203
54800	54944	216.650	−56.500	9.2079	9.0875	1.4806	1.2087
55000	55145	216.650	−56.500	9.1198 + 1	9.0005 − 2	1.4664 − 1	1.1971 − 1
55200	55346	216.650	−56.500	9.0326	8.9144	1.4524	1.1856
55400	55548	216.650	−56.500	8.9461	8.8292	1.4385	1.1743
55600	55749	216.650	−56.500	8.8606	8.7447	1.4248	1.1631
55800	55950	216.650	−56.500	8.7758	8.6610	1.4111	1.1519
56000	56151	216.650	−56.500	8.6918	8.5782	1.3976	1.1409
56200	56352	216.650	−56.500	8.6087	8.4961	1.3843	1.1300
56400	56553	216.650	−56.500	8.5263	8.4148	1.3710	1.1192
56600	56754	216.650	−56.500	8.4448	8.3343	1.3579	1.1085
56800	56955	216.650	−56.500	8.3640	8.2546	1.3449	1.0979
57000	57156	216.650	−56.500	8.2840 + 1	8.1756 − 2	1.3320 − 1	1.0874 − 1
57200	57357	216.650	−56.500	8.2047	8.0974	1.3193	1.0770
57400	57558	216.650	−56.500	8.1262	8.0199	1.3067	1.0667
57600	57760	216.650	−56.500	8.0485	7.9432	1.2942	1.0565
57800	57961	216.650	−56.500	7.9715	7.8672	1.2818	1.0464
58000	58162	216.650	−56.500	7.8952	7.7920	1.2695	1.0364
58200	58363	216.650	−56.500	7.8197	7.7174	1.2574	1.0264
58400	58564	216.650	−56.500	7.7449	7.6436	1.2454	1.0166
58600	58765	216.650	−56.500	7.6708	7.5705	1.2335	1.0069
58800	58966	216.650	−56.500	7.5974	7.4980	1.2217	9.9727 − 2

Table IV
Geometric Altitude, English Altitudes

Altitude		Temperature		Pressure		Density	
Z (ft)	H (ft)	T (K)	t (°C)	P (mb)	P/P$_0$	ρ (kg/m^3)	ρ/ρ$_0$
43000	42912	216.650	-56.500	1.6304 +2	1.6091 -1	2.6218 -1	2.1402 -1
43200	43111	216.650	-56.500	1.6149	1.5938	2.5968	2.1198
43400	43310	216.650	-56.500	1.5995	1.5786	2.5721	2.0996
43600	43509	216.650	-56.500	1.5843	1.5636	2.5476	2.0796
43800	43708	216.650	-56.500	1.5692	1.5487	2.5233	2.0598
44000	43907	216.650	-56.500	1.5542	1.5339	2.4993	2.0402
44200	44107	216.650	-56.500	1.5394	1.5193	2.4754	2.0208
44400	44306	216.650	-56.500	1.5248	1.5048	2.4519	2.0015
44600	44505	216.650	-56.500	1.5102	1.4905	2.4285	1.9825
44800	44704	216.650	-56.500	1.4959	1.4763	2.4054	1.9636
45000	44903	216.650	-56.500	1.4816 +2	1.4622 -1	2.3825 -1	1.9449 -1
45200	45102	216.650	-56.500	1.4675	1.4483	2.3598	1.9263
45400	45301	216.650	-56.500	1.4535	1.4345	2.3373	1.9080
45600	45501	216.650	-56.500	1.4397	1.4208	2.3150	1.8898
45800	45700	216.650	-56.500	1.4259	1.4073	2.2930	1.8718
46000	45899	216.650	-56.500	1.4124	1.3939	2.2711	1.8540
46200	46098	216.650	-56.500	1.3989	1.3806	2.2495	1.8363
46400	46297	216.650	-56.500	1.3856	1.3675	2.2281	1.8188
46600	46496	216.650	-56.500	1.3724	1.3544	2.2069	1.8015
46800	46695	216.650	-56.500	1.3593	1.3415	2.1858	1.7844
47000	46894	216.650	-56.500	1.3464 +2	1.3288 -1	2.1650 -1	1.7674 -1
47200	47093	216.650	-56.500	1.3336	1.3161	2.1444	1.7505
47400	47293	216.650	-56.500	1.3209	1.3036	2.1240	1.7339
47600	47492	216.650	-56.500	1.3083	1.2912	2.1038	1.7173
47800	47691	216.650	-56.500	1.2958	1.2789	2.0837	1.7010
48000	47890	216.650	-56.500	1.2835	1.2667	2.0639	1.6848
48200	48089	216.650	-56.500	1.2712	1.2546	2.0442	1.6687
48400	48288	216.650	-56.500	1.2591	1.2427	2.0248	1.6529
48600	48487	216.650	-56.500	1.2472	1.2308	2.0055	1.6371
48800	48686	216.650	-56.500	1.2353	1.2191	1.9864	1.6215
49000	48885	216.650	-56.500	1.2235 +2	1.2075 -1	1.9675 -1	1.6061 -1
49200	49084	216.650	-56.500	1.2119	1.1960	1.9487	1.5908
49400	49283	216.650	-56.500	1.2003	1.1846	1.9302	1.5756
49600	49482	216.650	-56.500	1.1889	1.1733	1.9118	1.5606
49800	49681	216.650	-56.500	1.1776	1.1622	1.8936	1.5458
50000	49880	216.650	-56.500	1.1664	1.1511	1.8756	1.5311
50200	50079	216.650	-56.500	1.1553	1.1401	1.8577	1.5165
50400	50278	216.650	-56.500	1.1443	1.1293	1.8400	1.5021
50600	50478	216.650	-56.500	1.1334	1.1185	1.8225	1.4878
50800	50677	216.650	-56.500	1.1226	1.1079	1.8051	1.4736
51000	50876	216.650	-56.500	1.1119 +2	1.0973 -1	1.7880 -1	1.4596 -1
51200	51075	216.650	-56.500	1.1013	1.0869	1.7709	1.4457
51400	51274	216.650	-56.500	1.0908	1.0765	1.7541	1.4319
51600	51473	216.650	-56.500	1.0804	1.0663	1.7374	1.4183
51800	51672	216.650	-56.500	1.0701	1.0561	1.7208	1.4048
52000	51871	216.650	-56.500	1.0600	1.0461	1.7045	1.3914
52200	52070	216.650	-56.500	1.0499	1.0361	1.6882	1.3782
52400	52269	216.650	-56.500	1.0399	1.0263	1.6722	1.3650
52600	52468	216.650	-56.500	1.0300	1.0165	1.6562	1.3520
52800	52667	216.650	-56.500	1.0202	1.0068	1.6405	1.3392
53000	52866	216.650	-56.500	1.0105 +2	9.9729 -2	1.6249 -1	1.3264 -1
53200	53065	216.650	-56.500	1.0008	9.8779	1.6094	1.3138
53400	53264	216.650	-56.500	9.9135 +1	9.7839	1.5941	1.3013
53600	53463	216.650	-56.500	9.8192	9.6908	1.5789	1.2889
53800	53662	216.650	-56.500	9.7257	9.5985	1.5639	1.2766
54000	53861	216.650	-56.500	9.6332	9.5072	1.5490	1.2645
54200	54059	216.650	-56.500	9.5415	9.4167	1.5343	1.2525
54400	54258	216.650	-56.500	9.4507	9.3271	1.5197	1.2405
54600	54457	216.650	-56.500	9.3607	9.2383	1.5052	1.2287
54800	54656	216.650	-56.500	9.2716	9.1504	1.4909	1.2170
55000	54855	216.650	-56.500	9.1834 +1	9.0633 -2	1.4767 -1	1.2055 -1
55200	55054	216.650	-56.500	9.0960	8.9771	1.4626	1.1940
55400	55253	216.650	-56.500	9.0095	8.8916	1.4487	1.1826
55600	55452	216.650	-56.500	8.9237	8.8070	1.4349	1.1714
55800	55651	216.650	-56.500	8.8388	8.7232	1.4213	1.1602
56000	55850	216.650	-56.500	8.7547	8.6402	1.4077	1.1492
56200	56049	216.650	-56.500	8.6714	8.5580	1.3943	1.1382
56400	56248	216.650	-56.500	8.5889	8.4766	1.3811	1.1274
56600	56447	216.650	-56.500	8.5071	8.3959	1.3679	1.1167
56800	56646	216.650	-56.500	8.4262	8.3160	1.3549	1.1061
57000	56845	216.650	-56.500	8.3460 +1	8.2369 -2	1.3420 -1	1.0955 -1
57200	57044	216.650	-56.500	8.2666	8.1585	1.3293	1.0851
57400	57242	216.650	-56.500	8.1880	8.0809	1.3166	1.0748
57600	57441	216.650	-56.500	8.1101	8.0040	1.3041	1.0646
57800	57640	216.650	-56.500	8.0329	7.9278	1.2917	1.0544
58000	57839	216.650	-56.500	7.9565	7.8524	1.2794	1.0444
58200	58038	216.650	-56.500	7.8808	7.7777	1.2672	1.0345
58400	58237	216.650	-56.500	7.8058	7.7037	1.2552	1.0246
58600	58436	216.650	-56.500	7.7315	7.6304	1.2432	1.0149
58800	58635	216.650	-56.500	7.6580	7.5578	1.2314	1.0052

Table IV
Geopotential Altitude, English Altitudes

Altitude		Temperature		Pressure		Density	
H (ft)	Z (ft)	T (K)	t (°C)	P (mb)	P/P$_0$	ρ (kg/m³)	ρ/ρ$_0$
59000	59167	216.650	−56.500	7.5247 + 1	7.4263 − 2	1.2100 − 1	9.8773 − 2
59200	59369	216.650	−56.500	7.4527	7.3553	1.1984	9.7828
59400	59570	216.650	−56.500	7.3814	7.2849	1.1869	9.6892
59600	59771	216.650	−56.500	7.3108	7.2152	1.1756	9.5965
59800	59972	216.650	−56.500	7.2409	7.1462	1.1643	9.5047
60000	60173	216.650	−56.500	7.1716	7.0778	1.1532	9.4137
60200	60374	216.650	−56.500	7.1030	7.0101	1.1422	9.3237
60400	60575	216.650	−56.500	7.0350	6.9430	1.1312	9.2345
60600	60777	216.650	−56.500	6.9677	6.8766	1.1204	9.1462
60800	60978	216.650	−56.500	6.9011	6.8108	1.1097	9.0587
61000	61179	216.650	−56.500	6.8351 + 1	6.7457 − 2	1.0991 − 1	8.9720 − 2
61200	61380	216.650	−56.500	6.7697	6.6811	1.0886	8.8862
61400	61581	216.650	−56.500	6.7049	6.6172	1.0781	8.8011
61600	61782	216.650	−56.500	6.6408	6.5539	1.0678	8.7170
61800	61984	216.650	−56.500	6.5772	6.4912	1.0576	8.6336
62000	62185	216.650	−56.500	6.5143	6.4291	1.0475	8.5510
62200	62386	216.650	−56.500	6.4520	6.3676	1.0375	8.4692
62400	62587	216.650	−56.500	6.3903	6.3067	1.0275	8.3881
62600	62788	216.650	−56.500	6.3291	6.2464	1.0177	8.3079
62800	62990	216.650	−56.500	6.2686	6.1866	1.0080	8.2284
63000	63191	216.650	−56.500	6.2086 + 1	6.1274 − 2	9.9834 − 2	8.1497 − 2
63200	63392	216.650	−56.500	6.1492	6.0688	9.8879	8.0717
63400	63593	216.650	−56.500	6.0904	6.0107	9.7933	7.9945
63600	63795	216.650	−56.500	6.0321	5.9532	9.6996	7.9180
63800	63996	216.650	−56.500	5.9744	5.8963	9.6068	7.8423
64000	64197	216.650	−56.500	5.9173	5.8399	9.5149	7.7673
64200	64398	216.650	−56.500	5.8607	5.7840	9.4239	7.6930
64400	64599	216.650	−56.500	5.8046	5.7287	9.3337	7.6194
64600	64801	216.650	−56.500	5.7491	5.6739	9.2444	7.5465
64800	65002	216.650	−56.500	5.6941	5.6196	9.1560	7.4743
65000	65203	216.650	−56.500	5.6396 + 1	5.5658 − 2	9.0684 − 2	7.4028 − 2
65200	65404	216.650	−56.500	5.5856	5.5126	8.9816	7.3319
65400	65606	216.650	−56.500	5.5322	5.4599	8.8957	7.2618
65600	65807	216.650	−56.500	5.4793	5.4076	8.8106	7.1923
65800	66008	216.706	−56.444	5.4269	5.3559	8.7241	7.1217
66000	66210	216.767	−56.383	5.3750	5.3047	8.6382	7.0516
66200	66411	216.828	−56.322	5.3236	5.2540	8.5532	6.9822
66400	66612	216.889	−56.261	5.2727	5.2037	8.4691	6.9136
66600	66813	216.950	−56.200	5.2223	5.1540	8.3858	6.8456
66800	67015	217.011	−56.139	5.1724	5.1048	8.3034	6.7783
67000	67216	217.072	−56.078	5.1230 + 1	5.0560 − 2	8.2218 − 2	6.7117 − 2
67200	67417	217.133	−56.017	5.0741	5.0078	8.1410	6.6457
67400	67619	217.194	−55.956	5.0257	4.9600	8.0611	6.5805
67600	67820	217.255	−55.895	4.9777	4.9127	7.9819	6.5158
67800	68021	217.316	−55.834	4.9303	4.8658	7.9035	6.4519
68000	68222	217.377	−55.773	4.8833	4.8194	7.8260	6.3886
68200	68424	217.438	−55.712	4.8367	4.7734	7.7492	6.3259
68400	68625	217.499	−55.651	4.7906	4.7279	7.6732	6.2638
68600	68826	217.559	−55.591	4.7450	4.6829	7.5980	6.2024
68800	69028	217.620	−55.530	4.6998	4.6383	7.5235	6.1416
69000	69229	217.681	−55.469	4.6550 + 1	4.5941 − 2	7.4497 − 2	6.0814 − 2
69200	69430	217.742	−55.408	4.6107	4.5504	7.3767	6.0218
69400	69632	217.803	−55.347	4.5668	4.5071	7.3045	5.9629
69600	69833	217.864	−55.286	4.5233	4.4642	7.2330	5.9045
69800	70034	217.925	−55.225	4.4803	4.4217	7.1622	5.8467
70000	70236	217.986	−55.164	4.4377	4.3797	7.0921	5.7894
70200	70437	218.047	−55.103	4.3955	4.3380	7.0227	5.7328
70400	70638	218.108	−55.042	4.3537	4.2968	6.9540	5.6767
70600	70840	218.169	−54.981	4.3124	4.2560	6.8860	5.6212
70800	71041	218.230	−54.920	4.2714	4.2156	6.8187	5.5663
71000	71243	218.291	−54.859	4.2308 + 1	4.1755 − 2	6.7520 − 2	5.5119 − 2
71200	71444	218.352	−54.798	4.1907	4.1359	6.6861	5.4580
71400	71645	218.413	−54.737	4.1509	4.0966	6.6208	5.4047
71600	71847	218.474	−54.676	4.1115	4.0578	6.5561	5.3519
71800	72048	218.535	−54.615	4.0725	4.0193	6.4921	5.2997
72000	72249	218.596	−54.554	4.0339	3.9811	6.4288	5.2480
72200	72451	218.657	−54.493	3.9957	3.9434	6.3660	5.1968
72400	72652	218.718	−54.432	3.9578	3.9060	6.3039	5.1461
72600	72854	218.779	−54.371	3.9203	3.8690	6.2425	5.0959
72800	73055	218.840	−54.310	3.8831	3.8324	6.1816	5.0462
73000	73256	218.901	−54.249	3.8464 + 1	3.7961 − 2	6.1214 − 2	4.9970 − 2
73200	73458	218.962	−54.188	3.8100	3.7601	6.0617	4.9483
73400	73659	219.023	−54.127	3.7739	3.7245	6.0027	4.9001
73600	73861	219.083	−54.067	3.7382	3.6893	5.9442	4.8524
73800	74062	219.144	−54.006	3.7028	3.6544	5.8864	4.8052
74000	74264	219.205	−53.945	3.6678	3.6198	5.8291	4.7584
74200	74465	219.266	−53.884	3.6331	3.5856	5.7724	4.7121
74400	74666	219.327	−53.823	3.5988	3.5517	5.7162	4.6663
74600	74868	219.388	−53.762	3.5648	3.5182	5.6606	4.6209
74800	75069	219.449	−53.701	3.5311	3.4849	5.6056	4.5760

Table IV
Geometric Altitude, English Altitudes

Altitude		Temperature		Pressure		Density	
Z (ft)	H (ft)	T (K)	t (°C)	P (mb)	P/P$_0$	ρ (kg/m^3)	ρ/ρ_0
59000	58834	216.650	-56.500	7.5851 + 1	7.4859 - 2	1.2197 - 1	9.9566 - 2
59200	59032	216.650	-56.500	7.5130	7.4147	1.2081	9.8618
59400	59231	216.650	-56.500	7.4415	7.3442	1.1966	9.7680
59600	59430	216.650	-56.500	7.3707	7.2743	1.1852	9.6751
59800	59629	216.650	-56.500	7.3006	7.2051	1.1739	9.5831
60000	59828	216.650	-56.500	7.2312	7.1366	1.1628	9.4919
60200	60027	216.650	-56.500	7.1624	7.0687	1.1517	9.4016
60400	60226	216.650	-56.500	7.0942	7.0015	1.1407	9.3122
60600	60424	216.650	-56.500	7.0268	6.9349	1.1299	9.2236
60800	60623	216.650	-56.500	6.9599	6.8689	1.1191	9.1359
61000	60822	216.650	-56.500	6.8937 + 1	6.8036 - 2	1.1085 - 1	9.0490 - 2
61200	61021	216.650	-56.500	6.8282	6.7389	1.0980	8.9629
61400	61220	216.650	-56.500	6.7632	6.6748	1.0875	8.8777
61600	61419	216.650	-56.500	6.6989	6.6113	1.0772	8.7933
61800	61617	216.650	-56.500	6.6352	6.5484	1.0669	8.7096
62000	61816	216.650	-56.500	6.5721	6.4861	1.0568	8.6268
62200	62015	216.650	-56.500	6.5096	6.4245	1.0467	8.5448
62400	62214	216.650	-56.500	6.4477	6.3634	1.0368	8.4635
62600	62413	216.650	-56.500	6.3864	6.3028	1.0269	8.3830
62800	62611	216.650	-56.500	6.3256	6.2429	1.0172	8.3033
63000	62810	216.650	-56.500	6.2655 + 1	6.1835 - 2	1.0075 - 1	8.2243 - 2
63200	63009	216.650	-56.500	6.2059	6.1247	9.9790 - 2	8.1461
63400	63208	216.650	-56.500	6.1469	6.0665	9.8841	8.0687
63600	63407	216.650	-56.500	6.0884	6.0088	9.7901	7.9919
63800	63605	216.650	-56.500	6.0305	5.9517	9.6970	7.9159
64000	63804	216.650	-56.500	5.9732	5.8951	9.6048	7.8407
64200	64003	216.650	-56.500	5.9164	5.8390	9.5135	7.7661
64400	64202	216.650	-56.500	5.8601	5.7835	9.4231	7.6923
64600	64401	216.650	-56.500	5.8044	5.7285	9.3335	7.6191
64800	64599	216.650	-56.500	5.7492	5.6741	9.2447	7.5467
65000	64798	216.650	-56.500	5.6946 + 1	5.6201 - 2	9.1568 - 2	7.4750 - 2
65200	64997	216.650	-56.500	5.6404	5.5667	9.0698	7.4039
65400	65196	216.650	-56.500	5.5868	5.5137	8.9835	7.3335
65600	65394	216.650	-56.500	5.5337	5.4613	8.8981	7.2638
65800	65593	216.650	-56.500	5.4811	5.4094	8.8135	7.1947
66000	65792	216.703	-56.447	5.4290	5.3580	8.7276	7.1246
66200	65991	216.764	-56.386	5.3774	5.3071	8.6423	7.0549
66400	66189	216.824	-56.326	5.3263	5.2567	8.5578	6.9859
66600	66388	216.885	-56.265	5.2757	5.2067	8.4741	6.9176
66800	66587	216.945	-56.205	5.2256	5.1573	8.3913	6.8500
67000	66785	217.006	-56.144	5.1760 + 1	5.1083 - 2	8.3094 - 2	6.7831 - 2
67200	66984	217.067	-56.083	5.1269	5.0599	8.2282	6.7169
67400	67183	217.127	-56.023	5.0783	5.0119	8.1479	6.6513
67600	67382	217.188	-55.962	5.0301	4.9643	8.0684	6.5864
67800	67580	217.248	-55.902	4.9824	4.9173	7.9896	6.5222
68000	67779	217.309	-55.841	4.9352	4.8707	7.9117	6.4585
68200	67978	217.369	-55.781	4.8885	4.8245	7.8346	6.3956
68400	68176	217.430	-55.720	4.8421	4.7788	7.7582	6.3332
68600	68375	217.491	-55.659	4.7963	4.7336	7.6826	6.2715
68800	68574	217.551	-55.599	4.7509	4.6888	7.6078	6.2104
69000	68772	217.612	-55.538	4.7059 + 1	4.6444 - 2	7.5337 - 2	6.1499 - 2
69200	68971	217.672	-55.478	4.6614	4.6004	7.4603	6.0900
69400	69170	217.733	-55.417	4.6173	4.5569	7.3877	6.0308
69600	69368	217.793	-55.357	4.5737	4.5139	7.3158	5.9721
69800	69567	217.854	-55.296	4.5304	4.4712	7.2446	5.9140
70000	69766	217.914	-55.236	4.4876	4.4289	7.1742	5.8565
70200	69964	217.975	-55.175	4.4452	4.3871	7.1044	5.7995
70400	70163	218.036	-55.114	4.4032	4.3457	7.0354	5.7432
70600	70362	218.096	-55.054	4.3617	4.3046	6.9670	5.6874
70800	70560	218.157	-54.993	4.3205	4.2640	6.8994	5.6321
71000	70759	218.217	-54.933	4.2797 + 1	4.2238 - 2	6.8324 - 2	5.5774 - 2
71200	70958	218.278	-54.872	4.2394	4.1839	6.7660	5.5233
71400	71156	218.338	-54.812	4.1994	4.1445	6.7004	5.4697
71600	71355	218.399	-54.751	4.1598	4.1054	6.6354	5.4166
71800	71554	218.459	-54.691	4.1206	4.0667	6.5710	5.3641
72000	71752	218.520	-54.630	4.0818	4.0284	6.5073	5.3121
72200	71951	218.581	-54.569	4.0433	3.9904	6.4442	5.2606
72400	72150	218.641	-54.509	4.0053	3.9529	6.3818	5.2096
72600	72348	218.702	-54.448	3.9675	3.9157	6.3200	5.1591
72800	72547	218.762	-54.388	3.9302	3.8788	6.2588	5.1092
73000	72745	218.823	-54.327	3.8932 + 1	3.8423 - 2	6.1982 - 2	5.0597 - 2
73200	72944	218.883	-54.267	3.8566	3.8062	6.1382	5.0107
73400	73143	218.944	-54.206	3.8204	3.7704	6.0788	4.9623
73600	73341	219.004	-54.146	3.7844	3.7350	6.0200	4.9143
73800	73540	219.065	-54.085	3.7489	3.6999	5.9618	4.8667
74000	73738	219.125	-54.025	3.7137	3.6651	5.9041	4.8197
74200	73937	219.186	-53.964	3.6788	3.6307	5.8471	4.7731
74400	74136	219.246	-53.904	3.6443	3.5966	5.7906	4.7270
74600	74334	219.307	-53.843	3.6100	3.5628	5.7346	4.6813
74800	74533	219.367	-53.783	3.5762	3.5294	5.6793	4.6361

Table IV
Geopotential Altitude, English Altitudes

Altitude		Temperature		Pressure		Density	
H (ft)	Z (ft)	T (K)	t (°C)	P (mb)	P/P$_0$	ρ (kg/m^3)	ρ/ρ$_0$
75000	75271	219.510	-53.640	3.4978 +1	3.4520 -2	5.5511 -2	4.5315 -2
75200	75472	219.571	-53.579	3.4647	3.4194	5.4972	4.4875
75400	75674	219.632	-53.518	3.4320	3.3872	5.4438	4.4439
75600	75875	219.693	-53.457	3.3996	3.3552	5.3909	4.4007
75800	76077	219.754	-53.396	3.3676	3.3235	5.3386	4.3580
76000	76278	219.815	-53.335	3.3358	3.2922	5.2868	4.3157
76200	76479	219.876	-53.274	3.3044	3.2612	5.2355	4.2738
76400	76681	219.937	-53.213	3.2732	3.2304	5.1847	4.2324
76600	76882	219.998	-53.152	3.2424	3.2000	5.1344	4.1913
76800	77084	220.059	-53.091	3.2118	3.1698	5.0846	4.1507
77000	77285	220.120	-53.030	3.1816 +1	3.1400 -2	5.0353 -2	4.1105 -2
77200	77487	220.181	-52.969	3.1516	3.1104	4.9866	4.0707
77400	77688	220.242	-52.908	3.1220	3.0811	4.9382	4.0312
77600	77890	220.303	-52.847	3.0926	3.0521	4.8904	3.9922
77800	78091	220.364	-52.786	3.0635	3.0234	4.8431	3.9535
78000	78293	220.425	-52.725	3.0347	2.9950	4.7962	3.9153
78200	78494	220.486	-52.664	3.0061	2.9668	4.7498	3.8774
78400	78696	220.547	-52.603	2.9779	2.9389	4.7038	3.8399
78600	78897	220.607	-52.543	2.9499	2.9113	4.6584	3.8027
78800	79099	220.668	-52.482	2.9222	2.8840	4.6133	3.7660
79000	79300	220.729	-52.421	2.8947 +1	2.8569 -2	4.5687 -2	3.7296 -2
79200	79502	220.790	-52.360	2.8676	2.8301	4.5246	3.6935
79400	79703	220.851	-52.299	2.8406	2.8035	4.4809	3.6579
79600	79905	220.912	-52.238	2.8140	2.7772	4.4376	3.6225
79800	80107	220.973	-52.177	2.7876	2.7511	4.3948	3.5876
80000	80308	221.034	-52.116	2.7614	2.7253	4.3523	3.5529
80200	80510	221.095	-52.055	2.7355	2.6998	4.3103	3.5186
80400	80711	221.156	-51.994	2.7099	2.6745	4.2688	3.4847
80600	80913	221.217	-51.933	2.6845	2.6494	4.2276	3.4511
80800	81114	221.278	-51.872	2.6594	2.6246	4.1868	3.4178
81000	81316	221.339	-51.811	2.6344 +1	2.6000 -2	4.1465 -2	3.3849 -2
81200	81517	221.400	-51.750	2.6098	2.5757	4.1065	3.3523
81400	81719	221.461	-51.689	2.5853	2.5515	4.0669	3.3200
81600	81921	221.522	-51.628	2.5612	2.5277	4.0278	3.2880
81800	82122	221.583	-51.567	2.5372	2.5040	3.9890	3.2563
82000	82324	221.644	-51.506	2.5135	2.4806	3.9506	3.2250
82200	82525	221.705	-51.445	2.4900	2.4574	3.9126	3.1939
82400	82727	221.766	-51.384	2.4667	2.4344	3.8749	3.1632
82600	82928	221.827	-51.323	2.4436	2.4117	3.8377	3.1328
82800	83130	221.888	-51.262	2.4208	2.3891	3.8008	3.1027
83000	83332	221.949	-51.201	2.3982 +1	2.3668 -2	3.7642 -2	3.0728 -2
83200	83533	222.010	-51.140	2.3758	2.3447	3.7281	3.0433
83400	83735	222.071	-51.079	2.3536	2.3228	3.6922	3.0141
83600	83936	222.131	-51.019	2.3316	2.3011	3.6568	2.9851
83800	84138	222.192	-50.958	2.3099	2.2797	3.6217	2.9565
84000	84340	222.253	-50.897	2.2883	2.2584	3.5869	2.9281
84200	84541	222.314	-50.836	2.2670	2.2374	3.5525	2.9000
84400	84743	222.375	-50.775	2.2459	2.2165	3.5184	2.8722
84600	84945	222.436	-50.714	2.2249	2.1958	3.4846	2.8446
84800	85146	222.497	-50.653	2.2042	2.1754	3.4512	2.8173
85000	85348	222.558	-50.592	2.1837 +1	2.1551 -2	3.4181 -2	2.7903 -2
85200	85550	222.619	-50.531	2.1633	2.1350	3.3854	2.7636
85400	85751	222.680	-50.470	2.1432	2.1152	3.3530	2.7371
85600	85953	222.741	-50.409	2.1232	2.0955	3.3208	2.7109
85800	86154	222.802	-50.348	2.1035	2.0760	3.2890	2.6849
86000	86356	222.863	-50.287	2.0839	2.0567	3.2575	2.6592
86200	86558	222.924	-50.226	2.0645	2.0375	3.2264	2.6338
86400	86759	222.985	-50.165	2.0453	2.0186	3.1955	2.6086
86600	86961	223.046	-50.104	2.0263	1.9998	3.1649	2.5836
86800	87163	223.107	-50.043	2.0075	1.9812	3.1347	2.5589
87000	87364	223.168	-49.982	1.9888 +1	1.9628 -2	3.1047 -2	2.5344 -2
87200	87566	223.229	-49.921	1.9704	1.9446	3.0750	2.5102
87400	87768	223.290	-49.860	1.9521	1.9266	3.0456	2.4862
87600	87970	223.351	-49.799	1.9340	1.9087	3.0165	2.4625
87800	88171	223.412	-49.738	1.9160	1.8910	2.9877	2.4390
88000	88373	223.473	-49.677	1.8982	1.8734	2.9592	2.4157
88200	88575	223.534	-49.616	1.8806	1.8560	2.9310	2.3926
88400	88776	223.595	-49.555	1.8632	1.8388	2.9030	2.3698
88600	88978	223.655	-49.495	1.8459	1.8218	2.8753	2.3472
88800	89180	223.716	-49.434	1.8288	1.8049	2.8479	2.3248
89000	89381	223.777	-49.373	1.8119 +1	1.7882 -2	2.8207 -2	2.3026 -2
89200	89583	223.838	-49.312	1.7951	1.7716	2.7938	2.2807
89400	89785	223.899	-49.251	1.7785	1.7552	2.7672	2.2590
89600	89987	223.960	-49.190	1.7620	1.7390	2.7409	2.2374
89800	90188	224.021	-49.129	1.7457	1.7229	2.7148	2.2161
90000	90390	224.082	-49.068	1.7295	1.7069	2.6889	2.1950
90200	90592	224.143	-49.007	1.7135	1.6911	2.6633	2.1741
90400	90794	224.204	-48.946	1.6977	1.6755	2.6380	2.1534
90600	90995	224.265	-48.885	1.6820	1.6600	2.6129	2.1330
90800	91197	224.326	-48.824	1.6665	1.6447	2.5880	2.1121

Table IV
Geometric Altitude, English Altitudes

Altitude		Temperature		Pressure				Density			
Z (ft)	H (ft)	T (K)	t (°C)	P (mb)		P/P$_0$		ρ (kg/m³)		ρ/ρ$_0$	
75000	74731	219.428	-53.722	3.5426	+ 1	3.4963	- 2	5.6244	- 2	4.5914	- 2
75200	74930	219.488	-53.662	3.5094		3.4635		5.5701		4.5471	
75400	75128	219.549	-53.601	3.4765		3.4310		5.5164		4.5032	
75600	75327	219.610	-53.540	3.4439		3.3989		5.4632		4.4598	
75800	75525	219.670	-53.480	3.4117		3.3670		5.4105		4.4168	
76000	75724	219.731	-53.419	3.3797		3.3355		5.3584		4.3742	
76200	75923	219.791	-53.359	3.3481		3.3043		5.3067		4.3320	
76400	76121	219.852	-53.298	3.3167		3.2733		5.2556		4.2903	
76600	76320	219.912	-53.238	3.2857		3.2427		5.2050		4.2490	
76800	76518	219.973	-53.177	3.2549		3.2124		5.1549		4.2081	
77000	76717	220.033	-53.117	3.2245	+ 1	3.1823	- 2	5.1053	- 2	4.1676	- 2
77200	76915	220.094	-53.056	3.1943		3.1526		5.0561		4.1275	
77400	77114	220.154	-52.996	3.1645		3.1231		5.0075		4.0878	
77600	77312	220.215	-52.935	3.1349		3.0939		4.9593		4.0484	
77800	77511	220.275	-52.875	3.1056		3.0650		4.9117		4.0095	
78000	77709	220.336	-52.814	3.0766		3.0364		4.8645		3.9710	
78200	77908	220.396	-52.754	3.0479		3.0080		4.8177		3.9328	
78400	78106	220.457	-52.693	3.0195		2.9800		4.7714		3.8951	
78600	78305	220.517	-52.633	2.9913		2.9522		4.7256		3.8577	
78800	78503	220.578	-52.572	2.9634		2.9246		4.6803		3.8206	
79000	78702	220.638	-52.512	2.9357	+ 1	2.8973	- 2	4.6353	- 2	3.7840	- 2
79200	78900	220.699	-52.451	2.9084		2.8703		4.5909		3.7476	
79400	79099	220.759	-52.391	2.8813		2.8436		4.5468		3.7117	
79600	79297	220.820	-52.330	2.8544		2.8171		4.5032		3.6761	
79800	79496	220.880	-52.270	2.8278		2.7908		4.4601		3.6409	
80000	79694	220.941	-52.209	2.8015		2.7649		4.4173		3.6060	
80200	79893	221.001	-52.149	2.7754		2.7391		4.3750		3.5714	
80400	80091	221.062	-52.088	2.7496		2.7136		4.3331		3.5372	
80600	80290	221.122	-52.028	2.7240		2.6884		4.2916		3.5034	
80800	80488	221.183	-51.967	2.6987		2.6634		4.2505		3.4698	
81000	80687	221.243	-51.907	2.6736	+ 1	2.6386	- 2	4.2099	- 2	3.4366	- 2
81200	80885	221.304	-51.846	2.6487		2.6141		4.1696		3.4037	
81400	81084	221.364	-51.786	2.6241		2.5898		4.1297		3.3712	
81600	81282	221.425	-51.725	2.5997		2.5657		4.0902		3.3390	
81800	81480	221.485	-51.665	2.5756		2.5419		4.0511		3.3071	
82000	81679	221.546	-51.604	2.5517		2.5183		4.0124		3.2755	
82200	81877	221.606	-51.544	2.5280		2.4949		3.9741		3.2442	
82400	82076	221.667	-51.483	2.5045		2.4718		3.9362		3.2132	
82600	82274	221.727	-51.423	2.4813		2.4488		3.8986		3.1825	
82800	82473	221.788	-51.362	2.4583		2.4261		3.8614		3.1521	
83000	82671	221.848	-51.302	2.4355	+ 1	2.4036	- 2	3.8245	- 2	3.1221	- 2
83200	82869	221.908	-51.242	2.4129		2.3814		3.7880		3.0923	
83400	83068	221.969	-51.181	2.3906		2.3593		3.7519		3.0628	
83600	83266	222.029	-51.121	2.3684		2.3374		3.7162		3.0336	
83800	83465	222.090	-51.060	2.3465		2.3158		3.6807		3.0047	
84000	83663	222.150	-51.000	2.3248		2.2943		3.6457		2.9761	
84200	83861	222.211	-50.939	2.3032		2.2731		3.6109		2.9477	
84400	84060	222.271	-50.879	2.2819		2.2521		3.5766		2.9196	
84600	84258	222.332	-50.818	2.2608		2.2313		3.5425		2.8918	
84800	84457	222.392	-50.758	2.2399		2.2106		3.5088		2.8643	
85000	84655	222.453	-50.697	2.2192	+ 1	2.1902	- 2	3.4754	- 2	2.8371	- 2
85200	84853	222.513	-50.637	2.1987		2.1699		3.4424		2.8101	
85400	85052	222.574	-50.576	2.1784		2.1499		3.4096		2.7834	
85600	85250	222.634	-50.516	2.1583		2.1300		3.3772		2.7569	
85800	85448	222.695	-50.455	2.1383		2.1104		3.3451		2.7307	
86000	85647	222.755	-50.395	2.1186		2.0909		3.3134		2.7048	
86200	85845	222.815	-50.335	2.0990		2.0716		3.2819		2.6791	
86400	86044	222.876	-50.274	2.0797		2.0525		3.2507		2.6536	
86600	86242	222.936	-50.214	2.0605		2.0335		3.2199		2.6285	
86800	86440	222.997	-50.153	2.0415		2.0148		3.1893		2.6035	
87000	86639	223.057	-50.093	2.0227	+ 1	1.9962	- 2	3.1591	- 2	2.5788	- 2
87200	86837	223.118	-50.032	2.0040		1.9778		3.1291		2.5544	
87400	87035	223.178	-49.972	1.9856		1.9596		3.0994		2.5301	
87600	87234	223.239	-49.911	1.9673		1.9416		3.0701		2.5062	
87800	87432	223.299	-49.851	1.9492		1.9237		3.0410		2.4824	
88000	87630	223.360	-49.790	1.9312		1.9060		3.0122		2.4589	
88200	87829	223.420	-49.730	1.9135		1.8884		2.9836		2.4356	
88400	88027	223.480	-49.670	1.8959		1.8711		2.9554		2.4126	
88600	88225	223.541	-49.609	1.8784		1.8539		2.9274		2.3897	
88800	88423	223.601	-49.549	1.8611		1.8368		2.8997		2.3671	
89000	88622	223.662	-49.488	1.8440	+ 1	1.8199	- 2	2.8723	- 2	2.3447	- 2
89200	88820	223.722	-49.428	1.8271		1.8032		2.8451		2.3226	
89400	89018	223.783	-49.367	1.8103		1.7866		2.8182		2.3006	
89600	89217	223.843	-49.307	1.7937		1.7702		2.7916		2.2789	
89800	89415	223.904	-49.246	1.7772		1.7540		2.7652		2.2573	
90000	89613	223.964	-49.186	1.7609		1.7379		2.7391		2.2360	
90200	89812	224.024	-49.126	1.7448		1.7219		2.7132		2.2149	
90400	90010	224.085	-49.065	1.7287		1.7061		2.6876		2.1940	
90600	90208	224.145	-49.005	1.7129		1.6905		2.6623		2.1733	
90800	90406	224.206	-48.944	1.6972		1.6750		2.6372		2.1528	

Table IV
Geopotential Altitude, English Altitudes

Altitude		Temperature		Pressure		Density	
H (ft)	Z (ft)	T (K)	t (°C)	P (mb)	P/P_0	ρ (kg/m³)	ρ/ρ_0
91000	91399	224.387	−48.763	1.6511 +1	1.6295 −2	2.5634 −2	2.0926 −2
91200	91601	224.448	−48.702	1.6358	1.6144	2.5390	2.0727
91400	91802	224.509	−48.641	1.6207	1.5995	2.5149	2.0530
91600	92004	224.570	−48.580	1.6057	1.5847	2.4910	2.0335
91800	92206	224.631	−48.519	1.5909	1.5701	2.4674	2.0142
92000	92408	224.692	−48.458	1.5762	1.5556	2.4439	1.9950
92200	92609	224.753	−48.397	1.5617	1.5413	2.4207	1.9761
92400	92811	224.814	−48.336	1.5473	1.5271	2.3977	1.9573
92600	93013	224.875	−48.275	1.5330	1.5130	2.3750	1.9388
92800	93215	224.936	−48.214	1.5189	1.4990	2.3525	1.9204
93000	93417	224.997	−48.153	1.5049 +1	1.4852 −2	2.3302 −2	1.9022 −2
93200	93618	225.058	−48.092	1.4910	1.4715	2.3081	1.8841
93400	93820	225.119	−48.031	1.4773	1.4580	2.2862	1.8663
93600	94022	225.179	−47.971	1.4637	1.4446	2.2645	1.8486
93800	94224	225.240	−47.910	1.4502	1.4313	2.2431	1.8311
94000	94426	225.301	−47.849	1.4369	1.4181	2.2218	1.8137
94200	94627	225.362	−47.788	1.4237	1.4051	2.2008	1.7966
94400	94829	225.423	−47.727	1.4106	1.3921	2.1800	1.7796
94600	95031	225.484	−47.666	1.3976	1.3793	2.1593	1.7627
94800	95233	225.545	−47.605	1.3848	1.3666	2.1389	1.7461
95000	95435	225.606	−47.544	1.3720 +1	1.3541 −2	2.1187 −2	1.7295 −2
95200	95637	225.667	−47.483	1.3594	1.3416	2.0987	1.7132
95400	95838	225.728	−47.422	1.3469	1.3293	2.0788	1.6970
95600	96040	225.789	−47.361	1.3346	1.3171	2.0592	1.6810
95800	96242	225.850	−47.300	1.3223	1.3050	2.0397	1.6651
96000	96444	225.911	−47.239	1.3102	1.2930	2.0205	1.6493
96200	96646	225.972	−47.178	1.2982	1.2812	2.0014	1.6338
96400	96848	226.033	−47.117	1.2863	1.2694	1.9825	1.6184
96600	97050	226.094	−47.056	1.2745	1.2578	1.9638	1.6031
96800	97251	226.155	−46.995	1.2628	1.2463	1.9452	1.5880
97000	97453	226.216	−46.934	1.2512 +1	1.2348 −2	1.9269 −2	1.5730 −2
97200	97655	226.277	−46.873	1.2397	1.2235	1.9087	1.5581
97400	97857	226.338	−46.812	1.2284	1.2123	1.8907	1.5435
97600	98059	226.399	−46.751	1.2171	1.2012	1.8729	1.5289
97800	98261	226.460	−46.690	1.2060	1.1902	1.8553	1.5145
98000	98463	226.521	−46.629	1.1949	1.1793	1.8378	1.5002
98200	98665	226.582	−46.568	1.1840	1.1685	1.8205	1.4861
98400	98866	226.643	−46.507	1.1732	1.1578	1.8033	1.4721
98600	99068	226.703	−46.447	1.1624	1.1472	1.7864	1.4583
98800	99270	226.764	−46.386	1.1518	1.1368	1.7696	1.4445
99000	99472	226.825	−46.325	1.1413 +1	1.1264 −2	1.7529 −2	1.4310 −2
99200	99674	226.886	−46.264	1.1309	1.1161	1.7364	1.4175
99400	99876	226.947	−46.203	1.1205	1.1059	1.7201	1.4042
99600	100078	227.008	−46.142	1.1103	1.0958	1.7039	1.3910
99800	100280	227.069	−46.081	1.1002	1.0858	1.6879	1.3779
100000	100482	227.130	−46.020	1.0901	1.0759	1.6721	1.3650
100200	100684	227.191	−45.959	1.0802	1.0660	1.6564	1.3521
100400	100886	227.252	−45.898	1.0703	1.0563	1.6408	1.3394
100600	101088	227.313	−45.837	1.0605	1.0467	1.6254	1.3269
100800	101290	227.374	−45.776	1.0509	1.0371	1.6102	1.3144
101000	101492	227.435	−45.715	1.0413 +1	1.0277 −2	1.5951 −2	1.3021 −2
101200	101693	227.496	−45.654	1.0318	1.0183	1.5801	1.2899
101400	101895	227.557	−45.593	1.0224	1.0090	1.5653	1.2778
101600	102097	227.618	−45.532	1.0131	9.9988 −3	1.5506	1.2658
101800	102299	227.679	−45.471	1.0039	9.9078	1.5361	1.2539
102000	102501	227.740	−45.410	9.9477 +0	9.8176	1.5217	1.2472
102200	102703	227.801	−45.349	9.8571	9.7282	1.5074	1.2306
102400	102905	227.862	−45.288	9.7674	9.6397	1.4933	1.2190
102600	103107	227.923	−45.227	9.6786	9.5520	1.4793	1.2076
102800	103309	227.984	−45.166	9.5906	9.4651	1.4655	1.1963
103000	103511	228.045	−45.105	9.5034 +0	9.3791 −3	1.4518 −2	1.1851 −2
103200	103713	228.106	−45.044	9.4170	9.2938	1.4382	1.1740
103400	103915	228.167	−44.983	9.3314	9.2094	1.4247	1.1631
103600	104117	228.227	−44.923	9.2466	9.1257	1.4114	1.1522
103800	104319	228.288	−44.862	9.1627	9.0428	1.3982	1.1414
104000	104521	228.349	−44.801	9.0795	8.9607	1.3852	1.1307
104200	104723	228.410	−44.740	8.9970	8.8794	1.3722	1.1202
104400	104925	228.471	−44.679	8.9154	8.7988	1.3594	1.1097
104600	105127	228.532	−44.618	8.8345	8.7190	1.3467	1.0994
104800	105329	228.593	−44.557	8.7544	8.6399	1.3341	1.0891
105000	105531	228.661	−44.489	8.6750 +0	8.5615 −3	1.3217 −2	1.0789 −2
105500	106036	229.088	−44.062	8.4799	8.3690	1.2895	1.0527
106000	106542	229.515	−43.635	8.2895	8.1811	1.2582	1.0271
106500	107047	229.942	−43.208	8.1037	7.9978	1.2277	1.0022
107000	107552	230.368	−42.782	7.9225	7.8189	1.1981	9.7801 −3
107500	108057	230.795	−42.355	7.7456	7.6443	1.1691	9.5441
108000	108562	231.222	−41.928	7.5730	7.4739	1.1410	9.3141
108500	109067	231.648	−41.502	7.4045	7.3077	1.1135	9.0902
109000	109573	232.075	−41.075	7.2401	7.1454	1.0868	8.8720
109500	110078	232.502	−40.648	7.0796	6.9870	1.0608	8.6594

Table IV
Geometric Altitude, English Altitudes

Altitude		Temperature		Pressure				Density			
Z (ft)	H (ft)	T (K)	t (°C)	P (mb)		P/P_0		ρ (kg/m³)		ρ/ρ_0	
91000	90605	224.266	-48.884	1.6816	+ 1	1.6596	- 2	2.6123	- 2	2.1325	- 2
91200	90803	224.327	-48.823	1.6662		1.6444		2.5876		2.1124	
91400	91001	224.387	-48.763	1.6510		1.6294		2.5633		2.0924	
91600	91199	224.447	-48.703	1.6358		1.6145		2.5391		2.0727	
91800	91398	224.508	-48.642	1.6209		1.5997		2.5152		2.0532	
92000	91596	224.568	-48.582	1.6060		1.5850		2.4915		2.0339	
92200	91794	224.629	-48.521	1.5913		1.5705		2.4680		2.0147	
92400	91992	224.689	-48.461	1.5768		1.5562		2.4448		1.9958	
92600	92191	224.750	-48.400	1.5624		1.5419		2.4218		1.9770	
92800	92389	224.810	-48.340	1.5481		1.5278		2.3990		1.9584	
93000	92587	224.870	-48.280	1.5339	+ 1	1.5139	- 2	2.3764	- 2	1.9400	- 2
93200	92785	224.931	-48.219	1.5199		1.5000		2.3541		1.9217	
93400	92984	224.991	-48.159	1.5060		1.4863		2.3320		1.9037	
93600	93182	225.052	-48.098	1.4923		1.4728		2.3101		1.8858	
93800	93380	225.112	-48.038	1.4787		1.4593		2.2884		1.8680	
94000	93578	225.173	-47.977	1.4652		1.4460		2.2669		1.8505	
94200	93776	225.233	-47.917	1.4518		1.4328		2.2456		1.8331	
94400	93975	225.293	-47.857	1.4386		1.4198		2.2245		1.8159	
94600	94173	225.354	-47.796	1.4254		1.4068		2.2036		1.7989	
94800	94371	225.414	-47.736	1.4125		1.3940		2.1830		1.7820	
95000	94569	225.475	-47.675	1.3996	+ 1	1.3813	- 2	2.1625	- 2	1.7653	- 2
95200	94767	225.535	-47.615	1.3868		1.3687		2.1422		1.7488	
95400	94966	225.595	-47.555	1.3742		1.3562		2.1221		1.7324	
95600	95164	225.656	-47.494	1.3617		1.3439		2.1023		1.7161	
95800	95362	225.716	-47.434	1.3493		1.3317		2.0826		1.7001	
96000	95560	225.777	-47.373	1.3370		1.3195		2.0631		1.6841	
96200	95758	225.837	-47.313	1.3249		1.3075		2.0438		1.6684	
96400	95956	225.897	-47.253	1.3128		1.2956		2.0246		1.6528	
96600	96155	225.958	-47.192	1.3009		1.2839		2.0057		1.6373	
96800	96353	226.018	-47.132	1.2890		1.2722		1.9869		1.6220	
97000	96551	226.079	-47.071	1.2773	+ 1	1.2606	- 2	1.9683	- 2	1.6068	- 2
97200	96749	226.139	-47.011	1.2657		1.2492		1.9499		1.5918	
97400	96947	226.199	-46.951	1.2542		1.2378		1.9317		1.5769	
97600	97145	226.260	-46.890	1.2428		1.2266		1.9137		1.5622	
97800	97343	226.320	-46.830	1.2316		1.2155		1.8958		1.5476	
98000	97542	226.381	-46.769	1.2204		1.2044		1.8781		1.5331	
98200	97740	226.441	-46.709	1.2093		1.1935		1.8606		1.5188	
98400	97938	226.501	-46.649	1.1984		1.1827		1.8432		1.5046	
98600	98136	226.562	-46.588	1.1875		1.1720		1.8260		1.4906	
98800	98334	226.622	-46.528	1.1767		1.1613		1.8090		1.4767	
99000	98532	226.682	-46.468	1.1661	+ 1	1.1508	- 2	1.7921	- 2	1.4629	- 2
99200	98730	226.743	-46.407	1.1555		1.1404		1.7754		1.4493	
99400	98928	226.803	-46.347	1.1450		1.1301		1.7588		1.4358	
99600	99127	226.864	-46.286	1.1347		1.1198		1.7425		1.4224	
99800	99325	226.924	-46.226	1.1244		1.1097		1.7262		1.4092	
100000	99523	226.984	-46.166	1.1142		1.0997		1.7102		1.3960	
100200	99721	227.045	-46.105	1.1041		1.0897		1.6942		1.3830	
100400	99919	227.105	-46.045	1.0942		1.0799		1.6785		1.3702	
100600	100117	227.166	-45.984	1.0843		1.0701		1.6629		1.3574	
100800	100315	227.226	-45.924	1.0745		1.0604		1.6474		1.3448	
101000	100513	227.286	-45.864	1.0648	+ 1	1.0508	- 2	1.6321	- 2	1.3323	- 2
101200	100711	227.347	-45.803	1.0551		1.0413		1.6169		1.3199	
101400	100909	227.407	-45.743	1.0456		1.0319		1.6019		1.3077	
101600	101107	227.467	-45.683	1.0362		1.0226		1.5870		1.2955	
101800	101305	227.528	-45.622	1.0268		1.0134		1.5723		1.2835	
102000	101504	227.588	-45.562	1.0176		1.0043		1.5577		1.2716	
102200	101702	227.649	-45.501	1.0084		9.9524	- 3	1.5432		1.2597	
102400	101900	227.709	-45.441	9.9934	+ 0	9.8627		1.5289		1.2481	
102600	102098	227.769	-45.381	9.9033		9.7738		1.5147		1.2365	
102800	102296	227.830	-45.320	9.8140		9.6857		1.5006		1.2250	
103000	102494	227.890	-45.260	9.7256	+ 0	9.5984	- 3	1.4867	- 2	1.2137	- 2
103200	102692	227.950	-45.200	9.6380		9.5120		1.4729		1.2024	
103400	102890	228.011	-45.139	9.5512		9.4263		1.4593		1.1913	
103600	103088	228.071	-45.079	9.4652		9.3415		1.4458		1.1802	
103800	103286	228.131	-45.019	9.3801		9.2574		1.4324		1.1693	
104000	103484	228.192	-44.958	9.2957		9.1741		1.4191		1.1585	
104200	103682	228.252	-44.898	9.2121		9.0916		1.4060		1.1477	
104400	103880	228.312	-44.838	9.1292		9.0099		1.3930		1.1371	
104600	104078	228.373	-44.777	9.0472		8.9289		1.3801		1.1266	
104800	104276	228.433	-44.717	8.9659		8.8486		1.3673		1.1162	
105000	104474	228.494	-44.656	8.8853	+ 0	8.7691	- 3	1.3547	- 2	1.1059	- 2
105500	104969	228.644	-44.506	8.6872		8.5736		1.3236		1.0805	
106000	105464	229.057	-44.093	8.4937		8.3827		1.2918		1.0545	
106500	105959	229.479	-43.671	8.3049		8.1963		1.2608		1.0292	
107000	106454	229.902	-43.248	8.1207		8.0145		1.2305		1.0045	
107500	106949	230.324	-42.826	7.9408		7.8370		1.2011		9.8046	- 3
108000	107444	230.747	-42.403	7.7653		7.6637		1.1724		9.5703	
108500	107938	231.169	-41.981	7.5940		7.4946		1.1444		9.3421	
109000	108433	231.591	-41.559	7.4267		7.3296		1.1172		9.1197	
109500	108928	232.013	-41.137	7.2635		7.1685		1.0906		8.9030	

Table IV
Geopotential Altitude, English Altitudes

Altitude		Temperature		Pressure				Density			
H (ft)	Z (ft)	T (K)	t (°C)	P (mb)		P/P$_0$		ρ (kg/m^3)		ρ/ρ$_0$	
110000	110583	232.929	-40.221	6.9230	+ 0	6.8325	- 3	1.0354	- 2	8.4523	- 3
110500	111089	233.355	-39.795	6.7701		6.6816		1.0107		8.2505	
111000	111594	233.782	-39.368	6.6209		6.5343		9.8661	- 3	8.0539	
111500	112099	234.209	-38.941	6.4752		6.3905		9.6314		7.8624	
112000	112605	234.635	-38.515	6.3329		6.2501		9.4027		7.6757	
112500	113110	235.062	-38.088	6.1941		6.1131		9.1799		7.4938	
113000	113616	235.489	-37.661	6.0585		5.9793		8.9627		7.3165	
113500	114121	235.916	-37.234	5.9262		5.8487		8.7510		7.1437	
114000	114627	236.342	-36.808	5.7969		5.7211		8.5447		6.9753	
114500	115132	236.769	-36.381	5.6707		5.5966		8.3436		6.8111	
115000	115638	237.196	-35.954	5.5475	+ 0	5.4749	- 3	8.1476	- 3	6.6511	- 3
115500	116143	237.623	-35.527	5.4272		5.3562		7.9566		6.4952	
116000	116649	238.049	-35.101	5.3096		5.2402		7.7704		6.3431	
116500	117154	238.476	-34.674	5.1949		5.1269		7.5888		6.1949	
117000	117660	238.903	-34.247	5.0828		5.0163		7.4118		6.0504	
117500	118166	239.329	-33.821	4.9733		4.9083		7.2392		5.9096	
118000	118671	239.756	-33.394	4.8664		4.8027		7.0710		5.7722	
118500	119177	240.183	-32.967	4.7619		4.6997		6.9069		5.6383	
119000	119683	240.610	-32.540	4.6599		4.5990		6.7469		5.5077	
119500	120189	241.036	-32.114	4.5602		4.5006		6.5910		5.3804	
120000	120695	241.463	-31.687	4.4629	+ 0	4.4045	- 3	6.4388	- 3	5.2562	- 3
120500	121200	241.890	-31.260	4.3678		4.3106		6.2905		5.1351	
121000	121706	242.316	-30.834	4.2748		4.2189		6.1458		5.0170	
121500	122212	242.743	-30.407	4.1840		4.1293		6.0047		4.9018	
122000	122718	243.170	-29.980	4.0953		4.0418		5.8671		4.7895	
122500	123224	243.597	-29.553	4.0087		3.9562		5.7329		4.6799	
123000	123730	244.023	-29.127	3.9240		3.8726		5.6019		4.5730	
123500	124236	244.450	-28.700	3.8412		3.7910		5.4742		4.4687	
124000	124742	244.877	-28.273	3.7603		3.7111		5.3496		4.3670	
124500	125248	245.303	-27.847	3.6813		3.6331		5.2280		4.2678	
125000	125754	245.730	-27.420	3.6040	+ 0	3.5569	- 3	5.1094	- 3	4.1710	- 3
125500	126260	246.157	-26.993	3.5285		3.4824		4.9937		4.0765	
126000	126766	246.584	-26.566	3.4547		3.4096		4.8809		3.9844	
126500	127272	247.010	-26.140	3.3826		3.3384		4.7707		3.8945	
127000	127778	247.437	-25.713	3.3121		3.2688		4.6632		3.8067	
127500	128284	247.864	-25.286	3.2432		3.2008		4.5584		3.7211	
128000	128790	248.291	-24.859	3.1759		3.1343		4.4560		3.6376	
128500	129297	248.717	-24.433	3.1100		3.0694		4.3562		3.5560	
129000	129803	249.144	-24.006	3.0456		3.0058		4.2587		3.4765	
129500	130309	249.571	-23.579	2.9827		2.9437		4.1636		3.3988	
130000	130815	249.997	-23.153	2.9212	+ 0	2.8830	- 3	4.0707	- 3	3.3230	- 3
130500	131322	250.424	-22.726	2.8610		2.8236		3.9801		3.2490	
131000	131828	250.851	-22.299	2.8022		2.7656		3.8916		3.1768	
131500	132334	251.278	-21.872	2.7447		2.7088		3.8053		3.1064	
132000	132841	251.704	-21.446	2.6885		2.6533		3.7210		3.0375	
132500	133347	252.131	-21.019	2.6335		2.5990		3.6387		2.9704	
133000	133854	252.558	-20.592	2.5797		2.5459		3.5584		2.9048	
133500	134360	252.984	-20.166	2.5271		2.4940		3.4800		2.8408	
134000	134867	253.411	-19.739	2.4757		2.4433		3.4034		2.7783	
134500	135373	253.838	-19.312	2.4254		2.3936		3.3286		2.7172	
135000	135880	254.265	-18.885	2.3762	+ 0	2.3451	- 3	3.2556	- 3	2.6577	- 3
135500	136386	254.691	-18.459	2.3280		2.2976		3.1844		2.5995	
136000	136893	255.118	-18.032	2.2810		2.2511		3.1148		2.5427	
136500	137399	255.545	-17.605	2.2349		2.2057		3.0468		2.4872	
137000	137906	255.971	-17.179	2.1899		2.1612		2.9804		2.4330	
137500	138413	256.398	-16.752	2.1458		2.1178		2.9156		2.3801	
138000	138919	256.825	-16.325	2.1027		2.0752		2.8523		2.3284	
138500	139426	257.252	-15.898	2.0606		2.0336		2.7905		2.2779	
139000	139933	257.678	-15.472	2.0193		1.9929		2.7301		2.2286	
139500	140439	258.105	-15.045	1.9790		1.9531		2.6711		2.1805	
140000	140946	258.532	-14.618	1.9395	+ 0	1.9141	- 3	2.6135	- 3	2.1334	- 3
140500	141453	258.959	-14.191	1.9008		1.8760		2.5572		2.0875	
141000	141960	259.385	-13.765	1.8630		1.8387		2.5022		2.0426	
141500	142467	259.812	-13.338	1.8260		1.8021		2.4485		1.9988	
142000	142974	260.239	-12.911	1.7898		1.7664		2.3960		1.9559	
142500	143480	260.665	-12.485	1.7544		1.7315		2.3448		1.9141	
143000	143987	261.092	-12.058	1.7197		1.6972		2.2947		1.8732	
143500	144494	261.519	-11.631	1.6858		1.6638		2.2457		1.8332	
144000	145001	261.946	-11.204	1.6526		1.6310		2.1979		1.7942	
144500	145508	262.372	-10.778	1.6201		1.5989		2.1512		1.7561	
145000	146015	262.799	-10.351	1.5883	+ 0	1.5675	- 3	2.1055	- 3	1.7188	- 3
145500	146522	263.226	-9.924	1.5572		1.5368		2.0609		1.6824	
146000	147029	263.652	-9.498	1.5267		1.5067		2.0173		1.6468	
146500	147536	264.079	-9.071	1.4969		1.4773		1.9747		1.6120	
147000	148044	264.506	-8.644	1.4677		1.4485		1.9331		1.5780	
147500	148551	264.933	-8.217	1.4391		1.4203		1.8924		1.5448	
148000	149058	265.359	-7.791	1.4111		1.3926		1.8526		1.5123	
148500	149565	265.786	-7.364	1.3837		1.3656		1.8137		1.4806	
149000	150072	266.213	-6.937	1.3569		1.3391		1.7757		1.4495	
149500	150579	266.639	-6.511	1.3306		1.3132		1.7385		1.4192	

Table IV
Geometric Altitude, English Altitudes

Altitude		Temperature		Pressure		Density	
Z (ft)	H (ft)	T (K)	t (°C)	P (mb)	P/P_0	ρ (kg/m³)	ρ/ρ_0
110000	109423	232.436	−40.714	7.1041 + 0	7.0112 − 3	1.0647 − 2	8.6918 − 3
110500	109918	232.858	−40.292	6.9485	6.8576	1.0395	8.4860
111000	110412	233.280	−39.870	6.7966	6.7077	1.0150	8.2855
111500	110907	233.702	−39.448	6.6483	6.5613	9.9103 − 3	8.0901
112000	111402	234.125	−39.025	6.5035	6.4184	9.6770	7.8996
112500	111896	234.547	−38.603	6.3621	6.2789	9.4496	7.7139
113000	112391	234.969	−38.181	6.2240	6.1426	9.2279	7.5330
113500	112886	235.391	−37.759	6.0892	6.0096	9.0118	7.3566
114000	113380	235.813	−37.337	5.9575	5.8796	8.8012	7.1846
114500	113875	236.235	−36.915	5.8289	5.7527	8.5958	7.0170
115000	114369	236.657	−36.493	5.7034 + 0	5.6288 − 3	8.3956 − 3	6.8536 − 3
115500	114864	237.079	−36.071	5.5807	5.5077	8.2005	6.6943
116000	115358	237.501	−35.649	5.4609	5.3895	8.0102	6.5389
116500	115853	237.923	−35.227	5.3439	5.2740	7.8246	6.3875
117000	116347	238.345	−34.805	5.2296	5.1612	7.6437	6.2398
117500	116842	238.767	−34.383	5.1180	5.0510	7.4673	6.0958
118000	117336	239.189	−33.961	5.0089	4.9434	7.2953	5.9553
118500	117830	239.611	−33.539	4.9023	4.8382	7.1275	5.8184
119000	118325	240.033	−33.117	4.7982	4.7355	6.9639	5.6848
119500	118819	240.455	−32.695	4.6965	4.6351	6.8043	5.5545
120000	119313	240.877	−32.273	4.5971 + 0	4.5370 − 3	6.6487 − 3	5.4275 − 3
120500	119808	241.299	−31.851	4.5000	4.4412	6.4968	5.3035
121000	120302	241.720	−31.430	4.4051	4.3475	6.3488	5.1827
121500	120796	242.142	−31.008	4.3124	4.2560	6.2043	5.0647
122000	121290	242.564	−30.586	4.2218	4.1666	6.0634	4.9497
122500	121785	242.986	−30.164	4.1333	4.0792	5.9259	4.8375
123000	122279	243.407	−29.743	4.0467	3.9938	5.7918	4.7280
123500	122773	243.829	−29.321	3.9621	3.9103	5.6609	4.6212
124000	123267	244.251	−28.899	3.8795	3.8287	5.5333	4.5169
124500	123761	244.673	−28.477	3.7987	3.7490	5.4087	4.4153
125000	124255	245.094	−28.056	3.7197 + 0	3.6711 − 3	5.2871 − 3	4.3160 − 3
125500	124749	245.516	−27.634	3.6425	3.5949	5.1685	4.2192
126000	125243	245.938	−27.212	3.5670	3.5204	5.0528	4.1247
126500	125737	246.359	−26.791	3.4933	3.4476	4.9398	4.0325
127000	126231	246.781	−26.369	3.4212	3.3764	4.8295	3.9425
127500	126725	247.202	−25.948	3.3506	3.3068	4.7219	3.8546
128000	127219	247.624	−25.526	3.2817	3.2388	4.6169	3.7689
128500	127713	248.045	−25.105	3.2143	3.1723	4.5144	3.6852
129000	128207	248.467	−24.683	3.1484	3.1072	4.4144	3.6036
129500	128701	248.888	−24.262	3.0840	3.0436	4.3167	3.5238
130000	129195	249.310	−23.840	3.0210 + 0	2.9815 − 3	4.2213 − 3	3.4460 − 3
130500	129688	249.731	−23.419	2.9593	2.9206	4.1283	3.3700
131000	130182	250.153	−22.997	2.8991	2.8612	4.0374	3.2958
131500	130676	250.574	−22.576	2.8401	2.8030	3.9487	3.2234
132000	131170	250.995	−22.155	2.7825	2.7461	3.8621	3.1527
132500	131663	251.417	−21.733	2.7261	2.6905	3.7775	3.0836
133000	132157	251.838	−21.312	2.6710	2.6361	3.6949	3.0162
133500	132651	252.259	−20.891	2.6171	2.5829	3.6142	2.9504
134000	133144	252.681	−20.469	2.5643	2.5308	3.5355	2.8861
134500	133638	253.102	−20.048	2.5127	2.4799	3.4586	2.8233
135000	134132	253.523	−19.627	2.4623 + 0	2.4301 − 3	3.3835 − 3	2.7620 − 3
135500	134625	253.944	−19.206	2.4129	2.3813	3.3102	2.7022
136000	135119	254.366	−18.784	2.3646	2.3337	3.2385	2.6437
136500	135612	254.787	−18.363	2.3173	2.2870	3.1686	2.5866
137000	136106	255.208	−17.942	2.2711	2.2414	3.1002	2.5308
137500	136599	255.629	−17.521	2.2259	2.1968	3.0335	2.4763
138000	137093	256.050	−17.100	2.1816	2.1531	2.9683	2.4231
138500	137586	256.471	−16.679	2.1383	2.1103	2.9046	2.3711
139000	138080	256.893	−16.257	2.0959	2.0685	2.8423	2.3203
139500	138573	257.314	−15.836	2.0545	2.0276	2.7815	2.2706
140000	139066	257.735	−15.415	2.0139 + 0	1.9875 − 3	2.7221 − 3	2.2221 − 3
140500	139560	258.156	−14.994	1.9742	1.9484	2.6641	2.1748
141000	140053	258.577	−14.573	1.9353	1.9100	2.6074	2.1285
141500	140546	258.998	−14.152	1.8973	1.8725	2.5520	2.0833
142000	141040	259.419	−13.731	1.8600	1.8357	2.4979	2.0391
142500	141533	259.840	−13.310	1.8236	1.7998	2.4450	1.9959
143000	142026	260.261	−12.889	1.7879	1.7646	2.3933	1.9537
143500	142519	260.682	−12.468	1.7530	1.7301	2.3428	1.9125
144000	143012	261.102	−12.048	1.7189	1.6964	2.2934	1.8722
144500	143506	261.523	−11.627	1.6854	1.6634	2.2452	1.8328
145000	143999	261.944	−11.206	1.6527 + 0	1.6311 − 3	2.1980 − 3	1.7943 − 3
145500	144492	262.365	−10.785	1.6206	1.5994	2.1519	1.7567
146000	144985	262.786	−10.364	1.5892	1.5684	2.1069	1.7199
146500	145478	263.207	−9.943	1.5585	1.5381	2.0628	1.6839
147000	145971	263.627	−9.523	1.5284	1.5084	2.0198	1.6488
147500	146464	264.048	−9.102	1.4990	1.4794	1.9777	1.6145
148000	146957	264.469	−8.681	1.4701	1.4509	1.9366	1.5809
148500	147450	264.890	−8.260	1.4419	1.4230	1.8964	1.5480
149000	147943	265.310	−7.840	1.4142	1.3957	1.8570	1.5160
149500	148436	265.731	−7.419	1.3872	1.3690	1.8186	1.4846

Table IV
Geopotential Altitude, English Altitudes

Altitude		Temperature		Pressure				Density			
H (ft)	Z (ft)	T (K)	t (°C)	P (mb)		P/P_0		ρ (kg/m³)		ρ/ρ_0	
150000	151087	267.066	−6.084	1.3049	+ 0	1.2878	− 3	1.7022	− 3	1.3896	− 3
150500	151594	267.493	−5.657	1.2797		1.2630		1.6667		1.3606	
151000	152101	267.920	−5.230	1.2551		1.2387		1.6320		1.3323	
151500	152609	268.346	−4.804	1.2309		1.2148		1.5981		1.3046	
152000	153116	268.773	−4.377	1.2073		1.1915		1.5649		1.2775	
152500	153623	269.200	−3.950	1.1842		1.1687		1.5325		1.2510	
153000	154131	269.627	−3.523	1.1615		1.1463		1.5008		1.2251	
153500	154638	270.053	−3.097	1.1393		1.1244		1.4698		1.1998	
154000	155146	270.480	−2.670	1.1176		1.1030		1.4394		1.1751	
154500	155653	270.650	−2.500	1.0963		1.0819		1.4111		1.1519	
155000	156161	270.650	−2.500	1.0754	+ 0	1.0613	− 3	1.3842	− 3	1.1300	− 3
155500	156668	270.650	−2.500	1.0549		1.0411		1.3579		1.1085	
156000	157176	270.650	−2.500	1.0348		1.0213		1.3320		1.0873	
156500	157683	270.650	−2.500	1.0151		1.0018		1.3066		1.0666	
157000	158191	270.650	−2.500	9.9578	− 1	9.8276	− 4	1.2817		1.0463	
157500	158699	270.650	−2.500	9.7681		9.6403		1.2573		1.0264	
158000	159206	270.650	−2.500	9.5819		9.4566		1.2333		1.0068	
158500	159714	270.650	−2.500	9.3994		9.2765		1.2098		9.8763	− 4
159000	160222	270.650	−2.500	9.2203		9.0997		1.1868		9.6881	
159500	160729	270.650	−2.500	9.0446		8.9263		1.1642		9.5036	
160000	161237	270.650	−2.500	8.8723	− 1	8.7563	− 4	1.1420	− 3	9.3225	− 4
160500	161745	270.650	−2.500	8.7032		8.5894		1.1202		9.1449	
161000	162253	270.650	−2.500	8.5374		8.4258		1.0989		8.9706	
161500	162760	270.650	−2.500	8.3747		8.2652		1.0780		8.7997	
162000	163268	270.650	−2.500	8.2152		8.1077		1.0574		8.6320	
162500	163776	270.650	−2.500	8.0587		7.9533		1.0373		8.4676	
163000	164284	270.650	−2.500	7.9051		7.8017		1.0175		8.3062	
163500	164792	270.650	−2.500	7.7545		7.6531		9.9813	− 4	8.1480	
164000	165300	270.650	−2.500	7.6067		7.5073		9.7911		7.9927	
164500	165808	270.650	−2.500	7.4618		7.3642		9.6046		7.8405	
165000	166316	270.650	−2.500	7.3196	− 1	7.2239	− 4	9.4216	− 4	7.6911	− 4
165500	166824	270.650	−2.500	7.1802		7.0863		9.2421		7.5445	
166000	167332	270.650	−2.500	7.0434		6.9513		9.0660		7.4008	
166500	167840	270.650	−2.500	6.9092		6.8188		8.8932		7.2598	
167000	168348	270.650	−2.500	6.7775		6.6889		8.7238		7.1215	
167500	168856	270.499	−2.651	6.6484		6.5614		8.5623		6.9897	
168000	169364	270.072	−3.078	6.5215		6.4363		8.4123		6.8671	
168500	169873	269.646	−3.504	6.3969		6.3133		8.2646		6.7466	
169000	170381	269.219	−3.931	6.2745		6.1924		8.1192		6.6280	
169500	170889	268.792	−4.358	6.1542		6.0737		7.9763		6.5112	
170000	171397	268.365	−4.785	6.0361	− 1	5.9571	− 4	7.8356	− 4	6.3964	− 4
170500	171905	267.939	−5.211	5.9200		5.8426		7.6971		6.2834	
171000	172414	267.512	−5.638	5.8060		5.7301		7.5609		6.1722	
171500	172922	267.085	−6.065	5.6940		5.6195		7.4269		6.0628	
172000	173430	266.659	−6.491	5.5840		5.5110		7.2951		5.9552	
172500	173939	266.232	−6.918	5.4759		5.4043		7.1654		5.8493	
173000	174447	265.805	−7.345	5.3698		5.2996		7.0378		5.7451	
173500	174956	265.378	−7.772	5.2656		5.1967		6.9123		5.6427	
174000	175464	264.952	−8.198	5.1632		5.0957		6.7888		5.5419	
174500	175972	264.525	−8.625	5.0626		4.9964		6.6673		5.4427	
175000	176481	264.098	−9.052	4.9639	− 1	4.8990	− 4	6.5478	− 4	5.3452	− 4
175500	176989	263.671	−9.479	4.8669		4.8032		6.4303		5.2492	
176000	177498	263.245	−9.905	4.7717		4.7093		6.3147		5.1549	
176500	178007	262.818	−10.332	4.6781		4.6170		6.2010		5.0620	
177000	178515	262.391	−10.759	4.5863		4.5263		6.0891		4.9707	
177500	179024	261.965	−11.185	4.4961		4.4373		5.9791		4.8809	
178000	179532	261.538	−11.612	4.4076		4.3499		5.8709		4.7926	
178500	180041	261.111	−12.039	4.3206		4.2641		5.7645		4.7057	
179000	180550	260.684	−12.466	4.2353		4.1799		5.6599		4.6203	
179500	181058	260.258	−12.892	4.1514		4.0971		5.5570		4.5363	
180000	181567	259.831	−13.319	4.0691	− 1	4.0159	− 4	5.4558	− 4	4.4537	− 4
180500	182076	259.404	−13.746	3.9884		3.9362		5.3562		4.3724	
181000	182585	258.978	−14.172	3.9090		3.8579		5.2584		4.2925	
181500	183094	258.551	−14.599	3.8312		3.7811		5.1621		4.2140	
182000	183602	258.124	−15.026	3.7547		3.7056		5.0675		4.1367	
182500	184111	257.697	−15.453	3.6797		3.6316		4.9745		4.0608	
183000	184620	257.271	−15.879	3.6060		3.5589		4.8830		3.9861	
183500	185129	256.844	−16.306	3.5337		3.4875		4.7930		3.9127	
184000	185638	256.417	−16.733	3.4628		3.4175		4.7046		3.8405	
184500	186147	255.991	−17.159	3.3931		3.3487		4.6176		3.7695	
185000	186656	255.564	−17.586	3.3247	− 1	3.2812	− 4	4.5321	− 4	3.6997	− 4
185500	187165	255.137	−18.013	3.2576		3.2150		4.4481		3.6311	
186000	187674	254.710	−18.440	3.1918		3.1500		4.3655		3.5636	
186500	188183	254.284	−18.866	3.1271		3.0862		4.2842		3.4973	
187000	188692	253.857	−19.293	3.0637		3.0236		4.2044		3.4321	
187500	189201	253.430	−19.720	3.0014		2.9622		4.1259		3.3681	
188000	189710	253.003	−20.147	2.9404		2.9019		4.0487		3.3051	
188500	190219	252.577	−20.573	2.8804		2.8428		3.9729		3.2432	
189000	190729	252.150	−21.000	2.8216		2.7847		3.8984		3.1823	
189500	191238	251.723	−21.427	2.7639		2.7277		3.8251		3.1225	

Table IV
Geometric Altitude, English Altitudes

Altitude		Temperature		Pressure		Density	
Z (ft)	H (ft)	T (K)	t (°C)	P (mb)	P/P$_0$	ρ (kg/m^3)	ρ/ρ_0
150000	148929	266.152	-6.998	1.3606 +0	1.3429 -3	1.7810 -3	1.4539 -3
150500	149422	266.572	-6.578	1.3347	1.3172	1.7443	1.4239
151000	149915	266.993	-6.157	1.3093	1.2921	1.7084	1.3946
151500	150407	267.414	-5.736	1.2843	1.2675	1.6732	1.3659
152000	150900	267.834	-5.316	1.2600	1.2435	1.6389	1.3379
152500	151393	268.255	-4.895	1.2361	1.2199	1.6053	1.3104
153000	151886	268.675	-4.475	1.2127	1.1968	1.5724	1.2836
153500	152378	269.096	-4.054	1.1897	1.1742	1.5403	1.2574
154000	152871	269.516	-3.634	1.1673	1.1520	1.5089	1.2317
154500	153364	269.937	-3.213	1.1453	1.1303	1.4781	1.2066
155000	153856	270.357	-2.793	1.1237 +0	1.1091 -3	1.4481 -3	1.1821 -3
155500	154349	270.650	-2.500	1.1026	1.0882	1.4193	1.1586
156000	154842	270.650	-2.500	1.0819	1.0678	1.3927	1.1369
156500	155334	270.650	-2.500	1.0616	1.0477	1.3665	1.1155
157000	155827	270.650	-2.500	1.0417	1.0281	1.3409	1.0946
157500	156319	270.650	-2.500	1.0221	1.0088	1.3157	1.0741
158000	156812	270.650	-2.500	1.0030	9.8988 -4	1.2910	1.0539
158500	157304	270.650	-2.500	9.8417 -1	9.7130	1.2668	1.0341
159000	157797	270.650	-2.500	9.6570	9.5307	1.2430	1.0147
159500	158289	270.650	-2.500	9.4758	9.3519	1.2197	9.9566 -4
160000	158782	270.650	-2.500	9.2979 -1	9.1763 -4	1.1968 -3	9.7697 -4
160500	159274	270.650	-2.500	9.1234	9.0041	1.1743	9.5864
161000	159767	270.650	-2.500	8.9522	8.8352	1.1523	9.4065
161500	160259	270.650	-2.500	8.7843	8.6694	1.1307	9.2300
162000	160751	270.650	-2.500	8.6194	8.5067	1.1095	9.0568
162500	161244	270.650	-2.500	8.4577	8.3471	1.0886	8.8869
163000	161736	270.650	-2.500	8.2990	8.1905	1.0682	8.7201
163500	162228	270.650	-2.500	8.1433	8.0368	1.0482	8.5565
164000	162720	270.650	-2.500	7.9905	7.8861	1.0285	8.3960
164500	163213	270.650	-2.500	7.8406	7.7381	1.0092	8.2385
165000	163705	270.650	-2.500	7.6936 -1	7.5930 -4	9.9029 -4	8.0840 -4
165500	164197	270.650	-2.500	7.5493	7.4505	9.7171	7.9323
166000	164689	270.650	-2.500	7.4077	7.3108	9.5349	7.7835
166500	165181	270.650	-2.500	7.2687	7.1737	9.3560	7.6376
167000	165673	270.650	-2.500	7.1324	7.0391	9.1806	7.4943
167500	166165	270.650	-2.500	6.9986	6.9071	9.0084	7.3538
168000	166657	270.650	-2.500	6.8674	6.7776	8.8394	7.2159
168500	167149	270.650	-2.500	6.7386	6.6505	8.6737	7.0806
169000	167641	270.378	-2.772	6.6122	6.5257	8.5196	6.9547
169500	168133	269.958	-3.192	6.4880	6.4032	8.3725	6.8347
170000	168625	269.538	-3.612	6.3660 -1	6.2827 -4	8.2278 -4	6.7166 -4
170500	169117	269.118	-4.032	6.2460	6.1643	8.0854	6.6003
171000	169609	268.699	-4.451	6.1282	6.0480	7.9452	6.4859
171500	170101	268.279	-4.871	6.0124	5.9337	7.8073	6.3733
172000	170593	267.859	-5.291	5.8986	5.8214	7.6716	6.2625
172500	171085	267.439	-5.711	5.7868	5.7111	7.5380	6.1534
173000	171577	267.019	-6.131	5.6769	5.6027	7.4065	6.0461
173500	172068	266.600	-6.550	5.5690	5.4962	7.2771	5.9405
174000	172560	266.180	-6.970	5.4630	5.3915	7.1499	5.8366
174500	173052	265.760	-7.390	5.3588	5.2887	7.0246	5.7344
175000	173544	265.341	-7.809	5.2565 -1	5.1877 -4	6.9013 -4	5.6337 -4
175500	174035	264.921	-8.229	5.1559	5.0885	6.7801	5.5347
176000	174527	264.501	-8.649	5.0572	4.9910	6.6607	5.4373
176500	175019	264.082	-9.068	4.9602	4.8953	6.5433	5.3415
177000	175510	263.662	-9.488	4.8649	4.8012	6.4278	5.2472
177500	176002	263.243	-9.907	4.7712	4.7088	6.3142	5.1544
178000	176494	262.823	-10.327	4.6793	4.6181	6.2024	5.0632
178500	176985	262.404	-10.746	4.5890	4.5289	6.0924	4.9734
179000	177477	261.984	-11.166	4.5002	4.4414	5.9842	4.8850
179500	177968	261.565	-11.585	4.4131	4.3554	5.8777	4.7981
180000	178460	261.145	-12.005	4.3275 -1	4.2709 -4	5.7730 -4	4.7126 -4
180500	178951	260.726	-12.424	4.2435	4.1880	5.6700	4.6286
181000	179443	260.306	-12.844	4.1609	4.1065	5.5687	4.5458
181500	179934	259.887	-13.263	4.0799	4.0265	5.4690	4.4645
182000	180425	259.468	-13.682	4.0003	3.9480	5.3709	4.3844
182500	180917	259.048	-14.102	3.9221	3.8708	5.2745	4.3057
183000	181408	258.629	-14.521	3.8453	3.7950	5.1796	4.2283
183500	181899	258.210	-14.940	3.7699	3.7206	5.0864	4.1521
184000	182391	257.790	-15.360	3.6959	3.6476	4.9946	4.0772
184500	182882	257.371	-15.779	3.6232	3.5759	4.9044	4.0036
185000	183373	256.952	-16.198	3.5519 -1	3.5054 -4	4.8156 -4	3.9311 -4
185500	183865	256.533	-16.617	3.4818	3.4363	4.7283	3.8599
186000	184356	256.113	-17.037	3.4130	3.3684	4.6425	3.7898
186500	184847	255.694	-17.456	3.3455	3.3017	4.5581	3.7209
187000	185338	255.275	-17.875	3.2792	3.2363	4.4751	3.6531
187500	185829	254.856	-18.294	3.2141	3.1721	4.3935	3.5865
188000	186320	254.437	-18.713	3.1502	3.1090	4.3132	3.5210
188500	186811	254.018	-19.132	3.0874	3.0471	4.2343	3.4566
189000	187302	253.598	-19.552	3.0259	2.9863	4.1567	3.3932
189500	187794	253.179	-19.971	2.9654	2.9266	4.0804	3.3309

Table IV
Geopotential Altitude, English Altitudes

Altitude		Temperature		Pressure		Density	
H (ft)	Z (ft)	T (K)	t (°C)	P (mb)	P/P_0	ρ (kg/m^3)	ρ/ρ_0
190000	191747	251.297	-21.853	2.7073 - 1	2.6719 - 4	3.7531 - 4	3.0638 - 4
190500	192256	250.870	-22.280	2.6517	2.6170	3.6823	3.0060
191000	192766	250.443	-22.707	2.5972	2.5632	3.6128	2.9492
191500	193275	250.016	-23.134	2.5437	2.5104	3.5444	2.8934
192000	193784	249.590	-23.560	2.4912	2.4587	3.4772	2.8386
192500	194293	249.163	-23.987	2.4398	2.4079	3.4112	2.7847
193000	194803	248.736	-24.414	2.3893	2.3580	3.3464	2.7317
193500	195312	248.310	-24.840	2.3397	2.3091	3.2826	2.6797
194000	195822	247.883	-25.267	2.2911	2.2612	3.2200	2.6286
194500	196331	247.456	-25.694	2.2435	2.2141	3.1584	2.5783
195000	196841	247.029	-26.121	2.1967 - 1	2.1680 - 4	3.0980 - 4	2.5290 - 4
195500	197350	246.603	-26.547	2.1509	2.1227	3.0385	2.4804
196000	197860	246.176	-26.974	2.1059	2.0784	2.9802	2.4328
196500	198369	245.749	-27.401	2.0618	2.0348	2.9228	2.3860
197000	198879	245.323	-27.827	2.0185	1.9921	2.8665	2.3400
197500	199388	244.896	-28.254	1.9761	1.9503	2.8111	2.2948
198000	199898	244.469	-28.681	1.9345	1.9092	2.7567	2.2504
198500	200408	244.042	-29.108	1.8937	1.8689	2.7033	2.2068
199000	200917	243.616	-29.534	1.8537	1.8295	2.6508	2.1639
199500	201427	243.189	-29.961	1.8145	1.7907	2.5993	2.1219
200000	201937	242.762	-30.388	1.7760 - 1	1.7528 - 4	2.5487 - 4	2.0805 - 4
200500	202446	242.335	-30.815	1.7383	1.7155	2.4989	2.0399
201000	202956	241.909	-31.241	1.7013	1.6790	2.4501	2.0001
201500	203466	241.482	-31.668	1.6650	1.6433	2.4021	1.9609
202000	203976	241.055	-32.095	1.6295	1.6082	2.3550	1.9224
202500	204486	240.629	-32.521	1.5946	1.5738	2.3087	1.8847
203000	204995	240.202	-32.948	1.5605	1.5401	2.2633	1.8476
203500	205505	239.775	-33.375	1.5270	1.5070	2.2186	1.8111
204000	206015	239.348	-33.802	1.4942	1.4746	2.1748	1.7753
204500	206525	238.922	-34.228	1.4620	1.4429	2.1318	1.7402
205000	207035	238.495	-34.655	1.4304 - 1	1.4117 - 4	2.0895 - 4	1.7057 - 4
205500	207545	238.068	-35.082	1.3995	1.3812	2.0480	1.6718
206000	208055	237.642	-35.508	1.3692	1.3513	2.0073	1.6386
206500	208565	237.215	-35.935	1.3395	1.3220	1.9673	1.6059
207000	209075	236.788	-36.362	1.3104	1.2933	1.9280	1.5739
207500	209585	236.361	-36.789	1.2819	1.2651	1.8894	1.5424
208000	210095	235.935	-37.215	1.2539	1.2375	1.8516	1.5115
208500	210606	235.508	-37.642	1.2265	1.2105	1.8144	1.4811
209000	211116	235.081	-38.069	1.1997	1.1840	1.7779	1.4514
209500	211626	234.655	-38.495	1.1734	1.1580	1.7421	1.4221
210000	212136	234.228	-38.922	1.1476 - 1	1.1326 - 4	1.7069 - 4	1.3934 - 4
210500	212646	233.801	-39.349	1.1224	1.1077	1.6724	1.3652
211000	213157	233.374	-39.776	1.0976	1.0833	1.6385	1.3376
211500	213667	232.948	-40.202	1.0734	1.0593	1.6053	1.3104
212000	214177	232.521	-40.629	1.0496	1.0359	1.5727	1.2838
212500	214688	232.094	-41.056	1.0264	1.0130	1.5406	1.2577
213000	215198	231.667	-41.483	1.0036	9.9050 - 5	1.5092	1.2320
213500	215708	231.241	-41.909	9.8131 - 2	9.6847	1.4784	1.2068
214000	216219	230.814	-42.336	9.5944	9.4689	1.4481	1.1821
214500	216729	230.387	-42.763	9.3802	9.2575	1.4184	1.1579
215000	217240	229.961	-43.189	9.1704 - 2	9.0505 - 5	1.3892 - 4	1.1341 - 4
215500	217750	229.534	-43.616	8.9649	8.8477	1.3606	1.1107
216000	218261	229.107	-44.043	8.7637	8.6491	1.3326	1.0878
216500	218771	228.680	-44.470	8.5666	8.4545	1.3050	1.0653
217000	219282	228.254	-44.896	8.3736	8.2640	1.2780	1.0433
217500	219792	227.827	-45.323	8.1845	8.0775	1.2515	1.0216
218000	220303	227.400	-45.750	7.9994	7.8948	1.2255	1.0004
218500	220814	226.974	-46.176	7.8182	7.7160	1.2000	9.7957 - 5
219000	221324	226.547	-46.603	7.6407	7.5408	1.1749	9.5914
219500	221835	226.120	-47.030	7.4670	7.3693	1.1504	9.3910
220000	222346	225.693	-47.457	7.2969 - 2	7.2014 - 5	1.1263 - 4	9.1944 - 5
220500	222856	225.267	-47.883	7.1303	7.0371	1.1027	9.0015
221000	223367	224.840	-48.310	6.9672	6.8761	1.0795	8.8124
221500	223878	224.413	-48.737	6.8076	6.7186	1.0568	8.6268
222000	224389	223.987	-49.163	6.6513	6.5644	1.0345	8.4449
222500	224900	223.560	-49.590	6.4984	6.4134	1.0126	8.2664
223000	225410	223.133	-50.017	6.3486	6.2656	9.9119 - 5	8.0914
223500	225921	222.706	-50.444	6.2021	6.1210	9.7017	7.9197
224000	226432	222.280	-50.870	6.0586	5.9794	9.4955	7.7514
224500	226943	221.853	-51.297	5.9182	5.8408	9.2933	7.5863
225000	227454	221.426	-51.724	5.7808 - 2	5.7052 - 5	9.0950 - 5	7.4245 - 5
225500	227965	220.999	-52.151	5.6463	5.5725	8.9006	7.2658
226000	228476	220.573	-52.577	5.5148	5.4426	8.7100	7.1102
226500	228987	220.146	-53.004	5.3860	5.3155	8.5231	6.9576
227000	229498	219.719	-53.431	5.2600	5.1912	8.3398	6.8080
227500	230009	219.293	-53.857	5.1367	5.0695	8.1602	6.6614
228000	230520	218.866	-54.284	5.0160	4.9504	7.9841	6.5176
228500	231031	218.439	-54.711	4.8980	4.8340	7.8115	6.3767
229000	231543	218.012	-55.138	4.7825	4.7200	7.6422	6.2386
229500	232054	217.586	-55.564	4.6696	4.6085	7.4763	6.1031

Table IV
Geometric Altitude, English Altitudes

Altitude		Temperature		Pressure		Density	
Z (ft)	H (ft)	T (K)	t (°C)	P (mb)	P/P$_0$	ρ (kg/m^3)	ρ/ρ_0
190000	188285	252.760	−20.390	2.9061 − 1	2.8681 − 4	4.0054 − 4	3.2697 − 4
190500	188776	252.341	−20.809	2.8478	2.8106	3.9316	3.2095
191000	189267	251.922	−21.228	2.7907	2.7542	3.8591	3.1503
191500	189757	251.503	−21.647	2.7346	2.6988	3.7878	3.0921
192000	190248	251.084	−22.066	2.6795	2.6445	3.7177	3.0349
192500	190739	250.665	−22.485	2.6255	2.5911	3.6489	2.9787
193000	191230	250.246	−22.904	2.5724	2.5388	3.5811	2.9234
193500	191721	249.827	−23.323	2.5204	2.4874	3.5145	2.8690
194000	192212	249.409	−23.741	2.4693	2.4370	3.4491	2.8156
194500	192703	248.990	−24.160	2.4191	2.3875	3.3848	2.7631
195000	193194	248.571	−24.579	2.3700 − 1	2.3390 − 4	3.3215 − 4	2.7114 − 4
195500	193684	248.152	−24.998	2.3217	2.2913	3.2594	2.6607
196000	194175	247.733	−25.417	2.2743	2.2446	3.1983	2.6108
196500	194666	247.314	−25.836	2.2279	2.1987	3.1382	2.5618
197000	195156	246.896	−26.254	2.1823	2.1537	3.0792	2.5137
197500	195647	246.477	−26.673	2.1375	2.1096	3.0212	2.4663
198000	196138	246.058	−27.092	2.0936	2.0663	2.9642	2.4198
198500	196628	245.639	−27.511	2.0506	2.0238	2.9082	2.3741
199000	197119	245.221	−27.929	2.0083	1.9821	2.8532	2.3291
199500	197610	244.802	−28.348	1.9669	1.9412	2.7991	2.2850
200000	198100	244.383	−28.767	1.9262 − 1	1.9011 − 4	2.7459 − 4	2.2416 − 4
200500	198591	243.965	−29.185	1.8864	1.8617	2.6937	2.1989
201000	199081	243.546	−29.604	1.8472	1.8231	2.6424	2.1570
201500	199572	243.127	−30.023	1.8089	1.7852	2.5919	2.1159
202000	200062	242.709	−30.441	1.7712	1.7481	2.5424	2.0754
202500	200553	242.290	−30.860	1.7343	1.7117	2.4937	2.0357
203000	201043	241.872	−31.278	1.6981	1.6759	2.4459	1.9966
203500	201533	241.453	−31.697	1.6626	1.6409	2.3989	1.9583
204000	202024	241.035	−32.115	1.6278	1.6065	2.3527	1.9206
204500	202514	240.616	−32.534	1.5936	1.5728	2.3074	1.8836
205000	203004	240.198	−32.952	1.5602 − 1	1.5398 − 4	2.2628 − 4	1.8472 − 4
205500	203495	239.779	−33.371	1.5273	1.5073	2.2191	1.8115
206000	203985	239.361	−33.789	1.4951	1.4756	2.1761	1.7764
206500	204475	238.942	−34.208	1.4635	1.4444	2.1338	1.7419
207000	204966	238.524	−34.626	1.4326	1.4138	2.0924	1.7081
207500	205456	238.106	−35.044	1.4022	1.3839	2.0516	1.6748
208000	205946	237.687	−35.463	1.3724	1.3545	2.0116	1.6421
208500	206436	237.269	−35.881	1.3433	1.3257	1.9723	1.6100
209000	206926	236.851	−36.299	1.3147	1.2975	1.9337	1.5785
209500	207416	236.432	−36.718	1.2866	1.2698	1.8958	1.5476
210000	207906	236.014	−37.136	1.2591 − 1	1.2426 − 4	1.8586 − 4	1.5172 − 4
210500	208396	235.596	−37.554	1.2321	1.2160	1.8220	1.4874
211000	208887	235.178	−37.972	1.2057	1.1900	1.7861	1.4580
211500	209377	234.760	−38.390	1.1798	1.1644	1.7509	1.4293
212000	209867	234.341	−38.809	1.1544	1.1393	1.7162	1.4010
212500	210357	233.923	−39.227	1.1295	1.1148	1.6822	1.3733
213000	210846	233.505	−39.645	1.1052	1.0907	1.6489	1.3460
213500	211336	233.087	−40.063	1.0812	1.0671	1.6161	1.3193
214000	211826	232.669	−40.481	1.0578	1.0440	1.5839	1.2930
214500	212316	232.251	−40.899	1.0349	1.0213	1.5523	1.2672
215000	212806	231.833	−41.317	1.0124 − 1	9.9916 − 5	1.5213 − 4	1.2419 − 4
215500	213296	231.415	−41.735	9.9035 − 2	9.7740	1.4909	1.2170
216000	213786	230.997	−42.153	9.6874	9.5607	1.4610	1.1926
216500	214275	230.579	−42.571	9.4757	9.3518	1.4316	1.1687
217000	214765	230.161	−42.989	9.2682	9.1470	1.4028	1.1452
217500	215255	229.743	−43.407	9.0649	8.9464	1.3746	1.1221
218000	215745	229.325	−43.825	8.8658	8.7498	1.3468	1.0994
218500	216234	228.907	−44.243	8.6706	8.5572	1.3196	1.0772
219000	216724	228.489	−44.661	8.4795	8.3686	1.2928	1.0554
219500	217214	228.071	−45.079	8.2922	8.1837	1.2666	1.0340
220000	217703	227.653	−45.497	8.1087 − 2	8.0026 − 5	1.2408 − 4	1.0129 − 4
220500	218193	227.235	−45.915	7.9289	7.8253	1.2156	9.9230 − 5
221000	218683	226.817	−46.333	7.7529	7.6515	1.1908	9.7206
221500	219172	226.400	−46.750	7.5804	7.4813	1.1664	9.5219
222000	219662	225.982	−47.168	7.4115	7.3146	1.1425	9.3269
222500	220151	225.564	−47.586	7.2460	7.1513	1.1191	9.1356
223000	220641	225.146	−48.004	7.0840	6.9914	1.0961	8.9478
223500	221130	224.729	−48.421	6.9253	6.8347	1.0735	8.7636
224000	221620	224.311	−48.839	6.7698	6.6813	1.0514	8.5829
224500	222109	223.893	−49.257	6.6176	6.5311	1.0297	8.4056
225000	222598	223.476	−49.674	6.4686 − 2	6.3840 − 5	1.0084 − 4	8.2316 − 5
225500	223088	223.058	−50.092	6.3226	6.2399	9.8746 − 5	8.0609
226000	223577	222.640	−50.510	6.1797	6.0989	9.6695	7.8935
226500	224066	222.223	−50.927	6.0397	5.9607	9.4683	7.7292
227000	224556	221.805	−51.345	5.9027	5.8255	9.2709	7.5681
227500	225045	221.387	−51.763	5.7685	5.6931	9.0772	7.4100
228000	225534	220.970	−52.180	5.6372	5.5635	8.8873	7.2549
228500	226023	220.552	−52.598	5.5086	5.4365	8.7010	7.1029
229000	226513	220.135	−53.015	5.3827	5.3123	8.5183	6.9537
229500	227002	219.717	−53.433	5.2594	5.1907	8.3391	6.8074

Table IV
Geopotential Altitude, English Altitudes

Altitude		Temperature		Pressure		Density	
H (ft)	Z (ft)	T (K)	t (°C)	P (mb)	P/P$_0$	ρ (kg/m^3)	ρ/ρ_0
230000	232565	217.159	−55.991	4.5591 − 2	4.4994 − 5	7.3137 − 5	5.9704 − 5
230500	233076	216.732	−56.418	4.4509	4.3927	7.1544	5.8403
231000	233587	216.306	−56.844	4.3452	4.2884	6.9982	5.7128
231500	234099	215.879	−57.271	4.2417	4.1863	6.8451	5.5878
232000	234610	215.452	−57.698	4.1406	4.0864	6.6950	5.4653
232500	235121	215.025	−58.125	4.0416	3.9888	6.5480	5.3453
233000	235633	214.613	−58.537	3.9448	3.8932	6.4035	5.2273
233500	236144	214.309	−58.841	3.8502	3.7999	6.2588	5.1092
234000	236655	214.004	−59.146	3.7577	3.7086	6.1171	4.9936
234500	237167	213.699	−59.451	3.6674	3.6194	5.9785	4.8804
235000	237678	213.394	−59.756	3.5790 − 2	3.5322 − 5	5.8429 − 5	4.7697 − 5
235500	238190	213.089	−60.061	3.4927	3.4470	5.7101	4.6613
236000	238701	212.785	−60.365	3.4083	3.3638	5.5801	4.5552
236500	239213	212.480	−60.670	3.3259	3.2824	5.4530	4.4514
237000	239724	212.175	−60.975	3.2453	3.2029	5.3285	4.3498
237500	240236	211.870	−61.280	3.1666	3.1252	5.2068	4.2504
238000	240748	211.565	−61.585	3.0897	3.0493	5.0876	4.1531
238500	241259	211.261	−61.889	3.0145	2.9751	4.9710	4.0580
239000	241771	210.956	−62.194	2.9411	2.9026	4.8569	3.9648
239500	242282	210.651	−62.499	2.8693	2.8318	4.7453	3.8737
240000	242794	210.346	−62.804	2.7992 − 2	2.7626 − 5	4.6361 − 5	3.7845 − 5
240500	243306	210.041	−63.109	2.7307	2.6950	4.5292	3.6973
241000	243818	209.737	−63.413	2.6638	2.6290	4.4246	3.6120
241500	244329	209.432	−63.718	2.5985	2.5645	4.3224	3.5285
242000	244841	209.127	−64.023	2.5346	2.5015	4.2223	3.4468
242500	245353	208.822	−64.328	2.4723	2.4399	4.1244	3.3669
243000	245865	208.517	−64.633	2.4113	2.3798	4.0287	3.2887
243500	246377	208.213	−64.937	2.3518	2.3211	3.9350	3.2122
244000	246889	207.908	−65.242	2.2937	2.2637	3.8434	3.1375
244500	247401	207.603	−65.547	2.2369	2.2077	3.7538	3.0643
245000	247913	207.298	−65.852	2.1815 − 2	2.1530 − 5	3.6661 − 5	2.9927 − 5
245500	248425	206.993	−66.157	2.1273	2.0995	3.5804	2.9228
246000	248937	206.689	−66.461	2.0745	2.0473	3.4965	2.8543
246500	249449	206.384	−66.766	2.0228	1.9964	3.4145	2.7874
247000	249961	206.079	−67.071	1.9724	1.9466	3.3343	2.7219
247500	250473	205.774	−67.376	1.9231	1.8980	3.2559	2.6579
248000	250985	205.469	−67.681	1.8751	1.8505	3.1792	2.5953
248500	251497	205.165	−67.985	1.8281	1.8042	3.1042	2.5340
249000	252009	204.860	−68.290	1.7823	1.7590	3.0309	2.4742
249500	252521	204.555	−68.595	1.7375	1.7148	2.9591	2.4156
250000	253033	204.250	−68.900	1.6938 − 2	1.6717 − 5	2.8890 − 5	2.3584 − 5
250500	253546	203.945	−69.205	1.6511	1.6295	2.8205	2.3024
251000	254058	203.641	−69.509	1.6095	1.5884	2.7534	2.2477
251500	254570	203.336	−69.814	1.5688	1.5483	2.6879	2.1942
252000	255082	203.031	−70.119	1.5291	1.5091	2.6238	2.1419
252500	255595	202.726	−70.424	1.4904	1.4709	2.5612	2.0908
253000	256107	202.421	−70.729	1.4526	1.4336	2.5000	2.0408
253500	256619	202.117	−71.033	1.4157	1.3971	2.4401	1.9919
254000	257132	201.812	−71.338	1.3796	1.3616	2.3816	1.9442
254500	257644	201.507	−71.643	1.3445	1.3269	2.3244	1.8975
255000	258157	201.202	−71.948	1.3101 − 2	1.2930 − 5	2.2685 − 5	1.8519 − 5
255500	258669	200.897	−72.253	1.2767	1.2600	2.2139	1.8072
256000	259182	200.593	−72.557	1.2440	1.2277	2.1605	1.7637
256500	259694	200.288	−72.862	1.2121	1.1962	2.1083	1.7210
257000	260207	199.983	−73.167	1.1809	1.1655	2.0573	1.6794
257500	260719	199.678	−73.472	1.1506	1.1355	2.0074	1.6387
258000	261232	199.373	−73.777	1.1209	1.1063	1.9587	1.5989
258500	261744	199.069	−74.081	1.0920	1.0777	1.9111	1.5601
259000	262257	198.764	−74.386	1.0638	1.0499	1.8646	1.5221
259500	262770	198.459	−74.691	1.0363	1.0227	1.8191	1.4850
260000	263282	198.154	−74.996	1.0094 − 2	9.9627 − 6	1.7747 − 5	1.4488 − 5
260500	263795	197.849	−75.301	9.8327 − 3	9.7041	1.7313	1.4133
261000	264308	197.545	−75.605	9.5771	9.4519	1.6889	1.3787
261500	264821	197.240	−75.910	9.3278	9.2059	1.6475	1.3449
262000	265333	196.935	−76.215	9.0846	8.9658	1.6070	1.3119
262500	265846	196.630	−76.520	8.8474	8.7317	1.5675	1.2796
263000	266359	196.325	−76.825	8.6161	8.5034	1.5289	1.2481
263500	266872	196.021	−77.129	8.3904	8.2807	1.4912	1.2173
264000	267385	195.716	−77.434	8.1703	8.0635	1.4543	1.1872
264500	267898	195.411	−77.739	7.9557	7.8516	1.4183	1.1578
265000	268411	195.106	−78.044	7.7463 − 3	7.6450 − 6	1.3831 − 5	1.1291 − 5
265500	268924	194.801	−78.349	7.5422	7.4436	1.3488	1.1011
266000	269437	194.497	−78.653	7.3431	7.2471	1.3153	1.0737
266500	269950	194.192	−78.958	7.1490	7.0555	1.2825	1.0469
267000	270463	193.887	−79.263	6.9597	6.8687	1.2505	1.0208
267500	270976	193.582	−79.568	6.7752	6.6866	1.2193	9.9532 − 6
268000	271489	193.277	−79.873	6.5953	6.5090	1.1888	9.7041
268500	272002	192.973	−80.177	6.4198	6.3359	1.1590	9.4609
269000	272515	192.668	−80.482	6.2488	6.1671	1.1299	9.2234
269500	273028	192.363	−80.787	6.0821	6.0025	1.1015	8.9916

Table IV
Geometric Altitude, English Altitudes

Altitude		Temperature		Pressure		Density	
Z (ft)	H (ft)	T (K)	t (°C)	P (mb)	P/P₀	ρ (kg/m³)	ρ/ρ₀
230000	227491	219.300	−53.850	5.1388 − 2	5.0716 − 5	8.1633 − 5	6.6639 − 5
230500	227980	218.882	−54.268	5.0207	4.9551	7.9909	6.5232
231000	228469	218.465	−54.685	4.9051	4.8410	7.8219	6.3852
231500	228958	218.048	−55.102	4.7920	4.7293	7.6561	6.2499
232000	229447	217.630	−55.520	4.6813	4.6200	7.4935	6.1172
232500	229936	217.213	−55.937	4.5729	4.5131	7.3341	5.9870
233000	230425	216.796	−56.354	4.4668	4.4084	7.1778	5.8594
233500	230914	216.378	−56.772	4.3630	4.3060	7.0246	5.7343
234000	231403	215.961	−57.189	4.2615	4.2057	6.8743	5.6117
234500	231892	215.544	−57.606	4.1621	4.1077	6.7270	5.4914
235000	232381	215.126	−58.024	4.0648 − 2	4.0117 − 5	6.5825 − 5	5.3735 − 5
235500	232870	214.709	−58.441	3.9697	3.9178	6.4409	5.2579
236000	233359	214.394	−58.756	3.8766	3.8259	6.2991	5.1421
236500	233848	214.096	−59.054	3.7856	3.7361	6.1598	5.0284
237000	234337	213.798	−59.352	3.6966	3.6482	6.0234	4.9170
237500	234826	213.500	−59.650	3.6095	3.5623	5.8898	4.8080
238000	235314	213.202	−59.948	3.5244	3.4784	5.7590	4.7012
238500	235803	212.904	−60.246	3.4412	3.3962	5.6309	4.5966
239000	236292	212.606	−60.544	3.3599	3.3160	5.5055	4.4943
239500	236781	212.308	−60.842	3.2804	3.2375	5.3827	4.3941
240000	237269	212.010	−61.140	3.2026 − 2	3.1608 − 5	5.2625 − 5	4.2959 − 5
240500	237758	211.713	−61.437	3.1266	3.0857	5.1449	4.1999
241000	238247	211.415	−61.735	3.0523	3.0124	5.0297	4.1059
241500	238735	211.117	−62.033	2.9797	2.9407	4.9169	4.0138
242000	239224	210.819	−62.331	2.9087	2.8706	4.8065	3.9237
242500	239713	210.521	−62.629	2.8393	2.8022	4.6985	3.8355
243000	240201	210.223	−62.927	2.7714	2.7352	4.5927	3.7492
243500	240690	209.925	−63.225	2.7051	2.6698	4.4892	3.6647
244000	241178	209.628	−63.522	2.6403	2.6058	4.3879	3.5819
244500	241667	209.330	−63.820	2.5770	2.5433	4.2887	3.5010
245000	242155	209.032	−64.118	2.5151 − 2	2.4822 − 5	4.1917 − 5	3.4218 − 5
245500	242644	208.734	−64.416	2.4546	2.4225	4.0967	3.3442
246000	243132	208.437	−64.713	2.3955	2.3641	4.0037	3.2683
246500	243620	208.139	−65.011	2.3377	2.3071	3.9127	3.1940
247000	244109	207.841	−65.309	2.2812	2.2514	3.8237	3.1214
247500	244597	207.543	−65.607	2.2260	2.1969	3.7365	3.0502
248000	245085	207.246	−65.904	2.1721	2.1437	3.6513	2.9806
248500	245574	206.948	−66.202	2.1194	2.0917	3.5678	2.9125
249000	246062	206.650	−66.500	2.0680	2.0409	3.4862	2.8459
249500	246550	206.353	−66.797	2.0177	1.9913	3.4063	2.7807
250000	247039	206.055	−67.095	1.9685 − 2	1.9428 − 5	3.3282 − 5	2.7169 − 5
250500	247527	205.758	−67.392	1.9205	1.8954	3.2517	2.6545
251000	248015	205.460	−67.690	1.8736	1.8491	3.1769	2.5934
251500	248503	205.162	−67.988	1.8278	1.8039	3.1037	2.5336
252000	248991	204.865	−68.285	1.7830	1.7597	3.0321	2.4752
252500	249479	204.567	−68.583	1.7393	1.7166	2.9620	2.4180
253000	249967	204.270	−68.880	1.6966	1.6744	2.8935	2.3620
253500	250456	203.972	−69.178	1.6549	1.6332	2.8265	2.3073
254000	250944	203.675	−69.475	1.6141	1.5930	2.7609	2.2538
254500	251432	203.377	−69.773	1.5743	1.5537	2.6967	2.2014
255000	251920	203.080	−70.070	1.5354 − 2	1.5154 − 5	2.6340 − 5	2.1502 − 5
255500	252408	202.782	−70.368	1.4975	1.4779	2.5726	2.1001
256000	252896	202.485	−70.665	1.4604	1.4413	2.5126	2.0511
256500	253383	202.187	−70.963	1.4242	1.4055	2.4539	2.0032
257000	253871	201.890	−71.260	1.3888	1.3706	2.3965	1.9563
257500	254359	201.592	−71.558	1.3543	1.3365	2.3404	1.9105
258000	254847	201.295	−71.855	1.3205	1.3033	2.2854	1.8657
258500	255335	200.998	−72.152	1.2876	1.2708	2.2317	1.8218
259000	255823	200.700	−72.450	1.2554	1.2390	2.1792	1.7790
259500	256311	200.403	−72.747	1.2240	1.2080	2.1279	1.7370
260000	256798	200.106	−73.044	1.1934 − 2	1.1778 − 5	2.0777 − 5	1.6961 − 5
260500	257286	199.808	−73.342	1.1635	1.1482	2.0286	1.6560
261000	257774	199.511	−73.639	1.1342	1.1194	1.9806	1.6168
261500	258262	199.214	−73.936	1.1057	1.0912	1.9336	1.5785
262000	258749	198.916	−74.234	1.0779	1.0638	1.8878	1.5410
262500	259237	198.619	−74.531	1.0507	1.0369	1.8429	1.5044
263000	259725	198.322	−74.828	1.0241	1.0107	1.7990	1.4686
263500	260212	198.025	−75.125	9.9826 − 3	9.8521 − 6	1.7562	1.4336
264000	260700	197.727	−75.423	9.7297	9.6025	1.7142	1.3994
264500	261187	197.430	−75.720	9.4829	9.3589	1.6733	1.3659
265000	261675	197.133	−76.017	9.2420 − 3	9.1211 − 6	1.6332 − 5	1.3332 − 5
265500	262162	196.836	−76.314	9.0068	8.8890	1.5941	1.3013
266000	262650	196.539	−76.611	8.7773	8.6626	1.5558	1.2700
266500	263137	196.241	−76.909	8.5534	8.4415	1.5184	1.2395
267000	263625	195.944	−77.206	8.3348	8.2258	1.4819	1.2097
267500	264112	195.647	−77.503	8.1215	8.0153	1.4461	1.1805
268000	264600	195.350	−77.800	7.9134	7.8099	1.4112	1.1520
268500	265087	195.053	−78.097	7.7103	7.6095	1.3771	1.1242
269000	265574	194.756	−78.394	7.5121	7.4139	1.3437	1.0969
269500	266062	194.459	−78.691	7.3188	7.2231	1.3112	1.0703

Table IV
Geopotential Altitude, English Altitudes

Altitude		Temperature		Pressure		Density	
H (ft)	Z (ft)	T (K)	t (°C)	P (mb)	P/P_0	ρ (kg/m³)	ρ/ρ_0
270000	273542	192.058	-81.092	5.9195 - 3	5.8421 - 6	1.0737 - 5	8.7652 - 6
270500	274055	191.753	-81.397	5.7611	5.6857	1.0467	8.5441
271000	274568	191.449	-81.701	5.6066	5.5333	1.0202	8.3283
271500	275081	191.144	-82.006	5.4561	5.3848	9.9441 - 6	8.1176
272000	275595	190.839	-82.311	5.3094	5.2399	9.6921	7.9119
272500	276108	190.534	-82.616	5.1664	5.0988	9.4462	7.7112
273000	276621	190.229	-82.921	5.0270	4.9613	9.2061	7.5152
273500	277135	189.925	-83.225	4.8912	4.8272	8.9717	7.3238
274000	277648	189.620	-83.530	4.7588	4.6966	8.7429	7.1371
274500	278161	189.315	-83.835	4.6298	4.5693	8.5196	6.9548
275000	278675	189.010	-84.140	4.5041 - 3	4.4452 - 6	8.3017 - 6	6.7769 - 6
275500	279188	188.705	-84.445	4.3816	4.3243	8.0890	6.6033
276000	279702	188.401	-84.749	4.2623	4.2066	7.8814	6.4338
276500	280215	188.096	-85.054	4.1460	4.0918	7.6789	6.2685
277000	280729	187.791	-85.359	4.0328	3.9800	7.4812	6.1071
277500	281242	187.486	-85.664	3.9224	3.8711	7.2883	5.9496
278000	281756	187.181	-85.969	3.8149	3.7650	7.1001	5.7960

Table IV
Geometric Altitude, English Altitudes

Altitude		Temperature		Pressure		Density	
Z (ft)	H (ft)	T (K)	t (°C)	P (mb)	P/P_0	ρ (kg/m^3)	ρ/ρ_0
270000	266549	194.162	-78.988	7.1301 − 3	7.0369 − 6	1.2793 − 5	1.0443 − 5
270500	267036	193.865	-79.285	6.9461	6.8552	1.2482	1.0199
271000	267524	193.568	-79.582	6.7665	6.6780	1.2178	9.9411 − 6
271500	268011	193.271	-79.879	6.5913	6.5051	1.1881	9.6987
272000	268498	192.973	-80.177	6.4204	6.3365	1.1591	9.4617
272500	268985	192.676	-80.474	6.2537	6.1719	1.1307	9.2302
273000	269472	192.380	-80.770	6.0911	6.0114	1.1030	9.0041
273500	269960	192.083	-81.067	5.9324	5.8549	1.0759	8.7832
274000	270447	191.786	-81.364	5.7777	5.7021	1.0495	8.5673
274500	270934	191.489	-81.661	5.6268	5.5532	1.0237	8.3565
275000	271421	191.192	-81.958	5.4796 − 3	5.4079 − 6	9.9844 − 6	8.1505 − 6
275500	271908	190.895	-82.255	5.3360	5.2663	9.7379	7.9493
276000	272395	190.598	-82.552	5.1960	5.1281	9.4972	7.7528
276500	272882	190.301	-82.849	5.0595	4.9933	9.2621	7.5609
277000	273369	190.004	-83.146	4.9264	4.8619	9.0324	7.3734
277500	273856	189.707	-83.443	4.7965	4.7338	8.8082	7.1903
278000	274343	189.410	-83.740	4.6699	4.6088	8.5891	7.0115
278500	274830	189.114	-84.036	4.5465	4.4870	8.3752	6.8369
279000	275317	188.817	-84.333	4.4261	4.3682	8.1663	6.6663
279500	275804	188.520	-84.630	4.3088	4.2524	7.9623	6.4998
280000	276290	188.223	-84.927	4.1943 − 3	4.1395 − 6	7.7631 − 6	6.3372 − 6
280500	276777	187.926	-85.224	4.0828	4.0294	7.5686	6.1784
281000	277264	187.630	-85.520	3.9741	3.9221	7.3786	6.0234
281500	277751	187.333	-85.817	3.8680	3.8175	7.1932	5.8720
282000	278238	187.036	-86.114	3.7647	3.7155	7.0121	5.7242

Table V
Geopotential Altitude, English Altitudes

Altitude		Gravity ratio	Number density	Collision frequency	Mean free path	Sound speed	Viscosity ratio	Thermal conductivity ratio
H (ft)	Z (ft)	g/g_0	n (m^{-3})	ν (s^{-1})	L (m)	C_s (m/s)	μ/μ_0	κ/κ_0
-16500	-16487	1.0016	4.0239 +25	1.1534 +10	4.1986 - 8	359.08	1.0858 + 0	1.0998 + 0
-16400	-16387	1.0016	4.0133	1.1500	4.2097	358.97	1.0853	1.0992
-16300	-16287	1.0016	4.0028	1.1467	4.2207	358.86	1.0848	1.0986
-16200	-16187	1.0016	3.9922	1.1433	4.2319	358.75	1.0843	1.0980
-16100	-16088	1.0015	3.9817	1.1399	4.2430	358.63	1.0838	1.0974
-16000	-15988	1.0015	3.9713 +25	1.1366 +10	4.2542 - 8	358.52	1.0833 + 0	1.0968 + 0
-15900	-15888	1.0015	3.9608	1.1332	4.2655	358.41	1.0828	1.0962
-15800	-15788	1.0015	3.9504	1.1299	4.2767	358.30	1.0822	1.0956
-15700	-15688	1.0015	3.9400	1.1266	4.2880	358.19	1.0817	1.0950
-15600	-15588	1.0015	3.9296	1.1233	4.2994	358.08	1.0812	1.0944
-15500	-15488	1.0015	3.9192	1.1199	4.3108	357.97	1.0807	1.0938
-15400	-15389	1.0015	3.9088	1.1166	4.3222	357.86	1.0802	1.0932
-15300	-15289	1.0015	3.8985	1.1133	4.3336	357.75	1.0797	1.0926
-15200	-15189	1.0015	3.8882	1.1101	4.3451	357.63	1.0792	1.0921
-15100	-15089	1.0014	3.8779	1.1068	4.3567	357.52	1.0787	1.0915
-15000	-14989	1.0014	3.8676 +25	1.1035 +10	4.3682 - 8	357.41	1.0782 + 0	1.0909 + 0
-14900	-14889	1.0014	3.8574	1.1002	4.3798	357.30	1.0777	1.0903
-14800	-14790	1.0014	3.8471	1.0970	4.3915	357.19	1.0772	1.0897
-14700	-14690	1.0014	3.8369	1.0937	4.4032	357.08	1.0766	1.0891
-14600	-14590	1.0014	3.8268	1.0905	4.4149	356.97	1.0761	1.0885
-14500	-14490	1.0014	3.8166	1.0872	4.4266	356.85	1.0756	1.0879
-14400	-14390	1.0014	3.8064	1.0840	4.4384	356.74	1.0751	1.0873
-14300	-14290	1.0014	3.7963	1.0808	4.4503	356.63	1.0746	1.0867
-14200	-14190	1.0014	3.7862	1.0776	4.4622	356.52	1.0741	1.0861
-14100	-14090	1.0014	3.7761	1.0744	4.4741	356.41	1.0736	1.0855
-14000	-13991	1.0013	3.7661 +25	1.0712 +10	4.4860 - 8	356.30	1.0731 + 0	1.0849 + 0
-13900	-13891	1.0013	3.7560	1.0680	4.4980	356.18	1.0726	1.0843
-13800	-13791	1.0013	3.7460	1.0648	4.5100	356.07	1.0721	1.0837
-13700	-13691	1.0013	3.7360	1.0616	4.5221	355.96	1.0715	1.0831
-13600	-13591	1.0013	3.7260	1.0584	4.5342	355.85	1.0710	1.0825
-13500	-13491	1.0013	3.7161	1.0553	4.5464	355.74	1.0705	1.0819
-13400	-13391	1.0013	3.7061	1.0521	4.5586	355.62	1.0700	1.0813
-13300	-13292	1.0013	3.6962	1.0490	4.5708	355.51	1.0695	1.0807
-13200	-13192	1.0013	3.6863	1.0458	4.5831	355.40	1.0690	1.0801
-13100	-13092	1.0013	3.6764	1.0427	4.5954	355.29	1.0685	1.0795
-13000	-12992	1.0012	3.6666 +25	1.0396 +10	4.6078 - 8	355.18	1.0680 + 0	1.0789 + 0
-12900	-12892	1.0012	3.6567	1.0365	4.6202	355.06	1.0674	1.0783
-12800	-12792	1.0012	3.6469	1.0334	4.6326	354.95	1.0669	1.0777
-12700	-12692	1.0012	3.6371	1.0303	4.6451	354.84	1.0664	1.0771
-12600	-12592	1.0012	3.6273	1.0272	4.6576	354.73	1.0659	1.0765
-12500	-12493	1.0012	3.6176	1.0241	4.6702	354.62	1.0654	1.0759
-12400	-12393	1.0012	3.6078	1.0210	4.6828	354.50	1.0649	1.0753
-12300	-12293	1.0012	3.5981	1.0179	4.6954	354.39	1.0644	1.0747
-12200	-12193	1.0012	3.5884	1.0149	4.7081	354.28	1.0639	1.0741
-12100	-12093	1.0012	3.5787	1.0118	4.7208	354.17	1.0633	1.0735
-12000	-11993	1.0012	3.5691 +25	1.0087 +10	4.7336 - 8	354.05	1.0628 + 0	1.0729 + 0
-11900	-11893	1.0011	3.5594	1.0057	4.7464	353.94	1.0623	1.0723
-11800	-11793	1.0011	3.5498	1.0027	4.7593	353.83	1.0618	1.0717
-11700	-11693	1.0011	3.5402	9.9964 + 9	4.7722	353.72	1.0613	1.0711
-11600	-11594	1.0011	3.5307	9.9662	4.7851	353.60	1.0608	1.0705
-11500	-11494	1.0011	3.5211	9.9360	4.7981	353.49	1.0603	1.0699
-11400	-11394	1.0011	3.5116	9.9060	4.8112	353.38	1.0597	1.0693
-11300	-11294	1.0011	3.5020	9.8760	4.8242	353.27	1.0592	1.0687
-11200	-11194	1.0011	3.4925	9.8460	4.8374	353.15	1.0587	1.0681
-11100	-11094	1.0011	3.4831	9.8162	4.8505	353.04	1.0582	1.0675
-11000	-10994	1.0011	3.4736 +25	9.7864 + 9	4.8637 - 8	352.93	1.0577 + 0	1.0669 + 0
-10900	-10894	1.0010	3.4642	9.7567	4.8770	352.82	1.0572	1.0663
-10800	-10794	1.0010	3.4547	9.7270	4.8903	352.70	1.0566	1.0657
-10700	-10695	1.0010	3.4453	9.6975	4.9036	352.59	1.0561	1.0651
-10600	-10595	1.0010	3.4360	9.6680	4.9170	352.48	1.0556	1.0645
-10500	-10495	1.0010	3.4266	9.6385	4.9304	352.36	1.0551	1.0639
-10400	-10395	1.0010	3.4173	9.6092	4.9439	352.25	1.0546	1.0633
-10300	-10295	1.0010	3.4079	9.5799	4.9574	352.14	1.0541	1.0627
-10200	-10195	1.0010	3.3986	9.5507	4.9710	352.02	1.0535	1.0621
-10100	-10095	1.0010	3.3893	9.5215	4.9846	351.91	1.0530	1.0615
-10000	-9995	1.0010	3.3801 +25	9.4924 + 9	4.9983 - 8	351.80	1.0525 + 0	1.0608 + 0
-9900	-9895	1.0009	3.3708	9.4634	5.0120	351.69	1.0520	1.0602
-9800	-9795	1.0009	3.3616	9.4345	5.0258	351.57	1.0515	1.0596
-9700	-9695	1.0009	3.3524	9.4056	5.0396	351.46	1.0510	1.0590
-9600	-9596	1.0009	3.3432	9.3768	5.0534	351.35	1.0504	1.0584
-9500	-9496	1.0009	3.3341	9.3481	5.0673	351.23	1.0499	1.0578
-9400	-9396	1.0009	3.3249	9.3194	5.0812	351.12	1.0494	1.0572
-9300	-9296	1.0009	3.3158	9.2909	5.0952	351.01	1.0489	1.0566
-9200	-9196	1.0009	3.3067	9.2623	5.1093	350.89	1.0484	1.0560
-9100	-9096	1.0009	3.2976	9.2339	5.1234	350.78	1.0479	1.0554

Table V
Geometric Altitude, English Altitudes

Altitude		Gravity ratio	Number density	Collision frequency	Mean free path	Sound speed	Viscosity ratio	Thermal conductivity ratio
Z (ft)	H (ft)	g/g_0	n (m^{-3})	ν (s^{-1})	L (m)	C_s (m/s)	μ/μ_0	κ/κ_0
-16500	-16513	1.0016	4.0253 +25	1.1539 +10	4.1972 - 8	359.09	1.0859 + 0	1.0999 + 0
-16400	-16413	1.0016	4.0147	1.1505	4.2082	358.98	1.0854	1.0993
-16300	-16313	1.0016	4.0041	1.1471	4.2193	358.87	1.0848	1.0987
-16200	-16213	1.0016	3.9936	1.1437	4.2305	358.76	1.0843	1.0981
-16100	-16112	1.0015	3.9831	1.1404	4.2416	358.65	1.0838	1.0975
-16000	-16012	1.0015	3.9726 +25	1.1370 +10	4.2528 - 8	358.54	1.0833 + 0	1.0969 + 0
-15900	-15912	1.0015	3.9621	1.1337	4.2641	358.43	1.0828	1.0963
-15800	-15812	1.0015	3.9516	1.1303	4.2754	358.31	1.0823	1.0957
-15700	-15712	1.0015	3.9412	1.1270	4.2867	358.20	1.0818	1.0951
-15600	-15612	1.0015	3.9308	1.1236	4.2980	358.09	1.0813	1.0945
-15500	-15512	1.0015	3.9204	1.1203	4.3094	357.98	1.0808	1.0939
-15400	-15411	1.0015	3.9100	1.1170	4.3209	357.87	1.0803	1.0933
-15300	-15311	1.0015	3.8997	1.1137	4.3323	357.76	1.0798	1.0927
-15200	-15211	1.0015	3.8893	1.1104	4.3438	357.65	1.0792	1.0921
-15100	-15111	1.0014	3.8790	1.1071	4.3554	357.53	1.0787	1.0915
-15000	-15011	1.0014	3.8687 +25	1.1038 +10	4.3670 - 8	357.42	1.0782 + 0	1.0909 + 0
-14900	-14911	1.0014	3.8585	1.1006	4.3786	357.31	1.0777	1.0903
-14800	-14811	1.0014	3.8482	1.0973	4.3902	357.20	1.0772	1.0897
-14700	-14710	1.0014	3.8380	1.0941	4.4019	357.09	1.0767	1.0891
-14600	-14610	1.0014	3.8278	1.0908	4.4137	356.98	1.0762	1.0885
-14500	-14510	1.0014	3.8176	1.0876	4.4254	356.87	1.0757	1.0879
-14400	-14410	1.0014	3.8075	1.0843	4.4373	356.75	1.0752	1.0873
-14300	-14310	1.0014	3.7973	1.0811	4.4491	356.64	1.0747	1.0867
-14200	-14210	1.0014	3.7872	1.0779	4.4610	356.53	1.0741	1.0861
-14100	-14110	1.0014	3.7771	1.0747	4.4729	356.42	1.0736	1.0855
-14000	-14009	1.0013	3.7670 +25	1.0715 +10	4.4849 - 8	356.31	1.0731 + 0	1.0849 + 0
-13900	-13909	1.0013	3.7570	1.0683	4.4969	356.19	1.0726	1.0843
-13800	-13809	1.0013	3.7469	1.0651	4.5089	356.08	1.0721	1.0837
-13700	-13709	1.0013	3.7369	1.0619	4.5210	355.97	1.0716	1.0831
-13600	-13609	1.0013	3.7269	1.0587	4.5332	355.86	1.0711	1.0825
-13500	-13509	1.0013	3.7169	1.0556	4.5453	355.75	1.0706	1.0819
-13400	-13409	1.0013	3.7070	1.0524	4.5575	355.63	1.0701	1.0813
-13300	-13308	1.0013	3.6970	1.0492	4.5698	355.52	1.0695	1.0807
-13200	-13208	1.0013	3.6871	1.0461	4.5821	355.41	1.0690	1.0801
-13100	-13108	1.0013	3.6772	1.0430	4.5944	355.30	1.0685	1.0795
-13000	-13008	1.0012	3.6674 +25	1.0398 +10	4.6068 - 8	355.19	1.0680 + 0	1.0789 + 0
-12900	-12908	1.0012	3.6575	1.0367	4.6192	355.07	1.0675	1.0783
-12800	-12808	1.0012	3.6477	1.0336	4.6316	354.96	1.0670	1.0777
-12700	-12708	1.0012	3.6379	1.0305	4.6441	354.85	1.0665	1.0771
-12600	-12608	1.0012	3.6281	1.0274	4.6566	354.74	1.0659	1.0765
-12500	-12507	1.0012	3.6183	1.0243	4.6692	354.62	1.0654	1.0759
-12400	-12407	1.0012	3.6086	1.0212	4.6818	354.51	1.0649	1.0753
-12300	-12307	1.0012	3.5988	1.0181	4.6945	354.40	1.0644	1.0747
-12200	-12207	1.0012	3.5891	1.0151	4.7072	354.29	1.0639	1.0741
-12100	-12107	1.0012	3.5794	1.0120	4.7199	354.17	1.0634	1.0735
-12000	-12007	1.0012	3.5698 +25	1.0090 +10	4.7327 - 8	354.06	1.0629 + 0	1.0729 + 0
-11900	-11907	1.0011	3.5601	1.0059	4.7455	353.95	1.0623	1.0723
-11800	-11807	1.0011	3.5505	1.0029	4.7584	353.84	1.0618	1.0717
-11700	-11707	1.0011	3.5409	9.9984 + 9	4.7713	353.72	1.0613	1.0711
-11600	-11606	1.0011	3.5313	9.9682	4.7843	353.61	1.0608	1.0705
-11500	-11506	1.0011	3.5217	9.9380	4.7973	353.50	1.0603	1.0699
-11400	-11406	1.0011	3.5122	9.9079	4.8103	353.39	1.0598	1.0693
-11300	-11306	1.0011	3.5026	9.8778	4.8234	353.27	1.0593	1.0687
-11200	-11206	1.0011	3.4931	9.8479	4.8366	353.16	1.0587	1.0681
-11100	-11106	1.0011	3.4836	9.8180	4.8497	353.05	1.0582	1.0675
-11000	-11006	1.0011	3.4742 +25	9.7881 + 9	4.8630 - 8	352.93	1.0577 + 0	1.0669 + 0
-10900	-10906	1.0010	3.4647	9.7584	4.8762	352.82	1.0572	1.0663
-10800	-10806	1.0010	3.4553	9.7287	4.8895	352.71	1.0567	1.0657
-10700	-10705	1.0010	3.4459	9.6991	4.9029	352.60	1.0562	1.0651
-10600	-10605	1.0010	3.4365	9.6696	4.9163	352.48	1.0556	1.0645
-10500	-10505	1.0010	3.4271	9.6401	4.9297	352.37	1.0551	1.0639
-10400	-10405	1.0010	3.4177	9.6107	4.9432	352.26	1.0546	1.0633
-10300	-10305	1.0010	3.4084	9.5814	4.9568	352.14	1.0541	1.0627
-10200	-10205	1.0010	3.3991	9.5521	4.9703	352.03	1.0536	1.0621
-10100	-10105	1.0010	3.3898	9.5230	4.9840	351.92	1.0531	1.0615
-10000	-10005	1.0010	3.3805 +25	9.4938 + 9	4.9976 - 8	351.80	1.0525 + 0	1.0609 + 0
-9900	-9905	1.0010	3.3713	9.4648	5.0114	351.69	1.0520	1.0603
-9800	-9805	1.0009	3.3620	9.4358	5.0251	351.58	1.0515	1.0597
-9700	-9705	1.0009	3.3528	9.4069	5.0389	351.46	1.0510	1.0591
-9600	-9604	1.0009	3.3436	9.3781	5.0528	351.35	1.0505	1.0585
-9500	-9504	1.0009	3.3345	9.3494	5.0667	351.24	1.0499	1.0579
-9400	-9404	1.0009	3.3253	9.3207	5.0806	351.12	1.0494	1.0573
-9300	-9304	1.0009	3.3162	9.2920	5.0946	351.01	1.0489	1.0567
-9200	-9204	1.0009	3.3070	9.2635	5.1087	350.90	1.0484	1.0560
-9100	-9104	1.0009	3.2979	9.2350	5.1228	350.78	1.0479	1.0554

Table V
Geopotential Altitude, English Altitudes

Altitude		Gravity ratio	Number density.	Collision frequency	Mean free path	Sound speed	Viscosity ratio	Thermal conductivity ratio
H (ft)	Z (ft)	g/g_0	n (m^{-3})	ν (s^{-1})	L (m)	C_s (m/s)	μ/μ_0	κ/κ_0
-9000	-8996	1.0009	3.2885 +25	9.2055 + 9	5.1375 - 8	350.66	1.0473 + 0	1.0548 + 0
-8900	-8896	1.0009	3.2795	9.1772	5.1517	350.55	1.0468	1.0542
-8800	-8796	1.0008	3.2704	9.1489	5.1659	350.44	1.0463	1.0536
-8700	-8696	1.0008	3.2614	9.1208	5.1802	350.32	1.0458	1.0530
-8600	-8596	1.0008	3.2524	9.0927	5.1945	350.21	1.0453	1.0524
-8500	-8497	1.0008	3.2434	9.0646	5.2089	350.10	1.0447	1.0518
-8400	-8397	1.0008	3.2345	9.0367	5.2233	349.98	1.0442	1.0512
-8300	-8297	1.0008	3.2255	9.0088	5.2378	349.87	1.0437	1.0506
-8200	-8197	1.0008	3.2166	8.9809	5.2523	349.76	1.0432	1.0500
-8100	-8097	1.0008	3.2077	8.9532	5.2669	349.64	1.0427	1.0494
-8000	-7997	1.0008	3.1988 +25	8.9255 + 9	5.2815 - 8	349.53	1.0421 + 0	1.0488 + 0
-7900	-7897	1.0008	3.1900	8.8978	5.2962	349.41	1.0416	1.0482
-7800	-7797	1.0007	3.1811	8.8703	5.3109	349.30	1.0411	1.0476
-7700	-7697	1.0007	3.1723	8.8428	5.3257	349.19	1.0406	1.0469
-7600	-7597	1.0007	3.1635	8.8153	5.3405	349.07	1.0401	1.0463
-7500	-7497	1.0007	3.1547	8.7880	5.3554	348.96	1.0395	1.0457
-7400	-7397	1.0007	3.1459	8.7607	5.3703	348.84	1.0390	1.0451
-7300	-7297	1.0007	3.1372	8.7335	5.3853	348.73	1.0385	1.0445
-7200	-7198	1.0007	3.1285	8.7063	5.4003	348.62	1.0380	1.0439
-7100	-7098	1.0007	3.1197	8.6792	5.4154	348.50	1.0374	1.0433
-7000	-6998	1.0007	3.1110 +25	8.6522 + 9	5.4305 - 8	348.39	1.0369 + 0	1.0427 + 0
-6900	-6898	1.0007	3.1024	8.6252	5.4457	348.27	1.0364	1.0421
-6800	-6798	1.0007	3.0937	8.5983	5.4610	348.16	1.0359	1.0415
-6700	-6698	1.0006	3.0851	8.5715	5.4763	348.04	1.0354	1.0409
-6600	-6598	1.0006	3.0765	8.5447	5.4916	347.93	1.0348	1.0403
-6500	-6498	1.0006	3.0679	8.5180	5.5070	347.82	1.0343	1.0397
-6400	-6398	1.0006	3.0593	8.4914	5.5224	347.70	1.0338	1.0391
-6300	-6298	1.0006	3.0507	8.4648	5.5380	347.59	1.0333	1.0385
-6200	-6198	1.0006	3.0422	8.4384	5.5535	347.47	1.0327	1.0378
-6100	-6098	1.0006	3.0336	8.4119	5.5691	347.36	1.0322	1.0372
-6000	-5998	1.0006	3.0251 +25	8.3856 + 9	5.5848 - 8	347.24	1.0317 + 0	1.0366 + 0
-5900	-5898	1.0006	3.0166	8.3593	5.6005	347.13	1.0312	1.0360
-5800	-5798	1.0006	3.0082	8.3330	5.6163	347.01	1.0306	1.0354
-5700	-5698	1.0005	2.9997	8.3068	5.6321	346.90	1.0301	1.0348
-5600	-5598	1.0005	2.9913	8.2807	5.6480	346.78	1.0296	1.0342
-5500	-5499	1.0005	2.9828	8.2547	5.6640	346.67	1.0291	1.0336
-5400	-5399	1.0005	2.9744	8.2287	5.6799	346.55	1.0285	1.0330
-5300	-5299	1.0005	2.9661	8.2028	5.6960	346.44	1.0280	1.0324
-5200	-5199	1.0005	2.9577	8.1770	5.7121	346.32	1.0275	1.0318
-5100	-5099	1.0005	2.9493	8.1512	5.7283	346.21	1.0270	1.0312
-5000	-4999	1.0005	2.9410 +25	8.1255 + 9	5.7445 - 8	346.09	1.0264 + 0	1.0305 + 0
-4900	-4899	1.0005	2.9327	8.0998	5.7608	345.98	1.0259	1.0299
-4800	-4799	1.0005	2.9244	8.0742	5.7771	345.86	1.0254	1.0293
-4700	-4699	1.0005	2.9161	8.0487	5.7935	345.75	1.0249	1.0287
-4600	-4599	1.0004	2.9079	8.0232	5.8100	345.63	1.0243	1.0281
-4500	-4499	1.0004	2.8996	7.9978	5.8265	345.52	1.0238	1.0275
-4400	-4399	1.0004	2.8914	7.9725	5.8430	345.40	1.0233	1.0269
-4300	-4299	1.0004	2.8832	7.9472	5.8597	345.29	1.0228	1.0263
-4200	-4199	1.0004	2.8750	7.9220	5.8763	345.17	1.0222	1.0257
-4100	-4099	1.0004	2.8669	7.8969	5.8931	345.06	1.0217	1.0251
-4000	-3999	1.0004	2.8587 +25	7.8718 + 9	5.9099 - 8	344.94	1.0212 + 0	1.0245 + 0
-3900	-3899	1.0004	2.8506	7.8468	5.9267	344.83	1.0207	1.0238
-3800	-3799	1.0004	2.8425	7.8218	5.9437	344.71	1.0201	1.0232
-3700	-3699	1.0004	2.8344	7.7969	5.9606	344.60	1.0196	1.0226
-3600	-3599	1.0003	2.8263	7.7721	5.9777	344.48	1.0191	1.0220
-3500	-3499	1.0003	2.8182	7.7473	5.9948	344.36	1.0185	1.0214
-3400	-3399	1.0003	2.8102	7.7226	6.0119	344.25	1.0180	1.0208
-3300	-3299	1.0003	2.8022	7.6980	6.0292	344.13	1.0175	1.0202
-3200	-3200	1.0003	2.7941	7.6734	6.0464	344.02	1.0170	1.0196
-3100	-3100	1.0003	2.7862	7.6489	6.0638	343.90	1.0164	1.0190
-3000	-3000	1.0003	2.7782 +25	7.6244 + 9	6.0812 - 8	343.79	1.0159 + 0	1.0183 + 0
-2900	-2900	1.0003	2.7702	7.6000	6.0987	343.67	1.0154	1.0177
-2800	-2800	1.0003	2.7623	7.5757	6.1162	343.55	1.0148	1.0171
-2700	-2700	1.0003	2.7544	7.5514	6.1338	343.44	1.0143	1.0165
-2600	-2600	1.0002	2.7465	7.5272	6.1514	343.32	1.0138	1.0159
-2500	-2500	1.0002	2.7386	7.5030	6.1691	343.21	1.0133	1.0153
-2400	-2400	1.0002	2.7307	7.4789	6.1869	343.09	1.0127	1.0147
-2300	-2300	1.0002	2.7229	7.4549	6.2048	342.97	1.0122	1.0141
-2200	-2200	1.0002	2.7150	7.4309	6.2227	342.86	1.0117	1.0134
-2100	-2100	1.0002	2.7072	7.4070	6.2406	342.74	1.0111	1.0128
-2000	-2000	1.0002	2.6994 +25	7.3832 + 9	6.2587 - 8	342.63	1.0106 + 0	1.0122 + 0
-1900	-1900	1.0002	2.6916	7.3594	6.2768	342.51	1.0101	1.0116
-1800	-1800	1.0002	2.6839	7.3357	6.2949	342.39	1.0095	1.0110
-1700	-1700	1.0002	2.6761	7.3120	6.3132	342.28	1.0090	1.0104
-1600	-1600	1.0002	2.6684	7.2884	6.3315	342.16	1.0085	1.0098
-1500	-1500	1.0001	2.6607	7.2649	6.3498	342.04	1.0079	1.0092
-1400	-1400	1.0001	2.6530	7.2414	6.3682	341.93	1.0074	1.0085
-1300	-1300	1.0001	2.6453	7.2180	6.3867	341.81	1.0069	1.0079
-1200	-1200	1.0001	2.6376	7.1946	6.4053	341.70	1.0063	1.0073
-1100	-1100	1.0001	2.6300	7.1713	6.4239	341.58	1.0058	1.0067

Table V
Geometric Altitude, English Altitudes

Altitude		Gravity ratio	Number density	Collision frequency	Mean free path	Sound speed	Viscosity ratio	Thermal conductivity ratio
Z (ft)	H (ft)	g/g_0	n (m^{-3})	ν (s^{-1})	L (m)	C_s (m/s)	μ/μ_0	κ/κ_0
-9000	-9004	1.0009	3.2889 +25	9.2066 + 9	5.1369 - 8	350.67	1.0474 + 0	1.0548 + 0
-8900	-8904	1.0009	3.2798	9.1783	5.1511	350.56	1.0468	1.0542
-8800	-8804	1.0008	3.2708	9.1500	5.1654	350.44	1.0463	1.0536
-8700	-8704	1.0008	3.2617	9.1218	5.1797	350.33	1.0458	1.0530
-8600	-8604	1.0008	3.2527	9.0937	5.1940	350.21	1.0453	1.0524
-8500	-8503	1.0008	3.2437	9.0656	5.2084	350.10	1.0448	1.0518
-8400	-8403	1.0008	3.2348	9.0376	5.2228	349.99	1.0442	1.0512
-8300	-8303	1.0008	3.2258	9.0097	5.2373	349.87	1.0437	1.0506
-8200	-8203	1.0008	3.2169	8.9818	5.2518	349.76	1.0432	1.0500
-8100	-8103	1.0008	3.2080	8.9540	5.2664	349.64	1.0427	1.0494
-8000	-8003	1.0008	3.1991 +25	8.9263 + 9	5.2810 - 8	349.53	1.0422 + 0	1.0488 + 0
-7900	-7903	1.0008	3.1902	8.8987	5.2957	349.42	1.0416	1.0482
-7800	-7803	1.0007	3.1814	8.8711	5.3105	349.30	1.0411	1.0476
-7700	-7703	1.0007	3.1726	8.8436	5.3252	349.19	1.0406	1.0470
-7600	-7603	1.0007	3.1637	8.8161	5.3401	349.07	1.0401	1.0464
-7500	-7503	1.0007	3.1549	8.7887	5.3550	348.96	1.0395	1.0458
-7400	-7403	1.0007	3.1462	8.7614	5.3699	348.85	1.0390	1.0451
-7300	-7303	1.0007	3.1374	8.7342	5.3849	348.73	1.0385	1.0445
-7200	-7202	1.0007	3.1287	8.7070	5.3999	348.62	1.0380	1.0439
-7100	-7102	1.0007	3.1200	8.6799	5.4150	348.50	1.0375	1.0433
-7000	-7002	1.0007	3.1113 +25	8.6528 + 9	5.4302 - 8	348.39	1.0369 + 0	1.0427 + 0
-6900	-6902	1.0007	3.1026	8.6258	5.4454	348.28	1.0364	1.0421
-6800	-6802	1.0007	3.0939	8.5989	5.4606	348.16	1.0359	1.0415
-6700	-6702	1.0006	3.0853	8.5721	5.4759	348.05	1.0354	1.0409
-6600	-6602	1.0006	3.0766	8.5453	5.4913	347.93	1.0348	1.0403
-6500	-6502	1.0006	3.0680	8.5186	5.5067	347.82	1.0343	1.0397
-6400	-6402	1.0006	3.0594	8.4919	5.5221	347.70	1.0338	1.0391
-6300	-6302	1.0006	3.0509	8.4654	5.5377	347.59	1.0333	1.0385
-6200	-6202	1.0006	3.0423	8.4388	5.5532	347.47	1.0327	1.0379
-6100	-6102	1.0006	3.0338	8.4124	5.5688	347.36	1.0322	1.0373
-6000	-6002	1.0006	3.0253 +25	8.3860 + 9	5.5845 - 8	347.24	1.0317 + 0	1.0366 + 0
-5900	-5902	1.0006	3.0168	8.3597	5.6002	347.13	1.0312	1.0360
-5800	-5802	1.0006	3.0083	8.3334	5.6160	347.01	1.0307	1.0354
-5700	-5702	1.0005	2.9998	8.3073	5.6319	346.90	1.0301	1.0348
-5600	-5602	1.0005	2.9914	8.2811	5.6478	346.78	1.0296	1.0342
-5500	-5501	1.0005	2.9830	8.2551	5.6637	346.67	1.0291	1.0336
-5400	-5401	1.0005	2.9746	8.2291	5.6797	346.56	1.0286	1.0330
-5300	-5301	1.0005	2.9662	8.2032	5.6958	346.44	1.0280	1.0324
-5200	-5201	1.0005	2.9578	8.1773	5.7119	346.33	1.0275	1.0318
-5100	-5101	1.0005	2.9495	8.1515	5.7281	346.21	1.0270	1.0312
-5000	-5001	1.0005	2.9411 +25	8.1258 + 9	5.7443 - 8	346.10	1.0265 + 0	1.0306 + 0
-4900	-4901	1.0005	2.9328	8.1001	5.7606	345.98	1.0259	1.0299
-4800	-4801	1.0005	2.9245	8.0745	5.7769	345.86	1.0254	1.0293
-4700	-4701	1.0005	2.9162	8.0490	5.7933	345.75	1.0249	1.0287
-4600	-4601	1.0004	2.9080	8.0235	5.8098	345.63	1.0243	1.0281
-4500	-4501	1.0004	2.8997	7.9981	5.8263	345.52	1.0238	1.0275
-4400	-4401	1.0004	2.8915	7.9727	5.8429	345.40	1.0233	1.0269
-4300	-4301	1.0004	2.8833	7.9474	5.8595	345.29	1.0228	1.0263
-4200	-4201	1.0004	2.8751	7.9222	5.8762	345.17	1.0222	1.0257
-4100	-4101	1.0004	2.8669	7.8971	5.8929	345.06	1.0217	1.0251
-4000	-4001	1.0004	2.8588 +25	7.8720 + 9	5.9097 - 8	344.94	1.0212 + 0	1.0245 + 0
-3900	-3901	1.0004	2.8506	7.8469	5.9266	344.83	1.0207	1.0238
-3800	-3801	1.0004	2.8425	7.8220	5.9435	344.71	1.0201	1.0232
-3700	-3701	1.0004	2.8344	7.7971	5.9605	344.60	1.0196	1.0226
-3600	-3601	1.0003	2.8263	7.7722	5.9776	344.48	1.0191	1.0220
-3500	-3501	1.0003	2.8183	7.7475	5.9947	344.36	1.0185	1.0214
-3400	-3401	1.0003	2.8102	7.7227	6.0118	344.25	1.0180	1.0208
-3300	-3301	1.0003	2.8022	7.6981	6.0291	344.13	1.0175	1.0202
-3200	-3200	1.0003	2.7942	7.6735	6.0464	344.02	1.0170	1.0196
-3100	-3100	1.0003	2.7862	7.6490	6.0637	343.90	1.0164	1.0190
-3000	-3000	1.0003	2.7782 +25	7.6245 + 9	6.0811 - 8	343.79	1.0159 + 0	1.0183 + 0
-2900	-2900	1.0003	2.7703	7.6001	6.0986	343.67	1.0154	1.0177
-2800	-2800	1.0003	2.7623	7.5758	6.1161	343.55	1.0148	1.0171
-2700	-2700	1.0003	2.7544	7.5515	6.1337	343.44	1.0143	1.0165
-2600	-2600	1.0002	2.7465	7.5273	6.1514	343.32	1.0138	1.0159
-2500	-2500	1.0002	2.7386	7.5031	6.1691	343.21	1.0133	1.0153
-2400	-2400	1.0002	2.7307	7.4790	6.1869	343.09	1.0127	1.0147
-2300	-2300	1.0002	2.7229	7.4550	6.2047	342.97	1.0122	1.0141
-2200	-2200	1.0002	2.7150	7.4310	6.2226	342.86	1.0117	1.0135
-2100	-2100	1.0002	2.7072	7.4071	6.2406	342.74	1.0111	1.0128
-2000	-2000	1.0002	2.6994 +25	7.3832 + 9	6.2586 - 8	342.63	1.0106 + 0	1.0122 + 0
-1900	-1900	1.0002	2.6916	7.3595	6.2767	342.51	1.0101	1.0116
-1800	-1800	1.0002	2.6839	7.3357	6.2949	342.39	1.0095	1.0110
-1700	-1700	1.0002	2.6761	7.3121	6.3131	342.28	1.0090	1.0104
-1600	-1600	1.0002	2.6684	7.2884	6.3314	342.16	1.0085	1.0098
-1500	-1500	1.0001	2.6607	7.2649	6.3498	342.04	1.0079	1.0092
-1400	-1400	1.0001	2.6530	7.2414	6.3682	341.93	1.0074	1.0085
-1300	-1300	1.0001	2.6453	7.2180	6.3867	341.81	1.0069	1.0079
-1200	-1200	1.0001	2.6376	7.1946	6.4053	341.69	1.0063	1.0073
-1100	-1100	1.0001	2.6300	7.1713	6.4239	341.58	1.0058	1.0067

Table V
Geopotential Altitude, English Altitudes

Altitude		Gravity ratio	Number density	Collision frequency	Mean free path	Sound speed	Viscosity ratio	Thermal conductivity ratio
H (ft)	Z (ft)	g/g_0	n (m^{-3})	ν (s^{-1})	L (m)	C_s (m/s)	μ/μ_0	κ/κ_0
-1000	-1000	1.0001	2.6223 +25	7.1481 + 9	6.4426 - 8	341.46	1.0053 + 0	1.0061 + 0
-900	-900	1.0001	2.6147	7.1249	6.4613	341.35	1.0048	1.0055
-800	-800	1.0001	2.6071	7.1017	6.4802	341.23	1.0042	1.0049
-700	-700	1.0001	2.5996	7.0787	6.4991	341.11	1.0037	1.0043
-600	-600	1.0001	2.5920	7.0557	6.5180	341.00	1.0032	1.0036
-500	-500	1.0000	2.5844	7.0327	6.5371	340.88	1.0026	1.0030
-400	-400	1.0000	2.5769	7.0098	6.5562	340.76	1.0021	1.0024
-300	-300	1.0000	2.5694	6.9870	6.5753	340.64	1.0016	1.0018
-200	-200	1.0000	2.5619	6.9642	6.5946	340.53	1.0010	1.0012
-100	-100	1.0000	2.5544	6.9415	6.6139	340.41	1.0005	1.0006
0	0	1.0000	2.5470 +25	6.9189 + 9	6.6332 - 8	340.29	1.0000 + 0	1.0000 + 0
100	100	1.0000	2.5395	6.8963	6.6527	340.18	9.9946 - 1	9.9938 - 1
200	200	1.0000	2.5321	6.8737	6.6722	340.06	9.9893	9.9876
300	300	1.0000	2.5247	6.8513	6.6918	339.94	9.9839	9.9815
400	400	1.0000	2.5173	6.8288	6.7114	339.83	9.9786	9.9753
500	500	1.0000	2.5099	6.8065	6.7312	339.71	9.9732	9.9692
600	600	.9999	2.5026	6.7842	6.7510	339.59	9.9679	9.9630
700	700	.9999	2.4952	6.7619	6.7708	339.47	9.9625	9.9569
800	800	.9999	2.4879	6.7397	6.7908	339.36	9.9572	9.9507
900	900	.9999	2.4806	6.7176	6.8108	339.24	9.9518	9.9446
1000	1000	.9999	2.4733 +25	6.6955 + 9	6.8309 - 8	339.12	9.9464 - 1	9.9384 - 1
1100	1100	.9999	2.4660	6.6735	6.8511	339.00	9.9411	9.9322
1200	1200	.9999	2.4587	6.6516	6.8713	338.89	9.9357	9.9261
1300	1300	.9999	2.4515	6.6297	6.8916	338.77	9.9303	9.9199
1400	1400	.9999	2.4443	6.6078	6.9120	338.65	9.9250	9.9137
1500	1500	.9999	2.4370	6.5860	6.9324	338.53	9.9196	9.9076
1600	1600	.9998	2.4298	6.5643	6.9530	338.42	9.9142	9.9014
1700	1700	.9998	2.4227	6.5426	6.9736	338.30	9.9089	9.8952
1800	1800	.9998	2.4155	6.5210	6.9943	338.18	9.9035	9.8891
1900	1900	.9998	2.4083	6.4994	7.0150	338.06	9.8981	9.8829
2000	2000	.9998	2.4012 +25	6.4779 + 9	7.0359 - 8	337.95	9.8927 - 1	9.8767 - 1
2100	2100	.9998	2.3941	6.4565	7.0568	337.83	9.8874	9.8705
2200	2200	.9998	2.3870	6.4351	7.0778	337.71	9.8820	9.8644
2300	2300	.9998	2.3799	6.4137	7.0988	337.59	9.8766	9.8582
2400	2400	.9998	2.3728	6.3925	7.1200	337.47	9.8712	9.8520
2500	2500	.9998	2.3658	6.3712	7.1412	337.36	9.8658	9.8458
2600	2600	.9998	2.3588	6.3501	7.1625	337.24	9.8604	9.8397
2700	2700	.9997	2.3517	6.3290	7.1839	337.12	9.8551	9.8335
2800	2800	.9997	2.3447	6.3079	7.2054	337.00	9.8497	9.8273
2900	2900	.9997	2.3378	6.2869	7.2269	336.88	9.8443	9.8211
3000	3000	.9997	2.3308 +25	6.2659 + 9	7.2485 - 8	336.77	9.8389 - 1	9.8149 - 1
3100	3100	.9997	2.3238	6.2450	7.2702	336.65	9.8335	9.8087
3200	3200	.9997	2.3169	6.2242	7.2920	336.53	9.8281	9.8026
3300	3301	.9997	2.3100	6.2034	7.3138	336.41	9.8227	9.7964
3400	3401	.9997	2.3030	6.1827	7.3358	336.29	9.8173	9.7902
3500	3501	.9997	2.2962	6.1620	7.3578	336.17	9.8119	9.7840
3600	3601	.9997	2.2893	6.1414	7.3799	336.06	9.8065	9.7778
3700	3701	.9996	2.2824	6.1208	7.4021	335.94	9.8011	9.7716
3800	3801	.9996	2.2756	6.1003	7.4243	335.82	9.7957	9.7654
3900	3901	.9996	2.2687	6.0799	7.4467	335.70	9.7902	9.7592
4000	4001	.9996	2.2619 +25	6.0595 + 9	7.4691 - 8	335.58	9.7848 - 1	9.7530 - 1
4100	4101	.9996	2.2551	6.0391	7.4916	335.46	9.7794	9.7468
4200	4201	.9996	2.2484	6.0188	7.5142	335.34	9.7740	9.7406
4300	4301	.9996	2.2416	5.9986	7.5369	335.23	9.7686	9.7344
4400	4401	.9996	2.2348	5.9784	7.5597	335.11	9.7632	9.7282
4500	4501	.9996	2.2281	5.9583	7.5826	334.99	9.7577	9.7220
4600	4601	.9996	2.2214	5.9382	7.6055	334.87	9.7523	9.7158
4700	4701	.9995	2.2147	5.9182	7.6285	334.75	9.7469	9.7096
4800	4801	.9995	2.2080	5.8982	7.6516	334.63	9.7415	9.7034
4900	4901	.9995	2.2013	5.8783	7.6748	334.51	9.7360	9.6972
5000	5001	.9995	2.1947 +25	5.8584 + 9	7.6981 - 8	334.39	9.7306 - 1	9.6910 - 1
5100	5101	.9995	2.1880	5.8386	7.7215	334.27	9.7252	9.6848
5200	5201	.9995	2.1814	5.8188	7.7449	334.16	9.7197	9.6785
5300	5301	.9995	2.1748	5.7991	7.7685	334.04	9.7143	9.6723
5400	5401	.9995	2.1682	5.7795	7.7921	333.92	9.7089	9.6661
5500	5501	.9995	2.1616	5.7599	7.8158	333.80	9.7034	9.6599
5600	5602	.9995	2.1550	5.7403	7.8397	333.68	9.6980	9.6537
5700	5702	.9995	2.1485	5.7208	7.8636	333.56	9.6925	9.6475
5800	5802	.9994	2.1419	5.7014	7.8876	333.44	9.6871	9.6413
5900	5902	.9994	2.1354	5.6820	7.9116	333.32	9.6816	9.6350
6000	6002	.9994	2.1289 +25	5.6627 + 9	7.9358 - 8	333.20	9.6762 - 1	9.6288 - 1
6100	6102	.9994	2.1224	5.6434	7.9601	333.08	9.6707	9.6226
6200	6202	.9994	2.1159	5.6241	7.9844	332.96	9.6653	9.6164
6300	6302	.9994	2.1095	5.6050	8.0089	332.84	9.6598	9.6101
6400	6402	.9994	2.1030	5.5858	8.0334	332.72	9.6544	9.6039
6500	6502	.9994	2.0966	5.5667	8.0581	332.60	9.6489	9.5977
6600	6602	.9994	2.0902	5.5477	8.0828	332.48	9.6434	9.5915
6700	6702	.9994	2.0838	5.5287	8.1076	332.36	9.6380	9.5852
6800	6802	.9993	2.0774	5.5098	8.1325	332.24	9.6325	9.5790
6900	6902	.9993	2.0710	5.4909	8.1576	332.12	9.6270	9.5728

Table V
Geometric Altitude, English Altitudes

Altitude		Gravity ratio	Number density	Collision frequency	Mean free path	Sound speed	Viscosity ratio	Thermal conductivity ratio
Z (ft)	H (ft)	g/g_0	n (m^{-3})	ν (s^{-1})	L (m)	C_s (m/s)	μ/μ_0	κ/κ_0
-1000	-1000	1.0001	2.6223 +25	7.1481 + 9	6.4426 - 8	341.46	1.0053 + 0	1.0061 + 0
-900	-900	1.0001	2.6147	7.1249	6.4613	341.35	1.0048	1.0055
-800	-800	1.0001	2.6071	7.1018	6.4802	341.23	1.0042	1.0049
-700	-700	1.0001	2.5996	7.0787	6.4991	341.11	1.0037	1.0043
-600	-600	1.0001	2.5920	7.0557	6.5180	341.00	1.0032	1.0036
-500	-500	1.0000	2.5844	7.0327	6.5370	340.88	1.0026	1.0030
-400	-400	1.0000	2.5769	7.0098	6.5561	340.76	1.0021	1.0024
-300	-300	1.0000	2.5694	6.9870	6.5753	340.64	1.0016	1.0018
-200	-200	1.0000	2.5619	6.9642	6.5945	340.53	1.0010	1.0012
-100	-100	1.0000	2.5544	6.9415	6.6139	340.41	1.0005	1.0006
0	0	1.0000	2.5470 +25	6.9189 + 9	6.6332 - 8	340.29	1.0000 + 0	1.0000 + 0
100	100	1.0000	2.5395	6.8963	6.6527	340.18	9.9946 - 1	9.9938 - 1
200	200	1.0000	2.5321	6.8737	6.6722	340.06	9.9893	9.9876
300	300	1.0000	2.5247	6.8513	6.6918	339.94	9.9839	9.9815
400	400	1.0000	2.5173	6.8288	6.7114	339.83	9.9786	9.9753
500	500	1.0000	2.5099	6.8065	6.7312	339.71	9.9732	9.9692
600	600	.9999	2.5026	6.7842	6.7510	339.59	9.9679	9.9630
700	700	.9999	2.4952	6.7619	6.7708	339.47	9.9625	9.9569
800	800	.9999	2.4879	6.7397	6.7908	339.36	9.9572	9.9507
900	900	.9999	2.4806	6.7176	6.8108	339.24	9.9518	9.9446
1000	1000	.9999	2.4733 +25	6.6955 + 9	6.8309 - 8	339.12	9.9464 - 1	9.9384 - 1
1100	1100	.9999	2.4660	6.6735	6.8510	339.00	9.9411	9.9322
1200	1200	.9999	2.4587	6.6516	6.8713	338.89	9.9357	9.9261
1300	1300	.9999	2.4515	6.6297	6.8916	338.77	9.9304	9.9199
1400	1400	.9999	2.4443	6.6078	6.9120	338.65	9.9250	9.9137
1500	1500	.9999	2.4371	6.5860	6.9324	338.53	9.9196	9.9076
1600	1600	.9998	2.4299	6.5643	6.9529	338.42	9.9143	9.9014
1700	1700	.9998	2.4227	6.5426	6.9736	338.30	9.9089	9.8952
1800	1800	.9998	2.4155	6.5210	6.9942	338.18	9.9035	9.8891
1900	1900	.9998	2.4084	6.4995	7.0150	338.06	9.8981	9.8829
2000	2000	.9998	2.4012 +25	6.4780 + 9	7.0358 - 8	337.95	9.8928 - 1	9.8767 - 1
2100	2100	.9998	2.3941	6.4565	7.0567	337.83	9.8874	9.8706
2200	2200	.9998	2.3870	6.4351	7.0777	337.71	9.8820	9.8644
2300	2300	.9998	2.3799	6.4138	7.0988	337.59	9.8766	9.8582
2400	2400	.9998	2.3729	6.3925	7.1199	337.47	9.8712	9.8520
2500	2500	.9998	2.3658	6.3713	7.1411	337.36	9.8659	9.8459
2600	2600	.9998	2.3588	6.3501	7.1624	337.24	9.8605	9.8397
2700	2700	.9997	2.3518	6.3290	7.1838	337.12	9.8551	9.8335
2800	2800	.9997	2.3448	6.3080	7.2053	337.00	9.8497	9.8273
2900	2900	.9997	2.3378	6.2870	7.2268	336.88	9.8443	9.8211
3000	3000	.9997	2.3308 +25	6.2660 + 9	7.2484 - 8	336.77	9.8389 - 1	9.8150 - 1
3100	3100	.9997	2.3239	6.2451	7.2701	336.65	9.8335	9.8088
3200	3200	.9997	2.3169	6.2243	7.2919	336.53	9.8281	9.8026
3300	3299	.9997	2.3100	6.2035	7.3137	336.41	9.8227	9.7964
3400	3399	.9997	2.3031	6.1828	7.3356	336.29	9.8173	9.7902
3500	3499	.9997	2.2962	6.1621	7.3577	336.18	9.8119	9.7840
3600	3599	.9997	2.2893	6.1415	7.3798	336.06	9.8065	9.7778
3700	3699	.9996	2.2825	6.1210	7.4019	335.94	9.8011	9.7716
3800	3799	.9996	2.2756	6.1005	7.4242	335.82	9.7957	9.7654
3900	3899	.9996	2.2688	6.0800	7.4465	335.70	9.7903	9.7592
4000	3999	.9996	2.2620 +25	6.0596 + 9	7.4690 - 8	335.58	9.7849 - 1	9.7531 - 1
4100	4099	.9996	2.2552	6.0393	7.4915	335.46	9.7795	9.7469
4200	4199	.9996	2.2484	6.0190	7.5140	335.35	9.7740	9.7407
4300	4299	.9996	2.2416	5.9988	7.5367	335.23	9.7686	9.7345
4400	4399	.9996	2.2349	5.9786	7.5595	335.11	9.7632	9.7283
4500	4499	.9996	2.2282	5.9585	7.5823	334.99	9.7578	9.7221
4600	4599	.9996	2.2214	5.9384	7.6053	334.87	9.7524	9.7159
4700	4699	.9995	2.2147	5.9184	7.6283	334.75	9.7469	9.7097
4800	4799	.9995	2.2081	5.8984	7.6514	334.63	9.7415	9.7035
4900	4899	.9995	2.2014	5.8785	7.6745	334.51	9.7361	9.6973
5000	4999	.9995	2.1947 +25	5.8587 + 9	7.6978 - 8	334.39	9.7307 - 1	9.6910 - 1
5100	5099	.9995	2.1881	5.8389	7.7212	334.28	9.7252	9.6848
5200	5199	.9995	2.1815	5.8191	7.7446	334.16	9.7198	9.6786
5300	5299	.9995	2.1749	5.7994	7.7682	334.04	9.7144	9.6724
5400	5399	.9995	2.1683	5.7798	7.7918	333.92	9.7089	9.6662
5500	5499	.9995	2.1617	5.7602	7.8155	333.80	9.7035	9.6600
5600	5598	.9995	2.1551	5.7406	7.8393	333.68	9.6980	9.6538
5700	5698	.9995	2.1486	5.7211	7.8632	333.56	9.6926	9.6476
5800	5798	.9994	2.1420	5.7017	7.8872	333.44	9.6872	9.6414
5900	5898	.9994	2.1355	5.6823	7.9112	333.32	9.6817	9.6351
6000	5998	.9994	2.1290 +25	5.6630 + 9	7.9354 - 8	333.20	9.6763 - 1	9.6289 - 1
6100	6098	.9994	2.1225	5.6437	7.9596	333.08	9.6708	9.6227
6200	6198	.9994	2.1161	5.6245	7.9840	332.96	9.6654	9.6165
6300	6298	.9994	2.1096	5.6053	8.0084	332.84	9.6599	9.6103
6400	6398	.9994	2.1032	5.5862	8.0329	332.72	9.6545	9.6040
6500	6498	.9994	2.0967	5.5671	8.0576	332.61	9.6490	9.5978
6600	6598	.9994	2.0903	5.5481	8.0823	332.49	9.6436	9.5916
6700	6698	.9994	2.0839	5.5291	8.1071	332.37	9.6381	9.5854
6800	6798	.9993	2.0776	5.5102	8.1320	332.25	9.6326	9.5791
6900	6898	.9993	2.0712	5.4914	8.1570	332.13	9.6272	9.5729

Table V
Geopotential Altitude, English Altitudes

Altitude		Gravity ratio	Number density	Collision frequency	Mean free path	Sound speed	Viscosity ratio	Thermal conductivity ratio
H (ft)	Z (ft)	g/g_0	n (m^{-3})	ν (s^{-1})	L (m)	C_s (m/s)	μ/μ_0	κ/κ_0
7000	7002	.9993	2.0647 +25	5.4721 + 9	8.1827 − 8	332.00	9.6216 − 1	9.5665 − 1
7100	7102	.9993	2.0584	5.4533	8.2079	331.88	9.6161	9.5603
7200	7202	.9993	2.0520	5.4346	8.2332	331.76	9.6106	9.5541
7300	7303	.9993	2.0457	5.4159	8.2586	331.64	9.6052	9.5478
7400	7403	.9993	2.0394	5.3973	8.2840	331.52	9.5997	9.5416
7500	7503	.9993	2.0331	5.3788	8.3096	331.40	9.5942	9.5353
7600	7603	.9993	2.0269	5.3602	8.3353	331.28	9.5887	9.5291
7700	7703	.9993	2.0206	5.3418	8.3611	331.16	9.5832	9.5229
7800	7803	.9993	2.0144	5.3234	8.3870	331.04	9.5778	9.5166
7900	7903	.9992	2.0082	5.3050	8.4130	330.92	9.5723	9.5104
8000	8003	.9992	2.0020 +25	5.2867 + 9	8.4391 − 8	330.80	9.5668 − 1	9.5041 − 1
8100	8103	.9992	1.9958	5.2684	8.4652	330.68	9.5613	9.4979
8200	8203	.9992	1.9896	5.2502	8.4915	330.56	9.5558	9.4916
8300	8303	.9992	1.9834	5.2320	8.5179	330.44	9.5503	9.4854
8400	8403	.9992	1.9773	5.2139	8.5444	330.32	9.5448	9.4791
8500	8503	.9992	1.9711	5.1958	8.5710	330.20	9.5393	9.4729
8600	8604	.9992	1.9650	5.1778	8.5977	330.08	9.5338	9.4666
8700	8704	.9992	1.9589	5.1598	8.6244	329.96	9.5283	9.4604
8800	8804	.9992	1.9528	5.1419	8.6513	329.84	9.5228	9.4541
8900	8904	.9991	1.9468	5.1240	8.6783	329.72	9.5173	9.4479
9000	9004	.9991	1.9407 +25	5.1062 + 9	8.7054 − 8	329.60	9.5118 − 1	9.4416 − 1
9100	9104	.9991	1.9347	5.0884	8.7326	329.48	9.5063	9.4354
9200	9204	.9991	1.9286	5.0707	8.7600	329.36	9.5008	9.4291
9300	9304	.9991	1.9226	5.0530	8.7874	329.23	9.4953	9.4228
9400	9404	.9991	1.9166	5.0354	8.8149	329.11	9.4898	9.4166
9500	9504	.9991	1.9106	5.0178	8.8425	328.99	9.4843	9.4103
9600	9604	.9991	1.9046	5.0003	8.8703	328.87	9.4787	9.4040
9700	9705	.9991	1.8987	4.9828	8.8981	328.75	9.4732	9.3978
9800	9805	.9991	1.8927	4.9654	8.9261	328.63	9.4677	9.3915
9900	9905	.9991	1.8868	4.9480	8.9541	328.51	9.4622	9.3852
10000	10005	.9990	1.8809 +25	4.9307 + 9	8.9823 − 8	328.39	9.4566 − 1	9.3790 − 1
10100	10105	.9990	1.8750	4.9134	9.0106	328.27	9.4511	9.3727
10200	10205	.9990	1.8691	4.8961	9.0390	328.14	9.4456	9.3664
10300	10305	.9990	1.8632	4.8789	9.0675	328.02	9.4401	9.3602
10400	10405	.9990	1.8574	4.8618	9.0961	327.90	9.4345	9.3539
10500	10505	.9990	1.8515	4.8447	9.1248	327.78	9.4290	9.3476
10600	10605	.9990	1.8457	4.8276	9.1536	327.66	9.4235	9.3413
10700	10705	.9990	1.8399	4.8106	9.1826	327.54	9.4179	9.3350
10800	10806	.9990	1.8341	4.7937	9.2116	327.42	9.4124	9.3288
10900	10906	.9990	1.8283	4.7768	9.2408	327.29	9.4068	9.3225
11000	11006	.9989	1.8225 +25	4.7599 + 9	9.2701 − 8	327.17	9.4013 − 1	9.3162 − 1
11100	11106	.9989	1.8167	4.7431	9.2995	327.05	9.3957	9.3099
11200	11206	.9989	1.8110	4.7263	9.3290	326.93	9.3902	9.3036
11300	11306	.9989	1.8052	4.7096	9.3586	326.81	9.3846	9.2973
11400	11406	.9989	1.7995	4.6929	9.3884	326.69	9.3791	9.2911
11500	11506	.9989	1.7938	4.6763	9.4183	326.56	9.3735	9.2848
11600	11606	.9989	1.7881	4.6597	9.4482	326.44	9.3680	9.2785
11700	11707	.9989	1.7824	4.6432	9.4783	326.32	9.3624	9.2722
11800	11807	.9989	1.7768	4.6267	9.5086	326.20	9.3569	9.2659
11900	11907	.9989	1.7711	4.6103	9.5389	326.08	9.3513	9.2596
12000	12007	.9988	1.7655 +25	4.5939 + 9	9.5694 − 8	325.95	9.3457 − 1	9.2533 − 1
12100	12107	.9988	1.7599	4.5775	9.5999	325.83	9.3402	9.2470
12200	12207	.9988	1.7543	4.5612	9.6306	325.71	9.3346	9.2407
12300	12307	.9988	1.7487	4.5450	9.6615	325.59	9.3290	9.2344
12400	12407	.9988	1.7431	4.5287	9.6924	325.46	9.3235	9.2281
12500	12507	.9988	1.7375	4.5126	9.7235	325.34	9.3179	9.2218
12600	12608	.9988	1.7320	4.4965	9.7547	325.22	9.3123	9.2155
12700	12708	.9988	1.7264	4.4804	9.7860	325.10	9.3067	9.2092
12800	12808	.9988	1.7209	4.4644	9.8174	324.98	9.3012	9.2029
12900	12908	.9988	1.7154	4.4484	9.8490	324.85	9.2956	9.1966
13000	13008	.9988	1.7099 +25	4.4324 + 9	9.8807 − 8	324.73	9.2900 − 1	9.1903 − 1
13100	13108	.9987	1.7044	4.4165	9.9125	324.61	9.2844	9.1840
13200	13208	.9987	1.6989	4.4007	9.9444	324.48	9.2788	9.1777
13300	13308	.9987	1.6934	4.3849	9.9765	324.36	9.2732	9.1714
13400	13409	.9987	1.6880	4.3691	1.0009 − 7	324.24	9.2676	9.1651
13500	13509	.9987	1.6826	4.3534	1.0041	324.12	9.2620	9.1588
13600	13609	.9987	1.6771	4.3377	1.0073	323.99	9.2564	9.1524
13700	13709	.9987	1.6717	4.3221	1.0106	323.87	9.2508	9.1461
13800	13809	.9987	1.6663	4.3065	1.0139	323.75	9.2452	9.1398
13900	13909	.9987	1.6610	4.2910	1.0172	323.62	9.2396	9.1335
14000	14009	.9987	1.6556 +25	4.2755 + 9	1.0205 − 7	323.50	9.2340 − 1	9.1272 − 1
14100	14110	.9986	1.6502	4.2601	1.0238	323.38	9.2284	9.1209
14200	14210	.9986	1.6449	4.2447	1.0271	323.26	9.2228	9.1145
14300	14310	.9986	1.6396	4.2293	1.0304	323.13	9.2172	9.1082
14400	14410	.9986	1.6343	4.2140	1.0338	323.01	9.2116	9.1019
14500	14510	.9986	1.6290	4.1987	1.0371	322.89	9.2060	9.0956
14600	14610	.9986	1.6237	4.1835	1.0405	322.76	9.2004	9.0892
14700	14710	.9986	1.6184	4.1683	1.0439	322.64	9.1948	9.0829
14800	14811	.9986	1.6131	4.1532	1.0473	322.52	9.1891	9.0766
14900	14911	.9986	1.6079	4.1381	1.0507	322.39	9.1835	9.0703

Table V
Geometric Altitude, English Altitudes

Altitude		Gravity ratio	Number density	Collision frequency	Mean free path	Sound speed	Viscosity ratio	Thermal conductivity ratio
Z (ft)	H (ft)	g/g_0	n (m^{-3})	ν (s^{-1})	L (m)	C_s (m/s)	μ/μ_0	κ/κ_0
7000	6998	.9993	2.0648 +25	5.4726 + 9	8.1821 - 8	332.01	9.6217 - 1	9.5667 - 1
7100	7098	.9993	2.0585	5.4538	8.2072	331.89	9.6162	9.5604
7200	7198	.9993	2.0522	5.4351	8.2325	331.77	9.6108	9.5542
7300	7297	.9993	2.0459	5.4164	8.2579	331.65	9.6053	9.5480
7400	7397	.9993	2.0396	5.3978	8.2834	331.53	9.5998	9.5418
7500	7497	.9993	2.0333	5.3793	8.3089	331.41	9.5944	9.5355
7600	7597	.9993	2.0271	5.3608	8.3346	331.29	9.5889	9.5293
7700	7697	.9993	2.0208	5.3423	8.3604	331.17	9.5834	9.5230
7800	7797	.9993	2.0146	5.3239	8.3862	331.05	9.5779	9.5168
7900	7897	.9992	2.0084	5.3055	8.4122	330.93	9.5724	9.5106
8000	7997	.9992	2.0022 +25	5.2872 + 9	8.4382 - 8	330.81	9.5670 - 1	9.5043 - 1
8100	8097	.9992	1.9960	5.2690	8.4644	330.69	9.5615	9.4981
8200	8197	.9992	1.9898	5.2508	8.4907	330.57	9.5560	9.4918
8300	8297	.9992	1.9836	5.2326	8.5170	330.45	9.5505	9.4856
8400	8397	.9992	1.9775	5.2145	8.5435	330.33	9.5450	9.4794
8500	8497	.9992	1.9714	5.1964	8.5700	330.20	9.5395	9.4731
8600	8596	.9992	1.9652	5.1784	8.5967	330.08	9.5340	9.4669
8700	8696	.9992	1.9591	5.1605	8.6235	329.96	9.5285	9.4606
8800	8796	.9992	1.9531	5.1426	8.6503	329.84	9.5230	9.4544
8900	8896	.9991	1.9470	5.1247	8.6773	329.72	9.5175	9.4481
9000	8996	.9991	1.9409 +25	5.1069 + 9	8.7044 - 8	329.60	9.5120 - 1	9.4419 - 1
9100	9096	.9991	1.9349	5.0891	8.7316	329.48	9.5065	9.4356
9200	9196	.9991	1.9289	5.0714	8.7588	329.36	9.5010	9.4293
9300	9296	.9991	1.9229	5.0538	8.7862	329.24	9.4955	9.4231
9400	9396	.9991	1.9169	5.0362	8.8137	329.12	9.4900	9.4168
9500	9496	.9991	1.9109	5.0186	8.8413	329.00	9.4845	9.4106
9600	9596	.9991	1.9049	5.0011	8.8690	328.88	9.4790	9.4043
9700	9695	.9991	1.8990	4.9836	8.8968	328.76	9.4735	9.3981
9800	9795	.9991	1.8930	4.9662	8.9248	328.63	9.4679	9.3918
9900	9895	.9991	1.8871	4.9488	8.9528	328.51	9.4624	9.3855
10000	9995	.9990	1.8812 +25	4.9315 + 9	8.9809 - 8	328.39	9.4569 - 1	9.3793 - 1
10100	10095	.9990	1.8753	4.9142	9.0092	328.27	9.4514	9.3730
10200	10195	.9990	1.8694	4.8970	9.0375	328.15	9.4459	9.3667
10300	10295	.9990	1.8635	4.8798	9.0660	328.03	9.4403	9.3605
10400	10395	.9990	1.8577	4.8627	9.0946	327.91	9.4348	9.3542
10500	10495	.9990	1.8518	4.8456	9.1233	327.79	9.4293	9.3479
10600	10595	.9990	1.8460	4.8286	9.1521	327.67	9.4237	9.3417
10700	10695	.9990	1.8402	4.8116	9.1810	327.54	9.4182	9.3354
10800	10794	.9990	1.8344	4.7946	9.2100	327.42	9.4127	9.3291
10900	10894	.9990	1.8286	4.7777	9.2391	327.30	9.4071	9.3228
11000	10994	.9989	1.8228 +25	4.7609 + 9	9.2684 - 8	327.18	9.4016 - 1	9.3166 - 1
11100	11094	.9989	1.8171	4.7441	9.2977	327.06	9.3961	9.3103
11200	11194	.9989	1.8113	4.7273	9.3272	326.94	9.3905	9.3040
11300	11294	.9989	1.8056	4.7106	9.3568	326.81	9.3850	9.2977
11400	11394	.9989	1.7999	4.6940	9.3865	326.69	9.3794	9.2915
11500	11494	.9989	1.7942	4.6774	9.4164	326.57	9.3739	9.2852
11600	11594	.9989	1.7885	4.6608	9.4463	326.45	9.3683	9.2789
11700	11693	.9989	1.7828	4.6443	9.4764	326.33	9.3628	9.2726
11800	11793	.9989	1.7772	4.6278	9.5065	326.21	9.3572	9.2663
11900	11893	.9989	1.7715	4.6114	9.5368	326.08	9.3517	9.2600
12000	11993	.9989	1.7659 +25	4.5950 + 9	9.5673 - 8	325.96	9.3461 - 1	9.2537 - 1
12100	12093	.9988	1.7603	4.5787	9.5978	325.84	9.3406	9.2475
12200	12193	.9988	1.7547	4.5624	9.6284	325.72	9.3350	9.2412
12300	12293	.9988	1.7491	4.5461	9.6592	325.60	9.3294	9.2349
12400	12393	.9988	1.7435	4.5299	9.6901	325.47	9.3239	9.2286
12500	12493	.9988	1.7379	4.5138	9.7211	325.35	9.3183	9.2223
12600	12592	.9988	1.7324	4.4977	9.7523	325.23	9.3127	9.2160
12700	12692	.9988	1.7268	4.4816	9.7836	325.11	9.3072	9.2097
12800	12792	.9988	1.7213	4.4656	9.8149	324.98	9.3016	9.2034
12900	12892	.9988	1.7158	4.4496	9.8465	324.86	9.2960	9.1971
13000	12992	.9988	1.7103 +25	4.4337 + 9	9.8781 - 8	324.74	9.2904 - 1	9.1908 - 1
13100	13092	.9987	1.7048	4.4178	9.9099	324.62	9.2849	9.1845
13200	13192	.9987	1.6994	4.4020	9.9417	324.49	9.2793	9.1782
13300	13292	.9987	1.6939	4.3862	9.9738	324.37	9.2737	9.1719
13400	13391	.9987	1.6885	4.3705	1.0006 - 7	324.25	9.2681	9.1656
13500	13491	.9987	1.6830	4.3548	1.0038	324.13	9.2625	9.1593
13600	13591	.9987	1.6776	4.3391	1.0071	324.00	9.2569	9.1530
13700	13691	.9987	1.6722	4.3235	1.0103	323.88	9.2513	9.1467
13800	13791	.9987	1.6668	4.3080	1.0136	323.76	9.2458	9.1404
13900	13891	.9987	1.6615	4.2924	1.0169	323.64	9.2402	9.1341
14000	13991	.9987	1.6561 +25	4.2770 + 9	1.0201 - 7	323.51	9.2346 - 1	9.1278 - 1
14100	14090	.9986	1.6508	4.2615	1.0235	323.39	9.2290	9.1215
14200	14190	.9986	1.6454	4.2461	1.0268	323.27	9.2234	9.1151
14300	14290	.9986	1.6401	4.2308	1.0301	323.14	9.2178	9.1088
14400	14390	.9986	1.6348	4.2155	1.0334	323.02	9.2122	9.1025
14500	14490	.9986	1.6295	4.2002	1.0368	322.90	9.2066	9.0962
14600	14590	.9986	1.6242	4.1850	1.0402	322.77	9.2010	9.0899
14700	14690	.9986	1.6189	4.1699	1.0436	322.65	9.1953	9.0836
14800	14790	.9986	1.6137	4.1547	1.0470	322.53	9.1897	9.0772
14900	14889	.9986	1.6084	4.1397	1.0504	322.41	9.1841	9.0709

Table V
Geopotential Altitude, English Altitudes

Altitude		Gravity ratio	Number density	Collision frequency	Mean free path	Sound speed	Viscosity ratio	Thermal conductivity ratio
H (ft)	Z (ft)	g/g_0	n (m^{-3})	ν (s^{-1})	L (m)	C_s (m/s)	μ/μ_0	κ/κ_0
15000	15011	.9986	1.6027 +25	4.1230 + 9	1.0542 − 7	322.27	9.1779 − 1	9.0639 − 1
15100	15111	.9986	1.5974	4.1080	1.0576	322.15	9.1723	9.0576
15200	15211	.9985	1.5922	4.0930	1.0611	322.02	9.1666	9.0513
15300	15311	.9985	1.5870	4.0781	1.0646	321.90	9.1610	9.0449
15400	15411	.9985	1.5818	4.0632	1.0680	321.77	9.1554	9.0386
15500	15512	.9985	1.5767	4.0484	1.0715	321.65	9.1498	9.0322
15600	15612	.9985	1.5715	4.0336	1.0751	321.53	9.1441	9.0259
15700	15712	.9985	1.5664	4.0188	1.0786	321.40	9.1385	9.0196
15800	15812	.9985	1.5612	4.0041	1.0821	321.28	9.1328	9.0132
15900	15912	.9985	1.5561	3.9895	1.0857	321.16	9.1272	9.0069
16000	16012	.9985	1.5510 +25	3.9748 + 9	1.0893 − 7	321.03	9.1216 − 1	9.0005 − 1
16100	16112	.9985	1.5459	3.9602	1.0929	320.91	9.1159	8.9942
16200	16213	.9984	1.5408	3.9457	1.0965	320.78	9.1103	8.9879
16300	16313	.9984	1.5358	3.9312	1.1001	320.66	9.1046	8.9815
16400	16413	.9984	1.5307	3.9168	1.1037	320.53	9.0990	8.9752
16500	16513	.9984	1.5257	3.9023	1.1074	320.41	9.0933	8.9688
16600	16613	.9984	1.5206	3.8880	1.1110	320.29	9.0877	8.9625
16700	16713	.9984	1.5156	3.8736	1.1147	320.16	9.0820	8.9561
16800	16814	.9984	1.5106	3.8593	1.1184	320.04	9.0763	8.9498
16900	16914	.9984	1.5056	3.8451	1.1221	319.91	9.0707	8.9434
17000	17014	.9984	1.5007 +25	3.8309 + 9	1.1258 − 7	319.79	9.0650 − 1	8.9370 − 1
17100	17114	.9984	1.4957	3.8167	1.1296	319.66	9.0594	8.9307
17200	17214	.9984	1.4907	3.8026	1.1333	319.54	9.0537	8.9243
17300	17314	.9983	1.4858	3.7885	1.1371	319.41	9.0480	8.9180
17400	17415	.9983	1.4809	3.7745	1.1409	319.29	9.0423	8.9116
17500	17515	.9983	1.4759	3.7605	1.1447	319.17	9.0367	8.9052
17600	17615	.9983	1.4710	3.7465	1.1485	319.04	9.0310	8.8989
17700	17715	.9983	1.4662	3.7326	1.1523	318.92	9.0253	8.8925
17800	17815	.9983	1.4613	3.7187	1.1562	318.79	9.0196	8.8862
17900	17915	.9983	1.4564	3.7049	1.1600	318.67	9.0140	8.8798
18000	18016	.9983	1.4516 +25	3.6911 + 9	1.1639 − 7	318.54	9.0083 − 1	8.8734 − 1
18100	18116	.9983	1.4467	3.6774	1.1678	318.42	9.0026	8.8671
18200	18216	.9983	1.4419	3.6636	1.1717	318.29	8.9969	8.8607
18300	18316	.9982	1.4371	3.6500	1.1756	318.17	8.9912	8.8543
18400	18416	.9982	1.4323	3.6363	1.1796	318.04	8.9855	8.8479
18500	18516	.9982	1.4275	3.6227	1.1835	317.92	8.9798	8.8416
18600	18617	.9982	1.4227	3.6092	1.1875	317.79	8.9741	8.8352
18700	18717	.9982	1.4179	3.5957	1.1915	317.67	8.9684	8.8288
18800	18817	.9982	1.4132	3.5822	1.1955	317.54	8.9627	8.8224
18900	18917	.9982	1.4084	3.5688	1.1995	317.41	8.9570	8.8161
19000	19017	.9982	1.4037 +25	3.5554 + 9	1.2036 − 7	317.29	8.9513 − 1	8.8097 − 1
19100	19118	.9982	1.3990	3.5420	1.2076	317.16	8.9456	8.8033
19200	19218	.9982	1.3943	3.5287	1.2117	317.04	8.9399	8.7969
19300	19318	.9982	1.3896	3.5154	1.2158	316.91	8.9342	8.7905
19400	19418	.9981	1.3849	3.5022	1.2199	316.79	8.9285	8.7841
19500	19518	.9981	1.3802	3.4890	1.2240	316.66	8.9228	8.7778
19600	19618	.9981	1.3756	3.4759	1.2282	316.54	8.9171	8.7714
19700	19719	.9981	1.3709	3.4627	1.2324	316.41	8.9113	8.7650
19800	19819	.9981	1.3663	3.4497	1.2365	316.28	8.9056	8.7586
19900	19919	.9981	1.3617	3.4366	1.2407	316.16	8.8999	8.7522
20000	20019	.9981	1.3571 +25	3.4236 + 9	1.2449 − 7	316.03	8.8942 − 1	8.7458 − 1
20100	20119	.9981	1.3525	3.4107	1.2492	315.91	8.8884	8.7394
20200	20220	.9981	1.3479	3.3977	1.2534	315.78	8.8827	8.7330
20300	20320	.9981	1.3433	3.3849	1.2577	315.65	8.8770	8.7266
20400	20420	.9980	1.3387	3.3720	1.2620	315.53	8.8712	8.7202
20500	20520	.9980	1.3342	3.3592	1.2663	315.40	8.8655	8.7138
20600	20620	.9980	1.3296	3.3464	1.2706	315.28	8.8598	8.7074
20700	20721	.9980	1.3251	3.3337	1.2750	315.15	8.8540	8.7010
20800	20821	.9980	1.3206	3.3210	1.2793	315.02	8.8483	8.6946
20900	20921	.9980	1.3161	3.3084	1.2837	314.90	8.8425	8.6882
21000	21021	.9980	1.3116 +25	3.2958 + 9	1.2881 − 7	314.77	8.8368 − 1	8.6818 − 1
21100	21121	.9980	1.3071	3.2832	1.2925	314.64	8.8311	8.6754
21200	21222	.9980	1.3027	3.2706	1.2969	314.52	8.8253	8.6690
21300	21322	.9980	1.2982	3.2581	1.3014	314.39	8.8196	8.6626
21400	21422	.9979	1.2938	3.2457	1.3059	314.26	8.8138	8.6562
21500	21522	.9979	1.2893	3.2332	1.3103	314.14	8.8080	8.6498
21600	21622	.9979	1.2849	3.2209	1.3149	314.01	8.8023	8.6434
21700	21723	.9979	1.2805	3.2085	1.3194	313.88	8.7965	8.6370
21800	21823	.9979	1.2761	3.1962	1.3239	313.76	8.7908	8.6305
21900	21923	.9979	1.2717	3.1839	1.3285	313.63	8.7850	8.6241
22000	22023	.9979	1.2673 +25	3.1717 + 9	1.3331 − 7	313.50	8.7792 − 1	8.6177 − 1
22100	22123	.9979	1.2630	3.1595	1.3377	313.38	8.7735	8.6113
22200	22224	.9979	1.2586	3.1473	1.3423	313.25	8.7677	8.6049
22300	22324	.9979	1.2543	3.1352	1.3470	313.12	8.7619	8.5985
22400	22424	.9979	1.2500	3.1231	1.3516	312.99	8.7561	8.5920
22500	22524	.9978	1.2456	3.1110	1.3563	312.87	8.7504	8.5856
22600	22625	.9978	1.2413	3.0990	1.3610	312.74	8.7446	8.5792
22700	22725	.9978	1.2370	3.0871	1.3657	312.61	8.7388	8.5728
22800	22825	.9978	1.2327	3.0751	1.3705	312.49	8.7330	8.5663
22900	22925	.9978	1.2285	3.0632	1.3753	312.36	8.7272	8.5599

Table V
Geometric Altitude, English Altitudes

Altitude		Gravity ratio	Number density	Collision frequency	Mean free path	Sound speed	Viscosity ratio	Thermal conductivity ratio
Z (ft)	H (ft)	g/g_0	n (m^{-3})	ν (s^{-1})	L (m)	C_s (m/s)	μ/μ_0	κ/κ_0
15000	14989	.9986	1.6032 +25	4.1246 + 9	1.0538 − 7	322.28	9.1785 − 1	9.0646 − 1
15100	15089	.9986	1.5980	4.1096	1.0572	322.16	9.1729	9.0583
15200	15189	.9985	1.5928	4.0947	1.0607	322.04	9.1673	9.0520
15300	15289	.9985	1.5876	4.0798	1.0642	321.91	9.1617	9.0456
15400	15389	.9985	1.5824	4.0649	1.0676	321.79	9.1560	9.0393
15500	15488	.9985	1.5773	4.0501	1.0711	321.66	9.1504	9.0330
15600	15588	.9985	1.5721	4.0353	1.0746	321.54	9.1448	9.0266
15700	15688	.9985	1.5670	4.0206	1.0782	321.42	9.1391	9.0203
15800	15788	.9985	1.5618	4.0059	1.0817	321.29	9.1335	9.0140
15900	15888	.9985	1.5567	3.9912	1.0853	321.17	9.1279	9.0077
16000	15988	.9985	1.5516 +25	3.9766 + 9	1.0888 − 7	321.05	9.1223 − 1	9.0013 − 1
16100	16088	.9985	1.5466	3.9621	1.0924	320.92	9.1166	8.9950
16200	16187	.9984	1.5415	3.9475	1.0960	320.80	9.1110	8.9886
16300	16287	.9984	1.5364	3.9331	1.0996	320.67	9.1053	8.9823
16400	16387	.9984	1.5314	3.9186	1.1032	320.55	9.0997	8.9760
16500	16487	.9984	1.5263	3.9042	1.1069	320.43	9.0941	8.9696
16600	16587	.9984	1.5213	3.8899	1.1105	320.30	9.0884	8.9633
16700	16687	.9984	1.5163	3.8755	1.1142	320.18	9.0828	8.9570
16800	16786	.9984	1.5113	3.8613	1.1179	320.05	9.0771	8.9506
16900	16886	.9984	1.5063	3.8470	1.1216	319.93	9.0715	8.9443
17000	16986	.9984	1.5013 +25	3.8329 + 9	1.1253 − 7	319.81	9.0658 − 1	8.9379 − 1
17100	17086	.9984	1.4964	3.8187	1.1290	319.68	9.0601	8.9316
17200	17186	.9984	1.4914	3.8046	1.1328	319.56	9.0545	8.9252
17300	17286	.9983	1.4865	3.7905	1.1365	319.43	9.0488	8.9189
17400	17385	.9983	1.4816	3.7765	1.1403	319.31	9.0432	8.9125
17500	17485	.9983	1.4767	3.7625	1.1441	319.18	9.0375	8.9062
17600	17585	.9983	1.4718	3.7486	1.1479	319.06	9.0318	8.8998
17700	17685	.9983	1.4669	3.7347	1.1517	318.93	9.0262	8.8935
17800	17785	.9983	1.4620	3.7208	1.1556	318.81	9.0205	8.8871
17900	17885	.9983	1.4572	3.7070	1.1594	318.69	9.0148	8.8808
18000	17984	.9983	1.4523 +25	3.6932 + 9	1.1633 − 7	318.56	9.0092 − 1	8.8744 − 1
18100	18084	.9983	1.4475	3.6795	1.1672	318.44	9.0035	8.8681
18200	18184	.9983	1.4427	3.6658	1.1711	318.31	8.9978	8.8617
18300	18284	.9982	1.4378	3.6522	1.1750	318.19	8.9921	8.8553
18400	18384	.9982	1.4330	3.6385	1.1789	318.06	8.9864	8.8490
18500	18484	.9982	1.4283	3.6250	1.1829	317.94	8.9808	8.8426
18600	18583	.9982	1.4235	3.6114	1.1869	317.81	8.9751	8.8362
18700	18683	.9982	1.4187	3.5979	1.1908	317.69	8.9694	8.8299
18800	18783	.9982	1.4140	3.5845	1.1948	317.56	8.9637	8.8235
18900	18883	.9982	1.4092	3.5711	1.1988	317.44	8.9580	8.8171
19000	18983	.9982	1.4045 +25	3.5577 + 9	1.2029 − 7	317.31	8.9523 − 1	8.8108 − 1
19100	19083	.9982	1.3998	3.5444	1.2069	317.19	8.9466	8.8044
19200	19182	.9982	1.3951	3.5311	1.2110	317.06	8.9409	8.7980
19300	19282	.9982	1.3904	3.5178	1.2151	316.93	8.9352	8.7917
19400	19382	.9981	1.3857	3.5046	1.2192	316.81	8.9295	8.7853
19500	19482	.9981	1.3811	3.4914	1.2233	316.68	8.9238	8.7789
19600	19582	.9981	1.3764	3.4783	1.2274	316.56	8.9181	8.7725
19700	19681	.9981	1.3718	3.4652	1.2316	316.43	8.9124	8.7662
19800	19781	.9981	1.3672	3.4521	1.2357	316.31	8.9067	8.7598
19900	19881	.9981	1.3625	3.4391	1.2399	316.18	8.9010	8.7534
20000	19981	.9981	1.3579 +25	3.4261 + 9	1.2441 − 7	316.06	8.8953 − 1	8.7470 − 1
20100	20081	.9981	1.3533	3.4132	1.2484	315.93	8.8895	8.7407
20200	20180	.9981	1.3488	3.4003	1.2526	315.80	8.8838	8.7343
20300	20280	.9981	1.3442	3.3874	1.2569	315.68	8.8781	8.7279
20400	20380	.9980	1.3396	3.3746	1.2611	315.55	8.8724	8.7215
20500	20480	.9980	1.3351	3.3618	1.2654	315.43	8.8667	8.7151
20600	20580	.9980	1.3306	3.3490	1.2697	315.30	8.8609	8.7087
20700	20679	.9980	1.3260	3.3363	1.2741	315.17	8.8552	8.7023
20800	20779	.9980	1.3215	3.3236	1.2784	315.05	8.8495	8.6960
20900	20879	.9980	1.3170	3.3110	1.2828	314.92	8.8437	8.6896
21000	20979	.9980	1.3126 +25	3.2984 + 9	1.2872 − 7	314.80	8.8380 − 1	8.6832 − 1
21100	21079	.9980	1.3081	3.2859	1.2916	314.67	8.8323	8.6768
21200	21178	.9980	1.3036	3.2733	1.2960	314.54	8.8265	8.6704
21300	21278	.9980	1.2992	3.2608	1.3004	314.42	8.8208	8.6640
21400	21378	.9980	1.2947	3.2484	1.3049	314.29	8.8151	8.6576
21500	21478	.9979	1.2903	3.2360	1.3094	314.16	8.8093	8.6512
21600	21578	.9979	1.2859	3.2236	1.3138	314.04	8.8036	8.6448
21700	21677	.9979	1.2815	3.2113	1.3184	313.91	8.7978	8.6384
21800	21777	.9979	1.2771	3.1990	1.3229	313.79	8.7921	8.6320
21900	21877	.9979	1.2727	3.1867	1.3274	313.66	8.7863	8.6256
22000	21977	.9979	1.2683 +25	3.1745 + 9	1.3320 − 7	313.53	8.7806 − 1	8.6192 − 1
22100	22077	.9979	1.2640	3.1623	1.3366	313.41	8.7748	8.6128
22200	22176	.9979	1.2596	3.1502	1.3412	313.28	8.7690	8.6064
22300	22276	.9979	1.2553	3.1381	1.3459	313.15	8.7633	8.6000
22400	22376	.9979	1.2510	3.1260	1.3505	313.02	8.7575	8.5936
22500	22476	.9978	1.2467	3.1140	1.3552	312.90	8.7518	8.5872
22600	22576	.9978	1.2424	3.1020	1.3599	312.77	8.7460	8.5808
22700	22675	.9978	1.2381	3.0900	1.3646	312.64	8.7402	8.5743
22800	22775	.9978	1.2338	3.0781	1.3693	312.52	8.7345	8.5679
22900	22875	.9978	1.2295	3.0662	1.3741	312.39	8.7287	8.5615

Table V
Geopotential Altitude, English Altitudes

Altitude		Gravity ratio	Number density	Collision frequency	Mean free path	Sound speed	Viscosity ratio	Thermal conductivity ratio
H (ft)	Z (ft)	g/g_0	n (m^{-3})	ν (s^{-1})	L (m)	C_s (m/s)	μ/μ_0	κ/κ_0
23000	23025	.9978	1.2242 +25	3.0513 + 9	1.3800 − 7	312.23	8.7214 − 1	8.5535 − 1
23100	23126	.9978	1.2200	3.0395	1.3848	312.10	8.7157	8.5470
23200	23226	.9978	1.2157	3.0277	1.3897	311.98	8.7099	8.5406
23300	23326	.9978	1.2115	3.0159	1.3945	311.85	8.7041	8.5342
23400	23426	.9978	1.2073	3.0042	1.3994	311.72	8.6983	8.5277
23500	23527	.9977	1.2031	2.9925	1.4043	311.59	8.6925	8.5213
23600	23627	.9977	1.1989	2.9809	1.4092	311.46	8.6867	8.5149
23700	23727	.9977	1.1947	2.9693	1.4141	311.34	8.6809	8.5084
23800	23827	.9977	1.1905	2.9577	1.4191	311.21	8.6751	8.5020
23900	23927	.9977	1.1864	2.9461	1.4241	311.08	8.6693	8.4956
24000	24028	.9977	1.1822 +25	2.9346 + 9	1.4291 − 7	310.95	8.6634 − 1	8.4891 − 1
24100	24128	.9977	1.1781	2.9231	1.4341	310.82	8.6576	8.4827
24200	24228	.9977	1.1740	2.9117	1.4391	310.70	8.6518	8.4762
24300	24328	.9977	1.1698	2.9003	1.4442	310.57	8.6460	8.4698
24400	24429	.9977	1.1657	2.8889	1.4493	310.44	8.6402	8.4633
24500	24529	.9977	1.1616	2.8776	1.4544	310.31	8.6344	8.4569
24600	24629	.9976	1.1576	2.8663	1.4595	310.18	8.6285	8.4504
24700	24729	.9976	1.1535	2.8550	1.4646	310.06	8.6227	8.4440
24800	24830	.9976	1.1494	2.8438	1.4698	309.93	8.6169	8.4375
24900	24930	.9976	1.1454	2.8326	1.4750	309.80	8.6111	8.4311
25000	25030	.9976	1.1413 +25	2.8215 + 9	1.4802 − 7	309.67	8.6052 − 1	8.4246 − 1
25100	25130	.9976	1.1373	2.8103	1.4855	309.54	8.5994	8.4182
25200	25230	.9976	1.1333	2.7992	1.4907	309.41	8.5936	8.4117
25300	25331	.9976	1.1293	2.7882	1.4960	309.28	8.5877	8.4053
25400	25431	.9976	1.1253	2.7772	1.5013	309.15	8.5819	8.3988
25500	25531	.9976	1.1213	2.7662	1.5067	309.03	8.5760	8.3923
25600	25631	.9975	1.1173	2.7552	1.5120	308.90	8.5702	8.3859
25700	25732	.9975	1.1134	2.7443	1.5174	308.77	8.5643	8.3794
25800	25832	.9975	1.1094	2.7334	1.5228	308.64	8.5585	8.3730
25900	25932	.9975	1.1055	2.7226	1.5283	308.51	8.5526	8.3665
26000	26032	.9975	1.1016 +25	2.7118 + 9	1.5337 − 7	308.38	8.5468 − 1	8.3600 − 1
26100	26133	.9975	1.0976	2.7010	1.5392	308.25	8.5409	8.3536
26200	26233	.9975	1.0937	2.6902	1.5447	308.12	8.5351	8.3471
26300	26333	.9975	1.0898	2.6795	1.5502	307.99	8.5292	8.3406
26400	26433	.9975	1.0859	2.6689	1.5558	307.86	8.5234	8.3342
26500	26534	.9975	1.0821	2.6582	1.5613	307.74	8.5175	8.3277
26600	26634	.9975	1.0782	2.6476	1.5669	307.61	8.5116	8.3212
26700	26734	.9974	1.0743	2.6370	1.5726	307.48	8.5058	8.3147
26800	26834	.9974	1.0705	2.6265	1.5782	307.35	8.4999	8.3083
26900	26935	.9974	1.0667	2.6160	1.5839	307.22	8.4940	8.3018
27000	27035	.9974	1.0628 +25	2.6055 + 9	1.5896 − 7	307.09	8.4881 − 1	8.2953 − 1
27100	27135	.9974	1.0590	2.5950	1.5953	306.96	8.4823	8.2888
27200	27236	.9974	1.0552	2.5846	1.6010	306.83	8.4764	8.2823
27300	27336	.9974	1.0514	2.5742	1.6068	306.70	8.4705	8.2759
27400	27436	.9974	1.0476	2.5639	1.6126	306.57	8.4646	8.2694
27500	27536	.9974	1.0439	2.5536	1.6185	306.44	8.4587	8.2629
27600	27637	.9974	1.0401	2.5433	1.6243	306.31	8.4528	8.2564
27700	27737	.9973	1.0364	2.5331	1.6302	306.18	8.4470	8.2499
27800	27837	.9973	1.0326	2.5228	1.6361	306.05	8.4411	8.2434
27900	27937	.9973	1.0289	2.5127	1.6420	305.92	8.4352	8.2369
28000	28038	.9973	1.0252 +25	2.5025 + 9	1.6480 − 7	305.79	8.4293 − 1	8.2305 − 1
28100	28138	.9973	1.0215	2.4924	1.6540	305.66	8.4234	8.2240
28200	28238	.9973	1.0178	2.4823	1.6600	305.53	8.4175	8.2175
28300	28338	.9973	1.0141	2.4722	1.6660	305.40	8.4116	8.2110
28400	28439	.9973	1.0104	2.4622	1.6721	305.27	8.4057	8.2045
28500	28539	.9973	1.0067	2.4522	1.6782	305.14	8.3998	8.1980
28600	28639	.9973	1.0031	2.4423	1.6843	305.01	8.3938	8.1915
28700	28740	.9972	9.9942 +24	2.4324	1.6904	304.88	8.3879	8.1850
28800	28840	.9972	9.9578	2.4225	1.6966	304.75	8.3820	8.1785
28900	28940	.9972	9.9215	2.4126	1.7028	304.61	8.3761	8.1720
29000	29040	.9972	9.8853 +24	2.4028 + 9	1.7091 − 7	304.48	8.3702 − 1	8.1655 − 1
29100	29141	.9972	9.8493	2.3930	1.7153	304.35	8.3643	8.1590
29200	29241	.9972	9.8133	2.3832	1.7216	304.22	8.3583	8.1525
29300	29341	.9972	9.7774	2.3735	1.7279	304.09	8.3524	8.1460
29400	29442	.9972	9.7416	2.3638	1.7343	303.96	8.3465	8.1395
29500	29542	.9972	9.7059	2.3541	1.7407	303.83	8.3405	8.1330
29600	29642	.9972	9.6704	2.3445	1.7471	303.70	8.3346	8.1264
29700	29742	.9972	9.6349	2.3348	1.7535	303.57	8.3287	8.1199
29800	29843	.9971	9.5995	2.3253	1.7599	303.44	8.3227	8.1134
29900	29943	.9971	9.5642	2.3157	1.7664	303.30	8.3168	8.1069
30000	30043	.9971	9.5291 +24	2.3062 + 9	1.7730 − 7	303.17	8.3109 − 1	8.1004 − 1
30100	30144	.9971	9.4940	2.2967	1.7795	303.04	8.3049	8.0939
30200	30244	.9971	9.4590	2.2873	1.7861	302.91	8.2990	8.0874
30300	30344	.9971	9.4241	2.2778	1.7927	302.78	8.2930	8.0808
30400	30444	.9971	9.3893	2.2684	1.7993	302.65	8.2871	8.0743
30500	30545	.9971	9.3546	2.2591	1.8060	302.52	8.2811	8.0678
30600	30645	.9971	9.3201	2.2498	1.8127	302.38	8.2752	8.0613
30700	30745	.9971	9.2856	2.2405	1.8195	302.25	8.2692	8.0548
30800	30846	.9970	9.2512	2.2312	1.8262	302.12	8.2632	8.0482
30900	30946	.9970	9.2169	2.2219	1.8330	301.99	8.2573	8.0417

Table V
Geometric Altitude, English Altitudes

Altitude		Gravity ratio	Number density	Collision frequency	Mean free path	Sound speed	Viscosity ratio	Thermal conductivity ratio
Z (ft)	H (ft)	g/g_0	n (m^{-3})	ν (s^{-1})	L (m)	C_s (m/s)	μ/μ_0	κ/κ_0
23000	22975	.9978	1.2253 +25	3.0543 + 9	1.3788 − 7	312.26	8.7229 − 1	8.5551 − 1
23100	23074	.9978	1.2211	3.0425	1.3836	312.13	8.7171	8.5487
23200	23174	.9978	1.2168	3.0307	1.3884	312.01	8.7114	8.5423
23300	23274	.9978	1.2126	3.0190	1.3933	311.88	8.7056	8.5358
23400	23374	.9978	1.2084	3.0073	1.3981	311.75	8.6998	8.5294
23500	23474	.9978	1.2042	2.9956	1.4030	311.63	8.6940	8.5230
23600	23573	.9977	1.2000	2.9840	1.4079	311.50	8.6882	8.5166
23700	23673	.9977	1.1958	2.9724	1.4128	311.37	8.6824	8.5102
23800	23773	.9977	1.1917	2.9608	1.4177	311.24	8.6766	8.5037
23900	23873	.9977	1.1875	2.9493	1.4227	311.12	8.6708	8.4973
24000	23972	.9977	1.1834 +25	2.9378 + 9	1.4277 − 7	310.99	8.6650 − 1	8.4909 − 1
24100	24072	.9977	1.1792	2.9263	1.4327	310.86	8.6592	8.4845
24200	24172	.9977	1.1751	2.9149	1.4377	310.73	8.6534	8.4780
24300	24272	.9977	1.1710	2.9035	1.4427	310.60	8.6476	8.4716
24400	24371	.9977	1.1669	2.8922	1.4478	310.48	8.6418	8.4652
24500	24471	.9977	1.1628	2.8808	1.4529	310.35	8.6360	8.4587
24600	24571	.9976	1.1587	2.8696	1.4580	310.22	8.6302	8.4523
24700	24671	.9976	1.1547	2.8583	1.4631	310.09	8.6244	8.4459
24800	24771	.9976	1.1506	2.8471	1.4683	309.96	8.6186	8.4394
24900	24870	.9976	1.1466	2.8359	1.4735	309.84	8.6128	8.4330
25000	24970	.9976	1.1426 +25	2.8248 + 9	1.4787 − 7	309.71	8.6070 − 1	8.4266 − 1
25100	25070	.9976	1.1385	2.8137	1.4839	309.58	8.6012	8.4201
25200	25170	.9976	1.1345	2.8026	1.4891	309.45	8.5953	8.4137
25300	25269	.9976	1.1305	2.7916	1.4944	309.32	8.5895	8.4072
25400	25369	.9976	1.1265	2.7806	1.4997	309.19	8.5837	8.4008
25500	25469	.9976	1.1226	2.7696	1.5050	309.07	8.5779	8.3944
25600	25569	.9975	1.1186	2.7587	1.5104	308.94	8.5720	8.3879
25700	25668	.9975	1.1146	2.7478	1.5157	308.81	8.5662	8.3815
25800	25768	.9975	1.1107	2.7369	1.5211	308.68	8.5604	8.3750
25900	25868	.9975	1.1068	2.7261	1.5265	308.55	8.5545	8.3686
26000	25968	.9975	1.1028 +25	2.7153 + 9	1.5319 − 7	308.42	8.5487 − 1	8.3621 − 1
26100	26067	.9975	1.0989	2.7045	1.5374	308.29	8.5428	8.3557
26200	26167	.9975	1.0950	2.6938	1.5429	308.17	8.5370	8.3492
26300	26267	.9975	1.0911	2.6831	1.5484	308.04	8.5312	8.3428
26400	26367	.9975	1.0872	2.6724	1.5539	307.91	8.5253	8.3363
26500	26466	.9975	1.0834	2.6618	1.5595	307.78	8.5195	8.3299
26600	26566	.9975	1.0795	2.6512	1.5650	307.65	8.5136	8.3234
26700	26666	.9974	1.0757	2.6406	1.5706	307.52	8.5078	8.3169
26800	26766	.9974	1.0718	2.6301	1.5763	307.39	8.5019	8.3105
26900	26865	.9974	1.0680	2.6196	1.5819	307.26	8.4961	8.3040
27000	26965	.9974	1.0642 +25	2.6091 + 9	1.5876 − 7	307.13	8.4902 − 1	8.2976 − 1
27100	27065	.9974	1.0604	2.5987	1.5933	307.00	8.4843	8.2911
27200	27165	.9974	1.0566	2.5883	1.5990	306.87	8.4785	8.2846
27300	27264	.9974	1.0528	2.5779	1.6048	306.74	8.4726	8.2782
27400	27364	.9974	1.0490	2.5676	1.6105	306.62	8.4667	8.2717
27500	27464	.9974	1.0452	2.5573	1.6163	306.49	8.4609	8.2652
27600	27564	.9974	1.0415	2.5470	1.6222	306.36	8.4550	8.2588
27700	27663	.9973	1.0377	2.5368	1.6280	306.23	8.4491	8.2523
27800	27763	.9973	1.0340	2.5266	1.6339	306.10	8.4432	8.2458
27900	27863	.9973	1.0303	2.5164	1.6398	305.97	8.4374	8.2394
28000	27962	.9973	1.0266 +25	2.5063 + 9	1.6457 − 7	305.84	8.4315 − 1	8.2329 − 1
28100	28062	.9973	1.0229	2.4962	1.6517	305.71	8.4256	8.2264
28200	28162	.9973	1.0192	2.4861	1.6577	305.58	8.4197	8.2199
28300	28262	.9973	1.0155	2.4761	1.6637	305.45	8.4138	8.2135
28400	28361	.9973	1.0118	2.4661	1.6697	305.32	8.4079	8.2070
28500	28461	.9973	1.0082	2.4561	1.6758	305.19	8.4020	8.2005
28600	28561	.9973	1.0045	2.4462	1.6819	305.06	8.3962	8.1940
28700	28661	.9973	1.0009	2.4363	1.6880	304.93	8.3903	8.1876
28800	28760	.9972	9.9722 +24	2.4264	1.6942	304.80	8.3844	8.1811
28900	28860	.9972	9.9360	2.4165	1.7003	304.67	8.3785	8.1746
29000	28960	.9972	9.8999 +24	2.4067 + 9	1.7065 − 7	304.54	8.3726 − 1	8.1681 − 1
29100	29059	.9972	9.8639	2.3969	1.7128	304.41	8.3667	8.1616
29200	29159	.9972	9.8280	2.3872	1.7190	304.28	8.3607	8.1551
29300	29259	.9972	9.7921	2.3775	1.7253	304.15	8.3548	8.1486
29400	29359	.9972	9.7564	2.3678	1.7316	304.01	8.3489	8.1422
29500	29458	.9972	9.7208	2.3581	1.7380	303.88	8.3430	8.1357
29600	29558	.9972	9.6853	2.3485	1.7444	303.75	8.3371	8.1292
29700	29658	.9972	9.6499	2.3389	1.7508	303.62	8.3312	8.1227
29800	29757	.9971	9.6145	2.3293	1.7572	303.49	8.3253	8.1162
29900	29857	.9971	9.5793	2.3198	1.7637	303.36	8.3193	8.1097
30000	29957	.9971	9.5442 +24	2.3103 + 9	1.7701 − 7	303.23	8.3134 − 1	8.1032 − 1
30100	30057	.9971	9.5092	2.3008	1.7767	303.10	8.3075	8.0967
30200	30156	.9971	9.4743	2.2914	1.7832	302.97	8.3016	8.0902
30300	30256	.9971	9.4394	2.2820	1.7898	302.84	8.2956	8.0837
30400	30356	.9971	9.4047	2.2726	1.7964	302.71	8.2897	8.0772
30500	30455	.9971	9.3701	2.2633	1.8030	302.57	8.2838	8.0707
30600	30555	.9971	9.3355	2.2539	1.8097	302.44	8.2778	8.0642
30700	30655	.9971	9.3011	2.2446	1.8164	302.31	8.2719	8.0577
30800	30755	.9971	9.2668	2.2354	1.8231	302.18	8.2659	8.0512
30900	30854	.9970	9.2325	2.2262	1.8299	302.05	8.2600	8.0447

Table V
Geopotential Altitude, English Altitudes

Altitude		Gravity ratio	Number density	Collision frequency	Mean free path	Sound speed	Viscosity ratio	Thermal conductivity ratio
H (ft)	Z (ft)	g/g_0	n (m^{-3})	ν (s^{-1})	L (m)	C_s (m/s)	μ/μ_0	κ/κ_0
31000	31046	.9970	9.1827 +24	2.2127 + 9	1.8398 − 7	301.86	8.2513 − 1	8.0352 − 1
31100	31146	.9970	9.1486	2.2036	1.8467	301.73	8.2453	8.0287
31200	31247	.9970	9.1146	2.1944	1.8536	301.59	8.2394	8.0221
31300	31347	.9970	9.0807	2.1853	1.8605	301.46	8.2334	8.0156
31400	31447	.9970	9.0469	2.1762	1.8675	301.33	8.2274	8.0091
31500	31548	.9970	9.0131	2.1671	1.8744	301.20	8.2214	8.0025
31600	31648	.9970	8.9795	2.1581	1.8815	301.07	8.2155	7.9960
31700	31748	.9970	8.9460	2.1491	1.8885	300.93	8.2095	7.9895
31800	31849	.9970	8.9126	2.1401	1.8956	300.80	8.2035	7.9829
31900	31949	.9969	8.8793	2.1312	1.9027	300.67	8.1975	7.9764
32000	32049	.9969	8.8460 +24	2.1223 + 9	1.9099 − 7	300.54	8.1915 − 1	7.9698 − 1
32100	32149	.9969	8.8129	2.1134	1.9170	300.40	8.1855	7.9633
32200	32250	.9969	8.7798	2.1045	1.9243	300.27	8.1796	7.9568
32300	32350	.9969	8.7469	2.0957	1.9315	300.14	8.1736	7.9502
32400	32450	.9969	8.7140	2.0869	1.9388	300.01	8.1676	7.9437
32500	32551	.9969	8.6813	2.0782	1.9461	299.87	8.1616	7.9371
32600	32651	.9969	8.6486	2.0694	1.9535	299.74	8.1556	7.9306
32700	32751	.9969	8.6160	2.0607	1.9608	299.61	8.1496	7.9240
32800	32852	.9969	8.5836	2.0520	1.9683	299.47	8.1435	7.9175
32900	32952	.9968	8.5512	2.0434	1.9757	299.34	8.1375	7.9109
33000	33052	.9968	8.5189 +24	2.0348 + 9	1.9832 − 7	299.21	8.1315 − 1	7.9044 − 1
33100	33153	.9968	8.4867	2.0262	1.9907	299.08	8.1255	7.8978
33200	33253	.9968	8.4546	2.0176	1.9983	298.94	8.1195	7.8913
33300	33353	.9968	8.4226	2.0091	2.0059	298.81	8.1135	7.8847
33400	33454	.9968	8.3907	2.0006	2.0135	298.68	8.1075	7.8782
33500	33554	.9968	8.3588	1.9921	2.0212	298.54	8.1014	7.8716
33600	33654	.9968	8.3271	1.9836	2.0289	298.41	8.0954	7.8651
33700	33755	.9968	8.2955	1.9752	2.0366	298.28	8.0894	7.8585
33800	33855	.9968	8.2639	1.9668	2.0444	298.14	8.0834	7.8519
33900	33955	.9968	8.2325	1.9585	2.0522	298.01	8.0773	7.8454
34000	34056	.9967	8.2011 +24	1.9501 + 9	2.0601 − 7	297.88	8.0713 − 1	7.8388 − 1
34100	34156	.9967	8.1698	1.9418	2.0679	297.74	8.0653	7.8322
34200	34256	.9967	8.1386	1.9335	2.0759	297.61	8.0592	7.8257
34300	34357	.9967	8.1075	1.9253	2.0838	297.47	8.0532	7.8191
34400	34457	.9967	8.0765	1.9171	2.0918	297.34	8.0471	7.8125
34500	34557	.9967	8.0456	1.9089	2.0999	297.21	8.0411	7.8060
34600	34658	.9967	8.0148	1.9007	2.1079	297.07	8.0350	7.7994
34700	34758	.9967	7.9841	1.8926	2.1160	296.94	8.0290	7.7928
34800	34858	.9967	7.9534	1.8844	2.1242	296.80	8.0229	7.7863
34900	34959	.9967	7.9229	1.8764	2.1324	296.67	8.0169	7.7797
35000	35059	.9966	7.8924 +24	1.8683 + 9	2.1406 − 7	296.54	8.0108 − 1	7.7731 − 1
35200	35260	.9966	7.8318	1.8523	2.1572	296.27	7.9987	7.7600
35400	35460	.9966	7.7715	1.8363	2.1739	296.00	7.9866	7.7468
35600	35661	.9966	7.7116	1.8205	2.1908	295.73	7.9744	7.7336
35800	35862	.9966	7.6520	1.8048	2.2079	295.46	7.9623	7.7205
36000	36062	.9966	7.5928	1.7892	2.2251	295.19	7.9501	7.7073
36200	36263	.9965	7.5263	1.7728	2.2448	295.07	7.9447	7.7014
36400	36464	.9965	7.4543	1.7558	2.2664	295.07	7.9447	7.7014
36600	36664	.9965	7.3830	1.7390	2.2883	295.07	7.9447	7.7014
36800	36865	.9965	7.3123	1.7224	2.3104	295.07	7.9447	7.7014
37000	37066	.9965	7.2424 +24	1.7059 + 9	2.3328 − 7	295.07	7.9447 − 1	7.7014 − 1
37200	37266	.9964	7.1731	1.6896	2.3553	295.07	7.9447	7.7014
37400	37467	.9964	7.1045	1.6735	2.3780	295.07	7.9447	7.7014
37600	37668	.9964	7.0365	1.6574	2.4010	295.07	7.9447	7.7014
37800	37869	.9964	6.9692	1.6416	2.4242	295.07	7.9447	7.7014
38000	38069	.9964	6.9025	1.6259	2.4476	295.07	7.9447	7.7014
38200	38270	.9963	6.8365	1.6103	2.4713	295.07	7.9447	7.7014
38400	38471	.9963	6.7711	1.5949	2.4951	295.07	7.9447	7.7014
38600	38672	.9963	6.7063	1.5797	2.5192	295.07	7.9447	7.7014
38800	38872	.9963	6.6421	1.5646	2.5436	295.07	7.9447	7.7014
39000	39073	.9963	6.5786 +24	1.5496 + 9	2.5681 − 7	295.07	7.9447 − 1	7.7014 − 1
39200	39274	.9962	6.5157	1.5348	2.5929	295.07	7.9447	7.7014
39400	39475	.9962	6.4533	1.5201	2.6180	295.07	7.9447	7.7014
39600	39675	.9962	6.3916	1.5055	2.6433	295.07	7.9447	7.7014
39800	39876	.9962	6.3305	1.4911	2.6688	295.07	7.9447	7.7014
40000	40077	.9962	6.2699	1.4769	2.6946	295.07	7.9447	7.7014
40200	40278	.9961	6.2099	1.4627	2.7206	295.07	7.9447	7.7014
40400	40478	.9961	6.1505	1.4487	2.7469	295.07	7.9447	7.7014
40600	40679	.9961	6.0917	1.4349	2.7734	295.07	7.9447	7.7014
40800	40880	.9961	6.0334	1.4212	2.8002	295.07	7.9447	7.7014
41000	41081	.9961	5.9757 +24	1.4076 + 9	2.8272 − 7	295.07	7.9447 − 1	7.7014 − 1
41200	41282	.9961	5.9185	1.3941	2.8546	295.07	7.9447	7.7014
41400	41482	.9960	5.8619	1.3808	2.8821	295.07	7.9447	7.7014
41600	41683	.9960	5.8058	1.3676	2.9100	295.07	7.9447	7.7014
41800	41884	.9960	5.7503	1.3545	2.9381	295.07	7.9447	7.7014
42000	42085	.9960	5.6952	1.3415	2.9664	295.07	7.9447	7.7014
42200	42286	.9960	5.6408	1.3287	2.9951	295.07	7.9447	7.7014
42400	42486	.9959	5.5868	1.3160	3.0240	295.07	7.9447	7.7014
42600	42687	.9959	5.5334	1.3034	3.0532	295.07	7.9447	7.7014
42800	42888	.9959	5.4804	1.2909	3.0827	295.07	7.9447	7.7014

Table V
Geometric Altitude, English Altitudes

Altitude		Gravity ratio	Number density	Collision frequency	Mean free path	Sound speed	Viscosity ratio	Thermal conductivity ratio
Z (ft)	H (ft)	g/g_0	n (m^{-3})	ν (s^{-1})	L (m)	C_s (m/s)	μ/μ_0	κ/κ_0
31000	30954	.9970	9.1984 +24	2.2170 + 9	1.8367 − 7	301.92	8.2541 − 1	8.0382 − 1
31100	31054	.9970	9.1644	2.2078	1.8435	301.79	8.2481	8.0317
31200	31153	.9970	9.1304	2.1987	1.8504	301.66	8.2422	8.0252
31300	31253	.9970	9.0966	2.1896	1.8573	301.52	8.2362	8.0187
31400	31353	.9970	9.0628	2.1805	1.8642	301.39	8.2302	8.0121
31500	31452	.9970	9.0292	2.1714	1.8711	301.26	8.2243	8.0056
31600	31552	.9970	8.9956	2.1624	1.8781	301.13	8.2183	7.9991
31700	31652	.9970	8.9621	2.1534	1.8851	301.00	8.2124	7.9926
31800	31752	.9970	8.9288	2.1445	1.8922	300.86	8.2064	7.9861
31900	31851	.9969	8.8955	2.1355	1.8992	300.73	8.2004	7.9796
32000	31951	.9969	8.8623 +24	2.1266 + 9	1.9064 − 7	300.60	8.1945 − 1	7.9730 − 1
32100	32051	.9969	8.8292	2.1178	1.9135	300.47	8.1885	7.9665
32200	32150	.9969	8.7962	2.1089	1.9207	300.34	8.1825	7.9600
32300	32250	.9969	8.7633	2.1001	1.9279	300.20	8.1765	7.9535
32400	32350	.9969	8.7305	2.0913	1.9351	300.07	8.1706	7.9470
32500	32449	.9969	8.6978	2.0826	1.9424	299.94	8.1646	7.9404
32600	32549	.9969	8.6652	2.0739	1.9497	299.81	8.1586	7.9339
32700	32649	.9969	8.6327	2.0652	1.9571	299.68	8.1526	7.9274
32800	32748	.9969	8.6003	2.0565	1.9644	299.54	8.1466	7.9209
32900	32848	.9969	8.5679	2.0479	1.9718	299.41	8.1406	7.9143
33000	32948	.9968	8.5357 +24	2.0393 + 9	1.9793 − 7	299.28	8.1347 − 1	7.9078 − 1
33100	33048	.9968	8.5036	2.0307	1.9868	299.14	8.1287	7.9013
33200	33147	.9968	8.4715	2.0221	1.9943	299.01	8.1227	7.8947
33300	33247	.9968	8.4396	2.0136	2.0018	298.88	8.1167	7.8882
33400	33347	.9968	8.4077	2.0051	2.0094	298.75	8.1107	7.8817
33500	33446	.9968	8.3759	1.9966	2.0171	298.61	8.1047	7.8751
33600	33546	.9968	8.3442	1.9882	2.0247	298.48	8.0987	7.8686
33700	33646	.9968	8.3126	1.9798	2.0324	298.35	8.0927	7.8621
33800	33745	.9968	8.2812	1.9714	2.0401	298.21	8.0866	7.8555
33900	33845	.9968	8.2497	1.9631	2.0479	298.08	8.0806	7.8490
34000	33945	.9967	8.2184 +24	1.9547 + 9	2.0557 − 7	297.95	8.0746 − 1	7.8424 − 1
34100	34044	.9967	8.1872	1.9464	2.0635	297.82	8.0686	7.8359
34200	34144	.9967	8.1561	1.9382	2.0714	297.68	8.0626	7.8294
34300	34244	.9967	8.1250	1.9299	2.0793	297.55	8.0566	7.8228
34400	34343	.9967	8.0941	1.9217	2.0873	297.42	8.0505	7.8163
34500	34443	.9967	8.0632	1.9135	2.0953	297.28	8.0445	7.8097
34600	34543	.9967	8.0325	1.9054	2.1033	297.15	8.0385	7.8032
34700	34642	.9967	8.0018	1.8972	2.1114	297.02	8.0325	7.7966
34800	34742	.9967	7.9712	1.8891	2.1195	296.88	8.0264	7.7901
34900	34842	.9967	7.9407	1.8811	2.1276	296.75	8.0204	7.7835
35000	34941	.9967	7.9103 +24	1.8730 + 9	2.1358 − 7	296.61	8.0144 − 1	7.7770 − 1
35200	35141	.9966	7.8497	1.8570	2.1523	296.35	8.0023	7.7639
35400	35340	.9966	7.7895	1.8411	2.1689	296.08	7.9902	7.7507
35600	35539	.9966	7.7297	1.8253	2.1857	295.81	7.9781	7.7376
35800	35739	.9966	7.6702	1.8096	2.2026	295.54	7.9660	7.7245
36000	35938	.9966	7.6111	1.7940	2.2197	295.27	7.9539	7.7114
36200	36137	.9965	7.5490	1.7782	2.2380	295.07	7.9447	7.7014
36400	36337	.9965	7.4770	1.7612	2.2595	295.07	7.9447	7.7014
36600	36536	.9965	7.4057	1.7444	2.2813	295.07	7.9447	7.7014
36800	36735	.9965	7.3351	1.7278	2.3032	295.07	7.9447	7.7014
37000	36934	.9965	7.2652 +24	1.7113 + 9	2.3254 − 7	295.07	7.9447 − 1	7.7014 − 1
37200	37134	.9964	7.1960	1.6950	2.3478	295.07	7.9447	7.7014
37400	37333	.9964	7.1274	1.6788	2.3704	295.07	7.9447	7.7014
37600	37532	.9964	7.0594	1.6628	2.3932	295.07	7.9447	7.7014
37800	37732	.9964	6.9921	1.6470	2.4162	295.07	7.9447	7.7014
38000	37931	.9964	6.9255	1.6313	2.4395	295.07	7.9447	7.7014
38200	38130	.9963	6.8595	1.6157	2.4630	295.07	7.9447	7.7014
38400	38329	.9963	6.7941	1.6003	2.4867	295.07	7.9447	7.7014
38600	38529	.9963	6.7293	1.5851	2.5106	295.07	7.9447	7.7014
38800	38728	.9963	6.6652	1.5700	2.5348	295.07	7.9447	7.7014
39000	38927	.9963	6.6017 +24	1.5550 + 9	2.5592 − 7	295.07	7.9447 − 1	7.7014 − 1
39200	39126	.9963	6.5387	1.5402	2.5838	295.07	7.9447	7.7014
39400	39326	.9962	6.4764	1.5255	2.6086	295.07	7.9447	7.7014
39600	39525	.9962	6.4147	1.5110	2.6337	295.07	7.9447	7.7014
39800	39724	.9962	6.3536	1.4966	2.6591	295.07	7.9447	7.7014
40000	39923	.9962	6.2930	1.4823	2.6847	295.07	7.9447	7.7014
40200	40123	.9962	6.2330	1.4682	2.7105	295.07	7.9447	7.7014
40400	40322	.9961	6.1736	1.4542	2.7366	295.07	7.9447	7.7014
40600	40521	.9961	6.1148	1.4403	2.7629	295.07	7.9447	7.7014
40800	40720	.9961	6.0565	1.4266	2.7895	295.07	7.9447	7.7014
41000	40920	.9961	5.9988 +24	1.4130 + 9	2.8163 − 7	295.07	7.9447 − 1	7.7014 − 1
41200	41119	.9961	5.9416	1.3995	2.8434	295.07	7.9447	7.7014
41400	41318	.9960	5.8850	1.3862	2.8708	295.07	7.9447	7.7014
41600	41517	.9960	5.8290	1.3730	2.8984	295.07	7.9447	7.7014
41800	41716	.9960	5.7734	1.3599	2.9263	295.07	7.9447	7.7014
42000	41916	.9960	5.7184	1.3470	2.9544	295.07	7.9447	7.7014
42200	42115	.9960	5.6639	1.3341	2.9829	295.07	7.9447	7.7014
42400	42314	.9959	5.6099	1.3214	3.0116	295.07	7.9447	7.7014
42600	42513	.9959	5.5565	1.3088	3.0405	295.07	7.9447	7.7014
42800	42712	.9959	5.5036	1.2964	3.0698	295.07	7.9447	7.7014

Table V
Geopotential Altitude, English Altitudes

Altitude		Gravity ratio	Number density	Collision frequency	Mean free path	Sound speed	Viscosity ratio	Thermal conductivity ratio
H (ft)	Z (ft)	g/g_0	n (m^{-3})	ν (s^{-1})	L (m)	C_s (m/s)	μ/μ_0	κ/κ_0
43000	43089	.9959	5.4280 +24	1.2786 + 9	3.1125 - 7	295.07	7.9447 - 1	7.7014 - 1
43200	43290	.9959	5.3761	1.2663	3.1426	295.07	7.9447	7.7014
43400	43491	.9958	5.3246	1.2542	3.1729	295.07	7.9447	7.7014
43600	43691	.9958	5.2737	1.2422	3.2036	295.07	7.9447	7.7014
43800	43892	.9958	5.2232	1.2303	3.2345	295.07	7.9447	7.7014
44000	44093	.9958	5.1733	1.2186	3.2658	295.07	7.9447	7.7014
44200	44294	.9958	5.1238	1.2069	3.2973	295.07	7.9447	7.7014
44400	44495	.9957	5.0748	1.1954	3.3292	295.07	7.9447	7.7014
44600	44696	.9957	5.0262	1.1839	3.3613	295.07	7.9447	7.7014
44800	44896	.9957	4.9781	1.1726	3.3938	295.07	7.9447	7.7014
45000	45097	.9957	4.9305 +24	1.1614 + 9	3.4266 - 7	295.07	7.9447 - 1	7.7014 - 1
45200	45298	.9957	4.8833	1.1503	3.4597	295.07	7.9447	7.7014
45400	45499	.9957	4.8366	1.1393	3.4931	295.07	7.9447	7.7014
45600	45700	.9956	4.7904	1.1284	3.5268	295.07	7.9447	7.7014
45800	45901	.9956	4.7445	1.1176	3.5609	295.07	7.9447	7.7014
46000	46102	.9956	4.6991	1.1069	3.5953	295.07	7.9447	7.7014
46200	46303	.9956	4.6542	1.0963	3.6300	295.07	7.9447	7.7014
46400	46503	.9956	4.6097	1.0858	3.6651	295.07	7.9447	7.7014
46600	46704	.9955	4.5656	1.0754	3.7005	295.07	7.9447	7.7014
46800	46905	.9955	4.5219	1.0651	3.7362	295.07	7.9447	7.7014
47000	47106	.9955	4.4786 +24	1.0549 + 9	3.7723 - 7	295.07	7.9447 - 1	7.7014 - 1
47200	47307	.9955	4.4358	1.0448	3.8087	295.07	7.9447	7.7014
47400	47508	.9955	4.3933	1.0348	3.8455	295.07	7.9447	7.7014
47600	47709	.9954	4.3513	1.0249	3.8827	295.07	7.9447	7.7014
47800	47910	.9954	4.3097	1.0151	3.9202	295.07	7.9447	7.7014
48000	48111	.9954	4.2685	1.0054	3.9580	295.07	7.9447	7.7014
48200	48312	.9954	4.2276	9.9581 + 8	3.9963	295.07	7.9447	7.7014
48400	48513	.9954	4.1872	9.8629	4.0349	295.07	7.9447	7.7014
48600	48714	.9953	4.1471	9.7685	4.0738	295.07	7.9447	7.7014
48800	48914	.9953	4.1074	9.6750	4.1132	295.07	7.9447	7.7014
49000	49115	.9953	4.0682 +24	9.5825 + 8	4.1529 - 7	295.07	7.9447 - 1	7.7014 - 1
49200	49316	.9953	4.0292	9.4908	4.1930	295.07	7.9447	7.7014
49400	49517	.9953	3.9907	9.4000	4.2335	295.07	7.9447	7.7014
49600	49718	.9952	3.9525	9.3101	4.2744	295.07	7.9447	7.7014
49800	49919	.9952	3.9147	9.2210	4.3157	295.07	7.9447	7.7014
50000	50120	.9952	3.8772	9.1328	4.3574	295.07	7.9447	7.7014
50200	50321	.9952	3.8402	9.0454	4.3995	295.07	7.9447	7.7014
50400	50522	.9952	3.8034	8.9589	4.4420	295.07	7.9447	7.7014
50600	50723	.9952	3.7670	8.8732	4.4849	295.07	7.9447	7.7014
50800	50924	.9951	3.7310	8.7883	4.5282	295.07	7.9447	7.7014
51000	51125	.9951	3.6953 +24	8.7042 + 8	4.5719 - 7	295.07	7.9447 - 1	7.7014 - 1
51200	51326	.9951	3.6599	8.6210	4.6161	295.07	7.9447	7.7014
51400	51527	.9951	3.6249	8.5385	4.6607	295.07	7.9447	7.7014
51600	51728	.9951	3.5903	8.4568	4.7057	295.07	7.9447	7.7014
51800	51929	.9950	3.5559	8.3759	4.7511	295.07	7.9447	7.7014
52000	52130	.9950	3.5219	8.2958	4.7970	295.07	7.9447	7.7014
52200	52331	.9950	3.4882	8.2164	4.8434	295.07	7.9447	7.7014
52400	52532	.9950	3.4548	8.1378	4.8902	295.07	7.9447	7.7014
52600	52733	.9950	3.4218	8.0600	4.9374	295.07	7.9447	7.7014
52800	52934	.9949	3.3890	7.9829	4.9851	295.07	7.9447	7.7014
53000	53135	.9949	3.3566 +24	7.9065 + 8	5.0332 - 7	295.07	7.9447 - 1	7.7014 - 1
53200	53336	.9949	3.3245	7.8308	5.0818	295.07	7.9447	7.7014
53400	53537	.9949	3.2927	7.7559	5.1309	295.07	7.9447	7.7014
53600	53738	.9949	3.2612	7.6817	5.1805	295.07	7.9447	7.7014
53800	53939	.9948	3.2300	7.6082	5.2305	295.07	7.9447	7.7014
54000	54140	.9948	3.1991	7.5355	5.2811	295.07	7.9447	7.7014
54200	54341	.9948	3.1685	7.4634	5.3321	295.07	7.9447	7.7014
54400	54542	.9948	3.1382	7.3920	5.3836	295.07	7.9447	7.7014
54600	54743	.9948	3.1082	7.3213	5.4356	295.07	7.9447	7.7014
54800	54944	.9948	3.0784	7.2512	5.4881	295.07	7.9447	7.7014
55000	55145	.9947	3.0490 +24	7.1818 + 8	5.5411 - 7	295.07	7.9447 - 1	7.7014 - 1
55200	55346	.9947	3.0198	7.1131	5.5946	295.07	7.9447	7.7014
55400	55548	.9947	2.9909	7.0451	5.6486	295.07	7.9447	7.7014
55600	55749	.9947	2.9623	6.9777	5.7032	295.07	7.9447	7.7014
55800	55950	.9947	2.9340	6.9109	5.7583	295.07	7.9447	7.7014
56000	56151	.9946	2.9059	6.8448	5.8139	295.07	7.9447	7.7014
56200	56352	.9946	2.8781	6.7793	5.8701	295.07	7.9447	7.7014
56400	56553	.9946	2.8506	6.7145	5.9268	295.07	7.9447	7.7014
56600	56754	.9946	2.8233	6.6503	5.9840	295.07	7.9447	7.7014
56800	56955	.9946	2.7963	6.5866	6.0418	295.07	7.9447	7.7014
57000	57156	.9945	2.7695 +24	6.5236 + 8	6.1002 - 7	295.07	7.9447 - 1	7.7014 - 1
57200	57357	.9945	2.7430	6.4612	6.1591	295.07	7.9447	7.7014
57400	57558	.9945	2.7168	6.3994	6.2186	295.07	7.9447	7.7014
57600	57760	.9945	2.6908	6.3382	6.2786	295.07	7.9447	7.7014
57800	57961	.9945	2.6651	6.2775	6.3393	295.07	7.9447	7.7014
58000	58162	.9944	2.6396	6.2175	6.4005	295.07	7.9447	7.7014
58200	58363	.9944	2.6143	6.1580	6.4623	295.07	7.9447	7.7014
58400	58564	.9944	2.5893	6.0991	6.5248	295.07	7.9447	7.7014
58600	58765	.9944	2.5645	6.0408	6.5878	295.07	7.9447	7.7014
58800	58966	.9944	2.5400	5.9830	6.6514	295.07	7.9447	7.7014

Table V
Geometric Altitude, English Altitudes

Altitude		Gravity ratio	Number density	Collision frequency	Mean free path	Sound speed	Viscosity ratio	Thermal conductivity ratio
Z (ft)	H (ft)	g/g_0	n (m^{-3})	ν (s^{-1})	L (m)	C_s (m/s)	μ/μ_0	κ/κ_0
43000	42912	.9959	5.4511 +24	1.2840 + 9	3.0993 − 7	295.07	7.9447 − 1	7.7014 − 1
43200	43111	.9959	5.3992	1.2718	3.1291	295.07	7.9447	7.7014
43400	43310	.9959	5.3477	1.2597	3.1592	295.07	7.9447	7.7014
43600	43509	.9958	5.2968	1.2477	3.1896	295.07	7.9447	7.7014
43800	43708	.9958	5.2463	1.2358	3.2203	295.07	7.9447	7.7014
44000	43907	.9958	5.1964	1.2240	3.2513	295.07	7.9447	7.7014
44200	44107	.9958	5.1468	1.2123	3.2825	295.07	7.9447	7.7014
44400	44306	.9958	5.0978	1.2008	3.3141	295.07	7.9447	7.7014
44600	44505	.9957	5.0493	1.1893	3.3460	295.07	7.9447	7.7014
44800	44704	.9957	5.0012	1.1780	3.3781	295.07	7.9447	7.7014
45000	44903	.9957	4.9535 +24	1.1668 + 9	3.4106 − 7	295.07	7.9447 − 1	7.7014 − 1
45200	45102	.9957	4.9063	1.1557	3.4434	295.07	7.9447	7.7014
45400	45301	.9957	4.8596	1.1447	3.4766	295.07	7.9447	7.7014
45600	45501	.9956	4.8133	1.1338	3.5100	295.07	7.9447	7.7014
45800	45700	.9956	4.7675	1.1230	3.5437	295.07	7.9447	7.7014
46000	45899	.9956	4.7221	1.1123	3.5778	295.07	7.9447	7.7014
46200	46098	.9956	4.6771	1.1017	3.6122	295.07	7.9447	7.7014
46400	46297	.9956	4.6325	1.0912	3.6470	295.07	7.9447	7.7014
46600	46496	.9955	4.5884	1.0808	3.6820	295.07	7.9447	7.7014
46800	46695	.9955	4.5447	1.0705	3.7174	295.07	7.9447	7.7014
47000	46894	.9955	4.5014 +24	1.0603 + 9	3.7532 − 7	295.07	7.9447 − 1	7.7014 − 1
47200	47093	.9955	4.4586	1.0502	3.7893	295.07	7.9447	7.7014
47400	47293	.9955	4.4161	1.0402	3.8257	295.07	7.9447	7.7014
47600	47492	.9955	4.3740	1.0303	3.8625	295.07	7.9447	7.7014
47800	47691	.9954	4.3324	1.0205	3.8996	295.07	7.9447	7.7014
48000	47890	.9954	4.2911	1.0108	3.9371	295.07	7.9447	7.7014
48200	48089	.9954	4.2503	1.0011	3.9750	295.07	7.9447	7.7014
48400	48288	.9954	4.2098	9.9161 + 8	4.0132	295.07	7.9447	7.7014
48600	48487	.9954	4.1697	9.8217	4.0518	295.07	7.9447	7.7014
48800	48686	.9953	4.1300	9.7281	4.0907	295.07	7.9447	7.7014
49000	48885	.9953	4.0907 +24	9.6355 + 8	4.1301 − 7	295.07	7.9447 − 1	7.7014 − 1
49200	49084	.9953	4.0517	9.5438	4.1698	295.07	7.9447	7.7014
49400	49283	.9953	4.0131	9.4529	4.2098	295.07	7.9447	7.7014
49600	49482	.9953	3.9749	9.3629	4.2503	295.07	7.9447	7.7014
49800	49681	.9952	3.9371	9.2737	4.2912	295.07	7.9447	7.7014
50000	49880	.9952	3.8996	9.1854	4.3324	295.07	7.9447	7.7014
50200	50079	.9952	3.8625	9.0980	4.3741	295.07	7.9447	7.7014
50400	50278	.9952	3.8257	9.0114	4.4161	295.07	7.9447	7.7014
50600	50478	.9952	3.7893	8.9256	4.4586	295.07	7.9447	7.7014
50800	50677	.9951	3.7532	8.8406	4.5014	295.07	7.9447	7.7014
51000	50876	.9951	3.7175 +24	8.7564 + 8	4.5447 − 7	295.07	7.9447 − 1	7.7014 − 1
51200	51075	.9951	3.6821	8.6731	4.5884	295.07	7.9447	7.7014
51400	51274	.9951	3.6470	8.5905	4.6325	295.07	7.9447	7.7014
51600	51473	.9951	3.6123	8.5087	4.6770	295.07	7.9447	7.7014
51800	51672	.9951	3.5779	8.4277	4.7219	295.07	7.9447	7.7014
52000	51871	.9950	3.5438	8.3475	4.7673	295.07	7.9447	7.7014
52200	52070	.9950	3.5101	8.2680	4.8131	295.07	7.9447	7.7014
52400	52269	.9950	3.4767	8.1893	4.8594	295.07	7.9447	7.7014
52600	52468	.9950	3.4436	8.1114	4.9061	295.07	7.9447	7.7014
52800	52667	.9950	3.4108	8.0342	4.9532	295.07	7.9447	7.7014
53000	52866	.9949	3.3784 +24	7.9577 + 8	5.0008 − 7	295.07	7.9447 − 1	7.7014 − 1
53200	53065	.9949	3.3462	7.8819	5.0489	295.07	7.9447	7.7014
53400	53264	.9949	3.3144	7.8069	5.0974	295.07	7.9447	7.7014
53600	53463	.9949	3.2828	7.7326	5.1464	295.07	7.9447	7.7014
53800	53662	.9949	3.2516	7.6590	5.1959	295.07	7.9447	7.7014
54000	53861	.9948	3.2206	7.5861	5.2458	295.07	7.9447	7.7014
54200	54059	.9948	3.1900	7.5139	5.2962	295.07	7.9447	7.7014
54400	54258	.9948	3.1596	7.4424	5.3471	295.07	7.9447	7.7014
54600	54457	.9948	3.1295	7.3716	5.3985	295.07	7.9447	7.7014
54800	54656	.9948	3.0998	7.3014	5.4503	295.07	7.9447	7.7014
55000	54855	.9947	3.0703 +24	7.2319 + 8	5.5027 − 7	295.07	7.9447 − 1	7.7014 − 1
55200	55054	.9947	3.0410	7.1631	5.5556	295.07	7.9447	7.7014
55400	55253	.9947	3.0121	7.0950	5.6089	295.07	7.9447	7.7014
55600	55452	.9947	2.9834	7.0274	5.6628	295.07	7.9447	7.7014
55800	55651	.9947	2.9550	6.9606	5.7172	295.07	7.9447	7.7014
56000	55850	.9947	2.9269	6.8943	5.7722	295.07	7.9447	7.7014
56200	56049	.9946	2.8991	6.8287	5.8276	295.07	7.9447	7.7014
56400	56248	.9946	2.8715	6.7637	5.8836	295.07	7.9447	7.7014
56600	56447	.9946	2.8442	6.6994	5.9401	295.07	7.9447	7.7014
56800	56646	.9946	2.8171	6.6356	5.9972	295.07	7.9447	7.7014
57000	56845	.9946	2.7903 +24	6.5725 + 8	6.0548 − 7	295.07	7.9447 − 1	7.7014 − 1
57200	57044	.9945	2.7637	6.5100	6.1130	295.07	7.9447	7.7014
57400	57242	.9945	2.7374	6.4480	6.1717	295.07	7.9447	7.7014
57600	57441	.9945	2.7114	6.3867	6.2310	295.07	7.9447	7.7014
57800	57640	.9945	2.6856	6.3259	6.2908	295.07	7.9447	7.7014
58000	57839	.9945	2.6601	6.2657	6.3512	295.07	7.9447	7.7014
58200	58038	.9944	2.6347	6.2061	6.4122	295.07	7.9447	7.7014
58400	58237	.9944	2.6097	6.1471	6.4738	295.07	7.9447	7.7014
58600	58436	.9944	2.5849	6.0886	6.5360	295.07	7.9447	7.7014
58800	58635	.9944	2.5603	6.0307	6.5988	295.07	7.9447	7.7014

Table V
Geopotential Altitude, English Altitudes

Altitude		Gravity ratio	Number density	Collision frequency	Mean free path	Sound speed	Viscosity ratio	Thermal conductivity ratio
H (ft)	Z (ft)	g/g_0	n (m^{-3})	ν (s^{-1})	L (m)	C_s (m/s)	μ/μ_0	κ/κ_0
59000	59167	.9944	2.5157 +24	5.9257 + 8	6.7157 - 7	295.07	7.9447 - 1	7.7014 - 1
59200	59369	.9943	2.4916	5.8690	6.7805	295.07	7.9447	7.7014
59400	59570	.9943	2.4678	5.8129	6.8460	295.07	7.9447	7.7014
59600	59771	.9943	2.4442	5.7573	6.9122	295.07	7.9447	7.7014
59800	59972	.9943	2.4208	5.7022	6.9789	295.07	7.9447	7.7014
60000	60173	.9943	2.3977	5.6477	7.0463	295.07	7.9447	7.7014
60200	60374	.9942	2.3747	5.5936	7.1144	295.07	7.9447	7.7014
60400	60575	.9942	2.3520	5.5401	7.1831	295.07	7.9447	7.7014
60600	60777	.9942	2.3295	5.4871	7.2525	295.07	7.9447	7.7014
60800	60978	.9942	2.3072	5.4346	7.3225	295.07	7.9447	7.7014
61000	61179	.9942	2.2851 +24	5.3826 + 8	7.3933 - 7	295.07	7.9447 - 1	7.7014 - 1
61200	61380	.9941	2.2633	5.3311	7.4647	295.07	7.9447	7.7014
61400	61581	.9941	2.2416	5.2801	7.5368	295.07	7.9447	7.7014
61600	61782	.9941	2.2202	5.2296	7.6096	295.07	7.9447	7.7014
61800	61984	.9941	2.1989	5.1796	7.6831	295.07	7.9447	7.7014
62000	62185	.9941	2.1779	5.1300	7.7573	295.07	7.9447	7.7014
62200	62386	.9940	2.1571	5.0810	7.8322	295.07	7.9447	7.7014
62400	62587	.9940	2.1364	5.0324	7.9079	295.07	7.9447	7.7014
62600	62788	.9940	2.1160	4.9842	7.9843	295.07	7.9447	7.7014
62800	62990	.9940	2.0958	4.9365	8.0614	295.07	7.9447	7.7014
63000	63191	.9940	2.0757 +24	4.8893 + 8	8.1392 - 7	295.07	7.9447 - 1	7.7014 - 1
63200	63392	.9939	2.0558	4.8425	8.2179	295.07	7.9447	7.7014
63400	63593	.9939	2.0362	4.7962	8.2972	295.07	7.9447	7.7014
63600	63795	.9939	2.0167	4.7503	8.3774	295.07	7.9447	7.7014
63800	63996	.9939	1.9974	4.7049	8.4583	295.07	7.9447	7.7014
64000	64197	.9939	1.9783	4.6599	8.5400	295.07	7.9447	7.7014
64200	64398	.9939	1.9594	4.6153	8.6225	295.07	7.9447	7.7014
64400	64599	.9938	1.9406	4.5711	8.7058	295.07	7.9447	7.7014
64600	64801	.9938	1.9221	4.5274	8.7899	295.07	7.9447	7.7014
64800	65002	.9938	1.9037	4.4841	8.8748	295.07	7.9447	7.7014
65000	65203	.9938	1.8855 +24	4.4412 + 8	8.9605 - 7	295.07	7.9447 - 1	7.7014 - 1
65200	65404	.9938	1.8674	4.3987	9.0470	295.07	7.9447	7.7014
65400	65606	.9937	1.8496	4.3566	9.1344	295.07	7.9447	7.7014
65600	65807	.9937	1.8319	4.3149	9.2226	295.07	7.9447	7.7014
65800	66008	.9937	1.8139	4.2731	9.3141	295.11	7.9464	7.7033
66000	66210	.9937	1.7960	4.2317	9.4067	295.15	7.9483	7.7053
66200	66411	.9937	1.7784	4.1906	9.5002	295.19	7.9501	7.7073
66400	66612	.9936	1.7609	4.1500	9.5945	295.23	7.9520	7.7093
66600	66813	.9936	1.7435	4.1098	9.6898	295.27	7.9539	7.7114
66800	67015	.9936	1.7264	4.0699	9.7860	295.32	7.9557	7.7134
67000	67216	.9936	1.7094 +24	4.0305 + 8	9.8831 - 7	295.36	7.9576 - 1	7.7154 - 1
67200	67417	.9936	1.6926	3.9915	9.9812	295.40	7.9595	7.7175
67400	67619	.9935	1.6760	3.9528	1.0080 - 6	295.44	7.9614	7.7195
67600	67820	.9935	1.6596	3.9145	1.0180	295.48	7.9632	7.7215
67800	68021	.9935	1.6433	3.8767	1.0281	295.52	7.9651	7.7235
68000	68222	.9935	1.6271	3.8391	1.0383	295.56	7.9670	7.7256
68200	68424	.9935	1.6112	3.8020	1.0486	295.61	7.9688	7.7276
68400	68625	.9935	1.5954	3.7653	1.0590	295.65	7.9707	7.7296
68600	68826	.9934	1.5797	3.7289	1.0695	295.69	7.9726	7.7316
68800	69028	.9934	1.5642	3.6928	1.0800	295.73	7.9744	7.7337
69000	69229	.9934	1.5489 +24	3.6571 + 8	1.0907 - 6	295.77	7.9763 - 1	7.7357 - 1
69200	69430	.9934	1.5337	3.6218	1.1015	295.81	7.9782	7.7377
69400	69632	.9934	1.5187	3.5868	1.1124	295.85	7.9801	7.7397
69600	69833	.9933	1.5039	3.5522	1.1234	295.90	7.9819	7.7418
69800	70034	.9933	1.4891	3.5179	1.1345	295.94	7.9838	7.7438
70000	70236	.9933	1.4746	3.4840	1.1457	295.98	7.9857	7.7458
70200	70437	.9933	1.4601	3.4504	1.1571	296.02	7.9875	7.7478
70400	70638	.9933	1.4458	3.4171	1.1685	296.06	7.9894	7.7499
70600	70840	.9932	1.4317	3.3842	1.1800	296.10	7.9913	7.7519
70800	71041	.9932	1.4177	3.3516	1.1917	296.14	7.9931	7.7539
71000	71243	.9932	1.4039 +24	3.3193 + 8	1.2034 - 6	296.18	7.9950 - 1	7.7559 - 1
71200	71444	.9932	1.3901	3.2873	1.2153	296.23	7.9969	7.7580
71400	71645	.9932	1.3765	3.2556	1.2273	296.27	7.9987	7.7600
71600	71847	.9931	1.3631	3.2243	1.2394	296.31	8.0006	7.7620
71800	72048	.9931	1.3498	3.1933	1.2516	296.35	8.0025	7.7640
72000	72249	.9931	1.3366	3.1625	1.2640	296.39	8.0043	7.7661
72200	72451	.9931	1.3236	3.1321	1.2764	296.43	8.0062	7.7681
72400	72652	.9931	1.3107	3.1020	1.2890	296.47	8.0080	7.7701
72600	72854	.9930	1.2979	3.0722	1.3017	296.52	8.0099	7.7721
72800	73055	.9930	1.2853	3.0427	1.3145	296.56	8.0118	7.7742
73000	73256	.9930	1.2727 +24	3.0134 + 8	1.3274 - 6	296.60	8.0136 - 1	7.7762 - 1
73200	73458	.9930	1.2603	2.9845	1.3405	296.64	8.0155	7.7782
73400	73659	.9930	1.2481	2.9558	1.3537	296.68	8.0174	7.7802
73600	73861	.9930	1.2359	2.9275	1.3670	296.72	8.0192	7.7822
73800	74062	.9929	1.2239	2.8994	1.3804	296.76	8.0211	7.7843
74000	74264	.9929	1.2120	2.8715	1.3940	296.80	8.0230	7.7863
74200	74465	.9929	1.2002	2.8440	1.4077	296.85	8.0248	7.7883
74400	74666	.9929	1.1885	2.8167	1.4215	296.89	8.0267	7.7903
74600	74868	.9929	1.1769	2.7897	1.4355	296.93	8.0285	7.7924
74800	75069	.9928	1.1655	2.7630	1.4496	296.97	8.0304	7.7944

Table V
Geometric Altitude, English Altitudes

Altitude		Gravity ratio	Number density	Collision frequency	Mean free path	Sound speed	Viscosity ratio	Thermal conductivity ratio
Z (ft)	H (ft)	g/g_0	n (m^{-3})	ν (s^{-1})	L (m)	C_s (m/s)	μ/μ_0	κ/κ_0
59000	58834	.9944	2.5359 +24	5.9733 + 8	6.6622 − 7	295.07	7.9447 − 1	7.7014 − 1
59200	59032	.9943	2.5118	5.9165	6.7262	295.07	7.9447	7.7014
59400	59231	.9943	2.4879	5.8602	6.7908	295.07	7.9447	7.7014
59600	59430	.9943	2.4642	5.8045	6.8560	295.07	7.9447	7.7014
59800	59629	.9943	2.4408	5.7492	6.9218	295.07	7.9447	7.7014
60000	59828	.9943	2.4176	5.6946	6.9883	295.07	7.9447	7.7014
60200	60027	.9943	2.3946	5.6404	7.0554	295.07	7.9447	7.7014
60400	60226	.9942	2.3718	5.5867	7.1232	295.07	7.9447	7.7014
60600	60424	.9942	2.3492	5.5336	7.1916	295.07	7.9447	7.7014
60800	60623	.9942	2.3269	5.4810	7.2606	295.07	7.9447	7.7014
61000	60822	.9942	2.3048 +24	5.4288 + 8	7.3303 − 7	295.07	7.9447 − 1	7.7014 − 1
61200	61021	.9942	2.2828	5.3772	7.4007	295.07	7.9447	7.7014
61400	61220	.9941	2.2611	5.3261	7.4718	295.07	7.9447	7.7014
61600	61419	.9941	2.2396	5.2754	7.5435	295.07	7.9447	7.7014
61800	61617	.9941	2.2183	5.2252	7.6160	295.07	7.9447	7.7014
62000	61816	.9941	2.1972	5.1755	7.6891	295.07	7.9447	7.7014
62200	62015	.9941	2.1763	5.1263	7.7629	295.07	7.9447	7.7014
62400	62214	.9940	2.1556	5.0776	7.8375	295.07	7.9447	7.7014
62600	62413	.9940	2.1351	5.0293	7.9127	295.07	7.9447	7.7014
62800	62611	.9940	2.1148	4.9815	7.9887	295.07	7.9447	7.7014
63000	62810	.9940	2.0947 +24	4.9341 + 8	8.0654 − 7	295.07	7.9447 − 1	7.7014 − 1
63200	63009	.9940	2.0748	4.8872	8.1428	295.07	7.9447	7.7014
63400	63208	.9939	2.0551	4.8407	8.2210	295.07	7.9447	7.7014
63600	63407	.9939	2.0355	4.7947	8.2999	295.07	7.9447	7.7014
63800	63605	.9939	2.0162	4.7491	8.3796	295.07	7.9447	7.7014
64000	63804	.9939	1.9970	4.7039	8.4600	295.07	7.9447	7.7014
64200	64003	.9939	1.9780	4.6592	8.5412	295.07	7.9447	7.7014
64400	64202	.9939	1.9592	4.6149	8.6232	295.07	7.9447	7.7014
64600	64401	.9938	1.9406	4.5710	8.7060	295.07	7.9447	7.7014
64800	64599	.9938	1.9221	4.5275	8.7896	295.07	7.9447	7.7014
65000	64798	.9938	1.9039 +24	4.4845 + 8	8.8739 − 7	295.07	7.9447 − 1	7.7014 − 1
65200	64997	.9938	1.8858	4.4419	8.9591	295.07	7.9447	7.7014
65400	65196	.9938	1.8678	4.3996	9.0451	295.07	7.9447	7.7014
65600	65394	.9937	1.8501	4.3578	9.1319	295.07	7.9447	7.7014
65800	65593	.9937	1.8325	4.3164	9.2196	295.07	7.9447	7.7014
66000	65792	.9937	1.8146	4.2748	9.3104	295.11	7.9463	7.7032
66200	65991	.9937	1.7969	4.2336	9.4023	295.15	7.9482	7.7052
66400	66189	.9937	1.7793	4.1928	9.4951	295.19	7.9500	7.7072
66600	66388	.9936	1.7619	4.1524	9.5889	295.23	7.9519	7.7092
66800	66587	.9936	1.7447	4.1124	9.6835	295.27	7.9537	7.7112
67000	66785	.9936	1.7276 +24	4.0728 + 8	9.7790 − 7	295.31	7.9556 − 1	7.7133 − 1
67200	66984	.9936	1.7108	4.0336	9.8754	295.35	7.9575	7.7153
67400	67183	.9936	1.6941	3.9948	9.9728	295.39	7.9593	7.7173
67600	67382	.9935	1.6775	3.9563	1.0071 − 6	295.44	7.9612	7.7193
67800	67580	.9935	1.6612	3.9183	1.0170	295.48	7.9630	7.7213
68000	67779	.9935	1.6450	3.8806	1.0270	295.52	7.9649	7.7233
68200	67978	.9935	1.6289	3.8433	1.0372	295.56	7.9668	7.7253
68400	68176	.9935	1.6131	3.8064	1.0474	295.60	7.9686	7.7273
68600	68375	.9935	1.5973	3.7698	1.0577	295.64	7.9705	7.7294
68800	68574	.9934	1.5818	3.7336	1.0681	295.68	7.9723	7.7314
69000	68772	.9934	1.5664 +24	3.6977 + 8	1.0786 − 6	295.72	7.9742 − 1	7.7334 − 1
69200	68971	.9934	1.5511	3.6623	1.0892	295.76	7.9760	7.7354
69400	69170	.9934	1.5360	3.6271	1.0999	295.81	7.9779	7.7374
69600	69368	.9934	1.5211	3.5923	1.1107	295.85	7.9798	7.7394
69800	69567	.9933	1.5063	3.5579	1.1216	295.89	7.9816	7.7414
70000	69766	.9933	1.4916	3.5238	1.1326	295.93	7.9835	7.7434
70200	69964	.9933	1.4771	3.4900	1.1438	295.97	7.9853	7.7455
70400	70163	.9933	1.4628	3.4565	1.1550	296.01	7.9872	7.7475
70600	70362	.9933	1.4486	3.4234	1.1663	296.05	7.9890	7.7495
70800	70560	.9932	1.4345	3.3907	1.1777	296.09	7.9909	7.7515
71000	70759	.9932	1.4206 +24	3.3582 + 8	1.1893 − 6	296.13	7.9927 − 1	7.7535 − 1
71200	70958	.9932	1.4068	3.3261	1.2010	296.18	7.9946	7.7555
71400	71156	.9932	1.3931	3.2942	1.2127	296.22	7.9964	7.7575
71600	71355	.9932	1.3796	3.2627	1.2246	296.26	7.9983	7.7595
71800	71554	.9931	1.3662	3.2315	1.2366	296.30	8.0002	7.7615
72000	71752	.9931	1.3530	3.2006	1.2487	296.34	8.0020	7.7635
72200	71951	.9931	1.3399	3.1701	1.2609	296.38	8.0039	7.7656
72400	72150	.9931	1.3269	3.1398	1.2733	296.42	8.0057	7.7676
72600	72348	.9931	1.3140	3.1098	1.2857	296.46	8.0076	7.7696
72800	72547	.9931	1.3013	3.0801	1.2983	296.50	8.0094	7.7716
73000	72745	.9930	1.2887 +24	3.0507 + 8	1.3110 − 6	296.55	8.0113 − 1	7.7736 − 1
73200	72944	.9930	1.2762	3.0216	1.3238	296.59	8.0131	7.7756
73400	73143	.9930	1.2639	2.9928	1.3367	296.63	8.0150	7.7776
73600	73341	.9930	1.2516	2.9642	1.3498	296.67	8.0168	7.7796
73800	73540	.9930	1.2395	2.9360	1.3630	296.71	8.0187	7.7816
74000	73738	.9929	1.2276	2.9080	1.3763	296.75	8.0205	7.7836
74200	73937	.9929	1.2157	2.8803	1.3897	296.79	8.0224	7.7857
74400	74136	.9929	1.2039	2.8528	1.4033	296.83	8.0242	7.7877
74600	74334	.9929	1.1923	2.8257	1.4170	296.87	8.0261	7.7897
74800	74533	.9929	1.1808	2.7988	1.4308	296.91	8.0279	7.7917

Table V
Geopotential Altitude, English Altitudes

Altitude		Gravity ratio	Number density	Collision frequency	Mean free path	Sound speed	Viscosity ratio	Thermal conductivity ratio
H (ft)	Z (ft)	g/g_0	n (m^{-3})	ν (s^{-1})	L (m)	C_s (m/s)	μ/μ_0	κ/κ_0
75000	75271	.9928	1.1542 +24	2.7365 + 8	1.4638 - 6	297.01	8.0323 - 1	7.7964 - 1
75200	75472	.9928	1.1429	2.7103	1.4782	297.05	8.0341	7.7984
75400	75674	.9928	1.1318	2.6843	1.4927	297.09	8.0360	7.8004
75600	75875	.9928	1.1209	2.6586	1.5073	297.13	8.0379	7.8025
75800	76077	.9927	1.1100	2.6332	1.5221	297.18	8.0397	7.8045
76000	76278	.9927	1.0992	2.6080	1.5370	297.22	8.0416	7.8065
76200	76479	.9927	1.0885	2.5831	1.5521	297.26	8.0434	7.8085
76400	76681	.9927	1.0780	2.5584	1.5673	297.30	8.0453	7.8106
76600	76882	.9927	1.0675	2.5339	1.5826	297.34	8.0472	7.8126
76800	77084	.9926	1.0572	2.5097	1.5981	297.38	8.0490	7.8146
77000	77285	.9926	1.0469 +24	2.4857 + 8	1.6137 - 6	297.42	8.0509 - 1	7.8166 - 1
77200	77487	.9926	1.0368	2.4620	1.6295	297.46	8.0527	7.8186
77400	77688	.9926	1.0267	2.4384	1.6455	297.51	8.0546	7.8207
77600	77890	.9926	1.0168	2.4152	1.6616	297.55	8.0565	7.8227
77800	78091	.9926	1.0070	2.3921	1.6778	297.59	8.0583	7.8247
78000	78293	.9925	9.9721 +23	2.3693	1.6942	297.63	8.0602	7.8267
78200	78494	.9925	9.8756	2.3467	1.7108	297.67	8.0620	7.8287
78400	78696	.9925	9.7801	2.3243	1.7275	297.71	8.0639	7.8308
78600	78897	.9925	9.6855	2.3021	1.7443	297.75	8.0657	7.8328
78800	79099	.9925	9.5918	2.2802	1.7614	297.79	8.0676	7.8348
79000	79300	.9924	9.4991 +23	2.2585 + 8	1.7786 - 6	297.83	8.0695 - 1	7.8368 - 1
79200	79502	.9924	9.4073	2.2370	1.7959	297.88	8.0713	7.8388
79400	79703	.9924	9.3165	2.2157	1.8134	297.92	8.0732	7.8409
79600	79905	.9924	9.2265	2.1946	1.8311	297.96	8.0750	7.8429
79800	80107	.9924	9.1374	2.1737	1.8490	298.00	8.0769	7.8449
80000	80308	.9923	9.0492	2.1530	1.8670	298.04	8.0787	7.8469
80200	80510	.9923	8.9619	2.1325	1.8852	298.08	8.0806	7.8489
80400	80711	.9923	8.8754	2.1122	1.9035	298.12	8.0825	7.8510
80600	80913	.9923	8.7898	2.0921	1.9221	298.16	8.0843	7.8530
80800	81114	.9923	8.7051	2.0723	1.9408	298.20	8.0862	7.8550
81000	81316	.9922	8.6212 +23	2.0526 + 8	1.9597 - 6	298.25	8.0880 - 1	7.8570 - 1
81200	81517	.9922	8.5381	2.0331	1.9787	298.29	8.0899	7.8590
81400	81719	.9922	8.4558	2.0138	1.9980	298.33	8.0917	7.8611
81600	81921	.9922	8.3744	1.9946	2.0174	298.37	8.0936	7.8631
81800	82122	.9922	8.2938	1.9757	2.0370	298.41	8.0954	7.8651
82000	82324	.9922	8.2139	1.9570	2.0568	298.45	8.0973	7.8671
82200	82525	.9921	8.1349	1.9384	2.0768	298.49	8.0991	7.8691
82400	82727	.9921	8.0566	1.9200	2.0970	298.53	8.1010	7.8711
82600	82928	.9921	7.9791	1.9018	2.1174	298.57	8.1029	7.8732
82800	83130	.9921	7.9024	1.8838	2.1379	298.61	8.1047	7.8752
83000	83332	.9921	7.8265 +23	1.8659 + 8	2.1587 - 6	298.66	8.1066 - 1	7.8772 - 1
83200	83533	.9920	7.7512	1.8482	2.1796	298.70	8.1084	7.8792
83400	83735	.9920	7.6768	1.8307	2.2008	298.74	8.1103	7.8812
83600	83936	.9920	7.6030	1.8134	2.2221	298.78	8.1121	7.8832
83800	84138	.9920	7.5300	1.7962	2.2436	298.82	8.1140	7.8853
84000	84340	.9920	7.4577	1.7792	2.2654	298.86	8.1158	7.8873
84200	84541	.9919	7.3862	1.7624	2.2873	298.90	8.1177	7.8893
84400	84743	.9919	7.3153	1.7457	2.3095	298.94	8.1195	7.8913
84600	84945	.9919	7.2451	1.7292	2.3319	298.98	8.1214	7.8933
84800	85146	.9919	7.1757	1.7129	2.3544	299.02	8.1232	7.8953
85000	85348	.9919	7.1069 +23	1.6967 + 8	2.3772 - 6	299.07	8.1251 - 1	7.8974 - 1
85200	85550	.9918	7.0388	1.6807	2.4002	299.11	8.1269	7.8994
85400	85751	.9918	6.9713	1.6648	2.4234	299.15	8.1288	7.9014
85600	85953	.9918	6.9046	1.6491	2.4469	299.19	8.1306	7.9034
85800	86154	.9918	6.8384	1.6335	2.4705	299.23	8.1325	7.9054
86000	86356	.9918	6.7730	1.6181	2.4944	299.27	8.1343	7.9074
86200	86558	.9918	6.7081	1.6028	2.5185	299.31	8.1362	7.9095
86400	86759	.9917	6.6440	1.5877	2.5429	299.35	8.1380	7.9115
86600	86961	.9917	6.5804	1.5727	2.5674	299.39	8.1399	7.9135
86800	87163	.9917	6.5175	1.5579	2.5922	299.43	8.1417	7.9155
87000	87364	.9917	6.4552 +23	1.5432 + 8	2.6172 - 6	299.48	8.1436 - 1	7.9175 - 1
87200	87566	.9917	6.3935	1.5287	2.6425	299.52	8.1454	7.9195
87400	87768	.9916	6.3324	1.5143	2.6680	299.56	8.1473	7.9216
87600	87970	.9916	6.2719	1.5000	2.6937	299.60	8.1491	7.9236
87800	88171	.9916	6.2120	1.4859	2.7197	299.64	8.1510	7.9256
88000	88373	.9916	6.1527	1.4719	2.7459	299.68	8.1528	7.9276
88200	88575	.9916	6.0940	1.4580	2.7724	299.72	8.1547	7.9296
88400	88776	.9915	6.0358	1.4443	2.7991	299.76	8.1565	7.9316
88600	88978	.9915	5.9782	1.4308	2.8260	299.80	8.1584	7.9336
88800	89180	.9915	5.9212	1.4173	2.8532	299.84	8.1602	7.9357
89000	89381	.9915	5.8648 +23	1.4040 + 8	2.8807 - 6	299.88	8.1620 - 1	7.9377 - 1
89200	89583	.9915	5.8089	1.3908	2.9084	299.92	8.1639	7.9397
89400	89785	.9914	5.7535	1.3777	2.9364	299.97	8.1657	7.9417
89600	89987	.9914	5.6987	1.3648	2.9647	300.01	8.1676	7.9437
89800	90188	.9914	5.6444	1.3520	2.9932	300.05	8.1694	7.9457
90000	90390	.9914	5.5907	1.3393	3.0219	300.09	8.1713	7.9477
90200	90592	.9914	5.5374	1.3267	3.0510	300.13	8.1731	7.9497
90400	90794	.9913	5.4848	1.3143	3.0803	300.17	8.1750	7.9518
90600	90995	.9913	5.4326	1.3019	3.1099	300.21	8.1768	7.9538
90800	91197	.9913	5.3809	1.2897	3.1397	300.25	8.1787	7.9558

Table V
Geometric Altitude, English Altitudes

Altitude		Gravity ratio	Number density	Collision frequency	Mean free path	Sound speed	Viscosity ratio	Thermal conductivity ratio
Z (ft)	H (ft)	g/g_0	n (m^{-3})	ν (s^{-1})	L (m)	C_s (m/s)	μ/μ_0	κ/κ_0
75000	74731	.9928	1.1694 +24	2.7721 + 8	1.4447 - 6	296.96	8.0298 - 1	7.7937 - 1
75200	74930	.9928	1.1581	2.7458	1.4588	297.00	8.0316	7.7957
75400	75128	.9928	1.1469	2.7196	1.4730	297.04	8.0335	7.7977
75600	75327	.9928	1.1359	2.6938	1.4874	297.08	8.0353	7.7997
75800	75525	.9928	1.1249	2.6682	1.5018	297.12	8.0372	7.8017
76000	75724	.9928	1.1141	2.6428	1.5165	297.16	8.0390	7.8037
76200	75923	.9927	1.1034	2.6177	1.5312	297.20	8.0409	7.8057
76400	76121	.9927	1.0927	2.5929	1.5461	297.24	8.0427	7.8077
76600	76320	.9927	1.0822	2.5682	1.5611	297.28	8.0445	7.8097
76800	76518	.9927	1.0718	2.5439	1.5763	297.32	8.0464	7.8117
77000	76717	.9927	1.0615 +24	2.5197 + 8	1.5916 - 6	297.36	8.0482 - 1	7.8138 - 1
77200	76915	.9926	1.0513	2.4958	1.6071	297.41	8.0501	7.8158
77400	77114	.9926	1.0411	2.4721	1.6227	297.45	8.0519	7.8178
77600	77312	.9926	1.0311	2.4487	1.6385	297.49	8.0538	7.8198
77800	77511	.9926	1.0212	2.4255	1.6544	297.53	8.0556	7.8218
78000	77709	.9926	1.0114	2.4025	1.6704	297.57	8.0575	7.8238
78200	77908	.9925	1.0017	2.3798	1.6866	297.61	8.0593	7.8258
78400	78106	.9925	9.9206 +23	2.3572	1.7030	297.65	8.0612	7.8278
78600	78305	.9925	9.8253	2.3349	1.7195	297.69	8.0630	7.8298
78800	78503	.9925	9.7310	2.3128	1.7362	297.73	8.0648	7.8318
79000	78702	.9925	9.6376 +23	2.2909 + 8	1.7530 - 6	297.77	8.0667 - 1	7.8338 - 1
79200	78900	.9924	9.5452	2.2693	1.7700	297.81	8.0685	7.8358
79400	79099	.9924	9.4536	2.2478	1.7871	297.85	8.0704	7.8378
79600	79297	.9924	9.3630	2.2266	1.8044	297.90	8.0722	7.8398
79800	79496	.9924	9.2732	2.2055	1.8219	297.94	8.0741	7.8418
80000	79694	.9924	9.1843	2.1847	1.8395	297.98	8.0759	7.8438
80200	79893	.9924	9.0964	2.1640	1.8573	298.02	8.0777	7.8458
80400	80091	.9923	9.0092	2.1436	1.8753	298.06	8.0796	7.8478
80600	80290	.9923	8.9230	2.1234	1.8934	298.10	8.0814	7.8498
80800	80488	.9923	8.8376	2.1033	1.9117	298.14	8.0833	7.8518
81000	80687	.9923	8.7530 +23	2.0835 + 8	1.9302 - 6	298.18	8.0851 - 1	7.8538 - 1
81200	80885	.9923	8.6693	2.0638	1.9488	298.22	8.0870	7.8559
81400	81084	.9922	8.5863	2.0444	1.9676	298.26	8.0888	7.8579
81600	81282	.9922	8.5043	2.0251	1.9866	298.30	8.0906	7.8599
81800	81480	.9922	8.4230	2.0060	2.0058	298.34	8.0925	7.8619
82000	81679	.9922	8.3425	1.9871	2.0251	298.38	8.0943	7.8639
82200	81877	.9922	8.2628	1.9684	2.0447	298.43	8.0962	7.8659
82400	82076	.9921	8.1839	1.9499	2.0644	298.47	8.0980	7.8679
82600	82274	.9921	8.1058	1.9315	2.0843	298.51	8.0998	7.8699
82800	82473	.9921	8.0284	1.9134	2.1044	298.55	8.1017	7.8719
83000	82671	.9921	7.9518 +23	1.8954 + 8	2.1246 - 6	298.59	8.1035 - 1	7.8739 - 1
83200	82869	.9921	7.8759	1.8775	2.1451	298.63	8.1053	7.8759
83400	83068	.9920	7.8008	1.8599	2.1657	298.67	8.1072	7.8779
83600	83266	.9920	7.7265	1.8424	2.1866	298.71	8.1090	7.8799
83800	83465	.9920	7.6528	1.8251	2.2076	298.75	8.1109	7.8819
84000	83663	.9920	7.5799	1.8080	2.2289	298.79	8.1127	7.8839
84200	83861	.9920	7.5077	1.7910	2.2503	298.83	8.1145	7.8859
84400	84060	.9920	7.4362	1.7742	2.2719	298.87	8.1164	7.8879
84600	84258	.9919	7.3655	1.7575	2.2938	298.91	8.1182	7.8899
84800	84457	.9919	7.2954	1.7410	2.3158	298.95	8.1200	7.8919
85000	84655	.9919	7.2260 +23	1.7247 + 8	2.3381 - 6	298.99	8.1219 - 1	7.8939 - 1
85200	84853	.9919	7.1572	1.7085	2.3605	299.04	8.1237	7.8959
85400	85052	.9919	7.0892	1.6925	2.3832	299.08	8.1256	7.8979
85600	85250	.9918	7.0218	1.6767	2.4060	299.12	8.1274	7.8999
85800	85448	.9918	6.9551	1.6610	2.4291	299.16	8.1292	7.9019
86000	85647	.9918	6.8890	1.6454	2.4524	299.20	8.1311	7.9039
86200	85845	.9918	6.8236	1.6300	2.4759	299.24	8.1329	7.9059
86400	86044	.9918	6.7588	1.6147	2.4997	299.28	8.1347	7.9079
86600	86242	.9917	6.6946	1.5996	2.5236	299.32	8.1366	7.9099
86800	86440	.9917	6.6311	1.5847	2.5478	299.36	8.1384	7.9119
87000	86639	.9917	6.5682 +23	1.5698 + 8	2.5722 - 6	299.40	8.1402 - 1	7.9139 - 1
87200	86837	.9917	6.5059	1.5552	2.5968	299.44	8.1421	7.9159
87400	87035	.9917	6.4442	1.5406	2.6217	299.48	8.1439	7.9179
87600	87234	.9917	6.3831	1.5262	2.6468	299.52	8.1457	7.9199
87800	87432	.9916	6.3227	1.5120	2.6721	299.56	8.1476	7.9219
88000	87630	.9916	6.2628	1.4979	2.6976	299.60	8.1494	7.9239
88200	87829	.9916	6.2035	1.4839	2.7234	299.64	8.1512	7.9259
88400	88027	.9916	6.1447	1.4700	2.7495	299.68	8.1531	7.9279
88600	88225	.9916	6.0866	1.4563	2.7757	299.73	8.1549	7.9299
88800	88423	.9915	6.0290	1.4427	2.8022	299.77	8.1567	7.9319
89000	88622	.9915	5.9720 +23	1.4293 + 8	2.8290 - 6	299.81	8.1586 - 1	7.9339 - 1
89200	88820	.9915	5.9155	1.4159	2.8560	299.85	8.1604	7.9359
89400	89018	.9915	5.8596	1.4028	2.8833	299.89	8.1622	7.9379
89600	89217	.9915	5.8042	1.3897	2.9108	299.93	8.1640	7.9398
89800	89415	.9914	5.7494	1.3767	2.9385	299.97	8.1659	7.9418
90000	89613	.9914	5.6950	1.3639	2.9666	300.01	8.1677	7.9438
90200	89812	.9914	5.6413	1.3512	2.9948	300.05	8.1695	7.9458
90400	90010	.9914	5.5880	1.3386	3.0234	300.09	8.1714	7.9478
90600	90208	.9914	5.5353	1.3262	3.0522	300.13	8.1732	7.9498
90800	90406	.9913	5.4831	1.3139	3.0812	300.17	8.1750	7.9518

Table V
Geopotential Altitude, English Altitudes

Altitude		Gravity ratio	Number density	Collision frequency	Mean free path	Sound speed	Viscosity ratio	Thermal conductivity ratio
H (ft)	Z (ft)	g/g_0	n (m^{-3})	ν (s^{-1})	L (m)	C_s (m/s)	μ/μ_0	κ/κ_0
91000	91399	.9913	5.3297 +23	1.2776 + 8	3.1699 − 6	300.29	8.1805 − 1	7.9578 − 1
91200	91601	.9913	5.2791	1.2657	3.2003	300.33	8.1823	7.9598
91400	91802	.9913	5.2289	1.2538	3.2310	300.37	8.1842	7.9618
91600	92004	.9912	5.1792	1.2421	3.2620	300.41	8.1860	7.9638
91800	92206	.9912	5.1300	1.2304	3.2933	300.46	8.1879	7.9659
92000	92408	.9912	5.0813	1.2189	3.3249	300.50	8.1897	7.9679
92200	92609	.9912	5.0331	1.2075	3.3567	300.54	8.1916	7.9699
92400	92811	.9912	4.9853	1.1962	3.3889	300.58	8.1934	7.9719
92600	93013	.9911	4.9380	1.1850	3.4214	300.62	8.1952	7.9739
92800	93215	.9911	4.8912	1.1739	3.4541	300.66	8.1971	7.9759
93000	93417	.9911	4.8448 +23	1.1630 + 8	3.4872 − 6	300.70	8.1989 − 1	7.9779 − 1
93200	93618	.9911	4.7988	1.1521	3.5206	300.74	8.2008	7.9799
93400	93820	.9911	4.7534	1.1413	3.5543	300.78	8.2026	7.9819
93600	94022	.9910	4.7083	1.1307	3.5883	300.82	8.2045	7.9840
93800	94224	.9910	4.6637	1.1201	3.6226	300.86	8.2063	7.9860
94000	94426	.9910	4.6196	1.1096	3.6572	300.90	8.2081	7.9880
94200	94627	.9910	4.5758	1.0993	3.6922	300.94	8.2100	7.9900
94400	94829	.9910	4.5325	1.0890	3.7274	300.98	8.2118	7.9920
94600	95031	.9909	4.4896	1.0789	3.7630	301.03	8.2137	7.9940
94800	95233	.9909	4.4471	1.0688	3.7990	301.07	8.2155	7.9960
95000	95435	.9909	4.4051 +23	1.0588 + 8	3.8353 − 6	301.11	8.2173 − 1	7.9980 − 1
95200	95637	.9909	4.3634	1.0490	3.8719	301.15	8.2192	8.0000
95400	95838	.9909	4.3222	1.0392	3.9088	301.19	8.2210	8.0021
95600	96040	.9909	4.2813	1.0295	3.9461	301.23	8.2229	8.0041
95800	96242	.9908	4.2409	1.0199	3.9837	301.27	8.2247	8.0061
96000	96444	.9908	4.2008	1.0104	4.0217	301.31	8.2265	8.0081
96200	96646	.9908	4.1612	1.0010	4.0601	301.35	8.2284	8.0101
96400	96848	.9908	4.1219	9.9171 + 7	4.0988	301.39	8.2302	8.0121
96600	97050	.9908	4.0830	9.8248	4.1378	301.43	8.2321	8.0141
96800	97251	.9907	4.0445	9.7335	4.1772	301.47	8.2339	8.0161
97000	97453	.9907	4.0063 +23	9.6430 + 7	4.2170 − 6	301.51	8.2357 − 1	8.0181 − 1
97200	97655	.9907	3.9686	9.5533	4.2571	301.55	8.2376	8.0201
97400	97857	.9907	3.9311	9.4645	4.2976	301.59	8.2394	8.0222
97600	98059	.9907	3.8941	9.3766	4.3385	301.64	8.2412	8.0242
97800	98261	.9906	3.8574	9.2895	4.3798	301.68	8.2431	8.0262
98000	98463	.9906	3.8211	9.2032	4.4215	301.72	8.2449	8.0282
98200	98665	.9906	3.7851	9.1178	4.4635	301.76	8.2467	8.0302
98400	98866	.9906	3.7494	9.0332	4.5059	301.80	8.2486	8.0322
98600	99068	.9906	3.7142	8.9493	4.5487	301.84	8.2504	8.0342
98800	99270	.9905	3.6792	8.8663	4.5919	301.88	8.2523	8.0362
99000	99472	.9905	3.6446 +23	8.7841 + 7	4.6355 − 6	301.92	8.2541 − 1	8.0382 − 1
99200	99674	.9905	3.6103	8.7027	4.6795	301.96	8.2559	8.0402
99400	99876	.9905	3.5764	8.6220	4.7240	302.00	8.2578	8.0422
99600	100078	.9905	3.5428	8.5421	4.7688	302.04	8.2596	8.0443
99800	100280	.9905	3.5095	8.4630	4.8140	302.08	8.2614	8.0463
100000	100482	.9904	3.4765	8.3846	4.8597	302.12	8.2633	8.0483
100200	100684	.9904	3.4439	8.3070	4.9057	302.16	8.2651	8.0503
100400	100886	.9904	3.4115	8.2301	4.9522	302.20	8.2669	8.0523
100600	101088	.9904	3.3795	8.1539	4.9992	302.24	8.2688	8.0543
100800	101290	.9904	3.3478	8.0785	5.0465	302.28	8.2706	8.0563
101000	101492	.9903	3.3164 +23	8.0037 + 7	5.0943 − 6	302.32	8.2724 − 1	8.0583 − 1
101200	101693	.9903	3.2853	7.9297	5.1426	302.37	8.2743	8.0603
101400	101895	.9903	3.2545	7.8564	5.1912	302.41	8.2761	8.0623
101600	102097	.9903	3.2240	7.7838	5.2404	302.45	8.2779	8.0643
101800	102299	.9903	3.1937	7.7119	5.2899	302.49	8.2798	8.0663
102000	102501	.9902	3.1638	7.6407	5.3400	302.53	8.2816	8.0683
102200	102703	.9902	3.1342	7.5701	5.3905	302.57	8.2834	8.0703
102400	102905	.9902	3.1048	7.5002	5.4414	302.61	8.2853	8.0724
102600	103107	.9902	3.0758	7.4310	5.4928	302.65	8.2871	8.0744
102800	103309	.9902	3.0470	7.3625	5.5447	302.69	8.2889	8.0764
103000	103511	.9901	3.0185 +23	7.2945 + 7	5.5971 − 6	302.73	8.2908 − 1	8.0784 − 1
103200	103713	.9901	2.9902	7.2273	5.6500	302.77	8.2926	8.0804
103400	103915	.9901	2.9623	7.1606	5.7033	302.81	8.2944	8.0824
103600	104117	.9901	2.9346	7.0946	5.7571	302.85	8.2962	8.0844
103800	104319	.9901	2.9071	7.0293	5.8114	302.89	8.2981	8.0864
104000	104521	.9901	2.8800	6.9645	5.8663	302.93	8.2999	8.0884
104200	104723	.9900	2.8531	6.9004	5.9216	302.97	8.3017	8.0904
104400	104925	.9900	2.8264	6.8368	5.9774	303.01	8.3036	8.0924
104600	105127	.9900	2.8000	6.7739	6.0337	303.05	8.3054	8.0944
104800	105329	.9900	2.7739	6.7116	6.0906	303.09	8.3072	8.0964
105000	105531	.9900	2.7479 +23	6.6497 + 7	6.1482 − 6	303.14	8.3093 − 1	8.0987 − 1
105500	106036	.9899	2.6811	6.4941	6.3014	303.42	8.3221	8.1127
106000	106542	.9899	2.6161	6.3424	6.4581	303.70	8.3349	8.1267
106500	107047	.9898	2.5527	6.1945	6.6184	303.99	8.3476	8.1407
107000	107552	.9898	2.4910	6.0503	6.7824	304.27	8.3604	8.1547
107500	108057	.9897	2.4308	5.9098	6.9501	304.55	8.3732	8.1688
108000	108562	.9897	2.3723	5.7728	7.1217	304.83	8.3859	8.1828
108500	109067	.9896	2.3152	5.6391	7.2972	305.11	8.3986	8.1968
109000	109573	.9896	2.2597	5.5088	7.4766	305.39	8.4114	8.2107
109500	110078	.9895	2.2055	5.3818	7.6601	305.67	8.4241	8.2247

Table V
Geometric Altitude, English Altitudes

Altitude		Gravity ratio	Number density	Collision frequency	Mean free path	Sound speed	Viscosity ratio	Thermal conductivity ratio
Z (ft)	H (ft)	g/g_0	n (m^{-3})	ν (s^{-1})	L (m)	C_s (m/s)	μ/μ_0	κ/κ_0
91000	90605	.9913	5.4313 +23	1.3016 + 8	3.1106 - 6	300.21	8.1769 - 1	7.9538 - 1
91200	90803	.9913	5.3801	1.2895	3.1402	300.25	8.1787	7.9558
91400	91001	.9913	5.3294	1.2776	3.1701	300.29	8.1805	7.9578
91600	91199	.9913	5.2792	1.2657	3.2002	300.33	8.1823	7.9598
91800	91398	.9913	5.2295	1.2539	3.2307	300.37	8.1842	7.9618
92000	91596	.9912	5.1802	1.2423	3.2614	300.41	8.1860	7.9638
92200	91794	.9912	5.1314	1.2308	3.2924	300.45	8.1878	7.9658
92400	91992	.9912	5.0831	1.2193	3.3237	300.49	8.1896	7.9678
92600	92191	.9912	5.0353	1.2080	3.3552	300.53	8.1915	7.9698
92800	92389	.9912	4.9879	1.1968	3.3871	300.57	8.1933	7.9718
93000	92587	.9911	4.9410 +23	1.1857 + 8	3.4193 - 6	300.62	8.1951 - 1	7.9738 - 1
93200	92785	.9911	4.8946	1.1747	3.4517	300.66	8.1970	7.9758
93400	92984	.9911	4.8485	1.1638	3.4845	300.70	8.1988	7.9778
93600	93182	.9911	4.8030	1.1531	3.5175	300.74	8.2006	7.9798
93800	93380	.9911	4.7579	1.1424	3.5509	300.78	8.2024	7.9817
94000	93578	.9910	4.7132	1.1318	3.5845	300.82	8.2043	7.9837
94200	93776	.9910	4.6689	1.1213	3.6185	300.86	8.2061	7.9857
94400	93975	.9910	4.6251	1.1110	3.6528	300.90	8.2079	7.9877
94600	94173	.9910	4.5817	1.1007	3.6874	300.94	8.2097	7.9897
94800	94371	.9910	4.5387	1.0905	3.7223	300.98	8.2116	7.9917
95000	94569	.9910	4.4962 +23	1.0804 + 8	3.7576 - 6	301.02	8.2134 - 1	7.9937 - 1
95200	94767	.9909	4.4540	1.0704	3.7931	301.06	8.2152	7.9957
95400	94966	.9909	4.4123	1.0605	3.8290	301.10	8.2170	7.9977
95600	95164	.9909	4.3709	1.0508	3.8652	301.14	8.2188	7.9997
95800	95362	.9909	4.3300	1.0410	3.9018	301.18	8.2207	8.0017
96000	95560	.9909	4.2894	1.0314	3.9387	301.22	8.2225	8.0037
96200	95758	.9908	4.2493	1.0219	3.9759	301.26	8.2243	8.0057
96400	95956	.9908	4.2095	1.0125	4.0134	301.30	8.2261	8.0076
96600	96155	.9908	4.1701	1.0031	4.0513	301.34	8.2280	8.0096
96800	96353	.9908	4.1311	9.9390 + 7	4.0896	301.38	8.2298	8.0116
97000	96551	.9908	4.0925 +23	9.8474 + 7	4.1282 - 6	301.42	8.2316 - 1	8.0136 - 1
97200	96749	.9907	4.0542	9.7566	4.1672	301.46	8.2334	8.0156
97400	96947	.9907	4.0163	9.6667	4.2065	301.50	8.2352	8.0176
97600	97145	.9907	3.9788	9.5777	4.2461	301.54	8.2371	8.0196
97800	97343	.9907	3.9417	9.4895	4.2862	301.58	8.2389	8.0216
98000	97542	.9907	3.9048	9.4021	4.3266	301.62	8.2407	8.0236
98200	97740	.9906	3.8684	9.3156	4.3674	301.66	8.2425	8.0256
98400	97938	.9906	3.8323	9.2299	4.4085	301.70	8.2443	8.0276
98600	98136	.9906	3.7965	9.1450	4.4500	301.74	8.2462	8.0295
98800	98334	.9906	3.7611	9.0609	4.4919	301.78	8.2480	8.0315
99000	98532	.9906	3.7261 +23	8.9776 + 7	4.5342 - 6	301.82	8.2498 - 1	8.0335 - 1
99200	98730	.9906	3.6913	8.8951	4.5769	301.86	8.2516	8.0355
99400	98928	.9905	3.6569	8.8134	4.6199	301.90	8.2534	8.0375
99600	99127	.9905	3.6229	8.7324	4.6634	301.94	8.2553	8.0395
99800	99325	.9905	3.5891	8.6522	4.7072	301.98	8.2571	8.0415
100000	99523	.9905	3.5557	8.5728	4.7514	302.03	8.2589	8.0435
100200	99721	.9905	3.5226	8.4941	4.7961	302.07	8.2607	8.0455
100400	99919	.9904	3.4898	8.4162	4.8411	302.11	8.2625	8.0474
100600	100117	.9904	3.4573	8.3390	4.8866	302.15	8.2643	8.0494
100800	100315	.9904	3.4252	8.2626	4.9325	302.19	8.2662	8.0514
101000	100513	.9904	3.3933 +23	8.1868 + 7	4.9788 - 6	302.23	8.2680 - 1	8.0534 - 1
101200	100711	.9904	3.3618	8.1118	5.0255	302.27	8.2698	8.0554
101400	100909	.9903	3.3306	8.0375	5.0726	302.31	8.2716	8.0574
101600	101107	.9903	3.2996	7.9639	5.1202	302.35	8.2734	8.0594
101800	101305	.9903	3.2690	7.8909	5.1682	302.39	8.2752	8.0614
102000	101504	.9903	3.2386	7.8187	5.2166	302.43	8.2770	8.0634
102200	101702	.9903	3.2086	7.7472	5.2655	302.47	8.2789	8.0653
102400	101900	.9903	3.1788	7.6763	5.3148	302.51	8.2807	8.0673
102600	102098	.9902	3.1493	7.6061	5.3646	302.55	8.2825	8.0693
102800	102296	.9902	3.1201	7.5365	5.4148	302.59	8.2843	8.0713
103000	102494	.9902	3.0911 +23	7.4677 + 7	5.4655 - 6	302.63	8.2861 - 1	8.0733 - 1
103200	102692	.9902	3.0625	7.3994	5.5166	302.67	8.2879	8.0753
103400	102890	.9902	3.0341	7.3318	5.5682	302.71	8.2897	8.0773
103600	103088	.9901	3.0060	7.2649	5.6203	302.75	8.2916	8.0792
103800	103286	.9901	2.9782	7.1985	5.6728	302.79	8.2934	8.0812
104000	103484	.9901	2.9506	7.1328	5.7258	302.83	8.2952	8.0832
104200	103682	.9901	2.9233	7.0677	5.7793	302.87	8.2970	8.0852
104400	103880	.9901	2.8962	7.0033	5.8333	302.91	8.2988	8.0872
104600	104078	.9900	2.8694	6.9394	5.8878	302.95	8.3006	8.0892
104800	104276	.9900	2.8429	6.8761	5.9428	302.99	8.3024	8.0912
105000	104474	.9900	2.8166 +23	6.8134 + 7	5.9982 - 6	303.03	8.3042 - 1	8.0931 - 1
105500	104969	.9900	2.7520	6.6593	6.1391	303.13	8.3088	8.0981
106000	105464	.9899	2.6859	6.5051	6.2902	303.40	8.3211	8.1117
106500	105959	.9899	2.6213	6.3547	6.4451	303.68	8.3338	8.1256
107000	106454	.9898	2.5585	6.2080	6.6035	303.96	8.3464	8.1394
107500	106949	.9898	2.4972	6.0649	6.7654	304.24	8.3591	8.1533
108000	107444	.9897	2.4375	5.9254	6.9310	304.52	8.3717	8.1672
108500	107938	.9897	2.3794	5.7894	7.1004	304.80	8.3843	8.1810
109000	108433	.9896	2.3228	5.6567	7.2735	305.07	8.3969	8.1949
109500	108928	.9896	2.2676	5.5274	7.4506	305.35	8.4095	8.2087

Table V
Geopotential Altitude, English Altitudes

Altitude		Gravity ratio	Number density	Collision frequency	Mean free path	Sound speed	Viscosity ratio	Thermal conductivity ratio
H (ft)	Z (ft)	g/g_0	$n\ (m^{-3})$	$\nu\ (s^{-1})$	$L\ (m)$	$C_s\ (m/s)$	μ/μ_0	κ/κ_0
110000	110583	.9895	2.1528 +23	5.2579 +7	7.8478 −6	305.95	8.4368 −1	8.2387 −1
110500	111089	.9894	2.1014	5.1371	8.0398	306.23	8.4495	8.2527
111000	111594	.9894	2.0513	5.0193	8.2360	306.51	8.4621	8.2667
111500	112099	.9893	2.0025	4.9043	8.4367	306.79	8.4748	8.2806
112000	112605	.9893	1.9550	4.7922	8.6419	307.07	8.4875	8.2946
112500	113110	.9892	1.9086	4.6829	8.8517	307.35	8.5001	8.3085
113000	113616	.9892	1.8635	4.5763	9.0662	307.63	8.5128	8.3225
113500	114121	.9891	1.8195	4.4722	9.2855	307.91	8.5254	8.3364
114000	114627	.9891	1.7766	4.3708	9.5096	308.19	8.5380	8.3503
114500	115132	.9890	1.7348	4.2718	9.7388	308.47	8.5506	8.3643
115000	115638	.9890	1.6940 +23	4.1752 +7	9.9731 −6	308.74	8.5632 −1	8.3782 −1
115500	116143	.9890	1.6543	4.0809	1.0213 −5	309.02	8.5758	8.3921
116000	116649	.9889	1.6156	3.9890	1.0457	309.30	8.5884	8.4060
116500	117154	.9889	1.5778	3.8993	1.0708	309.58	8.6010	8.4199
117000	117660	.9888	1.5410	3.8117	1.0963	309.85	8.6135	8.4338
117500	118166	.9888	1.5051	3.7263	1.1225	310.13	8.6261	8.4477
118000	118671	.9887	1.4702	3.6430	1.1492	310.41	8.6386	8.4616
118500	119177	.9887	1.4361	3.5616	1.1765	310.68	8.6512	8.4755
119000	119683	.9886	1.4028	3.4822	1.2044	310.96	8.6637	8.4894
119500	120189	.9886	1.3704	3.4047	1.2329	311.23	8.6762	8.5033
120000	120695	.9885	1.3387 +23	3.3291 +7	1.2620 −5	311.51	8.6887 −1	8.5171 −1
120500	121200	.9885	1.3079	3.2552	1.2917	311.78	8.7012	8.5310
121000	121706	.9884	1.2778	3.1832	1.3222	312.06	8.7137	8.5448
121500	122212	.9884	1.2485	3.1128	1.3532	312.33	8.7261	8.5587
122000	122718	.9883	1.2199	3.0442	1.3850	312.61	8.7386	8.5725
122500	123224	.9883	1.1920	2.9771	1.4174	312.88	8.7510	8.5864
123000	123730	.9882	1.1647	2.9117	1.4505	313.16	8.7635	8.6002
123500	124236	.9882	1.1382	2.8478	1.4844	313.43	8.7759	8.6140
124000	124742	.9881	1.1123	2.7854	1.5189	313.70	8.7883	8.6278
124500	125248	.9881	1.0870	2.7245	1.5543	313.98	8.8007	8.6417
125000	125754	.9880	1.0623 +23	2.6650 +7	1.5903 −5	314.25	8.8132 −1	8.6555 −1
125500	126260	.9880	1.0383	2.6069	1.6272	314.52	8.8255	8.6693
126000	126766	.9880	1.0148	2.5502	1.6648	314.79	8.8379	8.6831
126500	127272	.9879	9.9191 +22	2.4948	1.7032	315.07	8.8503	8.6969
127000	127778	.9879	9.6956	2.4407	1.7425	315.34	8.8627	8.7106
127500	128284	.9878	9.4776	2.3878	1.7826	315.61	8.8750	8.7244
128000	128790	.9878	9.2648	2.3362	1.8235	315.88	8.8874	8.7382
128500	129297	.9877	9.0571	2.2858	1.8653	316.15	8.8997	8.7520
129000	129803	.9877	8.8545	2.2366	1.9080	316.42	8.9120	8.7657
129500	130309	.9876	8.6567	2.1885	1.9516	316.70	8.9243	8.7795
130000	130815	.9876	8.4636 +22	2.1415 +7	1.9961 −5	316.97	8.9366 −1	8.7932 −1
130500	131322	.9875	8.2752	2.0957	2.0416	317.24	8.9489	8.8070
131000	131828	.9875	8.0913	2.0508	2.0880	317.51	8.9612	8.8207
131500	132334	.9874	7.9118	2.0070	2.1354	317.78	8.9735	8.8345
132000	132841	.9874	7.7365	1.9642	2.1837	318.05	8.9858	8.8482
132500	133347	.9873	7.5655	1.9224	2.2331	318.32	8.9980	8.8619
133000	133854	.9873	7.3984	1.8816	2.2835	318.58	9.0103	8.8756
133500	134360	.9872	7.2354	1.8417	2.3350	318.85	9.0225	8.8894
134000	134867	.9872	7.0762	1.8027	2.3875	319.12	9.0347	8.9031
134500	135373	.9871	6.9208	1.7645	2.4412	319.39	9.0469	8.9168
135000	135880	.9871	6.7690 +22	1.7273 +7	2.4959 −5	319.66	9.0592 −1	8.9305 −1
135500	136386	.9870	6.6208	1.6909	2.5518	319.93	9.0714	8.9441
136000	136893	.9870	6.4761	1.6553	2.6088	320.20	9.0835	8.9578
136500	137399	.9870	6.3348	1.6206	2.6670	320.46	9.0957	8.9715
137000	137906	.9869	6.1968	1.5866	2.7264	320.73	9.1079	8.9852
137500	138413	.9869	6.0620	1.5534	2.7870	321.00	9.1201	8.9989
138000	138919	.9868	5.9304	1.5209	2.8488	321.27	9.1322	9.0125
138500	139426	.9868	5.8018	1.4892	2.9120	321.53	9.1444	9.0262
139000	139933	.9867	5.6763	1.4582	2.9764	321.80	9.1565	9.0398
139500	140439	.9867	5.5536	1.4278	3.0421	322.06	9.1686	9.0535
140000	140946	.9866	5.4338 +22	1.3982 +7	3.1092 −5	322.33	9.1807 −1	9.0671 −1
140500	141453	.9866	5.3168	1.3692	3.1776	322.60	9.1928	9.0807
141000	141960	.9865	5.2025	1.3409	3.2474	322.86	9.2049	9.0944
141500	142467	.9865	5.0908	1.3132	3.3187	323.13	9.2170	9.1080
142000	142974	.9864	4.9817	1.2861	3.3913	323.39	9.2291	9.1216
142500	143480	.9864	4.8751	1.2596	3.4655	323.66	9.2412	9.1352
143000	143987	.9863	4.7710	1.2337	3.5411	323.92	9.2532	9.1488
143500	144494	.9863	4.6692	1.2084	3.6183	324.19	9.2653	9.1624
144000	145001	.9862	4.5698	1.1836	3.6970	324.45	9.2773	9.1760
144500	145508	.9862	4.4727	1.1594	3.7773	324.72	9.2894	9.1896
145000	146015	.9861	4.3777 +22	1.1357 +7	3.8592 −5	324.98	9.3014 −1	9.2032 −1
145500	146522	.9861	4.2850	1.1125	3.9428	325.24	9.3134	9.2168
146000	147029	.9860	4.1943	1.0899	4.0280	325.51	9.3254	9.2303
146500	147536	.9860	4.1057	1.0677	4.1149	325.77	9.3374	9.2439
147000	148044	.9860	4.0191	1.0460	4.2036	326.03	9.3494	9.2574
147500	148551	.9859	3.9345	1.0248	4.2940	326.30	9.3614	9.2710
148000	149058	.9859	3.8518	1.0041	4.3862	326.56	9.3733	9.2845
148500	149565	.9858	3.7710	9.8383 +6	4.4802	326.82	9.3853	9.2981
149000	150072	.9858	3.6919	9.6398	4.5761	327.08	9.3972	9.3116
149500	150579	.9857	3.6147	9.4457	4.6739	327.35	9.4092	9.3252

Table V
Geometric Altitude, English Altitudes

Altitude		Gravity ratio	Number density	Collision frequency	Mean free path	Sound speed	Viscosity ratio	Thermal conductivity ratio
Z (ft)	H (ft)	g/g_0	n (m^{-3})	ν (s^{-1})	L (m)	C_s (m/s)	μ/μ_0	κ/κ_0
110000	109423	.9895	2.2138 +23	5.4012 + 7	7.6316 - 6	305.63	8.4221 - 1	8.2226 - 1
110500	109918	.9895	2.1614	5.2781	7.8166	305.91	8.4347	8.2364
111000	110412	.9894	2.1103	5.1580	8.0058	306.18	8.4472	8.2502
111500	110907	.9894	2.0605	5.0409	8.1992	306.46	8.4598	8.2641
112000	111402	.9893	2.0120	4.9267	8.3969	306.74	8.4723	8.2779
112500	111896	.9893	1.9647	4.8152	8.5990	307.02	8.4849	8.2917
113000	112391	.9893	1.9186	4.7065	8.8056	307.29	8.4974	8.3055
113500	112886	.9892	1.8737	4.6004	9.0167	307.57	8.5099	8.3193
114000	113380	.9892	1.8299	4.4969	9.2325	307.84	8.5224	8.3331
114500	113875	.9891	1.7872	4.3959	9.4531	308.12	8.5349	8.3469
115000	114369	.9891	1.7456 +23	4.2974 + 7	9.6785 - 6	308.39	8.5473 - 1	8.3606 - 1
115500	114864	.9890	1.7050	4.2012	9.9088	308.67	8.5598	8.3744
116000	115358	.9890	1.6654	4.1074	1.0144 - 5	308.94	8.5723	8.3882
116500	115853	.9889	1.6269	4.0158	1.0385	309.22	8.5847	8.4019
117000	116347	.9889	1.5893	3.9264	1.0631	309.49	8.5971	8.4157
117500	116842	.9888	1.5526	3.8392	1.0882	309.76	8.6096	8.4294
118000	117336	.9888	1.5168	3.7541	1.1138	310.04	8.6220	8.4432
118500	117830	.9887	1.4819	3.6710	1.1401	310.31	8.6344	8.4569
119000	118325	.9887	1.4479	3.5899	1.1668	310.58	8.6468	8.4706
119500	118819	.9886	1.4147	3.5107	1.1942	310.86	8.6592	8.4844
120000	119313	.9886	1.3824 +23	3.4334 + 7	1.2222 - 5	311.13	8.6715 - 1	8.4981 - 1
120500	119808	.9885	1.3508	3.3579	1.2507	311.40	8.6839	8.5118
121000	120302	.9885	1.3200	3.2842	1.2799	311.67	8.6962	8.5255
121500	120796	.9884	1.2900	3.2123	1.3097	311.95	8.7086	8.5392
122000	121290	.9884	1.2607	3.1421	1.3401	312.22	8.7209	8.5529
122500	121785	.9884	1.2321	3.0735	1.3712	312.49	8.7332	8.5666
123000	122279	.9883	1.2042	3.0066	1.4030	312.76	8.7455	8.5802
123500	122773	.9883	1.1770	2.9412	1.4354	313.03	8.7578	8.5939
124000	123267	.9882	1.1505	2.8773	1.4685	313.30	8.7701	8.6076
124500	123761	.9882	1.1246	2.8150	1.5023	313.57	8.7824	8.6212
125000	124255	.9881	1.0993 +23	2.7541 + 7	1.5369 - 5	313.84	8.7947 - 1	8.6349 - 1
125500	124749	.9881	1.0746	2.6946	1.5722	314.11	8.8069	8.6485
126000	125243	.9880	1.0505	2.6365	1.6082	314.38	8.8192	8.6622
126500	125737	.9880	1.0271	2.5798	1.6449	314.65	8.8314	8.6758
127000	126231	.9879	1.0041	2.5244	1.6825	314.92	8.8436	8.6894
127500	126725	.9879	9.8177 +22	2.4702	1.7208	315.19	8.8559	8.7031
128000	127219	.9878	9.5993	2.4173	1.7600	315.46	8.8681	8.7167
128500	127713	.9878	9.3862	2.3657	1.7999	315.73	8.8803	8.7303
129000	128207	.9877	9.1782	2.3152	1.8407	315.99	8.8925	8.7439
129500	128701	.9877	8.9751	2.2659	1.8824	316.26	8.9046	8.7575
130000	129195	.9876	8.7769 +22	2.2177 + 7	1.9249 - 5	316.53	8.9168 - 1	8.7711 - 1
130500	129688	.9876	8.5833	2.1707	1.9683	316.80	8.9290	8.7847
131000	130182	.9876	8.3944	2.1247	2.0126	317.06	8.9411	8.7983
131500	130676	.9875	8.2099	2.0797	2.0578	317.33	8.9532	8.8118
132000	131170	.9875	8.0298	2.0358	2.1040	317.60	8.9654	8.8254
132500	131663	.9874	7.8540	1.9929	2.1511	317.86	8.9775	8.8390
133000	132157	.9874	7.6823	1.9510	2.1992	318.13	8.9896	8.8525
133500	132651	.9873	7.5146	1.9100	2.2482	318.40	9.0017	8.8661
134000	133144	.9873	7.3509	1.8699	2.2983	318.66	9.0138	8.8796
134500	133638	.9872	7.1910	1.8308	2.3494	318.93	9.0259	8.8931
135000	134132	.9872	7.0348 +22	1.7925 + 7	2.4016 - 5	319.19	9.0379 - 1	8.9067 - 1
135500	134625	.9871	6.8823	1.7551	2.4548	319.46	9.0500	8.9202
136000	135119	.9871	6.7334	1.7186	2.5091	319.72	9.0620	8.9337
136500	135612	.9870	6.5879	1.6828	2.5645	319.99	9.0741	8.9472
137000	136106	.9870	6.4458	1.6479	2.6210	320.25	9.0861	8.9607
137500	136599	.9869	6.3070	1.6137	2.6787	320.52	9.0981	8.9742
138000	137093	.9869	6.1715	1.5803	2.7375	320.78	9.1102	8.9877
138500	137586	.9868	6.0390	1.5477	2.7976	321.04	9.1222	9.0012
139000	138080	.9868	5.9096	1.5158	2.8588	321.31	9.1341	9.0147
139500	138573	.9868	5.7832	1.4846	2.9213	321.57	9.1461	9.0282
140000	139066	.9867	5.6598 +22	1.4541 + 7	2.9850 - 5	321.83	9.1581 - 1	9.0416 - 1
140500	139560	.9867	5.5391	1.4242	3.0501	322.10	9.1701	9.0551
141000	140053	.9866	5.4212	1.3951	3.1164	322.36	9.1820	9.0685
141500	140546	.9866	5.3060	1.3665	3.1840	322.62	9.1940	9.0820
142000	141040	.9865	5.1935	1.3386	3.2530	322.88	9.2059	9.0954
142500	141533	.9865	5.0835	1.3113	3.3234	323.15	9.2178	9.1089
143000	142026	.9864	4.9760	1.2847	3.3952	323.41	9.2297	9.1223
143500	142519	.9864	4.8710	1.2586	3.4684	323.67	9.2416	9.1357
144000	143012	.9863	4.7684	1.2330	3.5431	323.93	9.2535	9.1492
144500	143506	.9863	4.6680	1.2081	3.6192	324.19	9.2654	9.1626
145000	143999	.9862	4.5700 +22	1.1836 + 7	3.6969 - 5	324.45	9.2773 - 1	9.1760 - 1
145500	144492	.9862	4.4742	1.1598	3.7760	324.71	9.2892	9.1894
146000	144985	.9861	4.3805	1.1364	3.8568	324.97	9.3010	9.2028
146500	145478	.9861	4.2890	1.1135	3.9391	325.23	9.3129	9.2162
147000	145971	.9861	4.1995	1.0912	4.0231	325.49	9.3247	9.2295
147500	146464	.9860	4.1120	1.0693	4.1086	325.75	9.3365	9.2429
148000	146957	.9860	4.0265	1.0479	4.1959	326.01	9.3484	9.2563
148500	147450	.9859	3.9428	1.0269	4.2849	326.27	9.3602	9.2696
149000	147943	.9859	3.8611	1.0064	4.3756	326.53	9.3720	9.2830
149500	148436	.9858	3.7812	9.8639 + 6	4.4681	326.79	9.3838	9.2964

Table V
Geopotential Altitude, English Altitudes

Altitude		Gravity ratio	Number density	Collision frequency	Mean free path	Sound speed	Viscosity ratio	Thermal conductivity ratio
H (ft)	Z (ft)	g/g_0	n (m^{-3})	ν (s^{-1})	L (m)	C_s (m/s)	μ/μ_0	κ/κ_0
150000	151087	.9857	3.5392 +22	9.2558 + 6	4.7736 − 5	327.61	9.4211 − 1	9.3387 − 1
150500	151594	.9856	3.4654	9.0700	4.8753	327.87	9.4330	9.3522
151000	152101	.9856	3.3932	8.8882	4.9790	328.13	9.4450	9.3657
151500	152609	.9855	3.3227	8.7104	5.0847	328.39	9.4569	9.3792
152000	153116	.9855	3.2537	8.5364	5.1924	328.65	9.4688	9.3927
152500	153623	.9854	3.1863	8.3661	5.3023	328.91	9.4807	9.4062
153000	154131	.9854	3.1203	8.1995	5.4144	329.17	9.4925	9.4197
153500	154638	.9853	3.0559	8.0364	5.5286	329.43	9.5044	9.4332
154000	155146	.9853	2.9928	7.8769	5.6450	329.70	9.5163	9.4467
154500	155653	.9852	2.9340	7.7243	5.7583	329.80	9.5210	9.4521
155000	156161	.9852	2.8781 +22	7.5772 + 6	5.8701 − 5	329.80	9.5210 − 1	9.4521 − 1
155500	156668	.9851	2.8232	7.4328	5.9842	329.80	9.5210	9.4521
156000	157176	.9851	2.7694	7.2912	6.1004	329.80	9.5210	9.4521
156500	157683	.9850	2.7167	7.1523	6.2189	329.80	9.5210	9.4521
157000	158191	.9850	2.6649	7.0160	6.3397	329.80	9.5210	9.4521
157500	158699	.9850	2.6141	6.8823	6.4628	329.80	9.5210	9.4521
158000	159206	.9849	2.5643	6.7512	6.5883	329.80	9.5210	9.4521
158500	159714	.9849	2.5155	6.6225	6.7163	329.80	9.5210	9.4521
159000	160222	.9848	2.4675	6.4964	6.8468	329.80	9.5210	9.4521
159500	160729	.9848	2.4205	6.3726	6.9797	329.80	9.5210	9.4521
160000	161237	.9847	2.3744 +22	6.2512 + 6	7.1153 − 5	329.80	9.5210 − 1	9.4521 − 1
160500	161745	.9847	2.3292	6.1321	7.2535	329.80	9.5210	9.4521
161000	162253	.9846	2.2848	6.0152	7.3944	329.80	9.5210	9.4521
161500	162760	.9846	2.2413	5.9006	7.5380	329.80	9.5210	9.4521
162000	163268	.9845	2.1986	5.7882	7.6844	329.80	9.5210	9.4521
162500	163776	.9845	2.1567	5.6779	7.8337	329.80	9.5210	9.4521
163000	164284	.9844	2.1156	5.5697	7.9858	329.80	9.5210	9.4521
163500	164792	.9844	2.0753	5.4636	8.1410	329.80	9.5210	9.4521
164000	165300	.9843	2.0357	5.3595	8.2991	329.80	9.5210	9.4521
164500	165808	.9843	1.9969	5.2574	8.4603	329.80	9.5210	9.4521
165000	166316	.9842	1.9589 +22	5.1572 + 6	8.6246 − 5	329.80	9.5210 − 1	9.4521 − 1
165500	166824	.9842	1.9216	5.0590	8.7921	329.80	9.5210	9.4521
166000	167332	.9841	1.8850	4.9626	8.9629	329.80	9.5210	9.4521
166500	167840	.9841	1.8490	4.8680	9.1370	329.80	9.5210	9.4521
167000	168348	.9840	1.8138	4.7753	9.3144	329.80	9.5210	9.4521
167500	168856	.9840	1.7802	4.6856	9.4901	329.71	9.5168	9.4473
168000	169364	.9840	1.7490	4.5998	9.6594	329.45	9.5049	9.4338
168500	169873	.9839	1.7183	4.5155	9.8320	329.19	9.4931	9.4203
169000	170381	.9839	1.6881	4.4326	1.0008 − 4	328.93	9.4812	9.4068
169500	170889	.9838	1.6584	4.3511	1.0187	328.66	9.4693	9.3933
170000	171397	.9838	1.6291 +22	4.2709 + 6	1.0370 − 4	328.40	9.4574 − 1	9.3798 − 1
170500	171905	.9837	1.6004	4.1921	1.0557	328.14	9.4455	9.3663
171000	172414	.9837	1.5720	4.1147	1.0747	327.88	9.4336	9.3528
171500	172922	.9836	1.5442	4.0385	1.0941	327.62	9.4217	9.3393
172000	173430	.9836	1.5168	3.9637	1.1139	327.36	9.4097	9.3258
172500	173939	.9835	1.4898	3.8901	1.1340	327.10	9.3978	9.3122
173000	174447	.9835	1.4633	3.8178	1.1546	326.83	9.3858	9.2987
173500	174956	.9834	1.4372	3.7467	1.1755	326.57	9.3739	9.2852
174000	175464	.9834	1.4115	3.6768	1.1969	326.31	9.3619	9.2716
174500	175972	.9833	1.3862	3.6081	1.2187	326.05	9.3499	9.2581
175000	176481	.9833	1.3614 +22	3.5405 + 6	1.2410 − 4	325.78	9.3379 − 1	9.2445 − 1
175500	176989	.9832	1.3370	3.4742	1.2637	325.52	9.3259	9.2309
176000	177498	.9832	1.3129	3.4090	1.2868	325.26	9.3139	9.2174
176500	178007	.9831	1.2893	3.3449	1.3104	324.99	9.3019	9.2038
177000	178515	.9831	1.2660	3.2819	1.3345	324.73	9.2899	9.1902
177500	179024	.9831	1.2432	3.2200	1.3590	324.46	9.2779	9.1766
178000	179532	.9830	1.2207	3.1591	1.3841	324.20	9.2658	9.1630
178500	180041	.9830	1.1985	3.0993	1.4096	323.93	9.2538	9.1494
179000	180550	.9829	1.1768	3.0406	1.4357	323.67	9.2417	9.1358
179500	181058	.9829	1.1554	2.9828	1.4623	323.41	9.2296	9.1222
180000	181567	.9828	1.1343 +22	2.9261 + 6	1.4894 − 4	323.14	9.2176 − 1	9.1086 − 1
180500	182076	.9828	1.1136	2.8704	1.5171	322.87	9.2055	9.0950
181000	182585	.9827	1.0933	2.8156	1.5453	322.61	9.1934	9.0813
181500	183094	.9827	1.0733	2.7618	1.5741	322.34	9.1813	9.0677
182000	183602	.9826	1.0536	2.7089	1.6035	322.08	9.1692	9.0541
182500	184111	.9826	1.0343	2.6570	1.6335	321.81	9.1570	9.0404
183000	184620	.9825	1.0152	2.6060	1.6641	321.54	9.1449	9.0268
183500	185129	.9825	9.9654 +21	2.5558	1.6953	321.28	9.1328	9.0131
184000	185638	.9824	9.7815	2.5066	1.7272	321.01	9.1206	8.9995
184500	186147	.9824	9.6007	2.4582	1.7597	320.74	9.1084	8.9858
185000	186656	.9823	9.4230 +21	2.4107 + 6	1.7929 − 4	320.48	9.0963 − 1	8.9721 − 1
185500	187165	.9823	9.2483	2.3640	1.8268	320.21	9.0841	8.9584
186000	187674	.9822	9.0765	2.3182	1.8614	319.94	9.0719	8.9448
186500	188183	.9822	8.9076	2.2731	1.8967	319.67	9.0597	8.9311
187000	188692	.9821	8.7416	2.2289	1.9327	319.40	9.0475	8.9174
187500	189201	.9821	8.5784	2.1854	1.9694	319.13	9.0353	8.9037
188000	189710	.9821	8.4180	2.1428	2.0070	318.87	9.0230	8.8900
188500	190219	.9820	8.2603	2.1009	2.0453	318.60	9.0108	8.8763
189000	190729	.9820	8.1053	2.0597	2.0844	318.33	8.9986	8.8625
189500	191238	.9819	7.9530	2.0193	2.1243	318.06	8.9863	8.8488

Table V
Geometric Altitude, English Altitudes

Altitude		Gravity ratio	Number density	Collision frequency	Mean free path	Sound speed	Viscosity ratio	Thermal conductivity ratio
Z (ft)	H (ft)	g/g_0	n (m^{-3})	ν (s^{-1})	L (m)	C_s (m/s)	μ/μ_0	κ/κ_0
150000	148929	.9858	3.7030 +22	9.6678 + 6	4.5624 − 5	327.05	9.3955 − 1	9.3097 − 1
150500	149422	.9857	3.6266	9.4758	4.6585	327.30	9.4073	9.3230
151000	149915	.9857	3.5519	9.2879	4.7565	327.56	9.4191	9.3364
151500	150407	.9856	3.4789	9.1041	4.8563	327.82	9.4308	9.3497
152000	150900	.9856	3.4075	8.9241	4.9581	328.08	9.4426	9.3630
152500	151393	.9855	3.3376	8.7481	5.0619	328.34	9.4543	9.3763
153000	151886	.9855	3.2693	8.5757	5.1677	328.59	9.4660	9.3896
153500	152379	.9854	3.2025	8.4071	5.2755	328.85	9.4778	9.4029
154000	152871	.9854	3.1372	8.2420	5.3853	329.11	9.4895	9.4162
154500	153364	.9853	3.0733	8.0804	5.4973	329.36	9.5012	9.4295
155000	153856	.9853	3.0108 +22	7.9222 + 6	5.6114 − 5	329.62	9.5129 − 1	9.4428 − 1
155500	154349	.9853	2.9510	7.7692	5.7250	329.80	9.5210	9.4521
156000	154842	.9852	2.8956	7.6234	5.8346	329.80	9.5210	9.4521
156500	155334	.9852	2.8413	7.4803	5.9462	329.80	9.5210	9.4521
157000	155827	.9851	2.7879	7.3398	6.0599	329.80	9.5210	9.4521
157500	156319	.9851	2.7356	7.2021	6.1759	329.80	9.5210	9.4521
158000	156812	.9850	2.6842	7.0669	6.2940	329.80	9.5210	9.4521
158500	157304	.9850	2.6339	6.9342	6.4144	329.80	9.5210	9.4521
159000	157797	.9849	2.5844	6.8041	6.5371	329.80	9.5210	9.4521
159500	158289	.9849	2.5359	6.6764	6.6621	329.80	9.5210	9.4521
160000	158782	.9848	2.4883 +22	6.5511 + 6	6.7896 − 5	329.80	9.5210 − 1	9.4521 − 1
160500	159274	.9848	2.4416	6.4281	6.9194	329.80	9.5210	9.4521
161000	159767	.9847	2.3958	6.3075	7.0518	329.80	9.5210	9.4521
161500	160259	.9847	2.3509	6.1892	7.1866	329.80	9.5210	9.4521
162000	160751	.9846	2.3067	6.0730	7.3240	329.80	9.5210	9.4521
162500	161244	.9846	2.2635	5.9591	7.4641	329.80	9.5210	9.4521
163000	161736	.9846	2.2210	5.8473	7.6068	329.80	9.5210	9.4521
163500	162228	.9845	2.1793	5.7376	7.7522	329.80	9.5210	9.4521
164000	162720	.9845	2.1384	5.6299	7.9004	329.80	9.5210	9.4521
164500	163213	.9844	2.0983	5.5243	8.0515	329.80	9.5210	9.4521
165000	163705	.9844	2.0590 +22	5.4207 + 6	8.2054 − 5	329.80	9.5210 − 1	9.4521 − 1
165500	164197	.9843	2.0203	5.3190	8.3623	329.80	9.5210	9.4521
166000	164689	.9843	1.9824	5.2192	8.5221	329.80	9.5210	9.4521
166500	165181	.9842	1.9453	5.1214	8.6850	329.80	9.5210	9.4521
167000	165673	.9842	1.9088	5.0253	8.8510	329.80	9.5210	9.4521
167500	166165	.9841	1.8730	4.9311	9.0202	329.80	9.5210	9.4521
168000	166657	.9841	1.8379	4.8386	9.1926	329.80	9.5210	9.4521
168500	167149	.9840	1.8034	4.7479	9.3682	329.80	9.5210	9.4521
169000	167641	.9840	1.7714	4.6611	9.5377	329.63	9.5134	9.4435
169500	168133	.9839	1.7408	4.5771	9.7052	329.38	9.5018	9.4302
170000	168625	.9839	1.7107 +22	4.4945 + 6	9.8759 − 5	329.12	9.4901 − 1	9.4169 − 1
170500	169117	.9838	1.6811	4.4133	1.0050 − 4	328.86	9.4784	9.4037
171000	169609	.9838	1.6519	4.3334	1.0227	328.61	9.4667	9.3904
171500	170101	.9838	1.6233	4.2548	1.0408	328.35	9.4550	9.3771
172000	170593	.9837	1.5950	4.1776	1.0592	328.09	9.4433	9.3638
172500	171085	.9837	1.5673	4.1016	1.0780	327.84	9.4316	9.3505
173000	171577	.9836	1.5399	4.0269	1.0971	327.58	9.4198	9.3372
173500	172069	.9836	1.5130	3.9535	1.1166	327.32	9.4081	9.3239
174000	172560	.9835	1.4866	3.8813	1.1365	327.06	9.3963	9.3106
174500	173052	.9835	1.4605	3.8103	1.1568	326.81	9.3846	9.2973
175000	173544	.9834	1.4349 +22	3.7405 + 6	1.1774 − 4	326.55	9.3728 − 1	9.2840 − 1
175500	174035	.9834	1.4097	3.6718	1.1985	326.29	9.3610	9.2706
176000	174527	.9833	1.3849	3.6043	1.2199	326.03	9.3493	9.2573
176500	175019	.9833	1.3605	3.5380	1.2418	325.77	9.3375	9.2440
177000	175510	.9832	1.3364	3.4728	1.2641	325.51	9.3257	9.2306
177500	176002	.9832	1.3128	3.4087	1.2869	325.25	9.3139	9.2173
178000	176494	.9831	1.2896	3.3456	1.3101	325.00	9.3021	9.2040
178500	176985	.9831	1.2667	3.2837	1.3337	324.74	9.2903	9.1906
179000	177477	.9831	1.2442	3.2228	1.3579	324.48	9.2784	9.1772
179500	177968	.9830	1.2221	3.1629	1.3825	324.22	9.2666	9.1639
180000	178460	.9830	1.2003 +22	3.1041 + 6	1.4075 − 4	323.96	9.2547 − 1	9.1505 − 1
180500	178951	.9829	1.1789	3.0462	1.4331	323.70	9.2429	9.1371
181000	179443	.9829	1.1578	2.9894	1.4592	323.44	9.2310	9.1238
181500	179934	.9828	1.1371	2.9335	1.4858	323.17	9.2192	9.1104
182000	180425	.9828	1.1167	2.8786	1.5129	322.91	9.2073	9.0970
182500	180917	.9827	1.0967	2.8246	1.5406	322.65	9.1954	9.0836
183000	181408	.9827	1.0769	2.7716	1.5688	322.39	9.1835	9.0702
183500	181899	.9826	1.0575	2.7195	1.5976	322.13	9.1716	9.0568
184000	182391	.9826	1.0385	2.6682	1.6269	321.87	9.1597	9.0434
184500	182882	.9825	1.0197	2.6179	1.6568	321.61	9.1478	9.0300
185000	183373	.9825	1.0012 +22	2.5684 + 6	1.6874 − 4	321.34	9.1358 − 1	9.0166 − 1
185500	183865	.9824	9.8310 +21	2.5198	1.7185	321.08	9.1239	9.0032
186000	184356	.9824	9.6525	2.4721	1.7503	320.82	9.1119	8.9897
186500	184847	.9824	9.4770	2.4251	1.7827	320.56	9.1000	8.9763
187000	185339	.9823	9.3044	2.3790	1.8158	320.29	9.0880	8.9629
187500	185829	.9823	9.1347	2.3337	1.8495	320.03	9.0761	8.9494
188000	186320	.9822	8.9679	2.2892	1.8839	319.77	9.0641	8.9360
188500	186811	.9822	8.8038	2.2454	1.9190	319.50	9.0521	8.9225
189000	187302	.9821	8.6424	2.2025	1.9548	319.24	9.0401	8.9091
189500	187794	.9821	8.4838	2.1603	1.9914	318.98	9.0281	8.8956

Table V
Geopotential Altitude, English Altitudes

Altitude H (ft)	Z (ft)	Gravity ratio g/g_0	Number density n (m^{-3})	Collision frequency ν (s^{-1})	Mean free path L (m)	Sound speed C_s (m/s)	Viscosity ratio μ/μ_0	Thermal conductivity ratio κ/κ_0
190000	191747	.9819	7.8033 +21	1.9796 + 6	2.1651 − 4	317.79	8.9740 − 1	8.8351 − 1
190500	192256	.9818	7.6562	1.9406	2.2067	317.52	8.9618	8.8213
191000	192766	.9818	7.5115	1.9023	2.2492	317.25	8.9495	8.8076
191500	193275	.9817	7.3694	1.8647	2.2925	316.98	8.9372	8.7939
192000	193784	.9817	7.2298	1.8278	2.3368	316.71	8.9249	8.7801
192500	194293	.9816	7.0925	1.7916	2.3820	316.44	8.9126	8.7664
193000	194803	.9816	6.9576	1.7560	2.4282	316.17	8.9002	8.7526
193500	195312	.9815	6.8251	1.7211	2.4754	315.89	8.8879	8.7388
194000	195822	.9815	6.6949	1.6868	2.5235	315.62	8.8756	8.7250
194500	196331	.9814	6.5669	1.6531	2.5727	315.35	8.8632	8.7113
195000	196841	.9814	6.4412 +21	1.6201 + 6	2.6229 − 4	315.08	8.8508 − 1	8.6975 − 1
195500	197350	.9813	6.3176	1.5877	2.6742	314.81	8.8385	8.6837
196000	197860	.9813	6.1963	1.5558	2.7266	314.53	8.8261	8.6699
196500	198369	.9812	6.0770	1.5245	2.7801	314.26	8.8137	8.6561
197000	198879	.9812	5.9599	1.4938	2.8347	313.99	8.8013	8.6423
197500	199388	.9811	5.8448	1.4637	2.8906	313.72	8.7889	8.6285
198000	199898	.9811	5.7317	1.4342	2.9476	313.44	8.7765	8.6146
198500	200408	.9811	5.6206	1.4051	3.0058	313.17	8.7640	8.6008
199000	200917	.9810	5.5115	1.3767	3.0653	312.89	8.7516	8.5870
199500	201427	.9810	5.4043	1.3487	3.1261	312.62	8.7391	8.5731
200000	201937	.9809	5.2991 +21	1.3213 + 6	3.1882 − 4	312.35	8.7267 − 1	8.5593 − 1
200500	202446	.9809	5.1957	1.2943	3.2517	312.07	8.7142	8.5455
201000	202956	.9808	5.0941	1.2679	3.3165	311.80	8.7017	8.5316
201500	203466	.9808	4.9943	1.2420	3.3828	311.52	8.6893	8.5177
202000	203976	.9807	4.8964	1.2166	3.4504	311.25	8.6768	8.5039
202500	204486	.9807	4.8002	1.1916	3.5196	310.97	8.6642	8.4900
203000	204995	.9806	4.7057	1.1671	3.5903	310.69	8.6517	8.4761
203500	205505	.9806	4.6129	1.1431	3.6625	310.42	8.6392	8.4622
204000	206015	.9805	4.5218	1.1195	3.7363	310.14	8.6267	8.4484
204500	206525	.9805	4.4323	1.0964	3.8117	309.87	8.6141	8.4345
205000	207035	.9804	4.3444 +21	1.0737 + 6	3.8888 − 4	309.59	8.6015 − 1	8.4206 − 1
205500	207545	.9804	4.2581	1.0514	3.9676	309.31	8.5890	8.4067
206000	208055	.9803	4.1734	1.0296	4.0482	309.03	8.5764	8.3927
206500	208565	.9803	4.0902	1.0081	4.1305	308.76	8.5638	8.3788
207000	209075	.9802	4.0086	9.8712 + 5	4.2146	308.48	8.5512	8.3649
207500	209585	.9802	3.9284	9.6651	4.3007	308.20	8.5386	8.3510
208000	210095	.9802	3.8497	9.4629	4.3886	307.92	8.5260	8.3370
208500	210606	.9801	3.7724	9.2645	4.4785	307.64	8.5133	8.3231
209000	211116	.9801	3.6965	9.0700	4.5704	307.36	8.5007	8.3092
209500	211626	.9800	3.6221	8.8792	4.6644	307.09	8.4880	8.2952
210000	212136	.9800	3.5490 +21	8.6921 + 5	4.7604 − 4	306.81	8.4754 − 1	8.2812 − 1
210500	212646	.9799	3.4772	8.5086	4.8587	306.53	8.4627	8.2673
211000	213157	.9799	3.4068	8.3287	4.9591	306.25	8.4500	8.2533
211500	213667	.9798	3.3377	8.1522	5.0618	305.97	8.4373	8.2393
212000	214177	.9798	3.2698	7.9792	5.1668	305.69	8.4246	8.2254
212500	214688	.9797	3.2032	7.8095	5.2742	305.41	8.4119	8.2114
213000	215198	.9797	3.1379	7.6431	5.3841	305.12	8.3992	8.1974
213500	215708	.9796	3.0737	7.4800	5.4964	304.84	8.3865	8.1834
214000	216219	.9796	3.0108	7.3201	5.6113	304.56	8.3737	8.1694
214500	216729	.9795	2.9490	7.1633	5.7289	304.28	8.3610	8.1554
215000	217240	.9795	2.8884 +21	7.0096 + 5	5.8491 − 4	304.00	8.3482 − 1	8.1414 − 1
215500	217750	.9794	2.8290	6.8589	5.9720	303.72	8.3354	8.1273
216000	218261	.9794	2.7706	6.7111	6.0978	303.43	8.3226	8.1133
216500	218771	.9793	2.7134	6.5663	6.2265	303.15	8.3098	8.0993
217000	219282	.9793	2.6572	6.4244	6.3581	302.87	8.2970	8.0852
217500	219792	.9793	2.6021	6.2852	6.4928	302.59	8.2842	8.0712
218000	220303	.9792	2.5480	6.1489	6.6306	302.30	8.2714	8.0572
218500	220814	.9792	2.4949	6.0152	6.7716	302.02	8.2586	8.0431
219000	221324	.9791	2.4429	5.8842	6.9158	301.73	8.2457	8.0290
219500	221835	.9791	2.3919	5.7558	7.0634	301.45	8.2328	8.0150
220000	222346	.9790	2.3418 +21	5.6300 + 5	7.2145 − 4	301.16	8.2200 − 1	8.0009 − 1
220500	222856	.9790	2.2927	5.5067	7.3690	300.88	8.2071	7.9868
221000	223367	.9789	2.2445	5.3859	7.5272	300.59	8.1942	7.9728
221500	223878	.9789	2.1972	5.2675	7.6891	300.31	8.1813	7.9587
222000	224389	.9788	2.1509	5.1514	7.8548	300.02	8.1684	7.9446
222500	224900	.9788	2.1054	5.0378	8.0243	299.74	8.1555	7.9305
223000	225410	.9787	2.0608	4.9264	8.1979	299.45	8.1425	7.9164
223500	225921	.9787	2.0171	4.8173	8.3756	299.17	8.1296	7.9023
224000	226432	.9786	1.9743	4.7104	8.5575	298.88	8.1166	7.8881
224500	226943	.9786	1.9322	4.6056	8.7437	298.59	8.1037	7.8740
225000	227454	.9785	1.8910 +21	4.5030 + 5	8.9343 − 4	298.30	8.0907 − 1	7.8599 − 1
225500	227965	.9785	1.8506	4.4025	9.1294	298.02	8.0777	7.8458
226000	228476	.9784	1.8109	4.3041	9.3292	297.73	8.0647	7.8316
226500	228987	.9784	1.7721	4.2077	9.5338	297.44	8.0517	7.8175
227000	229498	.9783	1.7340	4.1132	9.7432	297.15	8.0387	7.8033
227500	230009	.9783	1.6966	4.0207	9.9577	296.86	8.0256	7.7892
228000	230520	.9783	1.6600	3.9301	1.0177 − 3	296.57	8.0126	7.7750
228500	231031	.9782	1.6241	3.8414	1.0402	296.29	7.9995	7.7609
229000	231543	.9782	1.5889	3.7545	1.0633	296.00	7.9865	7.7467
229500	232054	.9781	1.5545	3.6694	1.0869	295.71	7.9734	7.7325

Table V
Geometric Altitude, English Altitudes

Altitude		Gravity ratio	Number density	Collision frequency	Mean free path	Sound speed	Viscosity ratio	Thermal conductivity ratio
Z (ft)	H (ft)	g/g_0	n (m^{-3})	ν (s^{-1})	L (m)	C_s (m/s)	μ/μ_0	κ/κ_0
190000	188285	.9820	8.3278 +21	2.1188 + 6	2.0287 − 4	318.71	9.0161 − 1	8.8822 − 1
190500	188776	.9820	8.1745	2.0781	2.0668	318.45	9.0041	8.8687
191000	189267	.9819	8.0237	2.0380	2.1056	318.18	8.9920	8.8552
191500	189757	.9819	7.8755	1.9987	2.1452	317.92	8.9800	8.8417
192000	190248	.9818	7.7298	1.9601	2.1857	317.65	8.9679	8.8283
192500	190739	.9818	7.5865	1.9222	2.2269	317.39	8.9559	8.8148
193000	191230	.9817	7.4457	1.8849	2.2690	317.12	8.9438	8.8013
193500	191721	.9817	7.3073	1.8483	2.3120	316.86	8.9317	8.7878
194000	192212	.9817	7.1712	1.8124	2.3559	316.59	8.9197	8.7743
194500	192703	.9816	7.0375	1.7771	2.4007	316.33	8.9076	8.7608
195000	193194	.9816	6.9060 +21	1.7424 + 6	2.4464 − 4	316.06	8.8955 − 1	8.7473 − 1
195500	193684	.9815	6.7768	1.7084	2.4930	315.79	8.8834	8.7337
196000	194175	.9815	6.6497	1.6749	2.5406	315.53	8.8712	8.7202
196500	194666	.9814	6.5249	1.6421	2.5893	315.26	8.8591	8.7067
197000	195156	.9814	6.4022	1.6099	2.6389	314.99	8.8470	8.6932
197500	195647	.9813	6.2816	1.5782	2.6895	314.73	8.8348	8.6796
198000	196138	.9813	6.1631	1.5471	2.7413	314.46	8.8227	8.6661
198500	196628	.9812	6.0467	1.5166	2.7940	314.19	8.8105	8.6525
199000	197119	.9812	5.9322	1.4866	2.8480	313.92	8.7983	8.6390
199500	197610	.9811	5.8197	1.4572	2.9030	313.66	8.7862	8.6254
200000	198100	.9811	5.7092 +21	1.4283 + 6	2.9592 − 4	313.39	8.7740 − 1	8.6119 − 1
200500	198591	.9810	5.6006	1.3999	3.0166	313.12	8.7618	8.5983
201000	199081	.9810	5.4939	1.3721	3.0752	312.85	8.7496	8.5847
201500	199572	.9810	5.3891	1.3447	3.1350	312.58	8.7374	8.5712
202000	200062	.9809	5.2861	1.3179	3.1961	312.31	8.7251	8.5576
202500	200553	.9809	5.1848	1.2915	3.2585	312.04	8.7129	8.5440
203000	201043	.9808	5.0854	1.2657	3.3222	311.77	8.7007	8.5304
203500	201533	.9808	4.9877	1.2403	3.3873	311.50	8.6884	8.5168
204000	202024	.9807	4.8917	1.2154	3.4537	311.23	8.6762	8.5032
204500	202514	.9807	4.7974	1.1909	3.5216	310.96	8.6639	8.4896
205000	203004	.9806	4.7048 +21	1.1669 + 6	3.5909 − 4	310.69	8.6516 − 1	8.4760 − 1
205500	203495	.9806	4.6138	1.1433	3.6618	310.42	8.6393	8.4624
206000	203985	.9805	4.5244	1.1202	3.7341	310.15	8.6270	8.4488
206500	204475	.9805	4.4366	1.0975	3.8080	309.88	8.6147	8.4351
207000	204966	.9804	4.3504	1.0752	3.8835	309.61	8.6024	8.4215
207500	205456	.9804	4.2657	1.0534	3.9606	309.34	8.5901	8.4079
208000	205946	.9803	4.1825	1.0319	4.0394	309.06	8.5778	8.3942
208500	206436	.9803	4.1007	1.0108	4.1199	308.79	8.5654	8.3806
209000	206926	.9803	4.0205	9.9019 + 5	4.2021	308.52	8.5531	8.3670
209500	207416	.9802	3.9417	9.6992	4.2862	308.25	8.5407	8.3533
210000	207906	.9802	3.8643 +21	9.5003 + 5	4.3720 − 4	307.97	8.5283 − 1	8.3396 − 1
210500	208396	.9801	3.7882	9.3052	4.4598	307.70	8.5160	8.3260
211000	208887	.9801	3.7136	9.1137	4.5494	307.43	8.5036	8.3123
211500	209377	.9800	3.6403	8.9259	4.6410	307.15	8.4912	8.2986
212000	209867	.9800	3.5683	8.7416	4.7346	306.88	8.4788	8.2850
212500	210357	.9799	3.4976	8.5608	4.8303	306.61	8.4663	8.2713
213000	210846	.9799	3.4282	8.3834	4.9281	306.33	8.4539	8.2576
213500	211336	.9798	3.3601	8.2095	5.0280	306.05	8.4415	8.2439
214000	211826	.9798	3.2932	8.0388	5.1301	305.78	8.4290	8.2302
214500	212316	.9797	3.2275	7.8714	5.2345	305.51	8.4166	8.2165
215000	212805	.9797	3.1631 +21	7.7072 + 5	5.3413 − 4	305.23	8.4041 − 1	8.2028 − 1
215500	213296	.9796	3.0997	7.5461	5.4503	304.96	8.3917	8.1891
216000	213786	.9796	3.0376	7.3882	5.5618	304.68	8.3792	8.1754
216500	214275	.9796	2.9766	7.2332	5.6758	304.41	8.3667	8.1617
217000	214765	.9795	2.9167	7.0813	5.7924	304.13	8.3542	8.1479
217500	215255	.9795	2.8579	6.9323	5.9115	303.85	8.3417	8.1342
218000	215745	.9794	2.8002	6.7861	6.0333	303.58	8.3292	8.1205
218500	216234	.9794	2.7436	6.6428	6.1578	303.30	8.3166	8.1067
219000	216724	.9793	2.6880	6.5023	6.2852	303.02	8.3041	8.0930
219500	217214	.9793	2.6335	6.3645	6.4154	302.75	8.2916	8.0792
220000	217703	.9792	2.5799 +21	6.2294 + 5	6.5485 − 4	302.47	8.2790 − 1	8.0655 − 1
220500	218193	.9792	2.5274	6.0969	6.6847	302.19	8.2664	8.0517
221000	218683	.9791	2.4758	5.9670	6.8239	301.91	8.2539	8.0380
221500	219172	.9791	2.4252	5.8396	6.9663	301.64	8.2413	8.0242
222000	219662	.9790	2.3755	5.7148	7.1119	301.36	8.2287	8.0104
222500	220151	.9790	2.3268	5.5924	7.2609	301.08	8.2161	7.9967
223000	220641	.9790	2.2790	5.4724	7.4132	300.80	8.2035	7.9829
223500	221130	.9789	2.2321	5.3548	7.5690	300.52	8.1908	7.9691
224000	221620	.9789	2.1860	5.2394	7.7284	300.24	8.1782	7.9553
224500	222109	.9788	2.1409	5.1264	7.8915	299.96	8.1656	7.9415
225000	222598	.9788	2.0965 +21	5.0156 + 5	8.0583 − 4	299.68	8.1529 − 1	7.9277 − 1
225500	223088	.9787	2.0531	4.9070	8.2289	299.40	8.1403	7.9139
226000	223577	.9787	2.0104	4.8006	8.4035	299.12	8.1276	7.9001
226500	224066	.9786	1.9686	4.6963	8.5820	298.84	8.1149	7.8863
227000	224556	.9786	1.9276	4.5941	8.7648	298.56	8.1022	7.8725
227500	225045	.9785	1.8873	4.4939	8.9517	298.28	8.0895	7.8586
228000	225534	.9785	1.8478	4.3957	9.1431	298.00	8.0768	7.8448
228500	226023	.9784	1.8091	4.2995	9.3388	297.72	8.0641	7.8310
229000	226513	.9784	1.7711	4.2052	9.5391	297.43	8.0513	7.8171
229500	227002	.9783	1.7338	4.1128	9.7441	297.15	8.0386	7.8033

Table V
Geopotential Altitude, English Altitudes

Altitude		Gravity ratio	Number density	Collision frequency	Mean free path	Sound speed	Viscosity ratio	Thermal conductivity ratio
H (ft)	Z (ft)	g/g_0	n (m^{-3})	ν (s^{-1})	L (m)	C_s (m/s)	μ/μ_0	κ/κ_0
230000	232565	.9781	1.5206 +21	3.5861 + 5	1.1110 − 3	295.42	7.9603 − 1	7.7183 − 1
230500	233076	.9780	1.4875	3.5045	1.1358	295.13	7.9472	7.7041
231000	233587	.9780	1.4550	3.4246	1.1611	294.83	7.9341	7.6899
231500	234099	.9779	1.4232	3.3464	1.1871	294.54	7.9210	7.6757
232000	234610	.9779	1.3920	3.2698	1.2137	294.25	7.9078	7.6615
232500	235121	.9778	1.3614	3.1948	1.2409	293.96	7.8947	7.6473
233000	235633	.9778	1.3314	3.1213	1.2690	293.68	7.8820	7.6336
233500	236144	.9777	1.3013	3.0486	1.2983	293.47	7.8726	7.6234
234000	236655	.9777	1.2719	2.9775	1.3284	293.26	7.8632	7.6133
234500	237167	.9776	1.2430	2.9079	1.3591	293.05	7.8538	7.6031
235000	237678	.9776	1.2148 +21	2.8399 + 5	1.3907 − 3	292.84	7.8443 − 1	7.5930 − 1
235500	238190	.9775	1.1872	2.7734	1.4230	292.63	7.8349	7.5828
236000	238701	.9775	1.1602	2.7084	1.4562	292.43	7.8255	7.5726
236500	239213	.9774	1.1338	2.6447	1.4901	292.22	7.8161	7.5624
237000	239724	.9774	1.1079	2.5825	1.5249	292.01	7.8066	7.5523
237500	240236	.9774	1.0826	2.5217	1.5606	291.80	7.7972	7.5421
238000	240748	.9773	1.0578	2.4622	1.5972	291.59	7.7877	7.5319
238500	241259	.9773	1.0336	2.4040	1.6346	291.38	7.7782	7.5217
239000	241771	.9772	1.0098	2.3472	1.6730	291.17	7.7688	7.5115
239500	242282	.9772	9.8662 +20	2.2916	1.7124	290.96	7.7593	7.5013
240000	242794	.9771	9.6391 +20	2.2372 + 5	1.7527 − 3	290.75	7.7498 − 1	7.4911 − 1
240500	243306	.9771	9.4169	2.1841	1.7941	290.53	7.7403	7.4809
241000	243818	.9770	9.1996	2.1321	1.8365	290.32	7.7309	7.4707
241500	244329	.9770	8.9869	2.0813	1.8799	290.11	7.7214	7.4605
242000	244841	.9769	8.7789	2.0316	1.9245	289.90	7.7119	7.4503
242500	245353	.9769	8.5753	1.9831	1.9701	289.69	7.7024	7.4401
243000	245865	.9768	8.3762	1.9356	2.0170	289.48	7.6928	7.4299
243500	246377	.9768	8.1815	1.8892	2.0650	289.27	7.6833	7.4197
244000	246889	.9767	7.9910	1.8439	2.1142	289.05	7.6738	7.4095
244500	247401	.9767	7.8047	1.7996	2.1647	288.84	7.6643	7.3993
245000	247913	.9766	7.6224 +20	1.7563 + 5	2.2164 − 3	288.63	7.6547 − 1	7.3890 − 1
245500	248425	.9766	7.4442	1.7139	2.2695	288.42	7.6452	7.3788
246000	248937	.9765	7.2698	1.6726	2.3239	288.21	7.6356	7.3686
246500	249449	.9765	7.0993	1.6321	2.3798	287.99	7.6261	7.3584
247000	249961	.9765	6.9326	1.5926	2.4370	287.78	7.6165	7.3481
247500	250473	.9764	6.7695	1.5540	2.4957	287.57	7.6070	7.3379
248000	250985	.9764	6.6101	1.5163	2.5559	287.35	7.5974	7.3277
248500	251497	.9763	6.4541	1.4794	2.6177	287.14	7.5878	7.3174
249000	252009	.9763	6.3016	1.4434	2.6810	286.93	7.5782	7.3072
249500	252521	.9762	6.1525	1.4082	2.7460	286.71	7.5686	7.2969
250000	253033	.9762	6.0068 +20	1.3738 + 5	2.8126 − 3	286.50	7.5591 − 1	7.2867 − 1
250500	253546	.9761	5.8642	1.3402	2.8810	286.29	7.5495	7.2764
251000	254058	.9761	5.7248	1.3074	2.9511	286.07	7.5398	7.2662
251500	254570	.9760	5.5886	1.2753	3.0231	285.86	7.5302	7.2559
252000	255082	.9760	5.4554	1.2440	3.0969	285.64	7.5206	7.2456
252500	255595	.9759	5.3252	1.2134	3.1726	285.43	7.5110	7.2354
253000	256107	.9759	5.1979	1.1835	3.2503	285.22	7.5014	7.2251
253500	256619	.9758	5.0734	1.1543	3.3300	285.00	7.4917	7.2148
254000	257132	.9758	4.9518	1.1257	3.4119	284.79	7.4821	7.2046
254500	257644	.9757	4.8328	1.0979	3.4958	284.57	7.4724	7.1943
255000	258157	.9757	4.7166 +20	1.0707 + 5	3.5819 − 3	284.36	7.4628 − 1	7.1840 − 1
255500	258669	.9756	4.6030	1.0441	3.6703	284.14	7.4531	7.1737
256000	259182	.9756	4.4920	1.0181	3.7611	283.92	7.4434	7.1634
256500	259694	.9756	4.3835	9.9277 + 4	3.8542	283.71	7.4338	7.1532
257000	260207	.9755	4.2774	9.6801	3.9497	283.49	7.4241	7.1429
257500	260719	.9755	4.1738	9.4383	4.0478	283.28	7.4144	7.1326
258000	261232	.9754	4.0725	9.2023	4.1485	283.06	7.4047	7.1223
258500	261744	.9754	3.9735	8.9717	4.2518	282.84	7.3950	7.1120
259000	262257	.9753	3.8768	8.7467	4.3579	282.63	7.3853	7.1017
259500	262770	.9753	3.7823	8.5269	4.4668	282.41	7.3756	7.0914
260000	263282	.9752	3.6899 +20	8.3123 + 4	4.5786 − 3	282.19	7.3659 − 1	7.0811 − 1
260500	263795	.9752	3.5997	8.1028	4.6933	281.98	7.3562	7.0708
261000	264308	.9751	3.5116	7.8983	4.8112	281.76	7.3464	7.0605
261500	264821	.9751	3.4254	7.6986	4.9321	281.54	7.3367	7.0501
262000	265333	.9750	3.3413	7.5037	5.0563	281.32	7.3270	7.0398
262500	265846	.9750	3.2591	7.3135	5.1839	281.11	7.3172	7.0295
263000	266359	.9749	3.1788	7.1277	5.3148	280.89	7.3075	7.0192
263500	266872	.9749	3.1003	6.9464	5.4493	280.67	7.2977	7.0089
264000	267385	.9748	3.0237	6.7695	5.5874	280.45	7.2879	6.9985
264500	267898	.9748	2.9489	6.5968	5.7292	280.23	7.2782	6.9882
265000	268411	.9747	2.8758 +20	6.4282 + 4	5.8748 − 3	280.01	7.2684 − 1	6.9779 − 1
265500	268924	.9747	2.8044	6.2637	6.0244	279.80	7.2586	6.9675
266000	269437	.9747	2.7346	6.1032	6.1781	279.58	7.2488	6.9572
266500	269950	.9746	2.6665	5.9465	6.3359	279.36	7.2390	6.9469
267000	270463	.9746	2.6000	5.7936	6.4979	279.14	7.2292	6.9365
267500	270976	.9745	2.5350	5.6444	6.6644	278.92	7.2194	6.9262
268000	271489	.9745	2.4716	5.4989	6.8355	278.70	7.2096	6.9158
268500	272002	.9744	2.4097	5.3568	7.0112	278.48	7.1998	6.9055
269000	272515	.9744	2.3492	5.2182	7.1917	278.26	7.1899	6.8951
269500	273028	.9743	2.2901	5.0830	7.3772	278.04	7.1801	6.8848

Table V
Geometric Altitude, English Altitudes

Altitude		Gravity ratio	Number density	Collision frequency	Mean free path	Sound speed	Viscosity ratio	Thermal conductivity ratio
Z (ft)	H (ft)	g/g_0	n (m^{-3})	ν (s^{-1})	L (m)	C_s (m/s)	μ/μ_0	κ/κ_0
230000	227491	.9783	1.6973 +21	4.0223 + 5	9.9539 − 4	296.87	8.0259 − 1	7.7894 − 1
230500	227980	.9783	1.6614	3.9336	1.0169 − 3	296.59	8.0131	7.7756
231000	228469	.9782	1.6263	3.8467	1.0388	296.30	8.0003	7.7617
231500	228958	.9782	1.5918	3.7616	1.0613	296.02	7.9875	7.7479
232000	229447	.9781	1.5580	3.6782	1.0844	295.74	7.9748	7.7340
232500	229936	.9781	1.5249	3.5965	1.1079	295.45	7.9620	7.7201
233000	230425	.9780	1.4924	3.5165	1.1321	295.17	7.9491	7.7063
233500	230914	.9780	1.4605	3.4381	1.1568	294.88	7.9363	7.6924
234000	231403	.9779	1.4293	3.3613	1.1820	294.60	7.9235	7.6785
234500	231892	.9779	1.3986	3.2861	1.2079	294.32	7.9107	7.6646
235000	232381	.9778	1.3686 +21	3.2124 + 5	1.2344 − 3	294.03	7.8978 − 1	7.6507 − 1
235500	232870	.9778	1.3392	3.1402	1.2616	293.74	7.8849	7.6368
236000	233359	.9777	1.3097	3.0689	1.2900	293.53	7.8752	7.6263
236500	233848	.9777	1.2807	2.9989	1.3192	293.33	7.8660	7.6164
237000	234337	.9777	1.2524	2.9304	1.3490	293.12	7.8568	7.6064
237500	234826	.9776	1.2246	2.8634	1.3796	292.92	7.8476	7.5965
238000	235314	.9776	1.1974	2.7979	1.4110	292.71	7.8384	7.5866
238500	235803	.9775	1.1707	2.7337	1.4431	292.51	7.8292	7.5766
239000	236292	.9775	1.1447	2.6710	1.4759	292.30	7.8200	7.5667
239500	236781	.9774	1.1192	2.6096	1.5096	292.10	7.8107	7.5567
240000	237269	.9774	1.0942 +21	2.5495 + 5	1.5441 − 3	291.89	7.8015 − 1	7.5468 − 1
240500	237758	.9773	1.0697	2.4908	1.5794	291.69	7.7923	7.5368
241000	238247	.9773	1.0458	2.4333	1.6156	291.48	7.7830	7.5269
241500	238735	.9772	1.0223	2.3771	1.6526	291.28	7.7739	7.5169
242000	239224	.9772	9.9936 +20	2.3221	1.6906	291.07	7.7645	7.5070
242500	239713	.9771	9.7689	2.2683	1.7294	290.87	7.7553	7.4970
243000	240201	.9771	9.5490	2.2157	1.7693	290.66	7.7460	7.4870
243500	240690	.9771	9.3339	2.1642	1.8101	290.45	7.7367	7.4771
244000	241178	.9770	9.1231	2.1138	1.8518	290.25	7.7275	7.4671
244500	241667	.9770	8.9169	2.0646	1.8947	290.04	7.7182	7.4571
245000	242155	.9769	8.7151 +20	2.0164 + 5	1.9385 − 3	289.84	7.7089 − 1	7.4472 − 1
245500	242644	.9769	8.5176	1.9693	1.9835	289.63	7.6996	7.4372
246000	243132	.9768	8.3243	1.9233	2.0296	289.42	7.6903	7.4272
246500	243620	.9768	8.1351	1.8782	2.0767	289.22	7.6810	7.4172
247000	244109	.9767	7.9500	1.8342	2.1251	289.01	7.6717	7.4073
247500	244597	.9767	7.7689	1.7911	2.1747	288.80	7.6624	7.3973
248000	245085	.9766	7.5916	1.7489	2.2254	288.59	7.6531	7.3873
248500	245574	.9766	7.4181	1.7078	2.2775	288.39	7.6439	7.3773
249000	246062	.9765	7.2484	1.6675	2.3308	288.18	7.6345	7.3673
249500	246550	.9765	7.0823	1.6281	2.3855	287.97	7.6251	7.3573
250000	247039	.9764	6.9199 +20	1.5896 + 5	2.4415 − 3	287.76	7.6158 − 1	7.3473 − 1
250500	247527	.9764	6.7609	1.5520	2.4989	287.56	7.6065	7.3373
251000	248015	.9764	6.6053	1.5152	2.5578	287.35	7.5971	7.3273
251500	248503	.9763	6.4531	1.4792	2.6181	287.14	7.5878	7.3173
252000	248991	.9763	6.3042	1.4440	2.6799	286.93	7.5784	7.3073
252500	249479	.9762	6.1585	1.4096	2.7433	286.72	7.5690	7.2973
253000	249967	.9762	6.0161	1.3760	2.8083	286.51	7.5597	7.2873
253500	250456	.9761	5.8767	1.3431	2.8749	286.31	7.5503	7.2773
254000	250944	.9761	5.7403	1.3110	2.9431	286.10	7.5409	7.2673
254500	251432	.9760	5.6070	1.2796	3.0132	285.89	7.5315	7.2573
255000	251920	.9760	5.4765 +20	1.2489 + 5	3.0849 − 3	285.68	7.5222 − 1	7.2473 − 1
255500	252408	.9759	5.3489	1.2189	3.1585	285.47	7.5128	7.2373
256000	252896	.9759	5.2241	1.1896	3.2340	285.26	7.5034	7.2272
256500	253383	.9758	5.1021	1.1610	3.3113	285.05	7.4940	7.2172
257000	253871	.9758	4.9827	1.1330	3.3907	284.84	7.4846	7.2072
257500	254359	.9758	4.8660	1.1056	3.4720	284.63	7.4751	7.1972
258000	254847	.9757	4.7519	1.0789	3.5554	284.42	7.4657	7.1871
258500	255335	.9757	4.6402	1.0528	3.6410	284.21	7.4563	7.1771
259000	255823	.9756	4.5310	1.0272	3.7287	284.00	7.4469	7.1671
259500	256311	.9756	4.4242	1.0023	3.8187	283.79	7.4374	7.1571
260000	256798	.9755	4.3198 +20	9.7791 + 4	3.9110 − 3	283.58	7.4280 − 1	7.1470 − 1
260500	257286	.9755	4.2177	9.5409	4.0056	283.37	7.4185	7.1370
261000	257774	.9754	4.1179	9.3082	4.1027	283.16	7.4091	7.1269
261500	258262	.9754	4.0204	9.0808	4.2023	282.95	7.3996	7.1169
262000	258749	.9753	3.9250	8.8587	4.3044	282.74	7.3902	7.1068
262500	259237	.9753	3.8317	8.6417	4.4092	282.52	7.3807	7.0968
263000	259725	.9752	3.7405	8.4298	4.5167	282.31	7.3712	7.0868
263500	260212	.9752	3.6513	8.2227	4.6270	282.10	7.3618	7.0767
264000	260700	.9752	3.5642	8.0204	4.7401	281.89	7.3523	7.0666
264500	261187	.9751	3.4790	7.8228	4.8562	281.68	7.3428	7.0566
265000	261675	.9751	3.3957 +20	7.6298 + 4	4.9753 − 3	281.47	7.3333 − 1	7.0465 − 1
265500	262162	.9750	3.3143	7.4413	5.0974	281.25	7.3238	7.0365
266000	262650	.9750	3.2349	7.2572	5.2228	281.04	7.3143	7.0264
266500	263137	.9749	3.1570	7.0774	5.3515	280.83	7.3048	7.0163
267000	263625	.9749	3.0810	6.9018	5.4835	280.62	7.2953	7.0063
267500	264112	.9748	3.0067	6.7303	5.6190	280.40	7.2857	6.9962
268000	264600	.9748	2.9341	6.5628	5.7580	280.19	7.2762	6.9861
268500	265087	.9747	2.8632	6.3992	5.9007	279.98	7.2667	6.9761
269000	265574	.9747	2.7938	6.2395	6.0471	279.76	7.2571	6.9660
269500	266062	.9746	2.7261	6.0835	6.1974	279.55	7.2476	6.9559

Table V
Geopotential Altitude, English Altitudes

Altitude		Gravity ratio	Number density	Collision frequency	Mean free path	Sound speed	Viscosity ratio	Thermal conductivity ratio
H (ft)	Z (ft)	g/g_0	n (m^{-3})	ν (s^{-1})	L (m)	C$_s$ (m/s)	μ/μ_0	κ/κ_0
270000	273542	.9743	2.2325 +20	4.9511 + 4	7.5677 - 3	277.82	7.1703 - 1	6.8744 - 1
270500	274055	.9742	2.1762	4.8224	7.7635	277.60	7.1604	6.8640
271000	274568	.9742	2.1212	4.6969	7.9647	277.38	7.1506	6.8537
271500	275081	.9741	2.0675	4.5744	8.1714	277.16	7.1407	6.8433
272000	275595	.9741	2.0151	4.4549	8.3838	276.94	7.1308	6.8329
272500	276108	.9740	1.9640	4.3384	8.6021	276.71	7.1210	6.8226
273000	276621	.9740	1.9141	4.2248	8.8265	276.49	7.1111	6.8122
273500	277135	.9739	1.8654	4.1139	9.0571	276.27	7.1012	6.8018
274000	277648	.9739	1.8178	4.0058	9.2940	276.05	7.0913	6.7914
274500	278161	.9738	1.7714	3.9003	9.5376	275.83	7.0814	6.7810
275000	278675	.9738	1.7261 +20	3.7975 + 4	9.7880 - 3	275.61	7.0715 - 1	6.7706 - 1
275500	279188	.9738	1.6818	3.6972	1.0045 - 2	275.38	7.0616	6.7603
276000	279702	.9737	1.6387	3.5995	1.0310	275.16	7.0517	6.7499
276500	280215	.9737	1.5966	3.5041	1.0582	274.94	7.0418	6.7395
277000	280729	.9736	1.5555	3.4111	1.0862	274.71	7.0318	6.7291
277500	281242	.9736	1.5154	3.3205	1.1149	274.49	7.0219	6.7187
278000	281756	.9735	1.4762	3.2321	1.1445	274.27	7.0120	6.7083

Table V
Geometric Altitude, English Altitudes

Altitude		Gravity ratio	Number density	Collision frequency	Mean free path	Sound speed	Viscosity ratio	Thermal conductivity ratio
Z (ft)	H (ft)	g/g_0	n (m^{-3})	ν (s^{-1})	L (m)	C_s (m/s)	μ/μ_0	κ/κ_0
270000	266549	.9746	2.6599 +20	5.9313 + 4	6.3516 − 3	279.34	7.2381 − 1	6.9458 − 1
270500	267036	.9746	2.5952	5.7826	6.5100	279.12	7.2285	6.9358
271000	267524	.9745	2.5320	5.6374	6.6725	278.91	7.2189	6.9257
271500	268011	.9745	2.4702	5.4957	6.8393	278.69	7.2094	6.9156
272000	268498	.9744	2.4099	5.3573	7.0106	278.48	7.1998	6.9055
272500	268985	.9744	2.3509	5.2222	7.1864	278.27	7.1902	6.8954
273000	269472	.9743	2.2933	5.0903	7.3669	278.05	7.1806	6.8853
273500	269960	.9743	2.2370	4.9616	7.5522	277.84	7.1711	6.8752
274000	270447	.9742	2.1821	4.8359	7.7425	277.62	7.1615	6.8651
274500	270934	.9742	2.1284	4.7133	7.9378	277.41	7.1519	6.8550
275000	271421	.9741	2.0759 +20	4.5935 + 4	8.1384 − 3	277.19	7.1423 − 1	6.8449 − 1
275500	271908	.9741	2.0247	4.4767	8.3444	276.98	7.1327	6.8348
276000	272395	.9740	1.9746	4.3626	8.5559	276.76	7.1230	6.8247
276500	272882	.9740	1.9257	4.2513	8.7731	276.54	7.1134	6.8146
277000	273369	.9740	1.8780	4.1426	8.9961	276.33	7.1038	6.8045
277500	273856	.9739	1.8314	4.0366	9.2252	276.11	7.0942	6.7944
278000	274343	.9739	1.7858	3.9331	9.4605	275.90	7.0845	6.7843
278500	274830	.9738	1.7413	3.8322	9.7021	275.68	7.0749	6.7742
279000	275317	.9738	1.6979	3.7337	9.9503	275.46	7.0652	6.7641
279500	275804	.9737	1.6555	3.6375	1.0205 − 2	275.25	7.0556	6.7539
280000	276290	.9737	1.6141 +20	3.5437 + 4	1.0467 − 2	275.03	7.0459 − 1	6.7438 − 1
280500	276777	.9736	1.5736	3.4522	1.0736	274.81	7.0363	6.7337
281000	277264	.9736	1.5341	3.3629	1.1012	274.60	7.0266	6.7236
281500	277751	.9735	1.4956	3.2758	1.1296	274.39	7.0169	6.7135
282000	278238	.9735	1.4579	3.1908	1.1588	274.16	7.0072	6.7033

TABLE VI

GEOPOTENTIAL ALTITUDE IN METERS as a function of PRESSURE IN MILLIBARS

P, mb	0.00	0.01	0.02	0.03	0.04	0.05	0.06	0.07	0.08	0.09
8.60									32000	31992
8.70	31985	31977	31969	31962	31954	31946	31939	31931	31923	31916
8.80	31908	31901	31893	31885	31878	31870	31863	31855	31848	31840
8.90	31833	31825	31818	31810	31803	31795	31788	31780	31773	31765
9.00	31758	31751	31743	31736	31728	31721	31714	31706	31699	31691
9.10	31684	31677	31669	31662	31655	31647	31640	31633	31626	31618
9.20	31611	31604	31597	31589	31582	31575	31568	31560	31553	31546
9.30	31539	31532	31524	31517	31510	31503	31496	31489	31482	31474
9.40	31467	31460	31453	31446	31439	31432	31425	31418	31411	31404
9.50	31397	31390	31383	31376	31369	31362	31355	31348	31341	31334
9.60	31327	31320	31313	31306	31299	31292	31285	31278	31271	31265
9.70	31258	31251	31244	31237	31230	31223	31217	31210	31203	31196
9.80	31189	31182	31176	31169	31162	31155	31149	31142	31135	31128
9.90	31122	31115	31108	31101	31095	31088	31081	31075	31068	31061

TABLE VI - Continued

181

GEOPOTENTIAL ALTITUDE IN METERS as a function of PRESSURE IN MILLIBARS

P, mb	0.00	0.01	0.02	0.03	0.04	0.05	0.06	0.07	0.08	0.09
10.00	31055	31048	31041	31035	31028	31021	31015	31008	31002	30995
10.10	30988	30982	30975	30969	30962	30955	30949	30942	30936	30929
10.20	30923	30916	30910	30903	30897	30890	30884	30877	30871	30864
10.30	30858	30851	30845	30838	30832	30825	30819	30813	30806	30800
10.40	30793	30787	30781	30774	30768	30761	30755	30749	30742	30736
10.50	30730	30723	30717	30711	30704	30698	30692	30685	30679	30673
10.60	30667	30660	30654	30648	30642	30635	30629	30623	30617	30610
10.70	30604	30598	30592	30585	30579	30573	30567	30561	30555	30548
10.80	30542	30536	30530	30524	30518	30512	30505	30499	30493	30487
10.90	30481	30475	30469	30463	30457	30451	30444	30438	30432	30426
11.00	30420	30414	30408	30402	30396	30390	30384	30378	30372	30366
11.10	30360	30354	30348	30342	30336	30330	30324	30318	30312	30306
11.20	30300	30295	30289	30283	30277	30271	30265	30259	30253	30247
11.30	30241	30236	30230	30224	30218	30212	30206	30200	30195	30189
11.40	30183	30177	30171	30165	30160	30154	30148	30142	30137	30131
11.50	30125	30119	30113	30108	30102	30096	30090	30085	30079	30073
11.60	30067	30062	30056	30050	30045	30039	30033	30028	30022	30016
11.70	30011	30005	29999	29994	29988	29982	29977	29971	29965	29960
11.80	29954	29948	29943	29937	29932	29926	29920	29915	29909	29904
11.90	29898	29893	29887	29881	29876	29870	29865	29859	29854	29848
12.00	29843	29837	29832	29826	29821	29815	29810	29804	29799	29793
12.10	29788	29782	29777	29771	29766	29760	29755	29749	29744	29739
12.20	29733	29728	29722	29717	29711	29706	29701	29695	29690	29684
12.30	29679	29674	29668	29663	29657	29652	29647	29641	29636	29631
12.40	29625	29620	29615	29609	29604	29599	29593	29588	29583	29577
12.50	29572	29567	29562	29556	29551	29546	29540	29535	29530	29525
12.60	29519	29514	29509	29504	29498	29493	29488	29483	29477	29472
12.70	29467	29462	29457	29451	29446	29441	29436	29431	29426	29420
12.80	29415	29410	29405	29400	29395	29389	29384	29379	29374	29369
12.90	29364	29359	29353	29348	29343	29338	29333	29328	29323	29318
13.00	29313	29308	29302	29297	29292	29287	29282	29277	29272	29267
13.10	29262	29257	29252	29247	29242	29237	29232	29227	29222	29217
13.20	29212	29207	29202	29197	29192	29187	29182	29177	29172	29167
13.30	29162	29157	29152	29147	29142	29137	29132	29127	29122	29117
13.40	29112	29107	29102	29097	29093	29088	29083	29078	29073	29068
13.50	29063	29058	29053	29048	29044	29039	29034	29029	29024	29019
13.60	29014	29009	29005	29000	28995	28990	28985	28980	28976	28971
13.70	28966	28961	28956	28952	28947	28942	28937	28932	28928	28923
13.80	28918	28913	28908	28904	28899	28894	28889	28885	28880	28875
13.90	28870	28866	28861	28856	28851	28847	28842	28837	28832	28828
14.00	28823	28818	28814	28809	28804	28799	28795	28790	28785	28781
14.10	28776	28771	28767	28762	28757	28753	28748	28743	28739	28734
14.20	28729	28725	28720	28715	28711	28706	28702	28697	28692	28688
14.30	28683	28678	28674	28669	28665	28660	28655	28651	28646	28642
14.40	28637	28633	28628	28623	28619	28614	28610	28605	28601	28596
14.50	28591	28587	28582	28578	28573	28569	28564	28560	28555	28551
14.60	28546	28542	28537	28533	28528	28524	28519	28515	28510	28506
14.70	28501	28497	28492	28488	28483	28479	28474	28470	28465	28461
14.80	28456	28452	28448	28443	28439	28434	28430	28425	28421	28417
14.90	28412	28408	28403	28399	28394	28390	28386	28381	28377	28372
15.00	28368	28364	28359	28355	28351	28346	28342	28337	28333	28329
15.10	28324	28320	28316	28311	28307	28303	28298	28294	28290	28285
15.20	28281	28277	28272	28268	28264	28259	28255	28251	28246	28242
15.30	28238	28233	28229	28225	28220	28216	28212	28208	28203	28199
15.40	28195	28191	28186	28182	28178	28173	28169	28165	28161	28156
15.50	28152	28148	28144	28139	28135	28131	28127	28123	28118	28114
15.60	28110	28106	28101	28097	28093	28089	28085	28080	28076	28072
15.70	28068	28064	28059	28055	28051	28047	28043	28039	28034	28030
15.80	28026	28022	28018	28014	28009	28005	28001	27997	27993	27989
15.90	27985	27980	27976	27972	27968	27964	27960	27956	27952	27947
16.00	27943	27939	27935	27931	27927	27923	27919	27915	27911	27907
16.10	27902	27898	27894	27890	27886	27882	27878	27874	27870	27866
16.20	27862	27858	27854	27850	27846	27841	27837	27833	27829	27825
16.30	27821	27817	27813	27809	27805	27801	27797	27793	27789	27785
16.40	27781	27777	27773	27769	27765	27761	27757	27753	27749	27745
16.50	27741	27737	27733	27729	27725	27721	27717	27713	27709	27705
16.60	27701	27698	27694	27690	27686	27682	27678	27674	27670	27666
16.70	27662	27658	27654	27650	27646	27642	27639	27635	27631	27627
16.80	27623	27619	27615	27611	27607	27603	27599	27596	27592	27588
16.90	27584	27580	27576	27572	27568	27565	27561	27557	27553	27549
17.00	27545	27541	27537	27534	27530	27526	27522	27518	27514	27511
17.10	27507	27503	27499	27495	27491	27488	27484	27480	27476	27472
17.20	27468	27465	27461	27457	27453	27449	27446	27442	27438	27434
17.30	27430	27427	27423	27419	27415	27411	27408	27404	27400	27396
17.40	27393	27389	27385	27381	27378	27374	27370	27366	27363	27359
17.50	27355	27351	27348	27344	27340	27336	27333	27329	27325	27321
17.60	27318	27314	27310	27307	27303	27299	27295	27292	27288	27284
17.70	27281	27277	27273	27269	27266	27262	27258	27255	27251	27247
17.80	27244	27240	27236	27233	27229	27225	27222	27218	27214	27211
17.90	27207	27203	27200	27196	27192	27189	27185	27181	27178	27174
18.00	27170	27167	27163	27159	27156	27152	27149	27145	27141	27138
18.10	27134	27130	27127	27123	27120	27116	27112	27109	27105	27102
18.20	27098	27094	27091	27087	27084	27080	27076	27073	27069	27066
18.30	27062	27059	27055	27051	27048	27044	27041	27037	27034	27030
18.40	27026	27023	27019	27016	27012	27009	27005	27002	26998	26995
18.50	26991	26987	26984	26980	26977	26973	26970	26966	26963	26959
18.60	26956	26952	26949	26945	26942	26938	26935	26931	26928	26924
18.70	26921	26917	26914	26910	26907	26903	26900	26896	26893	26889
18.80	26886	26882	26879	26875	26872	26868	26865	26861	26858	26854
18.90	26851	26848	26844	26841	26837	26834	26830	26827	26823	26820
19.00	26816	26813	26810	26806	26803	26799	26796	26792	26789	26786
19.10	26782	26779	26775	26772	26768	26765	26762	26758	26755	26751
19.20	26748	26745	26741	26738	26734	26731	26728	26724	26721	26717
19.30	26714	26711	26707	26704	26700	26697	26694	26690	26687	26684
19.40	26680	26677	26673	26670	26667	26663	26660	26657	26653	26650
19.50	26647	26643	26640	26637	26633	26630	26627	26623	26620	26617
19.60	26613	26610	26607	26603	26600	26597	26593	26590	26587	26583
19.70	26580	26577	26573	26570	26567	26563	26560	26557	26553	26550
19.80	26547	26544	26540	26537	26534	26530	26527	26524	26521	26517
19.90	26514	26511	26507	26504	26501	26498	26494	26491	26488	26484

TABLE Ⅵ - Continued

GEOPOTENTIAL ALTITUDE IN METERS as a function of PRESSURE IN MILLIBARS

P, mb	0.0	0.1	0.2	0.3	0.4	0.5	0.6	0.7	0.8	0.9
20.0	26481	26449	26416	26384	26352	26320	26288	26257	26225	26194
21.0	26163	26132	26101	26070	26040	26009	25979	25949	25919	25889
22.0	25860	25830	25801	25771	25742	25713	25684	25656	25627	25599
23.0	25570	25542	25514	25486	25458	25430	25403	25375	25348	25321
24.0	25294	25267	25240	25213	25186	25160	25133	25107	25081	25055
25.0	25029	25003	24977	24951	24926	24900	24875	24849	24824	24799
26.0	24774	24749	24725	24700	24675	24651	24626	24602	24578	24554
27.0	24530	24506	24482	24458	24435	24411	24387	24364	24341	24318
28.0	24294	24271	24248	24225	24203	24180	24157	24135	24112	24090
29.0	24068	24045	24023	24001	23979	23957	23935	23914	23892	23870
30.0	23849	23827	23806	23784	23763	23742	23721	23700	23679	23658
31.0	23637	23616	23596	23575	23554	23534	23514	23493	23473	23453
32.0	23432	23412	23392	23372	23352	23333	23313	23293	23273	23254
33.0	23234	23215	23195	23176	23157	23138	23118	23099	23080	23061
34.0	23042	23023	23005	22986	22967	22948	22930	22911	22893	22874
35.0	22856	22838	22819	22801	22783	22765	22747	22729	22711	22693
36.0	22675	22657	22639	22622	22604	22586	22569	22551	22534	22517
37.0	22499	22482	22465	22447	22430	22413	22396	22379	22362	22345
38.0	22328	22311	22295	22278	22261	22244	22228	22211	22195	22178
39.0	22162	22145	22129	22113	22096	22080	22064	22048	22032	22016
40.0	22000	21984	21968	21952	21936	21920	21904	21889	21873	21857
41.0	21842	21826	21811	21795	21780	21764	21749	21733	21718	21703
42.0	21688	21672	21657	21642	21627	21612	21597	21582	21567	21552
43.0	21537	21522	21508	21493	21478	21463	21449	21434	21420	21405
44.0	21390	21376	21362	21347	21333	21318	21304	21290	21276	21261
45.0	21247	21233	21219	21205	21191	21177	21163	21149	21135	21121
46.0	21107	21093	21079	21066	21052	21038	21024	21011	20997	20984
47.0	20970	20956	20943	20929	20916	20903	20889	20876	20862	20849
48.0	20836	20823	20809	20796	20783	20770	20757	20744	20731	20718
49.0	20705	20692	20679	20666	20653	20640	20627	20614	20602	20589
50.0	20576	20563	20551	20538	20525	20513	20500	20488	20475	20463
51.0	20450	20438	20425	20413	20401	20388	20376	20364	20351	20339
52.0	20327	20315	20303	20290	20278	20266	20254	20242	20230	20218
53.0	20206	20194	20182	20170	20158	20146	20135	20123	20111	20099
54.0	20087	20076	20064	20052	20041	20029	20017	20006	19994	19982
55.0	19971	19959	19948	19936	19925	19914	19902	19891	19879	19868
56.0	19857	19845	19834	19823	19812	19800	19789	19778	19767	19756
57.0	19744	19733	19722	19711	19700	19689	19678	19667	19656	19645
58.0	19634	19623	19612	19601	19591	19580	19569	19558	19547	19537
59.0	19526	19515	19504	19494	19483	19472	19462	19451	19440	19430
60.0	19419	19409	19398	19388	19377	19367	19356	19346	19335	19325
61.0	19314	19304	19294	19283	19273	19263	19252	19242	19232	19221
62.0	19211	19201	19191	19181	19170	19160	19150	19140	19130	19120
63.0	19110	19100	19090	19080	19070	19060	19050	19040	19030	19020
64.0	19010	19000	18990	18980	18970	18961	18951	18941	18931	18921
65.0	18912	18902	18892	18882	18873	18863	18853	18844	18834	18824
66.0	18815	18805	18796	18786	18776	18767	18757	18748	18738	18729
67.0	18719	18710	18700	18691	18682	18672	18663	18653	18644	18635
68.0	18625	18616	18607	18598	18588	18579	18570	18560	18551	18542
69.0	18533	18524	18514	18505	18496	18487	18478	18469	18460	18451
70.0	18442	18433	18424	18414	18405	18396	18387	18378	18370	18361
71.0	18352	18343	18334	18325	18316	18307	18298	18289	18281	18272
72.0	18263	18254	18245	18237	18228	18219	18210	18202	18193	18184
73.0	18175	18167	18158	18149	18141	18132	18124	18115	18106	18098
74.0	18089	18081	18072	18064	18055	18046	18038	18029	18021	18013
75.0	18004	17996	17987	17979	17970	17962	17954	17945	17937	17928
76.0	17920	17912	17903	17895	17887	17878	17870	17862	17854	17845
77.0	17837	17829	17821	17813	17804	17796	17788	17780	17772	17763
78.0	17755	17747	17739	17731	17723	17715	17707	17699	17691	17683
79.0	17675	17667	17659	17651	17643	17635	17627	17619	17611	17603
80.0	17595	17587	17579	17571	17563	17555	17547	17540	17532	17524
81.0	17516	17508	17500	17493	17485	17477	17469	17461	17454	17446
82.0	17438	17430	17423	17415	17407	17400	17392	17384	17377	17369
83.0	17361	17354	17346	17338	17331	17323	17316	17308	17301	17293
84.0	17285	17278	17270	17263	17255	17248	17240	17233	17225	17218
85.0	17210	17203	17195	17188	17181	17173	17166	17158	17151	17144
86.0	17136	17129	17121	17114	17107	17099	17092	17085	17077	17070
87.0	17063	17056	17048	17041	17034	17027	17019	17012	17005	16998
88.0	16990	16983	16976	16969	16962	16954	16947	16940	16933	16926
89.0	16919	16912	16904	16897	16890	16883	16876	16869	16862	16855
90.0	16848	16841	16834	16827	16820	16813	16806	16799	16792	16785
91.0	16778	16771	16764	16757	16750	16743	16736	16729	16722	16715
92.0	16708	16702	16695	16688	16681	16674	16667	16660	16654	16647
93.0	16640	16633	16626	16620	16613	16606	16599	16592	16586	16579
94.0	16572	16565	16559	16552	16545	16538	16532	16525	16518	16512
95.0	16505	16498	16492	16485	16478	16472	16465	16458	16452	16445
96.0	16439	16432	16425	16419	16412	16406	16399	16393	16386	16379
97.0	16373	16366	16360	16353	16347	16340	16334	16327	16321	16314
98.0	16308	16301	16295	16288	16282	16276	16269	16263	16256	16250
99.0	16243	16237	16231	16224	16218	16211	16205	16199	16192	16186
100.0	16180	16173	16167	16161	16154	16148	16142	16135	16129	16123
101.0	16117	16110	16104	16098	16092	16085	16079	16073	16067	16060
102.0	16054	16048	16042	16036	16029	16023	16017	16011	16005	15998
103.0	15992	15986	15980	15974	15968	15962	15955	15949	15943	15937
104.0	15931	15925	15919	15913	15907	15901	15895	15888	15882	15876
105.0	15870	15864	15858	15852	15846	15840	15834	15828	15822	15816
106.0	15810	15804	15798	15792	15786	15780	15774	15768	15763	15757
107.0	15751	15745	15739	15733	15727	15721	15715	15709	15703	15698
108.0	15692	15686	15680	15674	15668	15662	15657	15651	15645	15639
109.0	15633	15627	15622	15616	15610	15604	15598	15593	15587	15581
110.0	15575	15570	15564	15558	15552	15547	15541	15535	15529	15524
111.0	15518	15512	15506	15501	15495	15489	15484	15478	15472	15467
112.0	15461	15455	15450	15444	15438	15433	15427	15422	15416	15410
113.0	15405	15399	15393	15388	15382	15377	15371	15365	15360	15354
114.0	15349	15343	15338	15332	15327	15321	15315	15310	15304	15299
115.0	15293	15288	15282	15277	15271	15266	15260	15255	15249	15244
116.0	15238	15233	15228	15222	15217	15211	15206	15200	15195	15189
117.0	15184	15179	15173	15168	15162	15157	15152	15146	15141	15135
118.0	15130	15125	15119	15114	15109	15103	15098	15093	15087	15082
119.0	15077	15071	15066	15061	15055	15050	15045	15039	15034	15029

TABLE VI - Continued   183

GEOPOTENTIAL ALTITUDE IN METERS as a function of PRESSURE IN MILLIBARS

P, mb	0.0	0.1	0.2	0.3	0.4	0.5	0.6	0.7	0.8	0.9
120.0	15023	15018	15013	15008	15002	14997	14992	14987	14981	14976
121.0	14971	14966	14960	14955	14950	14945	14940	14934	14929	14924
122.0	14919	14913	14908	14903	14898	14893	14888	14882	14877	14872
123.0	14867	14862	14857	14851	14846	14841	14836	14831	14826	14821
124.0	14816	14810	14805	14800	14795	14790	14785	14780	14775	14770
125.0	14765	14760	14754	14749	14744	14739	14734	14729	14724	14719
126.0	14714	14709	14704	14699	14694	14689	14684	14679	14674	14669
127.0	14664	14659	14654	14649	14644	14639	14634	14629	14624	14619
128.0	14614	14609	14604	14599	14594	14589	14585	14580	14575	14570
129.0	14565	14560	14555	14550	14545	14540	14535	14531	14526	14521
130.0	14516	14511	14506	14501	14496	14492	14487	14482	14477	14472
131.0	14467	14462	14458	14453	14448	14443	14438	14434	14429	14424
132.0	14419	14414	14409	14405	14400	14395	14390	14386	14381	14376
133.0	14371	14366	14362	14357	14352	14347	14343	14338	14333	14328
134.0	14324	14319	14314	14310	14305	14300	14295	14291	14286	14281
135.0	14277	14272	14267	14262	14258	14253	14248	14244	14239	14234
136.0	14230	14225	14220	14216	14211	14206	14202	14197	14193	14188
137.0	14183	14179	14174	14169	14165	14160	14156	14151	14146	14142
138.0	14137	14133	14128	14123	14119	14114	14110	14105	14101	14096
139.0	14091	14087	14082	14078	14073	14069	14064	14060	14055	14050
140.0	14046	14041	14037	14032	14028	14023	14019	14014	14010	14005
141.0	14001	13996	13992	13987	13983	13978	13974	13969	13965	13960
142.0	13956	13952	13947	13943	13938	13934	13929	13925	13920	13916
143.0	13911	13907	13903	13898	13894	13889	13885	13881	13876	13872
144.0	13867	13863	13858	13854	13850	13845	13841	13837	13832	13828
145.0	13823	13819	13815	13810	13806	13802	13797	13793	13789	13784
146.0	13780	13775	13771	13767	13762	13758	13754	13749	13745	13741
147.0	13737	13732	13728	13724	13719	13715	13711	13706	13702	13698
148.0	13694	13689	13685	13681	13676	13672	13668	13664	13659	13655
149.0	13651	13647	13642	13638	13634	13630	13625	13621	13617	13613
150.0	13608	13604	13600	13596	13592	13587	13583	13579	13575	13570
151.0	13566	13562	13558	13554	13549	13545	13541	13537	13533	13529
152.0	13524	13520	13516	13512	13508	13504	13499	13495	13491	13487
153.0	13483	13479	13475	13470	13466	13462	13458	13454	13450	13446
154.0	13442	13437	13433	13429	13425	13421	13417	13413	13409	13405
155.0	13400	13396	13392	13388	13384	13380	13376	13372	13368	13364
156.0	13360	13356	13352	13348	13343	13339	13335	13331	13327	13323
157.0	13319	13315	13311	13307	13303	13299	13295	13291	13287	13283
158.0	13279	13275	13271	13267	13263	13259	13255	13251	13247	13243
159.0	13239	13235	13231	13227	13223	13219	13215	13211	13207	13203
160.0	13199	13195	13191	13187	13183	13179	13175	13171	13167	13164
161.0	13160	13156	13152	13148	13144	13140	13136	13132	13128	13124
162.0	13120	13116	13113	13109	13105	13101	13097	13093	13089	13085
163.0	13081	13077	13074	13070	13066	13062	13058	13054	13050	13046
164.0	13043	13039	13035	13031	13027	13023	13019	13016	13012	13008
165.0	13004	13000	12996	12992	12989	12985	12981	12977	12973	12969
166.0	12966	12962	12958	12954	12950	12947	12943	12939	12935	12931
167.0	12928	12924	12920	12916	12912	12909	12905	12901	12897	12893
168.0	12890	12886	12882	12878	12875	12871	12867	12863	12860	12856
169.0	12852	12848	12845	12841	12837	12833	12830	12826	12822	12818
170.0	12815	12811	12807	12803	12800	12796	12792	12789	12785	12781
171.0	12777	12774	12770	12766	12763	12759	12755	12752	12748	12744
172.0	12740	12737	12733	12729	12726	12722	12718	12715	12711	12707
173.0	12704	12700	12696	12693	12689	12685	12682	12678	12674	12671
174.0	12667	12664	12660	12656	12653	12649	12645	12642	12638	12634
175.0	12631	12627	12624	12620	12616	12613	12609	12606	12602	12598
176.0	12595	12591	12588	12584	12580	12577	12573	12570	12566	12562
177.0	12559	12555	12552	12548	12544	12541	12537	12534	12530	12527
178.0	12523	12519	12516	12512	12509	12505	12502	12498	12495	12491
179.0	12488	12484	12480	12477	12473	12470	12466	12463	12459	12456
180.0	12452	12449	12445	12442	12438	12435	12431	12428	12424	12421
181.0	12417	12414	12410	12407	12403	12400	12396	12393	12389	12386
182.0	12382	12379	12375	12372	12368	12365	12361	12358	12354	12351
183.0	12347	12344	12340	12337	12334	12330	12327	12323	12320	12316
184.0	12313	12309	12306	12302	12299	12296	12292	12289	12285	12282
185.0	12278	12275	12272	12268	12265	12261	12258	12254	12251	12248
186.0	12244	12241	12237	12234	12231	12227	12224	12220	12217	12214
187.0	12210	12207	12203	12200	12197	12193	12190	12187	12183	12180
188.0	12176	12173	12170	12166	12163	12160	12156	12153	12149	12146
189.0	12143	12139	12136	12133	12129	12126	12123	12119	12116	12113
190.0	12109	12106	12103	12099	12096	12093	12089	12086	12083	12079
191.0	12076	12073	12069	12066	12063	12059	12056	12053	12050	12046
192.0	12043	12040	12036	12033	12030	12026	12023	12020	12017	12013
193.0	12010	12007	12003	12000	11997	11994	11990	11987	11984	11980
194.0	11977	11974	11971	11967	11964	11961	11958	11954	11951	11948
195.0	11945	11941	11938	11935	11932	11928	11925	11922	11919	11915
196.0	11912	11909	11906	11902	11899	11896	11893	11890	11886	11883
197.0	11880	11877	11873	11870	11867	11864	11861	11857	11854	11851
198.0	11848	11845	11841	11838	11835	11832	11829	11825	11822	11819
199.0	11816	11813	11809	11806	11803	11800	11797	11794	11790	11787
200.0	11784	11781	11778	11775	11771	11768	11765	11762	11759	11756
201.0	11752	11749	11746	11743	11740	11737	11734	11730	11727	11724
202.0	11721	11718	11715	11712	11708	11705	11702	11699	11696	11693
203.0	11690	11686	11683	11680	11677	11674	11671	11668	11665	11662
204.0	11658	11655	11652	11649	11646	11643	11640	11637	11634	11631
205.0	11627	11624	11621	11618	11615	11612	11609	11606	11603	11600
206.0	11597	11594	11590	11587	11584	11581	11578	11575	11572	11569
207.0	11566	11563	11560	11557	11554	11551	11548	11544	11541	11538
208.0	11535	11532	11529	11526	11523	11520	11517	11514	11511	11508
209.0	11505	11502	11499	11496	11493	11490	11487	11484	11481	11478
210.0	11475	11472	11469	11466	11463	11460	11457	11454	11451	11448
211.0	11445	11441	11438	11435	11432	11429	11426	11423	11421	11418
212.0	11415	11412	11409	11406	11403	11400	11397	11394	11391	11388
213.0	11385	11382	11379	11376	11373	11370	11367	11364	11361	11358
214.0	11355	11352	11349	11346	11343	11340	11337	11334	11331	11328
215.0	11325	11322	11320	11317	11314	11311	11308	11305	11302	11299
216.0	11296	11293	11290	11287	11284	11281	11278	11275	11273	11270
217.0	11267	11264	11261	11258	11255	11252	11249	11246	11243	11240
218.0	11238	11235	11232	11229	11226	11223	11220	11217	11214	11211
219.0	11209	11206	11203	11200	11197	11194	11191	11188	111185	11182

TABLE VI - Continued

GEOPOTENTIAL ALTITUDE IN METERS as a function of PRESSURE IN MILLIBARS

P,mb	0.0	0.1	0.2	0.3	0.4	0.5	0.6	0.7	0.8	0.9
220.0	11180	11177	11174	11171	11168	11165	11162	11159	11157	11154
221.0	11151	11148	11145	11142	11139	11137	11134	11131	11128	11125
222.0	11122	11119	11117	11114	11111	11108	11105	11102	11099	11097
223.0	11094	11091	11088	11085	11082	11080	11077	11074	11071	11068
224.0	11065	11063	11060	11057	11054	11051	11048	11046	11043	11040
225.0	11037	11034	11031	11029	11026	11023	11020	11017	11015	11012
226.0	11009	11006	11003	11001	10998	10995	10992	10989	10987	10984
227.0	10981	10978	10975	10973	10970	10967	10964	10961	10959	10956
228.0	10953	10950	10948	10945	10942	10939	10936	10934	10931	10928
229.0	10925	10922	10920	10917	10914	10911	10909	10906	10903	10900
230.0	10898	10895	10892	10889	10887	10884	10881	10878	10875	10873
231.0	10870	10867	10864	10862	10859	10856	10853	10851	10848	10845
232.0	10842	10840	10837	10834	10831	10829	10826	10823	10821	10818
233.0	10815	10812	10810	10807	10804	10801	10799	10796	10793	10790
234.0	10788	10785	10782	10780	10777	10774	10771	10769	10766	10763
235.0	10760	10758	10755	10752	10750	10747	10744	10741	10739	10736
236.0	10733	10731	10728	10725	10723	10720	10717	10714	10712	10709
237.0	10706	10704	10701	10698	10696	10693	10690	10687	10685	10682
238.0	10679	10677	10674	10671	10669	10666	10663	10661	10658	10655
239.0	10653	10650	10647	10644	10642	10639	10636	10634	10631	10628
240.0	10626	10623	10620	10618	10615	10612	10610	10607	10604	10602
241.0	10599	10596	10594	10591	10588	10586	10583	10580	10578	10575
242.0	10572	10570	10567	10565	10562	10559	10557	10554	10551	10549
243.0	10546	10543	10541	10538	10535	10533	10530	10527	10525	10522
244.0	10520	10517	10514	10512	10509	10506	10504	10501	10499	10496
245.0	10493	10491	10488	10485	10483	10480	10477	10475	10472	10470
246.0	10467	10464	10462	10459	10457	10454	10451	10449	10446	10443
247.0	10441	10438	10436	10433	10430	10428	10425	10423	10420	10417
248.0	10415	10412	10410	10407	10404	10402	10399	10397	10394	10391
249.0	10389	10386	10384	10381	10378	10376	10373	10371	10368	10366
250.0	10363	10360	10358	10355	10353	10350	10347	10345	10342	10340
251.0	10337	10335	10332	10329	10327	10324	10322	10319	10317	10314
252.0	10311	10309	10306	10304	10301	10299	10296	10293	10291	10288
253.0	10286	10283	10281	10278	10276	10273	10270	10268	10265	10263
254.0	10260	10258	10255	10253	10250	10247	10245	10242	10240	10237
255.0	10235	10232	10230	10227	10225	10222	10219	10217	10214	10212
256.0	10209	10207	10204	10202	10199	10197	10194	10192	10189	10187
257.0	10184	10181	10179	10176	10174	10171	10169	10166	10164	10161
258.0	10159	10156	10154	10151	10149	10146	10144	10141	10139	10136
259.0	10134	10131	10129	10126	10124	10121	10119	10116	10114	10111
260.0	10109	10106	10104	10101	10098	10096	10093	10091	10089	10086
261.0	10084	10081	10079	10076	10074	10071	10069	10066	10064	10061
262.0	10059	10056	10054	10051	10049	10046	10044	10041	10039	10036
263.0	10034	10031	10029	10026	10024	10021	10019	10016	10014	10011
264.0	10009	10006	10004	10002	9999	9997	9994	9992	9989	9987
265.0	9984	9982	9979	9977	9974	9972	9969	9967	9965	9962
266.0	9960	9957	9955	9952	9950	9947	9945	9942	9940	9938
267.0	9935	9933	9930	9928	9925	9923	9920	9918	9916	9913
268.0	9911	9908	9906	9903	9901	9898	9896	9894	9891	9889
269.0	9886	9884	9881	9879	9876	9874	9872	9869	9867	9864
270.0	9862	9859	9857	9855	9852	9850	9847	9845	9842	9840
271.0	9838	9835	9833	9830	9828	9826	9823	9821	9818	9816
272.0	9813	9811	9809	9806	9804	9801	9799	9797	9794	9792
273.0	9789	9787	9785	9782	9780	9777	9775	9773	9770	9768
274.0	9765	9763	9761	9758	9756	9753	9751	9749	9746	9744
275.0	9741	9739	9737	9734	9732	9729	9727	9725	9722	9720
276.0	9717	9715	9713	9710	9708	9706	9703	9701	9698	9696
277.0	9694	9691	9689	9686	9684	9682	9679	9677	9675	9672
278.0	9670	9667	9665	9663	9660	9658	9656	9653	9651	9649
279.0	9646	9644	9641	9639	9637	9634	9632	9630	9627	9625
280.0	9623	9620	9618	9615	9613	9611	9608	9606	9604	9601
281.0	9599	9597	9594	9592	9590	9587	9585	9583	9580	9578
282.0	9576	9573	9571	9568	9566	9564	9561	9559	9557	9554
283.0	9552	9550	9547	9545	9543	9540	9538	9536	9533	9531
284.0	9529	9526	9524	9522	9519	9517	9515	9512	9510	9508
285.0	9505	9503	9501	9499	9496	9494	9492	9489	9487	9485
286.0	9482	9480	9478	9475	9473	9471	9468	9466	9464	9461
287.0	9459	9457	9454	9452	9450	9448	9445	9443	9441	9438
288.0	9436	9434	9431	9429	9427	9425	9422	9420	9418	9415
289.0	9413	9411	9408	9406	9404	9402	9399	9397	9395	9392
290.0	9390	9388	9385	9383	9381	9379	9376	9374	9372	9369
291.0	9367	9365	9363	9360	9358	9356	9353	9351	9349	9347
292.0	9344	9342	9340	9337	9335	9333	9331	9328	9326	9324
293.0	9322	9319	9317	9315	9312	9310	9308	9306	9303	9301
294.0	9299	9297	9294	9292	9290	9288	9285	9283	9281	9278
295.0	9276	9274	9272	9269	9267	9265	9263	9260	9258	9256
296.0	9254	9251	9249	9247	9245	9242	9240	9238	9236	9233
297.0	9231	9229	9227	9224	9222	9220	9218	9215	9213	9211
298.0	9209	9206	9204	9202	9200	9197	9195	9193	9191	9189
299.0	9186	9184	9182	9180	9177	9175	9173	9171	9168	9166
300.0	9164	9162	9159	9157	9155	9153	9151	9148	9146	9144
301.0	9142	9139	9137	9135	9133	9131	9128	9126	9124	9122
302.0	9119	9117	9115	9113	9111	9108	9106	9104	9102	9100
303.0	9097	9095	9093	9091	9088	9086	9084	9082	9080	9077
304.0	9075	9073	9071	9069	9066	9064	9062	9060	9058	9055
305.0	9053	9051	9049	9047	9044	9042	9040	9038	9036	9033
306.0	9031	9029	9027	9025	9022	9020	9018	9016	9014	9011
307.0	9009	9007	9005	9003	9001	8998	8996	8994	8992	8990
308.0	8987	8985	8983	8981	8979	8977	8974	8972	8970	8968
309.0	8966	8963	8961	8959	8957	8955	8953	8950	8948	8946
310.0	8944	8942	8940	8937	8935	8933	8931	8929	8927	8924
311.0	8922	8920	8918	8916	8914	8911	8909	8907	8905	8903
312.0	8901	8898	8896	8894	8892	8890	8888	8885	8883	8881
313.0	8879	8877	8875	8873	8870	8868	8866	8864	8862	8860
314.0	8857	8855	8853	8851	8849	8847	8845	8842	8840	8838
315.0	8836	8834	8832	8830	8827	8825	8823	8821	8819	8817
316.0	8815	8812	8810	8808	8806	8804	8802	8800	8797	8795
317.0	8793	8791	8789	8787	8785	8783	8780	8778	8776	8774
318.0	8772	8770	8768	8766	8763	8761	8759	8757	8755	8753
319.0	8751	8771	8749	8746	8744	8742	8740	8738	8736	8734	8732

TABLE VI - Continued

185

GEOPOTENTIAL ALTITUDE IN METERS as a function of PRESSURE IN MILLIBARS

P, mb	0.0	0.1	0.2	0.3	0.4	0.5	0.6	0.7	0.8	0.9
320.0	8729	8727	8725	8723	8721	8719	8717	8715	8713	8710
321.0	8708	8706	8704	8702	8700	8698	8696	8694	8691	8689
322.0	8687	8685	8683	8681	8679	8677	8675	8673	8670	8668
323.0	8666	8664	8662	8660	8658	8656	8654	8652	8649	8647
324.0	8645	8643	8641	8639	8637	8635	8633	8631	8628	8626
325.0	8624	8622	8620	8618	8616	8614	8612	8610	8608	8605
326.0	8603	8601	8599	8597	8595	8593	8591	8589	8587	8585
327.0	8583	8581	8578	8576	8574	8572	8570	8568	8566	8564
328.0	8562	8560	8558	8556	8554	8551	8549	8547	8545	8543
329.0	8541	8539	8537	8535	8533	8531	8529	8527	8525	8522
330.0	8520	8518	8516	8514	8512	8510	8508	8506	8504	8502
331.0	8500	8498	8496	8494	8492	8490	8487	8485	8483	8481
332.0	8479	8477	8475	8473	8471	8469	8467	8465	8463	8461
333.0	8459	8457	8455	8453	8451	8448	8446	8444	8442	8440
334.0	8438	8436	8434	8432	8430	8428	8426	8424	8422	8420
335.0	8418	8416	8414	8412	8410	8408	8406	8404	8402	8399
336.0	8397	8395	8393	8391	8389	8387	8385	8383	8381	8379
337.0	8377	8375	8373	8371	8369	8367	8365	8363	8361	8359
338.0	8357	8355	8353	8351	8349	8347	8345	8343	8341	8339
339.0	8337	8335	8333	8331	8329	8327	8325	8322	8320	8318
340.0	8316	8314	8312	8310	8308	8306	8304	8302	8300	8298
341.0	8296	8294	8292	8290	8288	8286	8284	8282	8280	8278
342.0	8276	8274	8272	8270	8268	8266	8264	8262	8260	8258
343.0	8256	8254	8252	8250	8248	8246	8244	8242	8240	8238
344.0	8236	8234	8232	8230	8228	8226	8224	8222	8220	8218
345.0	8216	8214	8212	8210	8208	8206	8204	8202	8200	8198
346.0	8196	8194	8192	8190	8188	8186	8184	8182	8180	8179
347.0	8177	8175	8173	8171	8169	8167	8165	8163	8161	8159
348.0	8157	8155	8153	8151	8149	8147	8145	8143	8141	8139
349.0	8137	8135	8133	8131	8129	8127	8125	8123	8121	8119
350.0	8117	8115	8113	8111	8109	8107	8105	8103	8102	8100
351.0	8098	8096	8094	8092	8090	8088	8086	8084	8082	8080
352.0	8078	8076	8074	8072	8070	8068	8066	8064	8062	8060
353.0	8058	8056	8054	8053	8051	8049	8047	8045	8043	8041
354.0	8039	8037	8035	8033	8031	8029	8027	8025	8023	8021
355.0	8019	8017	8016	8014	8012	8010	8008	8006	8004	8002
356.0	8000	7998	7996	7994	7992	7990	7988	7986	7984	7982
357.0	7981	7979	7977	7975	7973	7971	7969	7967	7965	7963
358.0	7961	7959	7957	7955	7953	7952	7950	7948	7946	7944
359.0	7942	7940	7938	7936	7934	7932	7930	7928	7926	7925
360.0	7923	7921	7919	7917	7915	7913	7911	7909	7907	7905
361.0	7903	7901	7900	7898	7896	7894	7892	7890	7888	7886
362.0	7884	7882	7880	7878	7877	7875	7873	7871	7869	7867
363.0	7865	7863	7861	7859	7857	7856	7854	7852	7850	7848
364.0	7846	7844	7842	7840	7838	7836	7835	7833	7831	7829
365.0	7827	7825	7823	7821	7819	7817	7816	7814	7812	7810
366.0	7808	7806	7804	7802	7800	7798	7797	7795	7793	7791
367.0	7789	7787	7785	7783	7781	7780	7778	7776	7774	7772
368.0	7770	7768	7766	7764	7763	7761	7759	7757	7755	7753
369.0	7751	7749	7747	7746	7744	7742	7740	7738	7736	7734
370.0	7732	7730	7729	7727	7725	7723	7721	7719	7717	7715
371.0	7714	7712	7710	7708	7706	7704	7702	7700	7699	7697
372.0	7695	7693	7691	7689	7687	7685	7684	7682	7680	7678
373.0	7676	7674	7672	7670	7669	7667	7665	7663	7661	7659
374.0	7657	7656	7654	7652	7650	7648	7646	7644	7642	7641
375.0	7639	7637	7635	7633	7631	7629	7628	7626	7624	7622
376.0	7620	7618	7616	7615	7613	7611	7609	7607	7605	7603
377.0	7602	7600	7598	7596	7594	7592	7590	7589	7587	7585
378.0	7583	7581	7579	7578	7576	7574	7572	7570	7568	7566
379.0	7565	7563	7561	7559	7557	7555	7554	7552	7550	7548
380.0	7546	7544	7542	7541	7539	7537	7535	7533	7531	7530
381.0	7528	7526	7524	7522	7520	7519	7517	7515	7513	7511
382.0	7509	7508	7506	7504	7502	7500	7498	7497	7495	7493
383.0	7491	7489	7487	7486	7484	7482	7480	7478	7476	7475
384.0	7473	7471	7469	7467	7466	7464	7462	7460	7458	7456
385.0	7455	7453	7451	7449	7447	7445	7444	7442	7440	7438
386.0	7436	7435	7433	7431	7429	7427	7425	7424	7422	7420
387.0	7418	7416	7415	7413	7411	7409	7407	7406	7404	7402
388.0	7400	7398	7396	7395	7393	7391	7389	7387	7386	7384
389.0	7382	7380	7378	7377	7375	7373	7371	7369	7368	7366
390.0	7364	7362	7360	7359	7357	7355	7353	7351	7350	7348
391.0	7346	7344	7342	7341	7339	7337	7335	7333	7332	7330
392.0	7328	7326	7324	7323	7321	7319	7317	7315	7314	7312
393.0	7310	7308	7306	7305	7303	7301	7299	7297	7296	7294
394.0	7292	7290	7289	7287	7285	7283	7281	7280	7278	7276
395.0	7274	7272	7271	7269	7267	7265	7264	7262	7260	7258
396.0	7256	7255	7253	7251	7249	7247	7246	7244	7242	7240
397.0	7239	7237	7235	7233	7231	7230	7228	7226	7224	7223
398.0	7221	7219	7217	7216	7214	7212	7210	7208	7207	7205
399.0	7203	7201	7200	7198	7196	7194	7192	7191	7189	7187
400.0	7185	7184	7182	7180	7178	7177	7175	7173	7171	7170
401.0	7168	7166	7164	7162	7161	7159	7157	7155	7154	7152
402.0	7150	7148	7147	7145	7143	7141	7140	7138	7136	7134
403.0	7133	7131	7129	7127	7126	7124	7122	7120	7119	7117
404.0	7115	7113	7112	7110	7108	7106	7105	7103	7101	7099
405.0	7098	7096	7094	7092	7091	7089	7087	7085	7084	7082
406.0	7080	7078	7077	7075	7073	7071	7070	7068	7066	7064
407.0	7063	7061	7059	7057	7056	7054	7052	7050	7049	7047
408.0	7045	7043	7042	7040	7038	7037	7035	7033	7031	7030
409.0	7028	7026	7024	7023	7021	7019	7017	7016	7014	7012
410.0	7011	7009	7007	7005	7004	7002	7000	6998	6997	6995
411.0	6993	6991	6990	6988	6986	6985	6983	6981	6979	6978
412.0	6976	6974	6972	6971	6969	6967	6966	6964	6962	6960
413.0	6959	6957	6955	6954	6952	6950	6948	6947	6945	6943
414.0	6942	6940	6938	6936	6935	6933	6931	6929	6928	6926
415.0	6924	6923	6921	6919	6917	6916	6914	6912	6911	6909
416.0	6907	6905	6904	6902	6900	6899	6897	6895	6894	6892
417.0	6890	6888	6887	6885	6883	6882	6880	6878	6876	6875
418.0	6873	6871	6870	6868	6866	6865	6863	6861	6859	6858
419.0	6856	6854	6853	6851	6849	6847	6846	6844	6842	6841

TABLE VI - Continued

GEOPOTENTIAL ALTITUDE IN METERS as a function of PRESSURE IN MILLIBARS

P, mb	0.0	0.1	0.2	0.3	0.4	0.5	0.6	0.7	0.8	0.9
420.0	6839	6837	6836	6834	6832	6831	6829	6827	6825	6824
421.0	6822	6820	6819	6817	6815	6814	6812	6810	6808	6807
422.0	6805	6803	6802	6800	6798	6797	6795	6793	6792	6790
423.0	6788	6787	6785	6783	6781	6780	6778	6776	6775	6773
424.0	6771	6770	6768	6766	6765	6763	6761	6760	6758	6756
425.0	6754	6753	6751	6749	6748	6746	6744	6743	6741	6739
426.0	6738	6736	6734	6733	6731	6729	6728	6726	6724	6723
427.0	6721	6719	6718	6716	6714	6713	6711	6709	6708	6706
428.0	6704	6702	6701	6699	6697	6696	6694	6692	6691	6689
429.0	6687	6686	6684	6682	6681	6679	6677	6676	6674	6672
430.0	6671	6669	6667	6666	6664	6662	6661	6659	6657	6656
431.0	6654	6652	6651	6649	6647	6646	6644	6642	6641	6639
432.0	6638	6636	6634	6633	6631	6629	6628	6626	6624	6623
433.0	6621	6619	6618	6616	6614	6613	6611	6609	6608	6606
434.0	6604	6603	6601	6599	6598	6596	6594	6593	6591	6589
435.0	6588	6586	6585	6583	6581	6580	6578	6576	6575	6573
436.0	6571	6570	6568	6566	6565	6563	6561	6560	6558	6557
437.0	6555	6553	6552	6550	6548	6547	6545	6543	6542	6540
438.0	6538	6537	6535	6534	6532	6530	6529	6527	6525	6524
439.0	6522	6520	6519	6517	6516	6514	6512	6511	6509	6507
440.0	6506	6504	6502	6501	6499	6498	6496	6494	6493	6491
441.0	6489	6488	6486	6484	6483	6481	6480	6478	6476	6475
442.0	6473	6471	6470	6468	6467	6465	6463	6462	6460	6458
443.0	6457	6455	6454	6452	6450	6449	6447	6445	6444	6442
444.0	6441	6439	6437	6436	6434	6432	6431	6429	6428	6426
445.0	6424	6423	6421	6419	6418	6416	6415	6413	6411	6410
446.0	6408	6406	6405	6403	6402	6400	6398	6397	6395	6394
447.0	6392	6390	6389	6387	6385	6384	6382	6381	6379	6377
448.0	6376	6374	6373	6371	6369	6368	6366	6365	6363	6361
449.0	6360	6358	6356	6355	6353	6352	6350	6348	6347	6345
450.0	6344	6342	6340	6339	6337	6336	6334	6332	6331	6329
451.0	6328	6326	6324	6323	6321	6320	6318	6316	6315	6313
452.0	6312	6310	6308	6307	6305	6304	6302	6300	6299	6297
453.0	6296	6294	6292	6291	6289	6288	6286	6284	6283	6281
454.0	6280	6278	6276	6275	6273	6272	6270	6268	6267	6265
455.0	6264	6262	6260	6259	6257	6256	6254	6253	6251	6249
456.0	6248	6246	6245	6243	6241	6240	6238	6237	6235	6233
457.0	6232	6230	6229	6227	6226	6224	6222	6221	6219	6218
458.0	6216	6214	6213	6211	6210	6208	6207	6205	6203	6202
459.0	6200	6199	6197	6195	6194	6192	6191	6189	6188	6186
460.0	6184	6183	6181	6180	6178	6177	6175	6173	6172	6170
461.0	6169	6167	6166	6164	6162	6161	6159	6158	6156	6154
462.0	6153	6151	6150	6148	6147	6145	6143	6142	6140	6139
463.0	6137	6136	6134	6133	6131	6129	6128	6126	6125	6123
464.0	6122	6120	6118	6117	6115	6114	6112	6111	6109	6107
465.0	6106	6104	6103	6101	6100	6098	6097	6095	6093	6092
466.0	6090	6089	6087	6086	6084	6082	6081	6079	6078	6076
467.0	6075	6073	6072	6070	6068	6067	6065	6064	6062	6061
468.0	6059	6058	6056	6054	6053	6051	6050	6048	6047	6045
469.0	6044	6042	6040	6039	6037	6036	6034	6033	6031	6030
470.0	6028	6026	6025	6023	6022	6020	6019	6017	6016	6014
471.0	6013	6011	6009	6008	6006	6005	6003	6002	6000	5999
472.0	5997	5996	5994	5992	5991	5989	5988	5986	5985	5983
473.0	5982	5980	5979	5977	5975	5974	5972	5971	5969	5968
474.0	5966	5965	5963	5962	5960	5959	5957	5955	5954	5952
475.0	5951	5949	5948	5946	5945	5943	5942	5940	5939	5937
476.0	5935	5934	5932	5931	5929	5928	5926	5925	5923	5922
477.0	5920	5919	5917	5916	5914	5912	5911	5909	5908	5906
478.0	5905	5903	5902	5900	5899	5897	5896	5894	5893	5891
479.0	5890	5888	5886	5885	5883	5882	5880	5879	5877	5876
480.0	5874	5873	5871	5870	5868	5867	5865	5864	5862	5861
481.0	5859	5858	5856	5854	5853	5851	5850	5848	5847	5845
482.0	5844	5842	5841	5839	5838	5836	5835	5833	5832	5830
483.0	5829	5827	5826	5824	5823	5821	5820	5818	5817	5815
484.0	5814	5812	5810	5809	5807	5806	5804	5803	5801	5800
485.0	5798	5797	5795	5794	5792	5791	5789	5788	5786	5785
486.0	5783	5782	5780	5779	5777	5776	5774	5773	5771	5770
487.0	5768	5767	5765	5764	5762	5761	5759	5758	5756	5755
488.0	5753	5752	5750	5749	5747	5746	5744	5743	5741	5740
489.0	5738	5737	5735	5734	5732	5731	5729	5728	5726	5725
490.0	5723	5722	5720	5719	5717	5716	5714	5713	5711	5710
491.0	5708	5707	5705	5704	5702	5701	5699	5698	5696	5695
492.0	5693	5692	5690	5689	5687	5686	5684	5683	5681	5680
493.0	5678	5677	5675	5674	5672	5671	5669	5668	5666	5665
494.0	5663	5662	5660	5659	5657	5656	5654	5653	5651	5650
495.0	5648	5647	5645	5644	5643	5641	5640	5638	5637	5635
496.0	5634	5632	5631	5629	5628	5626	5625	5623	5622	5620
497.0	5619	5617	5616	5614	5613	5611	5610	5608	5607	5605
498.0	5604	5602	5601	5600	5598	5597	5595	5594	5592	5591
499.0	5589	5588	5586	5585	5583	5582	5580	5579	5577	5576
500.0	5574	5573	5571	5570	5569	5567	5566	5564	5563	5561
501.0	5560	5558	5557	5555	5554	5552	5551	5549	5548	5546
502.0	5545	5544	5542	5541	5539	5538	5536	5535	5533	5532
503.0	5530	5529	5527	5526	5524	5523	5521	5520	5519	5517
504.0	5516	5514	5513	5511	5510	5508	5507	5505	5504	5502
505.0	5501	5500	5498	5497	5495	5494	5492	5491	5489	5488
506.0	5486	5485	5483	5482	5481	5479	5478	5476	5475	5473
507.0	5472	5470	5469	5467	5466	5464	5463	5462	5460	5459
508.0	5457	5456	5454	5453	5451	5450	5448	5447	5446	5444
509.0	5443	5441	5440	5438	5437	5435	5434	5432	5431	5430
510.0	5428	5427	5425	5424	5422	5421	5419	5418	5417	5415
511.0	5414	5412	5411	5409	5408	5406	5405	5403	5402	5401
512.0	5399	5398	5396	5395	5393	5392	5390	5389	5388	5386
513.0	5385	5383	5382	5380	5379	5377	5376	5375	5373	5372
514.0	5370	5369	5367	5366	5364	5363	5362	5360	5359	5357
515.0	5356	5354	5353	5352	5350	5349	5347	5346	5344	5343
516.0	5341	5340	5339	5337	5336	5334	5333	5331	5330	5329
517.0	5327	5326	5324	5323	5321	5320	5318	5317	5316	5314
518.0	5313	5311	5310	5308	5307	5306	5304	5303	5301	5300
519.0	5299	5297	5296	5294	5293	5291	5290	5288	5287	5286

GEOPOTENTIAL ALTITUDE IN METERS as a function of PRESSURE IN MILLIBARS

P, mb	0.0	0.1	0.2	0.3	0.4	0.5	0.6	0.7	0.8	0.9
520.0	5284	5283	5281	5280	5278	5277	5276	5274	5273	5271
521.0	5270	5268	5267	5266	5264	5263	5261	5260	5258	5257
522.0	5256	5254	5253	5251	5250	5248	5247	5246	5244	5243
523.0	5241	5240	5239	5237	5236	5234	5233	5231	5230	5229
524.0	5227	5226	5224	5223	5221	5220	5219	5217	5216	5214
525.0	5213	5212	5210	5209	5207	5206	5204	5203	5202	5200
526.0	5199	5197	5196	5195	5193	5192	5190	5189	5187	5186
527.0	5185	5183	5182	5180	5179	5178	5176	5175	5173	5172
528.0	5171	5169	5168	5166	5165	5163	5162	5161	5159	5158
529.0	5156	5155	5154	5152	5151	5149	5148	5147	5145	5144
530.0	5142	5141	5140	5138	5137	5135	5134	5133	5131	5130
531.0	5128	5127	5126	5124	5123	5121	5120	5118	5117	5116
532.0	5114	5113	5111	5110	5109	5107	5106	5104	5103	5102
533.0	5100	5099	5097	5096	5095	5093	5092	5090	5089	5088
534.0	5086	5085	5083	5082	5081	5079	5078	5076	5075	5074
535.0	5072	5071	5070	5068	5067	5065	5064	5063	5061	5060
536.0	5058	5057	5056	5054	5053	5051	5050	5049	5047	5046
537.0	5044	5043	5042	5040	5039	5037	5036	5035	5033	5032
538.0	5031	5029	5028	5026	5025	5024	5022	5021	5019	5018
539.0	5017	5015	5014	5012	5011	5010	5008	5007	5006	5004
540.0	5003	5001	5000	4999	4997	4996	4994	4993	4992	4990
541.0	4989	4988	4986	4985	4983	4982	4981	4979	4978	4976
542.0	4975	4974	4972	4971	4970	4968	4967	4965	4964	4963
543.0	4961	4960	4959	4957	4956	4954	4953	4952	4950	4949
544.0	4947	4946	4945	4943	4942	4941	4939	4938	4936	4935
545.0	4934	4932	4931	4930	4928	4927	4925	4924	4923	4921
546.0	4920	4919	4917	4916	4914	4913	4912	4910	4909	4908
547.0	4906	4905	4904	4902	4901	4899	4898	4897	4895	4894
548.0	4893	4891	4890	4888	4887	4886	4884	4883	4882	4880
549.0	4879	4878	4876	4875	4873	4872	4871	4869	4868	4867
550.0	4865	4864	4862	4861	4860	4858	4857	4856	4854	4853
551.0	4852	4850	4849	4847	4846	4845	4843	4842	4841	4839
552.0	4838	4837	4835	4834	4833	4831	4830	4828	4827	4826
553.0	4824	4823	4822	4820	4819	4818	4816	4815	4813	4812
554.0	4811	4809	4808	4807	4805	4804	4803	4801	4800	4799
555.0	4797	4796	4794	4793	4792	4790	4789	4788	4786	4785
556.0	4784	4782	4781	4780	4778	4777	4776	4774	4773	4771
557.0	4770	4769	4767	4766	4765	4763	4762	4761	4759	4758
558.0	4757	4755	4754	4753	4751	4750	4749	4747	4746	4744
559.0	4743	4742	4740	4739	4738	4736	4735	4734	4732	4731
560.0	4730	4728	4727	4726	4724	4723	4722	4720	4719	4718
561.0	4716	4715	4714	4712	4711	4710	4708	4707	4705	4704
562.0	4703	4701	4700	4699	4697	4696	4695	4693	4692	4691
563.0	4689	4688	4687	4685	4684	4683	4681	4680	4679	4677
564.0	4676	4675	4673	4672	4671	4669	4668	4667	4665	4664
565.0	4663	4661	4660	4659	4657	4656	4655	4653	4652	4651
566.0	4649	4648	4647	4645	4644	4643	4641	4640	4639	4637
567.0	4636	4635	4633	4632	4631	4629	4628	4627	4625	4624
568.0	4623	4621	4620	4619	4617	4616	4615	4613	4612	4611
569.0	4609	4608	4607	4605	4604	4603	4601	4600	4599	4597
570.0	4596	4595	4593	4592	4591	4589	4588	4587	4585	4584
571.0	4583	4582	4580	4579	4578	4576	4575	4574	4572	4571
572.0	4570	4568	4567	4566	4564	4563	4562	4560	4559	4558
573.0	4556	4555	4554	4552	4551	4550	4548	4547	4546	4545
574.0	4543	4542	4541	4539	4538	4537	4535	4534	4533	4531
575.0	4530	4529	4527	4526	4525	4523	4522	4521	4519	4518
576.0	4517	4516	4514	4513	4512	4510	4509	4508	4506	4505
577.0	4504	4502	4501	4500	4498	4497	4496	4495	4493	4492
578.0	4491	4489	4488	4487	4485	4484	4483	4481	4480	4479
579.0	4477	4476	4475	4474	4472	4471	4470	4468	4467	4466
580.0	4464	4463	4462	4460	4459	4458	4457	4455	4454	4453
581.0	4451	4450	4449	4447	4446	4445	4443	4442	4441	4440
582.0	4438	4437	4436	4434	4433	4432	4430	4429	4428	4427
583.0	4425	4424	4423	4421	4420	4419	4417	4416	4415	4414
584.0	4412	4411	4410	4408	4407	4406	4404	4403	4402	4401
585.0	4399	4398	4397	4395	4394	4393	4391	4390	4389	4388
586.0	4386	4385	4384	4382	4381	4380	4378	4377	4376	4375
587.0	4373	4372	4371	4369	4368	4367	4366	4364	4363	4362
588.0	4360	4359	4358	4356	4355	4354	4353	4351	4350	4349
589.0	4347	4346	4345	4344	4342	4341	4340	4338	4337	4336
590.0	4335	4333	4332	4331	4329	4328	4327	4325	4324	4323
591.0	4322	4320	4319	4318	4316	4315	4314	4313	4311	4310
592.0	4309	4307	4306	4305	4304	4302	4301	4300	4298	4297
593.0	4296	4295	4293	4292	4291	4289	4288	4287	4286	4284
594.0	4283	4282	4281	4279	4278	4277	4275	4274	4273	4272
595.0	4270	4269	4268	4266	4265	4264	4263	4261	4260	4259
596.0	4257	4256	4255	4254	4252	4251	4250	4249	4247	4246
597.0	4245	4243	4242	4241	4240	4238	4237	4236	4234	4233
598.0	4232	4231	4229	4228	4227	4226	4224	4223	4222	4220
599.0	4219	4218	4217	4215	4214	4213	4212	4210	4209	4208
600.0	4206	4205	4204	4203	4201	4200	4199	4198	4196	4195
601.0	4194	4192	4191	4190	4189	4187	4186	4185	4184	4182
602.0	4181	4180	4178	4177	4176	4175	4173	4172	4171	4170
603.0	4168	4167	4166	4165	4163	4162	4161	4159	4158	4157
604.0	4156	4154	4153	4152	4151	4149	4148	4147	4146	4144
605.0	4143	4142	4140	4139	4138	4137	4135	4134	4133	4132
606.0	4130	4129	4128	4127	4125	4124	4123	4122	4120	4119
607.0	4118	4117	4115	4114	4113	4111	4110	4109	4108	4106
608.0	4105	4104	4103	4101	4100	4099	4098	4096	4095	4094
609.0	4093	4091	4090	4089	4088	4086	4085	4084	4083	4081
610.0	4080	4079	4078	4076	4075	4074	4073	4071	4070	4069
611.0	4067	4066	4065	4064	4062	4061	4060	4059	4057	4056
612.0	4055	4054	4052	4051	4050	4049	4047	4046	4045	4044
613.0	4042	4041	4040	4039	4037	4036	4035	4034	4032	4031
614.0	4030	4029	4027	4026	4025	4024	4022	4021	4020	4019
615.0	4017	4016	4015	4014	4012	4011	4010	4009	4007	4006
616.0	4005	4004	4003	4001	4000	3999	3998	3996	3995	3994
617.0	3993	3991	3990	3989	3988	3986	3985	3984	3983	3981
618.0	3980	3979	3978	3976	3975	3974	3973	3971	3970	3969
619.0	3968	3966	3965	3964	3963	3962	3960	3959	3958	3957

GEOPOTENTIAL ALTITUDE IN METERS as a function of PRESSURE IN MILLIBARS

P, mb	0.0	0.1	0.2	0.3	0.4	0.5	0.6	0.7	0.8	0.9
620.0	3955	3954	3953	3952	3950	3949	3948	3947	3945	3944
621.0	3943	3942	3940	3939	3938	3937	3936	3934	3933	3932
622.0	3931	3929	3928	3927	3926	3924	3923	3922	3921	3919
623.0	3918	3917	3916	3915	3913	3912	3911	3910	3908	3907
624.0	3906	3905	3903	3902	3901	3900	3898	3897	3896	3895
625.0	3894	3892	3891	3890	3889	3887	3886	3885	3884	3882
626.0	3881	3880	3879	3878	3876	3875	3874	3873	3871	3870
627.0	3869	3868	3867	3865	3864	3863	3862	3860	3859	3858
628.0	3857	3855	3854	3853	3852	3851	3849	3848	3847	3846
629.0	3844	3843	3842	3841	3840	3838	3837	3836	3835	3833
630.0	3832	3831	3830	3829	3827	3826	3825	3824	3822	3821
631.0	3820	3819	3818	3816	3815	3814	3813	3811	3810	3809
632.0	3808	3807	3805	3804	3803	3802	3800	3799	3798	3797
633.0	3796	3794	3793	3792	3791	3789	3788	3787	3786	3785
634.0	3783	3782	3781	3780	3779	3777	3776	3775	3774	3772
635.0	3771	3770	3769	3768	3766	3765	3764	3763	3762	3760
636.0	3759	3758	3757	3755	3754	3753	3752	3751	3749	3748
637.0	3747	3746	3745	3743	3742	3741	3740	3738	3737	3736
638.0	3735	3734	3732	3731	3730	3729	3728	3726	3725	3724
639.0	3723	3722	3720	3719	3718	3717	3716	3714	3713	3712
640.0	3711	3709	3708	3707	3706	3705	3703	3702	3701	3700
641.0	3699	3697	3696	3695	3694	3693	3691	3690	3689	3688
642.0	3687	3685	3684	3683	3682	3681	3679	3678	3677	3676
643.0	3675	3673	3672	3671	3670	3669	3667	3666	3665	3664
644.0	3663	3661	3660	3659	3658	3656	3655	3654	3653	3652
645.0	3650	3649	3648	3647	3646	3644	3643	3642	3641	3640
646.0	3639	3637	3636	3635	3634	3633	3631	3630	3629	3628
647.0	3627	3625	3624	3623	3622	3621	3619	3618	3617	3616
648.0	3615	3613	3612	3611	3610	3609	3607	3606	3605	3604
649.0	3603	3601	3600	3599	3598	3597	3595	3594	3593	3592
650.0	3591	3589	3588	3587	3586	3585	3584	3582	3581	3580
651.0	3579	3578	3576	3575	3574	3573	3572	3570	3569	3568
652.0	3567	3566	3564	3563	3562	3561	3560	3559	3557	3556
653.0	3555	3554	3553	3551	3550	3549	3548	3547	3545	3544
654.0	3543	3542	3541	3540	3538	3537	3536	3535	3534	3532
655.0	3531	3530	3529	3528	3527	3525	3524	3523	3522	3521
656.0	3519	3518	3517	3516	3515	3513	3512	3511	3510	3509
657.0	3508	3506	3505	3504	3503	3502	3500	3499	3498	3497
658.0	3496	3495	3493	3492	3491	3490	3489	3487	3486	3485
659.0	3484	3483	3482	3480	3479	3478	3477	3476	3475	3473
660.0	3472	3471	3470	3469	3467	3466	3465	3464	3463	3462
661.0	3460	3459	3458	3457	3456	3455	3453	3452	3451	3450
662.0	3449	3447	3446	3445	3444	3443	3442	3440	3439	3438
663.0	3437	3436	3435	3433	3432	3431	3430	3429	3428	3426
664.0	3425	3424	3423	3422	3420	3419	3418	3417	3416	3415
665.0	3413	3412	3411	3410	3409	3408	3406	3405	3404	3403
666.0	3402	3401	3399	3398	3397	3396	3395	3394	3392	3391
667.0	3390	3389	3388	3387	3385	3384	3383	3382	3381	3380
668.0	3378	3377	3376	3375	3374	3373	3371	3370	3369	3368
669.0	3367	3366	3364	3363	3362	3361	3360	3359	3357	3356
670.0	3355	3354	3353	3352	3350	3349	3348	3347	3346	3345
671.0	3343	3342	3341	3340	3339	3338	3336	3335	3334	3333
672.0	3332	3331	3330	3328	3327	3326	3325	3324	3323	3321
673.0	3320	3319	3318	3317	3316	3314	3313	3312	3311	3310
674.0	3309	3308	3306	3305	3304	3303	3302	3301	3299	3298
675.0	3297	3296	3295	3294	3292	3291	3290	3289	3288	3287
676.0	3286	3284	3283	3282	3281	3280	3279	3277	3276	3275
677.0	3274	3273	3272	3271	3269	3268	3267	3266	3265	3264
678.0	3262	3261	3260	3259	3258	3257	3256	3254	3253	3252
679.0	3251	3250	3249	3247	3246	3245	3244	3243	3242	3241
680.0	3239	3238	3237	3236	3235	3234	3233	3231	3230	3229
681.0	3228	3227	3226	3224	3223	3222	3221	3220	3219	3218
682.0	3216	3215	3214	3213	3212	3211	3210	3208	3207	3206
683.0	3205	3204	3203	3202	3200	3199	3198	3197	3196	3195
684.0	3194	3192	3191	3190	3189	3188	3187	3186	3184	3183
685.0	3182	3181	3180	3179	3178	3176	3175	3174	3173	3172
686.0	3171	3170	3168	3167	3166	3165	3164	3163	3162	3160
687.0	3159	3158	3157	3156	3155	3154	3152	3151	3150	3149
688.0	3148	3147	3146	3144	3143	3142	3141	3140	3139	3138
689.0	3137	3135	3134	3133	3132	3131	3130	3129	3127	3126
690.0	3125	3124	3123	3122	3121	3119	3118	3117	3116	3115
691.0	3114	3113	3112	3110	3109	3108	3107	3106	3105	3104
692.0	3102	3101	3100	3099	3098	3097	3096	3095	3093	3092
693.0	3091	3090	3089	3088	3087	3085	3084	3083	3082	3081
694.0	3080	3079	3078	3076	3075	3074	3073	3072	3071	3070
695.0	3068	3067	3066	3065	3064	3063	3062	3061	3059	3058
696.0	3057	3056	3055	3054	3053	3052	3050	3049	3048	3047
697.0	3046	3045	3044	3043	3041	3040	3039	3038	3037	3036
698.0	3035	3034	3032	3031	3030	3029	3028	3027	3026	3025
699.0	3023	3022	3021	3020	3019	3018	3017	3016	3014	3013
700.0	3012	3011	3010	3009	3008	3007	3005	3004	3003	3002
701.0	3001	3000	2999	2998	2996	2995	2994	2993	2992	2991
702.0	2990	2989	2988	2986	2985	2984	2983	2982	2981	2980
703.0	2979	2977	2976	2975	2974	2973	2972	2971	2970	2968
704.0	2967	2966	2965	2964	2963	2962	2961	2960	2958	2957
705.0	2956	2955	2954	2953	2952	2951	2949	2948	2947	2946
706.0	2945	2944	2943	2942	2941	2939	2938	2937	2936	2935
707.0	2934	2933	2932	2931	2929	2928	2927	2926	2925	2924
708.0	2923	2922	2921	2919	2918	2917	2916	2915	2914	2913
709.0	2912	2911	2909	2908	2907	2906	2905	2904	2903	2902
710.0	2901	2899	2898	2897	2896	2895	2894	2893	2892	2891
711.0	2889	2888	2887	2886	2885	2884	2883	2882	2881	2879
712.0	2878	2877	2876	2875	2874	2873	2872	2871	2869	2868
713.0	2867	2866	2865	2864	2863	2862	2861	2860	2858	2857
714.0	2856	2855	2854	2853	2852	2851	2850	2848	2847	2846
715.0	2845	2844	2843	2842	2841	2840	2839	2837	2836	2835
716.0	2834	2833	2832	2831	2830	2829	2828	2826	2825	2824
717.0	2823	2822	2821	2820	2819	2818	2817	2815	2814	2813
718.0	2812	2811	2800	2799	2798	2797	2796	2795	2793	2792

TABLE VI - Continued   189

GEOPOTENTIAL ALTITUDE IN METERS as a function of PRESSURE IN MILLIBARS

P, mb	0.0	0.1	0.2	0.3	0.4	0.5	0.6	0.7	0.8	0.9
720.0	2790	2789	2788	2787	2786	2785	2784	2782	2781	2780
721.0	2779	2778	2777	2776	2775	2774	2773	2771	2770	2769
722.0	2768	2767	2766	2765	2764	2763	2762	2761	2759	2758
723.0	2757	2756	2755	2754	2753	2752	2751	2750	2748	2747
724.0	2746	2745	2744	2743	2742	2741	2740	2739	2738	2736
725.0	2735	2734	2733	2732	2731	2730	2729	2728	2727	2726
726.0	2724	2723	2722	2721	2720	2719	2718	2717	2716	2715
727.0	2714	2712	2711	2710	2709	2708	2707	2706	2705	2704
728.0	2703	2702	2701	2699	2698	2697	2696	2695	2694	2693
729.0	2692	2691	2690	2689	2687	2686	2685	2684	2683	2682
730.0	2681	2680	2679	2678	2677	2676	2674	2673	2672	2671
731.0	2670	2669	2668	2667	2666	2665	2664	2663	2661	2660
732.0	2659	2658	2657	2656	2655	2654	2653	2652	2651	2650
733.0	2648	2647	2646	2645	2644	2643	2642	2641	2640	2639
734.0	2638	2637	2635	2634	2633	2632	2631	2630	2629	2628
735.0	2627	2626	2625	2624	2623	2621	2620	2619	2618	2617
736.0	2616	2615	2614	2613	2612	2611	2610	2608	2607	2606
737.0	2605	2604	2603	2602	2601	2600	2599	2598	2597	2596
738.0	2594	2593	2592	2591	2590	2589	2588	2587	2586	2585
739.0	2584	2583	2582	2581	2579	2578	2577	2576	2575	2574
740.0	2573	2572	2571	2570	2569	2568	2567	2565	2564	2563
741.0	2562	2561	2560	2559	2558	2557	2556	2555	2554	2553
742.0	2552	2550	2549	2548	2547	2546	2545	2544	2543	2542
743.0	2541	2540	2539	2538	2537	2535	2534	2533	2532	2531
744.0	2530	2529	2528	2527	2526	2525	2524	2523	2522	2521
745.0	2519	2518	2517	2516	2515	2514	2513	2512	2511	2510
746.0	2509	2508	2507	2506	2505	2503	2502	2501	2500	2499
747.0	2498	2497	2496	2495	2494	2493	2492	2491	2490	2489
748.0	2487	2486	2485	2484	2483	2482	2481	2480	2479	2478
749.0	2477	2476	2475	2474	2473	2472	2470	2469	2468	2467
750.0	2466	2465	2464	2463	2462	2461	2460	2459	2458	2457
751.0	2456	2455	2454	2453	2452	2451	2450	2449	2448	2447
752.0	2445	2444	2443	2442	2441	2440	2439	2438	2437	2435
753.0	2434	2433	2432	2431	2430	2429	2428	2427	2426	2425
754.0	2424	2423	2422	2421	2420	2419	2417	2416	2415	2414
755.0	2413	2412	2411	2410	2409	2408	2407	2406	2405	2404
756.0	2403	2402	2401	2400	2398	2397	2396	2395	2394	2393
757.0	2392	2391	2390	2389	2388	2387	2386	2385	2384	2383
758.0	2382	2381	2380	2378	2377	2376	2375	2374	2373	2372
759.0	2371	2370	2369	2368	2367	2366	2365	2364	2363	2362
760.0	2361	2360	2358	2357	2356	2355	2354	2353	2352	2351
761.0	2350	2349	2348	2347	2346	2345	2344	2343	2342	2341
762.0	2340	2339	2337	2336	2335	2334	2333	2332	2331	2330
763.0	2329	2328	2327	2326	2325	2324	2323	2322	2321	2320
764.0	2319	2318	2317	2316	2314	2313	2312	2311	2310	2309
765.0	2308	2307	2306	2305	2304	2303	2302	2301	2300	2299
766.0	2298	2297	2296	2295	2294	2293	2291	2290	2289	2288
767.0	2287	2286	2285	2284	2283	2282	2281	2280	2279	2278
768.0	2277	2276	2275	2274	2273	2272	2271	2270	2269	2268
769.0	2266	2265	2264	2263	2262	2261	2260	2259	2258	2257
770.0	2256	2255	2254	2253	2252	2251	2250	2249	2248	2247
771.0	2246	2245	2244	2243	2242	2240	2239	2238	2237	2236
772.0	2235	2234	2233	2232	2231	2230	2229	2228	2227	2226
773.0	2225	2224	2223	2222	2221	2220	2219	2218	2217	2216
774.0	2215	2214	2213	2211	2210	2209	2208	2207	2206	2205
775.0	2204	2203	2202	2201	2200	2199	2198	2197	2196	2195
776.0	2194	2193	2192	2191	2190	2189	2188	2187	2186	2185
777.0	2184	2183	2181	2180	2179	2178	2177	2176	2175	2174
778.0	2173	2172	2171	2170	2169	2168	2167	2166	2165	2164
779.0	2163	2162	2161	2160	2159	2158	2157	2156	2155	2154
780.0	2153	2152	2151	2150	2149	2148	2146	2145	2144	2143
781.0	2142	2141	2140	2139	2138	2137	2136	2135	2134	2133
782.0	2132	2131	2130	2129	2128	2127	2126	2125	2124	2123
783.0	2122	2121	2120	2119	2118	2117	2116	2115	2114	2113
784.0	2112	2111	2110	2109	2107	2106	2105	2104	2103	2102
785.0	2101	2100	2099	2098	2097	2096	2095	2094	2093	2092
786.0	2091	2090	2089	2088	2087	2086	2085	2084	2083	2082
787.0	2081	2080	2079	2078	2077	2076	2075	2074	2073	2072
788.0	2071	2070	2069	2068	2067	2066	2065	2064	2063	2062
789.0	2060	2059	2058	2057	2056	2055	2054	2053	2052	2051
790.0	2050	2049	2048	2047	2046	2045	2044	2043	2042	2041
791.0	2040	2039	2038	2037	2036	2035	2034	2033	2032	2031
792.0	2030	2029	2028	2027	2026	2025	2024	2023	2022	2021
793.0	2020	2019	2018	2017	2016	2015	2014	2013	2012	2011
794.0	2010	2009	2008	2007	2006	2005	2004	2003	2002	2001
795.0	2000	1998	1997	1996	1995	1994	1993	1992	1991	1990
796.0	1989	1988	1987	1986	1985	1984	1983	1982	1981	1980
797.0	1979	1978	1977	1976	1975	1974	1973	1972	1971	1970
798.0	1969	1968	1967	1966	1965	1964	1963	1962	1961	1960
799.0	1959	1958	1957	1956	1955	1954	1953	1952	1951	1950
800.0	1949	1948	1947	1946	1945	1944	1943	1942	1941	1940
801.0	1939	1938	1937	1936	1935	1934	1933	1932	1931	1930
802.0	1929	1928	1927	1926	1925	1924	1923	1922	1921	1920
803.0	1919	1918	1917	1916	1915	1914	1913	1912	1911	1910
804.0	1909	1908	1907	1906	1905	1904	1903	1902	1901	1900
805.0	1899	1898	1897	1896	1895	1894	1893	1892	1891	1890
806.0	1889	1888	1887	1886	1885	1884	1883	1882	1881	1880
807.0	1879	1878	1877	1876	1875	1874	1873	1872	1871	1870
808.0	1869	1868	1867	1866	1865	1864	1863	1862	1861	1860
809.0	1859	1858	1857	1856	1855	1854	1853	1852	1851	1850
810.0	1849	1848	1847	1846	1845	1844	1843	1842	1841	1840
811.0	1839	1838	1837	1836	1835	1834	1833	1832	1831	1830
812.0	1829	1828	1827	1826	1825	1824	1823	1822	1821	1820
813.0	1819	1818	1817	1816	1815	1814	1813	1812	1811	1810
814.0	1809	1808	1807	1806	1805	1804	1803	1802	1801	1800
815.0	1799	1798	1797	1796	1795	1794	1793	1792	1791	1790
816.0	1789	1788	1787	1786	1785	1784	1783	1782	1781	1780
817.0	1779	1778	1777	1776	1775	1774	1773	1772	1771	1770
818.0	1769	1768	1767	1766	1765	1764	1763	1762	1761	1760
819.0	1759	1758	1757	1756	1755	1754	1753	1752	1751	1750

TABLE VI – Continued

GEOPOTENTIAL ALTITUDE IN METERS as a function of PRESSURE IN MILLIBARS

P, mb	0.0	0.1	0.2	0.3	0.4	0.5	0.6	0.7	0.8	0.9
820.0	1749	1748	1747	1746	1745	1744	1743	1742	1742	1741
821.0	1740	1739	1738	1737	1736	1735	1734	1733	1732	1731
822.0	1730	1729	1728	1727	1726	1725	1724	1723	1722	1721
823.0	1720	1719	1718	1717	1716	1715	1714	1713	1712	1711
824.0	1710	1709	1708	1707	1706	1705	1704	1703	1702	1701
825.0	1700	1699	1698	1697	1696	1695	1694	1693	1692	1691
826.0	1690	1689	1688	1687	1686	1685	1684	1683	1682	1681
827.0	1680	1679	1679	1678	1677	1676	1675	1674	1673	1672
828.0	1671	1670	1669	1668	1667	1666	1665	1664	1663	1662
829.0	1661	1660	1659	1658	1657	1656	1655	1654	1653	1652
830.0	1651	1650	1649	1648	1647	1646	1645	1644	1643	1642
831.0	1641	1640	1639	1638	1637	1636	1635	1634	1633	1633
832.0	1632	1631	1630	1629	1628	1627	1626	1625	1624	1623
833.0	1622	1621	1620	1619	1618	1617	1616	1615	1614	1613
834.0	1612	1611	1610	1609	1608	1607	1606	1605	1604	1603
835.0	1602	1601	1600	1599	1598	1597	1596	1595	1595	1594
836.0	1593	1592	1591	1590	1589	1588	1587	1586	1585	1584
837.0	1583	1582	1581	1580	1579	1578	1577	1576	1575	1574
838.0	1573	1572	1571	1570	1569	1568	1567	1566	1565	1564
839.0	1563	1562	1561	1561	1560	1559	1558	1557	1556	1555
840.0	1554	1553	1552	1551	1550	1549	1548	1547	1546	1545
841.0	1544	1543	1542	1541	1540	1539	1538	1537	1536	1535
842.0	1534	1533	1532	1531	1530	1530	1529	1528	1527	1526
843.0	1525	1524	1523	1522	1521	1520	1519	1518	1517	1516
844.0	1515	1514	1513	1512	1511	1510	1509	1508	1507	1506
845.0	1505	1504	1503	1503	1502	1501	1500	1499	1498	1497
846.0	1496	1495	1494	1493	1492	1491	1490	1489	1488	1487
847.0	1486	1485	1484	1483	1482	1481	1480	1479	1478	1477
848.0	1477	1476	1475	1474	1473	1472	1471	1470	1469	1468
849.0	1467	1466	1465	1464	1463	1462	1461	1460	1459	1458
850.0	1457	1456	1455	1454	1453	1452	1452	1451	1450	1449
851.0	1448	1447	1446	1445	1444	1443	1442	1441	1440	1439
852.0	1438	1437	1436	1435	1434	1433	1432	1431	1430	1430
853.0	1429	1428	1427	1426	1425	1424	1423	1422	1421	1420
854.0	1419	1418	1417	1416	1415	1414	1413	1412	1411	1410
855.0	1409	1408	1408	1407	1406	1405	1404	1403	1402	1401
856.0	1400	1399	1398	1397	1396	1395	1394	1393	1392	1391
857.0	1390	1389	1388	1387	1387	1386	1385	1384	1383	1382
858.0	1381	1380	1379	1378	1377	1376	1375	1374	1373	1372
859.0	1371	1370	1369	1368	1367	1367	1366	1365	1364	1363
860.0	1362	1361	1360	1359	1358	1357	1356	1355	1354	1353
861.0	1352	1351	1350	1349	1348	1347	1346	1345	1344	1344
862.0	1343	1342	1341	1340	1339	1338	1337	1336	1335	1334
863.0	1333	1332	1331	1330	1329	1328	1327	1326	1325	1325
864.0	1324	1323	1322	1321	1320	1319	1318	1317	1316	1315
865.0	1314	1313	1312	1311	1310	1309	1308	1307	1306	1306
866.0	1305	1304	1303	1302	1301	1300	1299	1298	1297	1296
867.0	1295	1295	1294	1293	1292	1291	1290	1289	1288	1287
868.0	1286	1285	1284	1283	1282	1281	1280	1279	1278	1278
869.0	1277	1276	1275	1274	1273	1272	1271	1270	1269	1268
870.0	1267	1266	1265	1264	1263	1262	1262	1261	1260	1259
871.0	1258	1257	1256	1255	1254	1253	1252	1251	1250	1249
872.0	1248	1247	1246	1245	1244	1243	1242	1241	1240	1240
873.0	1239	1238	1237	1236	1235	1234	1233	1232	1231	1231
874.0	1230	1229	1228	1227	1226	1225	1224	1223	1222	1221
875.0	1220	1219	1218	1217	1216	1215	1215	1214	1213	1212
876.0	1211	1210	1209	1208	1207	1206	1205	1204	1203	1202
877.0	1201	1201	1200	1199	1198	1197	1196	1195	1194	1193
878.0	1192	1191	1190	1189	1188	1187	1186	1186	1185	1184
879.0	1183	1182	1181	1180	1179	1178	1177	1176	1175	1174
880.0	1173	1172	1172	1171	1170	1169	1168	1167	1166	1165
881.0	1164	1163	1162	1161	1160	1159	1158	1157	1156	1156
882.0	1155	1154	1153	1152	1151	1150	1149	1148	1147	1146
883.0	1145	1145	1144	1143	1142	1141	1140	1139	1138	1137
884.0	1136	1135	1134	1133	1132	1131	1130	1129	1128	1128
885.0	1127	1126	1125	1124	1123	1122	1121	1120	1119	1119
886.0	1118	1117	1116	1115	1114	1113	1112	1111	1110	1109
887.0	1108	1107	1106	1106	1105	1104	1103	1102	1101	1100
888.0	1099	1098	1097	1096	1095	1094	1093	1092	1091	1091
889.0	1090	1089	1088	1087	1086	1085	1084	1083	1082	1081
890.0	1081	1080	1079	1078	1077	1076	1075	1074	1073	1072
891.0	1071	1070	1069	1069	1068	1067	1066	1065	1064	1063
892.0	1062	1061	1060	1059	1058	1057	1057	1056	1055	1054
893.0	1053	1052	1051	1050	1049	1048	1047	1046	1045	1045
894.0	1044	1043	1042	1041	1040	1039	1038	1037	1036	1035
895.0	1034	1033	1033	1032	1031	1030	1029	1028	1027	1026
896.0	1025	1024	1023	1022	1022	1021	1020	1019	1018	1017
897.0	1016	1015	1014	1013	1012	1011	1011	1010	1009	1008
898.0	1007	1006	1005	1004	1003	1002	1001	1000	999	999
899.0	998	997	996	995	994	993	992	991	990	989
900.0	988	988	987	986	985	984	983	982	981	980
901.0	979	978	978	977	976	975	974	973	972	971
902.0	970	969	968	967	967	966	965	964	963	962
903.0	961	960	959	958	957	956	956	955	954	953
904.0	952	951	950	949	948	947	946	945	945	944
905.0	943	942	941	940	939	938	937	936	935	935
906.0	934	933	932	931	930	929	928	927	926	925
907.0	925	924	923	922	921	920	919	918	917	916
908.0	915	915	914	913	912	911	910	909	908	907
909.0	906	905	905	904	903	902	901	900	899	898
910.0	897	896	895	895	894	893	892	891	890	889
911.0	888	887	886	885	885	884	883	882	881	880
912.0	879	878	877	876	876	875	874	873	872	871
913.0	870	869	868	867	866	866	865	864	863	862
914.0	861	860	859	858	857	856	856	855	854	853
915.0	852	851	850	849	848	847	847	846	845	844
916.0	843	842	841	840	839	838	838	837	836	835
917.0	834	833	832	831	830	829	828	828	827	826
918.0	825	824	823	822	821	820	819	819	818	817
919.0	816	815	814	813	812	811	810	810	809	808

TABLE VI - Continued

GEOPOTENTIAL ALTITUDE IN METERS as a function of PRESSURE IN MILLIBARS

P, mb	0.0	0.1	0.2	0.3	0.4	0.5	0.6	0.7	0.8	0.9
920.0	807	806	805	804	803	802	801	801	800	799
921.0	798	797	796	795	794	793	792	792	791	790
922.0	789	788	787	786	785	784	783	783	782	781
923.0	780	779	778	777	776	775	775	774	773	772
924.0	771	770	769	768	767	766	766	765	764	763
925.0	762	761	760	759	758	757	757	756	755	754
926.0	753	752	751	750	749	749	748	747	746	745
927.0	744	743	742	741	740	740	739	738	737	736
928.0	735	734	733	732	732	731	730	729	728	727
929.0	726	725	724	724	723	722	721	720	719	718
930.0	717	716	715	715	714	713	712	711	710	709
931.0	708	707	707	706	705	704	703	702	701	700
932.0	699	699	698	697	696	695	694	693	692	691
933.0	691	690	689	688	687	686	685	684	683	683
934.0	682	681	680	679	678	677	676	675	675	674
935.0	673	672	671	670	669	668	667	667	666	665
936.0	664	663	662	661	660	659	659	658	657	656
937.0	655	654	653	652	651	651	650	649	648	647
938.0	646	645	644	643	643	642	641	640	639	638
939.0	637	636	635	635	634	633	632	631	630	629
940.0	628	628	627	626	625	624	623	622	621	620
941.0	620	619	618	617	616	615	614	613	613	612
942.0	611	610	609	608	607	606	605	605	604	603
943.0	602	601	600	599	598	597	597	596	595	594
944.0	593	592	591	590	590	589	588	587	586	585
945.0	584	583	583	582	581	580	579	578	577	576
946.0	575	575	574	573	572	571	570	569	568	568
947.0	567	566	565	564	563	562	561	561	560	559
948.0	558	557	556	555	554	553	553	552	551	550
949.0	549	548	547	546	546	545	544	543	542	541
950.0	540	539	539	538	537	536	535	534	533	532
951.0	532	531	530	529	528	527	526	525	525	524
952.0	523	522	521	520	519	518	518	517	516	515
953.0	514	513	512	511	511	510	509	508	507	506
954.0	505	504	504	503	502	501	500	499	498	497
955.0	497	496	495	494	493	492	491	490	490	489
956.0	488	487	486	485	484	483	483	482	481	480
957.0	479	478	477	477	476	475	474	473	472	471
958.0	470	470	469	468	467	466	465	464	463	463
959.0	462	461	460	459	458	457	456	456	455	454
960.0	453	452	451	450	450	449	448	447	446	445
961.0	444	443	443	442	441	440	439	438	437	436
962.0	436	435	434	433	432	431	430	430	429	428
963.0	427	426	425	424	423	423	422	421	420	419
964.0	418	417	417	416	415	414	413	412	411	410
965.0	410	409	408	407	406	405	404	404	403	402
966.0	401	400	399	398	397	397	396	395	394	393
967.0	392	391	391	390	389	388	387	386	385	385
968.0	384	383	382	381	380	379	378	378	377	376
969.0	375	374	373	372	372	371	370	369	368	367
970.0	366	366	365	364	363	362	361	360	360	359
971.0	358	357	356	355	354	353	353	352	351	350
972.0	349	348	347	347	346	345	344	343	342	341
973.0	341	340	339	338	337	336	335	335	334	333
974.0	332	331	330	329	329	328	327	326	325	324
975.0	323	323	322	321	320	319	318	317	317	316
976.0	315	314	313	312	311	311	310	309	308	307
977.0	306	305	305	304	303	302	301	300	299	299
978.0	298	297	296	295	294	293	293	292	291	290
979.0	289	288	287	287	286	285	284	283	282	281
980.0	281	280	279	278	277	276	275	275	274	273
981.0	272	271	270	269	269	268	267	266	265	264
982.0	263	263	262	261	260	259	258	257	257	256
983.0	255	254	253	252	251	251	250	249	248	247
984.0	246	246	245	244	243	242	241	240	240	239
985.0	238	237	236	235	234	234	233	232	231	230
986.0	229	228	228	227	226	225	224	223	223	222
987.0	221	220	219	218	217	217	216	215	214	213
988.0	212	211	211	210	209	208	207	206	206	205
989.0	204	203	202	201	200	200	199	198	197	196
990.0	195	195	194	193	192	191	190	189	189	188
991.0	187	186	185	184	183	183	182	181	180	179
992.0	178	178	177	176	175	174	173	172	172	171
993.0	170	169	168	167	167	166	165	164	163	162
994.0	161	161	160	159	158	157	156	156	155	154
995.0	153	152	151	151	150	149	148	147	146	145
996.0	145	144	143	142	141	140	140	139	138	137
997.0	136	135	134	134	133	132	131	130	129	129
998.0	128	127	126	125	124	124	123	122	121	120
999.0	119	118	118	117	116	115	114	113	113	112
1000.0	111	110	109	108	108	107	106	105	104	103
1001.0	102	102	101	100	99	98	97	97	96	95
1002.0	94	93	92	92	91	90	89	88	87	87
1003.0	86	85	84	83	82	81	81	80	79	78
1004.0	77	76	76	75	74	73	72	71	71	70
1005.0	69	68	67	66	66	65	64	63	62	61
1006.0	61	60	59	58	57	56	56	55	54	53
1007.0	52	51	50	50	49	48	47	46	45	45
1008.0	44	43	42	41	40	40	39	38	37	36
1009.0	35	35	34	33	32	31	30	30	29	28
1010.0	27	26	25	25	24	23	22	21	20	20
1011.0	19	18	17	16	15	15	14	13	12	11
1012.0	10	10	9	8	7	6	5	5	4	3
1013.0	2	1	0	-0	-1	-2	-3	-4	-5	-5
1014.0	-6	-7	-8	-9	-10	-10	-11	-12	-13	-14
1015.0	-15	-15	-16	-17	-18	-19	-20	-20	-21	-22
1016.0	-23	-24	-25	-26	-26	-27	-28	-29	-30	-30
1017.0	-31	-32	-33	-34	-34	-35	-36	-37	-38	-39
1018.0	-39	-40	-41	-42	-43	-44	-44	-45	-46	-47
1019.0	-48	-49	-49	-50	-51	-52	-53	-54	-54	-55

TABLE VI - Continued

GEOPOTENTIAL ALTITUDE IN METERS as a function of PRESSURE IN MILLIBARS

P, mb	0.0	0.1	0.2	0.3	0.4	0.5	0.6	0.7	0.8	0.9
1020.0	-56	-57	-58	-59	-59	-60	-61	-62	-63	-63
1021.0	-64	-65	-66	-67	-68	-68	-69	-70	-71	-72
1022.0	-73	-73	-74	-75	-76	-77	-78	-78	-79	-80
1023.0	-81	-82	-83	-83	-84	-85	-86	-87	-87	-88
1024.0	-89	-90	-91	-92	-92	-93	-94	-95	-96	-97
1025.0	-97	-98	-99	-100	-101	-101	-102	-103	-104	-105
1026.0	-106	-106	-107	-108	-109	-110	-111	-111	-112	-113
1027.0	-114	-115	-115	-116	-117	-118	-119	-120	-120	-121
1028.0	-122	-123	-124	-125	-125	-126	-127	-128	-129	-129
1029.0	-130	-131	-132	-133	-134	-134	-135	-136	-137	-138
1030.0	-139	-139	-140	-141	-142	-143	-143	-144	-145	-146
1031.0	-147	-148	-148	-149	-150	-151	-152	-152	-153	-154
1032.0	-155	-156	-157	-157	-158	-159	-160	-161	-161	-162
1033.0	-163	-164	-165	-166	-166	-167	-168	-169	-170	-170
1034.0	-171	-172	-173	-174	-175	-175	-176	-177	-178	-179
1035.0	-180	-180	-181	-182	-183	-184	-184	-185	-186	-187
1036.0	-188	-188	-189	-190	-191	-192	-193	-193	-194	-195
1037.0	-196	-197	-197	-198	-199	-200	-201	-202	-202	-203
1038.0	-204	-205	-206	-206	-207	-208	-209	-210	-211	-211
1039.0	-212	-213	-214	-215	-215	-216	-217	-218	-219	-220
1040.0	-220	-221	-222	-223	-224	-224	-225	-226	-227	-228
1041.0	-228	-229	-230	-231	-232	-233	-233	-234	-235	-236
1042.0	-237	-237	-238	-239	-240	-241	-242	-242	-243	-244
1043.0	-245	-246	-246	-247	-248	-249	-250	-250	-251	-252
1044.0	-253	-254	-255	-255	-256	-257	-258	-259	-259	-260
1045.0	-261	-262	-263	-263	-264	-265	-266	-267	-267	-268
1046.0	-269	-270	-271	-272	-272	-273	-274	-275	-276	-276
1047.0	-277	-278	-279	-280	-280	-281	-282	-283	-284	-285
1048.0	-285	-286	-287	-288	-289	-289	-290	-291	-292	-293
1049.0	-293	-294	-295	-296	-297	-297	-298	-299	-300	-301
1050.0	-302	-302	-303	-304	-305	-306	-306	-307	-308	-309
1051.0	-310	-310	-311	-312	-313	-314	-314	-315	-316	-317
1052.0	-318	-318	-319	-320	-321	-322	-323	-323	-324	-325
1053.0	-326	-327	-327	-328	-329	-330	-331	-331	-332	-333
1054.0	-334	-335	-335	-336	-337	-338	-339	-339	-340	-341
1055.0	-342	-343	-343	-344	-345	-346	-347	-348	-348	-349
1056.0	-350	-351	-352	-352	-353	-354	-355	-356	-356	-357
1057.0	-358	-359	-360	-360	-361	-362	-363	-364	-364	-365
1058.0	-366	-367	-368	-368	-369	-370	-371	-372	-372	-373
1059.0	-374	-375	-376	-376	-377	-378	-379	-380	-380	-381
1060.0	-382	-383	-384	-384	-385	-386	-387	-388	-389	-389
1061.0	-390	-391	-392	-393	-393	-394	-395	-396	-397	-397
1062.0	-398	-399	-400	-401	-401	-402	-403	-404	-405	-405
1063.0	-406	-407	-408	-409	-409	-410	-411	-412	-413	-413
1064.0	-414	-415	-416	-417	-417	-418	-419	-420	-421	-421
1065.0	-422	-423	-424	-425	-425	-426	-427	-428	-429	-429
1066.0	-430	-431	-432	-433	-433	-434	-435	-436	-437	-437
1067.0	-438	-439	-440	-441	-441	-442	-443	-444	-445	-445
1068.0	-446	-447	-448	-448	-449	-450	-451	-452	-452	-453
1069.0	-454	-455	-456	-456	-457	-458	-459	-460	-460	-461
1070.0	-462	-463	-464	-464	-465	-466	-467	-468	-468	-469
1071.0	-470	-471	-472	-472	-473	-474	-475	-476	-484	-485
1072.0	-478	-479	-480	-480	-481	-482	-483	-484	-484	-485
1073.0	-486	-487	-487	-488	-489	-490	-491	-491	-492	-493
1074.0	-494	-495	-495	-496	-497	-498	-499	-499	-500	-501
1075.0	-502	-503	-503	-504	-505	-506	-507	-507	-508	-509
1076.0	-510	-511	-511	-512	-513	-514	-514	-515	-516	-517
1077.0	-518	-518	-519	-520	-521	-522	-522	-523	-524	-525
1078.0	-526	-526	-527	-528	-529	-530	-530	-531	-532	-533
1079.0	-533	-534	-535	-536	-537	-537	-538	-539	-540	-541
1080.0	-541	-542	-543	-544	-545	-545	-546	-547	-548	-548
1081.0	-549	-550	-551	-552	-552	-553	-554	-555	-556	-556
1082.0	-557	-558	-559	-560	-560	-561	-562	-563	-563	-564
1083.0	-565	-566	-567	-567	-568	-569	-570	-571	-571	-572
1084.0	-573	-574	-575	-575	-576	-577	-578	-578	-579	-580
1085.0	-581	-582	-582	-583	-584	-585	-586	-586	-587	-588
1086.0	-589	-589	-590	-591	-592	-593	-593	-594	-595	-596
1087.0	-597	-597	-598	-599	-600	-601	-601	-602	-603	-604
1088.0	-604	-605	-606	-607	-608	-608	-609	-610	-611	-612
1089.0	-612	-613	-614	-615	-615	-616	-617	-618	-619	-619
1090.0	-620	-621	-622	-622	-623	-624	-625	-626	-626	-627
1091.0	-628	-629	-630	-630	-631	-632	-633	-633	-634	-635
1092.0	-636	-637	-637	-638	-639	-640	-641	-641	-642	-643
1093.0	-644	-644	-645	-646	-647	-648	-648	-649	-650	-651
1094.0	-651	-652	-653	-654	-655	-655	-656	-657	-658	-659
1095.0	-659	-660	-661	-662	-662	-663	-664	-665	-666	-666
1096.0	-667	-668	-669	-669	-670	-671	-672	-673	-673	-674
1097.0	-675	-676	-676	-677	-678	-679	-680	-680	-681	-682
1098.0	-683	-684	-684	-685	-686	-687	-687	-688	-689	-690
1099.0	-691	-691	-692	-693	-694	-694	-695	-696	-697	-698
1100.0	-698	-699	-700	-701	-701	-702	-703	-704	-705	-705
1101.0	-706	-707	-708	-708	-709	-710	-711	-712	-712	-713
1102.0	-714	-715	-715	-716	-717	-718	-719	-719	-720	-721
1103.0	-722	-722	-723	-724	-725	-726	-726	-727	-728	-729
1104.0	-729	-730	-731	-732	-733	-733	-734	-735	-736	-736
1105.0	-737	-738	-739	-740	-740	-741	-742	-743	-743	-744
1106.0	-745	-746	-746	-747	-748	-749	-750	-750	-751	-752
1107.0	-753	-753	-754	-755	-756	-757	-757	-758	-759	-760
1108.0	-760	-761	-762	-763	-764	-764	-765	-766	-767	-767
1109.0	-768	-769	-770	-771	-771	-772	-773	-774	-774	-775
1110.0	-776	-777	-777	-778	-779	-780	-781	-781	-782	-783
1111.0	-784	-784	-785	-786	-787	-788	-788	-789	-790	-791
1112.0	-791	-792	-793	-794	-794	-795	-796	-797	-798	-798
1113.0	-799	-800	-801	-801	-802	-803	-804	-804	-805	-806
1114.0	-807	-808	-808	-809	-810	-811	-811	-812	-813	-814
1115.0	-815	-815	-816	-817	-818	-818	-819	-820	-821	-821
1116.0	-822	-823	-824	-825	-825	-826	-827	-828	-828	-829
1117.0	-830	-831	-831	-832	-833	-834	-834	-835	-836	-837
1118.0	-838	-838	-839	-840	-841	-841	-842	-843	-844	-845
1119.0	-845	-846	-847	-848	-848	-849	-850	-851	-851	-852

TABLE VI - Continued   193

GEOPOTENTIAL ALTITUDE IN METERS as a function of PRESSURE IN MILLIBARS

P,mb	0.0	0.1	0.2	0.3	0.4	0.5	0.6	0.7	0.8	0.9
1120.0	-853	-854	-854	-855	-856	-857	-858	-858	-859	-860
1121.0	-861	-861	-862	-863	-864	-864	-865	-866	-867	-868
1122.0	-868	-869	-870	-871	-871	-872	-873	-874	-874	-875
1123.0	-876	-877	-877	-878	-879	-880	-881	-881	-882	-883
1124.0	-884	-884	-885	-886	-887	-887	-888	-889	-890	-890
1125.0	-891	-892	-893	-894	-894	-895	-896	-897	-897	-898
1126.0	-899	-900	-900	-901	-902	-903	-903	-904	-905	-906
1127.0	-907	-907	-908	-909	-910	-910	-911	-912	-913	-913
1128.0	-914	-915	-916	-916	-917	-918	-919	-920	-920	-921
1129.0	-922	-923	-923	-924	-925	-926	-926	-927	-928	-929
1130.0	-929	-930	-931	-932	-932	-933	-934	-935	-936	-936
1131.0	-937	-938	-939	-939	-940	-941	-942	-942	-943	-944
1132.0	-945	-945	-946	-947	-948	-948	-949	-950	-951	-952
1133.0	-952	-953	-954	-955	-955	-956	-957	-958	-958	-959
1134.0	-960	-961	-961	-962	-963	-964	-964	-965	-966	-967
1135.0	-967	-968	-969	-970	-971	-971	-972	-973	-974	-974
1136.0	-975	-976	-977	-977	-978	-979	-980	-980	-981	-982
1137.0	-983	-983	-984	-985	-986	-986	-987	-988	-989	-989
1138.0	-990	-991	-992	-992	-993	-994	-995	-996	-996	-997
1139.0	-998	-999	-999	-1000	-1001	-1002	-1002	-1003	-1004	-1005
1140.0	-1005	-1006	-1007	-1008	-1008	-1009	-1010	-1011	-1011	-1012
1141.0	-1013	-1014	-1014	-1015	-1016	-1017	-1017	-1018	-1019	-1020
1142.0	-1020	-1021	-1022	-1023	-1024	-1024	-1025	-1026	-1027	-1027
1143.0	-1028	-1029	-1030	-1030	-1031	-1032	-1033	-1033	-1034	-1035
1144.0	-1036	-1036	-1037	-1038	-1039	-1039	-1040	-1041	-1042	-1042
1145.0	-1043	-1044	-1045	-1045	-1046	-1047	-1048	-1048	-1049	-1050
1146.0	-1051	-1051	-1052	-1053	-1054	-1054	-1055	-1056	-1057	-1057
1147.0	-1058	-1059	-1060	-1060	-1061	-1062	-1063	-1063	-1064	-1065
1148.0	-1066	-1066	-1067	-1068	-1069	-1069	-1070	-1071	-1072	-1072
1149.0	-1073	-1074	-1075	-1076	-1076	-1077	-1078	-1079	-1079	-1080
1150.0	-1081	-1082	-1082	-1083	-1084	-1085	-1085	-1086	-1087	-1088
1151.0	-1088	-1089	-1090	-1091	-1091	-1092	-1093	-1094	-1094	-1095
1152.0	-1096	-1097	-1097	-1098	-1099	-1100	-1100	-1101	-1102	-1103
1153.0	-1103	-1104	-1105	-1106	-1106	-1107	-1108	-1109	-1109	-1110
1154.0	-1111	-1112	-1112	-1113	-1114	-1115	-1115	-1116	-1117	-1118
1155.0	-1118	-1119	-1120	-1121	-1121	-1122	-1123	-1124	-1124	-1125
1156.0	-1126	-1126	-1127	-1128	-1129	-1129	-1130	-1131	-1132	-1132
1157.0	-1133	-1134	-1135	-1135	-1136	-1137	-1138	-1138	-1139	-1140
1158.0	-1141	-1141	-1142	-1143	-1144	-1144	-1145	-1146	-1147	-1147
1159.0	-1148	-1149	-1150	-1150	-1151	-1152	-1153	-1153	-1154	-1155
1160.0	-1156	-1156	-1157	-1158	-1159	-1159	-1160	-1161	-1162	-1162
1161.0	-1163	-1164	-1165	-1165	-1166	-1167	-1168	-1168	-1169	-1170
1162.0	-1171	-1171	-1172	-1173	-1174	-1174	-1175	-1176	-1177	-1177
1163.0	-1178	-1179	-1179	-1180	-1181	-1182	-1182	-1183	-1184	-1185
1164.0	-1185	-1186	-1187	-1188	-1188	-1189	-1190	-1191	-1191	-1192
1165.0	-1193	-1194	-1194	-1195	-1196	-1197	-1197	-1198	-1199	-1200
1166.0	-1200	-1201	-1202	-1203	-1203	-1204	-1205	-1206	-1206	-1207
1167.0	-1208	-1208	-1209	-1210	-1211	-1211	-1212	-1213	-1214	-1214
1168.0	-1215	-1216	-1217	-1217	-1218	-1219	-1220	-1220	-1221	-1222
1169.0	-1223	-1223	-1224	-1225	-1226	-1226	-1227	-1228	-1229	-1229
1170.0	-1230	-1231	-1231	-1232	-1233	-1234	-1234	-1235	-1236	-1237
1171.0	-1237	-1238	-1239	-1240	-1240	-1241	-1242	-1243	-1243	-1244
1172.0	-1245	-1246	-1246	-1247	-1248	-1248	-1249	-1250	-1251	-1251
1173.0	-1252	-1253	-1254	-1254	-1255	-1256	-1257	-1257	-1258	-1259
1174.0	-1260	-1260	-1261	-1262	-1263	-1263	-1264	-1265	-1265	-1266
1175.0	-1267	-1268	-1268	-1269	-1270	-1271	-1271	-1272	-1273	-1274
1176.0	-1274	-1275	-1276	-1277	-1277	-1278	-1279	-1280	-1280	-1281
1177.0	-1282	-1282	-1283	-1284	-1285	-1285	-1286	-1287	-1288	-1288
1178.0	-1289	-1290	-1291	-1291	-1292	-1293	-1294	-1294	-1295	-1296
1179.0	-1296	-1297	-1298	-1299	-1299	-1300	-1301	-1302	-1302	-1303
1180.0	-1304	-1305	-1305	-1306	-1307	-1307	-1308	-1309	-1310	-1310
1181.0	-1311	-1312	-1313	-1313	-1314	-1315	-1316	-1316	-1317	-1318
1182.0	-1319	-1319	-1320	-1321	-1321	-1322	-1323	-1324	-1324	-1325
1183.0	-1326	-1327	-1327	-1328	-1329	-1330	-1330	-1331	-1332	-1332
1184.0	-1333	-1334	-1335	-1335	-1336	-1337	-1338	-1338	-1339	-1340
1185.0	-1341	-1341	-1342	-1343	-1343	-1344	-1345	-1346	-1346	-1347
1186.0	-1348	-1349	-1349	-1350	-1351	-1352	-1352	-1353	-1354	-1354
1187.0	-1355	-1356	-1357	-1357	-1358	-1359	-1360	-1360	-1361	-1362
1188.0	-1363	-1363	-1364	-1365	-1365	-1366	-1367	-1368	-1368	-1369
1189.0	-1370	-1371	-1371	-1372	-1373	-1373	-1374	-1375	-1376	-1376
1190.0	-1377	-1378	-1379	-1379	-1380	-1381	-1382	-1382	-1383	-1384
1191.0	-1384	-1385	-1386	-1387	-1387	-1388	-1389	-1390	-1390	-1391
1192.0	-1392	-1392	-1393	-1394	-1395	-1395	-1396	-1397	-1398	-1398
1193.0	-1399	-1400	-1401	-1401	-1402	-1403	-1403	-1404	-1405	-1406
1194.0	-1406	-1407	-1408	-1409	-1409	-1410	-1411	-1411	-1412	-1413
1195.0	-1414	-1414	-1415	-1416	-1417	-1417	-1418	-1419	-1419	-1420
1196.0	-1421	-1422	-1422	-1423	-1424	-1425	-1425	-1426	-1427	-1427
1197.0	-1428	-1429	-1430	-1430	-1431	-1432	-1433	-1433	-1434	-1435
1198.0	-1435	-1436	-1437	-1438	-1438	-1439	-1440	-1441	-1441	-1442
1199.0	-1443	-1443	-1444	-1445	-1446	-1446	-1447	-1448	-1449	-1449

TABLE VI – Concluded

GEOPOTENTIAL ALTITUDE IN METERS as a function of PRESSURE IN MILLIBARS

P, mb	0	1	2	3	4	5	6	7	8	9
1200.	-1450	-1457	-1464	-1472	-1479	-1486	-1493	-1501	-1508	-1515
1210.	-1522	-1530	-1537	-1544	-1551	-1558	-1565	-1573	-1580	-1587
1220.	-1594	-1601	-1608	-1616	-1623	-1630	-1637	-1644	-1651	-1658
1230.	-1666	-1673	-1680	-1687	-1694	-1701	-1708	-1715	-1722	-1729
1240.	-1736	-1744	-1751	-1758	-1765	-1772	-1779	-1786	-1793	-1800
1250.	-1807	-1814	-1821	-1828	-1835	-1842	-1849	-1856	-1863	-1870
1260.	-1877	-1884	-1891	-1898	-1905	-1912	-1919	-1926	-1933	-1940
1270.	-1946	-1953	-1960	-1967	-1974	-1981	-1988	-1995	-2002	-2009
1280.	-2016	-2022	-2029	-2036	-2043	-2050	-2057	-2064	-2071	-2077
1290.	-2084	-2091	-2098	-2105	-2112	-2118	-2125	-2132	-2139	-2146
1300.	-2153	-2159	-2166	-2173	-2180	-2186	-2193	-2200	-2207	-2214
1310.	-2220	-2227	-2234	-2241	-2247	-2254	-2261	-2268	-2274	-2281
1320.	-2288	-2294	-2301	-2308	-2315	-2321	-2328	-2335	-2341	-2348
1330.	-2355	-2361	-2368	-2375	-2381	-2388	-2395	-2401	-2408	-2415
1340.	-2421	-2428	-2435	-2441	-2448	-2454	-2461	-2468	-2474	-2481
1350.	-2487	-2494	-2501	-2507	-2514	-2520	-2527	-2534	-2540	-2547
1360.	-2553	-2560	-2566	-2573	-2579	-2586	-2593	-2599	-2606	-2612
1370.	-2619	-2625	-2632	-2638	-2645	-2651	-2658	-2664	-2671	-2677
1380.	-2684	-2690	-2697	-2703	-2710	-2716	-2723	-2729	-2735	-2742
1390.	-2748	-2755	-2761	-2768	-2774	-2780	-2787	-2793	-2800	-2806
1400.	-2813	-2819	-2825	-2832	-2838	-2845	-2851	-2857	-2864	-2870
1410.	-2876	-2883	-2889	-2896	-2902	-2908	-2915	-2921	-2927	-2934
1420.	-2940	-2946	-2953	-2959	-2965	-2972	-2978	-2984	-2991	-2997
1430.	-3003	-3009	-3016	-3022	-3028	-3035	-3041	-3047	-3053	-3060
1440.	-3066	-3072	-3078	-3085	-3091	-3097	-3103	-3110	-3116	-3122
1450.	-3128	-3135	-3141	-3147	-3153	-3159	-3166	-3172	-3178	-3184
1460.	-3190	-3197	-3203	-3209	-3215	-3221	-3228	-3234	-3240	-3246
1470.	-3252	-3258	-3265	-3271	-3277	-3283	-3289	-3295	-3301	-3308
1480.	-3314	-3320	-3326	-3332	-3338	-3344	-3350	-3356	-3363	-3369
1490.	-3375	-3381	-3387	-3393	-3399	-3405	-3411	-3417	-3423	-3429
1500.	-3435	-3442	-3448	-3454	-3460	-3466	-3472	-3478	-3484	-3490
1510.	-3496	-3502	-3508	-3514	-3520	-3526	-3532	-3538	-3544	-3550
1520.	-3556	-3562	-3568	-3574	-3580	-3586	-3592	-3598	-3604	-3610
1530.	-3616	-3622	-3628	-3634	-3640	-3646	-3652	-3657	-3663	-3669
1540.	-3675	-3681	-3687	-3693	-3699	-3705	-3711	-3717	-3723	-3729
1550.	-3734	-3740	-3746	-3752	-3758	-3764	-3770	-3776	-3782	-3787
1560.	-3793	-3799	-3805	-3811	-3817	-3823	-3828	-3834	-3840	-3846
1570.	-3852	-3858	-3863	-3869	-3875	-3881	-3887	-3893	-3898	-3904
1580.	-3910	-3916	-3922	-3927	-3933	-3939	-3945	-3951	-3956	-3962
1590.	-3968	-3974	-3980	-3985	-3991	-3997	-4003	-4008	-4014	-4020
1600.	-4026	-4031	-4037	-4043	-4049	-4054	-4060	-4066	-4072	-4077
1610.	-4083	-4089	-4094	-4100	-4106	-4112	-4117	-4123	-4129	-4134
1620.	-4140	-4146	-4151	-4157	-4163	-4169	-4174	-4180	-4186	-4191
1630.	-4197	-4203	-4208	-4214	-4219	-4225	-4231	-4236	-4242	-4248
1640.	-4253	-4259	-4265	-4270	-4276	-4282	-4287	-4293	-4298	-4304
1650.	-4310	-4315	-4321	-4326	-4332	-4338	-4343	-4349	-4354	-4360
1660.	-4366	-4371	-4377	-4382	-4388	-4393	-4399	-4454	-4410	-4416
1670.	-4421	-4427	-4432	-4438	-4443	-4449	-4454	-4460	-4466	-4471
1680.	-4477	-4482	-4488	-4493	-4499	-4504	-4510	-4515	-4521	-4526
1690.	-4532	-4537	-4543	-4548	-4554	-4559	-4565	-4570	-4576	-4581
1700.	-4587	-4592	-4598	-4603	-4609	-4614	-4619	-4625	-4630	-4636
1710.	-4641	-4647	-4652	-4658	-4663	-4668	-4674	-4679	-4685	-4690
1720.	-4696	-4701	-4706	-4712	-4717	-4723	-4728	-4734	-4739	-4744
1730.	-4750	-4755	-4761	-4765	-4771	-4777	-4782	-4787	-4793	-4798
1740.	-4804	-4809	-4814	-4820	-4825	-4830	-4836	-4841	-4846	-4852
1750.	-4857	-4863	-4868	-4873	-4879	-4884	-4889	-4895	-4900	-4905
1760.	-4911	-4916	-4921	-4927	-4932	-4937	-4942	-4948	-4953	-4958
1770.	-4964	-4969	-4974	-4980	-4985	-4990	-4995			

TABLE VII

GEOPOTENTIAL ALTITUDE IN FEET as a function of PRESSURE IN MILLIBARS

P, mb	0.00	0.01	0.02	0.03	0.04	0.05	0.06	0.07	0.08	0.09
8.60									104987	104962
8.70	104937	104911	104886	104861	104836	104811	104786	104761	104736	104711
8.80	104686	104661	104636	104611	104586	104561	104537	104512	104487	104462
8.90	104438	104413	104389	104364	104339	104315	104290	104266	104241	104217
9.00	104193	104168	104144	104120	104095	104071	104047	104023	103999	103974
9.10	103950	103926	103902	103878	103854	103830	103806	103782	103758	103735
9.20	103711	103687	103663	103639	103616	103592	103568	103545	103521	103497
9.30	103474	103450	103427	103403	103380	103356	103333	103309	103286	103263
9.40	103239	103216	103193	103170	103146	103123	103100	103077	103054	103031
9.50	103008	102985	102962	102939	102916	102893	102870	102847	102824	102801
9.60	102778	102756	102733	102710	102687	102665	102642	102619	102597	102574
9.70	102552	102529	102506	102484	102461	102439	102417	102394	102372	102349
9.80	102327	102305	102282	102260	102238	102216	102194	102171	102149	102127
9.90	102105	102083	102061	102039	102017	101995	101973	101951	101929	101907

TABLE VII- Continued

GEOPOTENTIAL ALTITUDE IN FEET as a function of PRESSURE IN MILLIBARS

P, mb	0.00	0.01	0.02	0.03	0.04	0.05	0.06	0.07	0.08	0.09
10.00	101885	101863	101841	101820	101798	101776	101754	101733	101711	101689
10.10	101668	101646	101624	101603	101581	101560	101538	101517	101495	101474
10.20	101452	101431	101409	101388	101367	101345	101324	101303	101282	101260
10.30	101239	101218	101197	101176	101154	101133	101112	101091	101070	101049
10.40	101028	101007	100986	100965	100944	100923	100902	100882	100861	100840
10.50	100819	100798	100777	100757	100736	100715	100695	100674	100653	100633
10.60	100612	100591	100571	100550	100530	100509	100489	100468	100448	100428
10.70	100407	100387	100366	100346	100326	100305	100285	100265	100245	100224
10.80	100204	100184	100164	100144	100123	100103	100083	100063	100043	100023
10.90	100003	99983	99963	99943	99923	99903	99883	99863	99844	99824
11.00	99804	99784	99764	99745	99725	99705	99685	99666	99646	99626
11.10	99607	99587	99567	99548	99528	99509	99489	99470	99450	99431
11.20	99411	99392	99372	99353	99333	99314	99295	99275	99256	99237
11.30	99217	99198	99179	99160	99140	99121	99102	99083	99064	99045
11.40	99025	99006	98987	98968	98949	98930	98911	98892	98873	98854
11.50	98835	98816	98797	98778	98760	98741	98722	98703	98684	98665
11.60	98647	98628	98609	98590	98572	98553	98534	98516	98497	98478
11.70	98460	98441	98423	98404	98385	98367	98348	98330	98311	98293
11.80	98275	98256	98238	98219	98201	98183	98164	98146	98128	98109
11.90	98091	98073	98054	98036	98018	98000	97982	97963	97945	97927
12.00	97909	97891	97873	97855	97837	97818	97800	97782	97764	97746
12.10	97728	97710	97692	97675	97657	97639	97621	97603	97585	97567
12.20	97549	97532	97514	97496	97478	97461	97443	97425	97407	97390
12.30	97372	97354	97337	97319	97301	97284	97266	97249	97231	97214
12.40	97196	97179	97161	97144	97126	97109	97091	97074	97056	97039
12.50	97022	97004	96987	96969	96952	96935	96917	96900	96883	96866
12.60	96848	96831	96814	96797	96780	96762	96745	96728	96711	96694
12.70	96677	96660	96643	96625	96608	96591	96574	96557	96540	96523
12.80	96506	96489	96473	96456	96439	96422	96405	96388	96371	96354
12.90	96338	96321	96304	96287	96270	96254	96237	96220	96203	96187
13.00	96170	96153	96137	96120	96103	96087	96070	96053	96037	96020
13.10	96004	95987	95971	95954	95938	95921	95905	95888	95872	95855
13.20	95839	95822	95806	95789	95773	95757	95740	95724	95708	95691
13.30	95675	95659	95642	95626	95610	95594	95577	95561	95545	95529
13.40	95513	95496	95480	95464	95448	95432	95416	95400	95384	95367
13.50	95351	95335	95319	95303	95287	95271	95255	95239	95223	95207
13.60	95191	95176	95160	95144	95128	95112	95096	95080	95064	95049
13.70	95033	95017	95001	94985	94970	94954	94938	94922	94907	94891
13.80	94875	94859	94844	94828	94812	94797	94781	94766	94750	94734
13.90	94719	94703	94688	94672	94657	94641	94625	94610	94594	94579
14.00	94564	94548	94533	94517	94502	94486	94471	94456	94440	94425
14.10	94409	94394	94379	94363	94348	94333	94317	94302	94287	94272
14.20	94256	94241	94226	94211	94196	94180	94165	94150	94135	94120
14.30	94105	94089	94074	94059	94044	94029	94014	93999	93984	93969
14.40	93954	93939	93924	93909	93894	93879	93864	93849	93834	93819
14.50	93804	93789	93774	93759	93744	93730	93715	93700	93685	93670
14.60	93655	93641	93626	93611	93596	93581	93567	93552	93537	93523
14.70	93508	93493	93478	93464	93449	93434	93420	93405	93390	93376
14.80	93361	93347	93332	93317	93303	93288	93274	93259	93245	93230
14.90	93216	93201	93187	93172	93158	93143	93129	93114	93100	93086
15.00	93071	93057	93042	93028	93014	92999	92985	92970	92956	92942
15.10	92928	92913	92899	92885	92870	92856	92842	92828	92813	92799
15.20	92785	92771	92757	92742	92728	92714	92700	92686	92672	92657
15.30	92643	92629	92615	92601	92587	92573	92559	92545	92531	92517
15.40	92503	92489	92475	92461	92447	92433	92419	92405	92391	92377
15.50	92363	92349	92335	92321	92307	92293	92279	92266	92252	92238
15.60	92224	92210	92196	92183	92169	92155	92141	92127	92114	92100
15.70	92086	92072	92059	92045	92031	92018	92004	91990	91976	91963
15.80	91949	91935	91922	91908	91895	91881	91867	91854	91840	91827
15.90	91813	91799	91786	91772	91759	91745	91732	91718	91705	91691
16.00	91678	91664	91651	91637	91624	91610	91597	91584	91570	91557
16.10	91543	91530	91517	91503	91490	91477	91463	91450	91437	91423
16.20	91410	91397	91383	91370	91357	91343	91330	91317	91304	91290
16.30	91277	91264	91251	91238	91224	91211	91198	91185	91172	91159
16.40	91145	91132	91119	91106	91093	91080	91067	91054	91041	91027
16.50	91014	91001	90988	90975	90962	90949	90936	90923	90910	90897
16.60	90884	90871	90858	90845	90832	90819	90806	90794	90781	90768
16.70	90755	90742	90729	90716	90703	90690	90678	90665	90652	90639
16.80	90626	90613	90601	90588	90575	90562	90549	90537	90524	90511
16.90	90498	90486	90473	90460	90447	90435	90422	90409	90397	90384
17.00	90371	90359	90346	90333	90321	90308	90295	90283	90270	90258
17.10	90245	90232	90220	90207	90195	90182	90170	90157	90145	90132
17.20	90120	90107	90095	90082	90070	90057	90045	90032	90020	90007
17.30	89995	89982	89970	89958	89945	89933	89920	89908	89896	89883
17.40	89871	89858	89846	89834	89821	89809	89797	89784	89772	89760
17.50	89747	89735	89723	89711	89698	89686	89674	89662	89649	89637
17.60	89625	89613	89600	89588	89576	89564	89552	89540	89527	89515
17.70	89503	89491	89479	89467	89455	89442	89430	89418	89406	89394
17.80	89382	89370	89358	89346	89334	89322	89310	89298	89286	89273
17.90	89261	89249	89237	89225	89213	89202	89190	89178	89166	89154
18.00	89142	89130	89118	89106	89094	89082	89070	89058	89046	89035
18.10	89023	89011	88999	88987	88975	88963	88952	88940	88928	88916
18.20	88904	88892	88881	88869	88857	88845	88834	88822	88810	88798
18.30	88787	88775	88763	88751	88740	88728	88716	88705	88693	88681
18.40	88669	88658	88646	88634	88623	88611	88600	88588	88576	88565
18.50	88553	88541	88530	88518	88507	88495	88484	88472	88460	88449
18.60	88437	88426	88414	88403	88391	88380	88368	88357	88345	88334
18.70	88322	88311	88299	88288	88276	88265	88253	88242	88230	88219
18.80	88208	88196	88185	88173	88162	88151	88139	88128	88116	88105
18.90	88094	88082	88071	88060	88048	88037	88026	88014	88003	87992
19.00	87981	87969	87958	87947	87935	87924	87913	87902	87890	87879
19.10	87868	87857	87845	87834	87823	87812	87801	87789	87778	87767
19.20	87756	87745	87733	87722	87711	87700	87689	87678	87667	87656
19.30	87644	87633	87622	87611	87600	87589	87578	87567	87556	87545
19.40	87534	87522	87511	87500	87489	87478	87467	87456	87445	87434
19.50	87423	87412	87401	87390	87379	87368	87357	87346	87335	87325
19.60	87314	87303	87292	87281	87270	87259	87248	87237	87226	87215
19.70	87204	87194	87183	87172	87161	87150	87139	87128	87118	87107
19.80	87096	87086	87075	87064	87053	87042	87031	87020	87010	86999
19.90	86988	86977	86966	86955	86943	86932	86921	86910	86899	86888

TABLE VII - Continued

GEOPOTENTIAL ALTITUDE IN FEET as a function of PRESSURE IN MILLIBARS

P, mb	0.0	0.1	0.2	0.3	0.4	0.5	0.6	0.7	0.8	0.9
20.0	86881	86774	86667	86562	86456	86352	86247	86144	86041	85938
21.0	85836	85734	85633	85532	85432	85332	85233	85135	85036	84938
22.0	84841	84744	84648	84552	84456	84361	84266	84172	84078	83985
23.0	83892	83799	83707	83615	83524	83433	83342	83252	83163	83073
24.0	82984	82896	82807	82719	82632	82545	82458	82372	82286	82200
25.0	82115	82030	81945	81861	81777	81693	81610	81527	81444	81362
26.0	81280	81198	81117	81036	80956	80875	80795	80715	80636	80557
27.0	80478	80399	80321	80243	80166	80088	80011	79935	79858	79782
28.0	79706	79630	79555	79480	79405	79330	79256	79182	79108	79035
29.0	78962	78889	78816	78744	78671	78600	78528	78456	78385	78314
30.0	78244	78173	78103	78033	77963	77894	77824	77755	77686	77618
31.0	77550	77481	77413	77346	77278	77211	77144	77077	77011	76944
32.0	76878	76812	76746	76681	76616	76551	76486	76421	76356	76292
33.0	76228	76164	76101	76037	75974	75911	75848	75785	75722	75660
34.0	75598	75536	75474	75413	75351	75290	75229	75168	75107	75047
35.0	74987	74927	74867	74807	74747	74688	74628	74569	74510	74452
36.0	74393	74335	74276	74218	74160	74103	74045	73988	73930	73873
37.0	73816	73759	73703	73646	73590	73534	73478	73422	73366	73311
38.0	73255	73200	73145	73090	73035	72980	72926	72871	72817	72763
39.0	72709	72655	72602	72548	72495	72441	72388	72335	72283	72230
40.0	72177	72125	72073	72020	71968	71917	71865	71813	71762	71710
41.0	71659	71608	71557	71506	71455	71405	71354	71304	71254	71204
42.0	71154	71104	71054	71004	70955	70905	70856	70807	70758	70709
43.0	70660	70612	70563	70515	70466	70418	70370	70322	70274	70226
44.0	70179	70131	70084	70037	69989	69942	69895	69848	69802	69755
45.0	69708	69662	69616	69569	69523	69477	69431	69385	69340	69294
46.0	69249	69203	69158	69113	69068	69023	68978	68933	68888	68844
47.0	68799	68755	68710	68666	68622	68578	68534	68490	68446	68403
48.0	68359	68316	68272	68229	68186	68143	68100	68057	68014	67971
49.0	67929	67886	67844	67801	67759	67717	67675	67633	67591	67549
50.0	67507	67465	67424	67382	67341	67299	67258	67217	67176	67135
51.0	67094	67053	67012	66972	66931	66891	66850	66810	66770	66729
52.0	66689	66649	66609	66569	66530	66490	66450	66411	66371	66332
53.0	66293	66253	66214	66175	66136	66097	66058	66019	65981	65942
54.0	65903	65865	65826	65788	65750	65712	65673	65635	65597	65559
55.0	65522	65484	65446	65408	65371	65333	65296	65258	65221	65184
56.0	65147	65110	65072	65035	64999	64962	64925	64888	64852	64815
57.0	64778	64742	64705	64669	64633	64597	64561	64524	64488	64452
58.0	64417	64381	64345	64309	64274	64238	64202	64167	64132	64096
59.0	64061	64026	63990	63955	63920	63885	63850	63815	63781	63746
60.0	63711	63677	63642	63607	63573	63539	63504	63470	63436	63401
61.0	63367	63333	63299	63265	63231	63197	63164	63130	63096	63063
62.0	63029	62995	62962	62929	62895	62862	62829	62795	62762	62729
63.0	62696	62663	62630	62597	62564	62532	62499	62466	62434	62401
64.0	62368	62336	62303	62271	62239	62206	62174	62142	62110	62078
65.0	62046	62014	61982	61950	61918	61886	61855	61823	61791	61760
66.0	61728	61697	61665	61634	61602	61571	61540	61509	61477	61446
67.0	61415	61384	61353	61322	61291	61261	61230	61199	61168	61138
68.0	61107	61076	61046	61015	60985	60955	60924	60894	60864	60833
69.0	60803	60773	60743	60713	60683	60653	60623	60593	60563	60534
70.0	60504	60474	60445	60415	60385	60356	60326	60297	60268	60238
71.0	60209	60180	60150	60121	60092	60063	60034	60005	59976	59947
72.0	59918	59889	59860	59831	59803	59774	59745	59717	59688	59659
73.0	59631	59602	59574	59546	59517	59489	59461	59432	59404	59376
74.0	59348	59320	59292	59264	59236	59208	59180	59152	59124	59096
75.0	59068	59041	59013	58985	58958	58930	58903	58875	58848	58820
76.0	58793	58766	58738	58711	58684	58656	58629	58602	58575	58548
77.0	58521	58494	58467	58440	58413	58386	58359	58333	58306	58279
78.0	58252	58226	58199	58173	58146	58120	58093	58067	58040	58014
79.0	57987	57961	57935	57909	57882	57856	57830	57804	57778	57752
80.0	57726	57700	57674	57648	57622	57596	57570	57544	57519	57493
81.0	57467	57442	57416	57390	57365	57339	57314	57288	57263	57237
82.0	57212	57187	57161	57136	57111	57085	57060	57035	57010	56985
83.0	56960	56935	56910	56885	56860	56835	56810	56785	56760	56735
84.0	56711	56686	56661	56636	56612	56587	56563	56538	56513	56489
85.0	56464	56440	56415	56391	56367	56342	56318	56294	56269	56245
86.0	56221	56197	56173	56149	56124	56100	56076	56052	56028	56004
87.0	55980	55957	55933	55909	55885	55861	55837	55814	55790	55766
88.0	55743	55719	55695	55672	55648	55625	55601	55578	55554	55531
89.0	55508	55484	55461	55438	55414	55391	55368	55345	55321	55298
90.0	55275	55252	55229	55206	55183	55160	55137	55114	55091	55068
91.0	55045	55022	55000	54977	54954	54931	54909	54886	54863	54840
92.0	54818	54795	54773	54750	54728	54705	54683	54660	54638	54615
93.0	54593	54571	54548	54526	54504	54481	54459	54437	54415	54393
94.0	54370	54348	54326	54304	54282	54260	54238	54216	54194	54172
95.0	54150	54128	54106	54085	54063	54041	54019	53997	53976	53954
96.0	53932	53911	53889	53867	53846	53824	53803	53781	53760	53738
97.0	53717	53695	53674	53653	53631	53610	53588	53567	53546	53525
98.0	53503	53482	53461	53440	53419	53397	53376	53355	53334	53313
99.0	53292	53271	53250	53229	53208	53187	53166	53146	53125	53104
100.0	53083	53062	53041	53021	53000	52979	52959	52938	52917	52897
101.0	52876	52855	52835	52814	52794	52773	52753	52732	52712	52691
102.0	52671	52651	52630	52610	52590	52569	52549	52529	52508	52488
103.0	52468	52448	52428	52408	52387	52367	52347	52327	52307	52287
104.0	52267	52247	52227	52207	52187	52167	52147	52127	52108	52088
105.0	52068	52048	52028	52009	51989	51969	51949	51930	51910	51890
106.0	51871	51851	51831	51812	51792	51773	51753	51734	51714	51695
107.0	51675	51656	51636	51617	51598	51578	51559	51540	51520	51501
108.0	51482	51463	51443	51424	51405	51386	51367	51347	51328	51309
109.0	51290	51271	51252	51233	51214	51195	51176	51157	51138	51119
110.0	51100	51081	51062	51043	51025	51006	50987	50968	50949	50930
111.0	50912	50893	50874	50856	50837	50818	50800	50781	50762	50744
112.0	50725	50707	50688	50669	50651	50632	50614	50596	50577	50559
113.0	50540	50522	50503	50485	50467	50448	50430	50412	50393	50375
114.0	50357	50339	50320	50302	50284	50266	50248	50230	50211	50193
115.0	50175	50157	50139	50121	50103	50085	50067	50049	50031	50013
116.0	49995	49977	49959	49941	49923	49906	49888	49870	49852	49834
117.0	49816	49799	49781	49763	49745	49728	49710	49692	49675	49657
118.0	49639	49622	49604	49587	49569	49551	49534	49516	49499	49481
119.0	49464	49446	49429	49411	49394	49377	49359	49342	49324	49307

TABLE VII - Continued

GEOPOTENTIAL ALTITUDE IN FEET as a function of PRESSURE IN MILLIBARS

P, mb	0.0	0.1	0.2	0.3	0.4	0.5	0.6	0.7	0.8	0.9
120.0	49290	49272	49255	49238	49220	49203	49186	49169	49151	49134
121.0	49117	49100	49083	49065	49048	49031	49014	48997	48980	48963
122.0	48946	48929	48912	48895	48878	48861	48844	48827	48810	48793
123.0	48776	48759	48742	48725	48708	48692	48675	48658	48641	48624
124.0	48607	48591	48574	48557	48540	48524	48507	48490	48474	48457
125.0	48440	48424	48407	48390	48374	48357	48341	48324	48308	48291
126.0	48275	48258	48242	48225	48209	48192	48176	48159	48143	48126
127.0	48110	48094	48077	48061	48045	48028	48012	47996	47979	47963
128.0	47947	47931	47914	47898	47882	47866	47850	47833	47817	47801
129.0	47785	47769	47753	47737	47721	47705	47688	47672	47656	47640
130.0	47624	47608	47592	47576	47560	47544	47529	47513	47497	47481
131.0	47465	47449	47433	47417	47401	47386	47370	47354	47338	47322
132.0	47307	47291	47275	47259	47244	47228	47212	47197	47181	47165
133.0	47150	47134	47118	47103	47087	47072	47056	47040	47025	47009
134.0	46994	46978	46963	46947	46932	46916	46901	46885	46870	46855
135.0	46839	46824	46808	46793	46778	46762	46747	46732	46716	46701
136.0	46686	46670	46655	46640	46624	46609	46594	46579	46564	46548
137.0	46533	46518	46503	46488	46472	46457	46442	46427	46412	46397
138.0	46382	46367	46352	46337	46322	46307	46292	46277	46262	46247
139.0	46232	46217	46202	46187	46172	46157	46142	46127	46112	46097
140.0	46082	46068	46053	46038	46023	46008	45993	45979	45964	45949
141.0	45934	45920	45905	45890	45875	45861	45846	45831	45817	45802
142.0	45787	45773	45758	45743	45729	45714	45700	45685	45670	45656
143.0	45641	45627	45612	45598	45583	45569	45554	45540	45525	45511
144.0	45496	45482	45467	45453	45439	45424	45410	45395	45381	45367
145.0	45352	45338	45324	45309	45295	45281	45266	45252	45238	45224
146.0	45209	45195	45181	45167	45152	45138	45124	45110	45096	45081
147.0	45067	45053	45039	45025	45011	44997	44983	44968	44954	44940
148.0	44926	44912	44898	44884	44870	44856	44842	44828	44814	44800
149.0	44786	44772	44758	44744	44730	44716	44703	44689	44675	44661
150.0	44647	44633	44619	44605	44592	44578	44564	44550	44536	44523
151.0	44509	44495	44481	44467	44454	44440	44426	44413	44399	44385
152.0	44371	44358	44344	44330	44317	44303	44289	44276	44262	44249
153.0	44235	44221	44208	44194	44181	44167	44154	44140	44126	44113
154.0	44099	44086	44072	44059	44045	44032	44019	44005	43992	43978
155.0	43965	43951	43938	43925	43911	43898	43884	43871	43858	43844
156.0	43831	43818	43804	43791	43778	43764	43751	43738	43725	43711
157.0	43698	43685	43672	43658	43645	43632	43619	43605	43592	43579
158.0	43566	43553	43540	43526	43513	43500	43487	43474	43461	43448
159.0	43435	43422	43409	43395	43382	43369	43356	43343	43330	43317
160.0	43304	43291	43278	43265	43252	43239	43226	43213	43200	43188
161.0	43175	43162	43149	43136	43123	43110	43097	43084	43071	43059
162.0	43046	43033	43020	43007	42994	42982	42969	42956	42943	42930
163.0	42918	42905	42892	42879	42867	42854	42841	42829	42816	42803
164.0	42790	42778	42765	42752	42740	42727	42714	42702	42689	42677
165.0	42664	42651	42639	42626	42614	42601	42588	42576	42563	42551
166.0	42538	42526	42513	42501	42488	42476	42463	42451	42438	42426
167.0	42413	42401	42388	42376	42364	42351	42339	42326	42314	42301
168.0	42289	42277	42264	42252	42240	42227	42215	42203	42190	42178
169.0	42166	42153	42141	42129	42116	42104	42092	42080	42067	42055
170.0	42043	42031	42018	42006	41994	41982	41970	41957	41945	41933
171.0	41921	41909	41897	41884	41872	41860	41848	41836	41824	41812
172.0	41800	41787	41775	41763	41751	41739	41727	41715	41703	41691
173.0	41679	41667	41655	41643	41631	41619	41607	41595	41583	41571
174.0	41559	41547	41535	41523	41511	41499	41487	41475	41464	41452
175.0	41440	41428	41416	41404	41392	41380	41369	41357	41345	41333
176.0	41321	41309	41298	41286	41274	41262	41250	41239	41227	41215
177.0	41203	41192	41180	41168	41156	41145	41133	41121	41110	41098
178.0	41086	41074	41063	41051	41039	41028	41016	41004	40993	40981
179.0	40970	40958	40946	40935	40923	40912	40900	40888	40877	40865
180.0	40854	40842	40831	40819	40807	40796	40784	40773	40761	40750
181.0	40738	40727	40715	40704	40692	40681	40670	40658	40647	40635
182.0	40624	40612	40601	40589	40578	40567	40555	40544	40532	40521
183.0	40510	40498	40487	40476	40464	40453	40442	40430	40419	40408
184.0	40396	40385	40374	40362	40351	40340	40329	40317	40306	40295
185.0	40284	40272	40261	40250	40239	40227	40216	40204	40194	40183
186.0	40171	40160	40149	40138	40127	40116	40104	40093	40082	40071
187.0	40060	40049	40038	40027	40015	40004	39993	39982	39971	39960
188.0	39949	39938	39927	39916	39905	39894	39883	39872	39861	39850
189.0	39839	39828	39817	39806	39795	39784	39773	39762	39751	39740
190.0	39729	39718	39707	39696	39685	39674	39663	39652	39641	39630
191.0	39620	39609	39598	39587	39576	39565	39554	39543	39533	39522
192.0	39511	39500	39489	39478	39468	39457	39446	39435	39424	39414
193.0	39403	39392	39381	39370	39360	39349	39338	39327	39317	39306
194.0	39295	39285	39274	39263	39252	39242	39231	39220	39210	39199
195.0	39188	39178	39167	39156	39146	39135	39124	39114	39103	39092
196.0	39082	39071	39061	39050	39039	39029	39018	39008	38997	38987
197.0	38976	38965	38955	38944	38934	38923	38913	38902	38892	38881
198.0	38871	38860	38850	38839	38829	38818	38808	38797	38787	38776
199.0	38766	38755	38745	38734	38724	38714	38703	38693	38682	38672
200.0	38662	38651	38641	38630	38620	38610	38599	38589	38578	38568
201.0	38558	38547	38537	38527	38516	38506	38496	38485	38475	38465
202.0	38455	38444	38434	38424	38413	38403	38393	38383	38372	38362
203.0	38352	38342	38331	38321	38311	38301	38290	38280	38270	38260
204.0	38250	38239	38229	38219	38209	38199	38188	38178	38168	38158
205.0	38148	38138	38127	38117	38107	38097	38087	38077	38067	38057
206.0	38047	38036	38026	38016	38006	37996	37986	37976	37966	37956
207.0	37946	37936	37926	37916	37906	37896	37886	37876	37866	37856
208.0	37846	37836	37826	37816	37806	37796	37786	37776	37766	37756
209.0	37746	37736	37726	37716	37706	37696	37686	37676	37666	37656
210.0	37646	37637	37627	37617	37607	37597	37587	37577	37567	37557
211.0	37548	37538	37528	37518	37508	37498	37488	37479	37469	37459
212.0	37449	37439	37430	37420	37410	37400	37390	37381	37371	37361
213.0	37351	37342	37332	37322	37312	37303	37293	37283	37273	37264
214.0	37254	37244	37234	37225	37215	37205	37196	37186	37176	37167
215.0	37157	37147	37137	37128	37118	37109	37099	37089	37080	37070
216.0	37060	37051	37041	37031	37022	37012	37003	36993	36983	36974
217.0	36964	36955	36945	36935	36926	36916	36907	36897	36888	36878
218.0	36869	36859	36849	36840	36830	36821	36811	36802	36792	36783
219.0	36773	36764	36754	36745	36735	36726	36716	36707	36697	36688

TABLE VII - Continued

GEOPOTENTIAL ALTITUDE IN FEET as a function of PRESSURE IN MILLIBARS

P, mb	0.0	0.1	0.2	0.3	0.4	0.5	0.6	0.7	0.8	0.9
220.0	36679	36669	36660	36650	36641	36631	36622	36612	36603	36594
221.0	36584	36575	36565	36556	36547	36537	36528	36518	36509	36500
222.0	36490	36481	36472	36462	36453	36443	36434	36425	36415	36406
223.0	36397	36387	36378	36369	36359	36350	36341	36332	36322	36313
224.0	36304	36294	36285	36276	36267	36257	36248	36239	36229	36220
225.0	36211	36202	36192	36183	36174	36165	36156	36146	36137	36128
226.0	36119	36109	36100	36091	36082	36073	36064	36054	36045	36036
227.0	36027	36018	36008	35999	35990	35981	35972	35963	35954	35944
228.0	35935	35926	35917	35908	35899	35890	35881	35871	35862	35853
229.0	35844	35835	35826	35817	35808	35799	35789	35780	35771	35762
230.0	35753	35744	35735	35726	35717	35708	35699	35690	35681	35672
231.0	35663	35654	35645	35635	35626	35617	35608	35599	35590	35581
232.0	35572	35563	35554	35545	35536	35527	35518	35509	35500	35491
233.0	35482	35473	35464	35455	35446	35438	35429	35420	35411	35402
234.0	35393	35384	35375	35366	35357	35348	35339	35330	35321	35312
235.0	35303	35294	35286	35277	35268	35259	35250	35241	35232	35223
236.0	35214	35206	35197	35188	35179	35170	35161	35152	35143	35135
237.0	35126	35117	35108	35099	35090	35081	35073	35064	35055	35046
238.0	35037	35028	35020	35011	35002	34993	34984	34976	34967	34958
239.0	34949	34940	34932	34923	34914	34905	34896	34888	34879	34870
240.0	34861	34853	34844	34835	34826	34818	34809	34800	34791	34783
241.0	34774	34765	34756	34748	34739	34730	34721	34713	34704	34695
242.0	34687	34678	34669	34660	34652	34643	34634	34626	34617	34608
243.0	34600	34591	34582	34574	34565	34556	34548	34539	34530	34522
244.0	34513	34504	34496	34487	34478	34470	34461	34453	34444	34435
245.0	34427	34418	34409	34401	34392	34384	34375	34366	34358	34349
246.0	34341	34332	34323	34315	34306	34298	34289	34281	34272	34263
247.0	34255	34246	34238	34229	34221	34212	34203	34195	34186	34178
248.0	34169	34161	34152	34144	34135	34127	34118	34110	34101	34093
249.0	34084	34076	34067	34059	34050	34042	34033	34025	34016	34008
250.0	33999	33991	33982	33974	33965	33957	33948	33940	33931	33923
251.0	33914	33906	33898	33889	33881	33872	33864	33855	33847	33838
252.0	33830	33822	33813	33805	33796	33788	33780	33771	33763	33754
253.0	33746	33738	33729	33721	33712	33704	33696	33687	33679	33670
254.0	33662	33654	33645	33637	33629	33620	33612	33604	33595	33587
255.0	33578	33570	33562	33553	33545	33537	33528	33520	33512	33503
256.0	33495	33487	33478	33470	33462	33454	33445	33437	33429	33420
257.0	33412	33404	33395	33387	33379	33371	33362	33354	33346	33338
258.0	33329	33321	33313	33304	33296	33288	33280	33271	33263	33255
259.0	33247	33238	33230	33222	33214	33206	33197	33189	33181	33173
260.0	33164	33156	33148	33140	33132	33123	33115	33107	33099	33091
261.0	33082	33074	33066	33058	33050	33041	33033	33025	33017	33009
262.0	33001	32992	32984	32976	32968	32960	32952	32943	32935	32927
263.0	32919	32911	32903	32895	32887	32878	32870	32862	32854	32846
264.0	32838	32830	32822	32813	32805	32797	32789	32781	32773	32765
265.0	32757	32749	32741	32732	32724	32716	32708	32700	32692	32684
266.0	32676	32668	32660	32652	32644	32636	32628	32620	32612	32603
267.0	32595	32587	32579	32571	32563	32555	32547	32539	32531	32523
268.0	32515	32507	32499	32491	32483	32475	32467	32459	32451	32443
269.0	32435	32427	32419	32411	32403	32395	32387	32379	32371	32363
270.0	32355	32347	32339	32331	32323	32315	32308	32300	32292	32284
271.0	32276	32268	32260	32252	32244	32236	32228	32220	32212	32204
272.0	32196	32188	32181	32173	32165	32157	32149	32141	32133	32125
273.0	32117	32109	32101	32094	32086	32078	32070	32062	32054	32046
274.0	32038	32031	32023	32015	32007	31999	31991	31983	31975	31968
275.0	31960	31952	31944	31936	31928	31921	31913	31905	31897	31889
276.0	31881	31874	31866	31858	31850	31842	31834	31827	31819	31811
277.0	31803	31795	31788	31780	31772	31764	31756	31749	31741	31733
278.0	31725	31717	31710	31702	31694	31686	31679	31671	31663	31655
279.0	31648	31640	31632	31624	31617	31609	31601	31593	31586	31578
280.0	31570	31562	31555	31547	31539	31531	31524	31516	31508	31501
281.0	31493	31485	31477	31470	31462	31454	31447	31439	31431	31423
282.0	31416	31408	31400	31393	31385	31377	31370	31362	31354	31347
283.0	31339	31331	31324	31316	31308	31301	31293	31285	31278	31270
284.0	31262	31255	31247	31239	31232	31224	31216	31209	31201	31194
285.0	31186	31178	31171	31163	31155	31148	31140	31133	31125	31117
286.0	31110	31102	31095	31087	31079	31072	31064	31057	31049	31041
287.0	31034	31026	31019	31011	31004	30996	30988	30981	30973	30966
288.0	30958	30951	30943	30935	30928	30920	30913	30905	30898	30890
289.0	30883	30875	30867	30860	30852	30845	30837	30830	30822	30815
290.0	30807	30800	30792	30785	30777	30770	30762	30755	30747	30740
291.0	30732	30725	30717	30710	30702	30695	30687	30680	30672	30665
292.0	30657	30650	30642	30635	30627	30620	30612	30605	30597	30590
293.0	30583	30575	30568	30560	30553	30545	30538	30530	30523	30516
294.0	30508	30501	30493	30486	30478	30471	30463	30456	30449	30441
295.0	30434	30426	30419	30412	30404	30397	30389	30382	30375	30367
296.0	30360	30352	30345	30338	30330	30323	30315	30308	30301	30293
297.0	30286	30278	30271	30264	30256	30249	30242	30234	30227	30220
298.0	30212	30205	30197	30190	30183	30175	30168	30161	30153	30146
299.0	30139	30131	30124	30117	30109	30102	30095	30087	30080	30073
300.0	30065	30058	30051	30043	30036	30029	30022	30014	30007	30000
301.0	29992	29985	29978	29970	29963	29956	29949	29941	29934	29927
302.0	29919	29912	29905	29898	29890	29883	29876	29869	29861	29854
303.0	29847	29840	29832	29825	29818	29811	29803	29796	29789	29782
304.0	29774	29767	29760	29753	29745	29738	29731	29724	29716	29709
305.0	29702	29695	29688	29680	29673	29666	29659	29652	29644	29637
306.0	29630	29623	29616	29608	29601	29594	29587	29580	29572	29565
307.0	29558	29551	29544	29536	29529	29522	29515	29508	29501	29493
308.0	29486	29479	29472	29465	29458	29450	29443	29436	29429	29422
309.0	29415	29408	29400	29393	29386	29379	29372	29365	29358	29351
310.0	29343	29336	29329	29322	29315	29308	29301	29294	29286	29279
311.0	29272	29265	29258	29251	29244	29237	29230	29223	29215	29208
312.0	29201	29194	29187	29180	29173	29166	29159	29152	29145	29138
313.0	29130	29123	29116	29109	29102	29095	29088	29081	29074	29067
314.0	29060	29053	29046	29039	29032	29025	29018	29011	29003	28996
315.0	28989	28982	28975	28968	28961	28954	28947	28940	28933	28926
316.0	28919	28912	28905	28898	28891	28884	28877	28870	28863	28856
317.0	28849	28842	28835	28828	28821	28814	28807	28800	28793	28786
318.0	28779	28772	28765	28758	28751	28744	28737	28730	28723	28716
319.0	28709	28703	28696	28689	28682	28675	28668	28661	28654	28647

TABLE VII- Continued

GEOPOTENTIAL ALTITUDE IN FEET as a function of PRESSURE IN MILLIBARS

P, mb	0.0	0.1	0.2	0.3	0.4	0.5	0.6	0.7	0.8	0.9
320.0	28640	28633	28626	28619	28612	28605	28598	28591	28584	28578
321.0	28571	28564	28557	28550	28543	28536	28529	28522	28515	28508
322.0	28501	28495	28488	28481	28474	28467	28460	28453	28446	28439
323.0	28432	28426	28419	28412	28405	28398	28391	28384	28377	28370
324.0	28364	28357	28350	28343	28336	28329	28322	28315	28309	28302
325.0	28295	28288	28281	28274	28267	28261	28254	28247	28240	28233
326.0	28226	28220	28213	28206	28199	28192	28185	28179	28172	28165
327.0	28158	28151	28144	28138	28131	28124	28117	28110	28104	28097
328.0	28090	28083	28076	28070	28063	28056	28049	28042	28036	28029
329.0	28022	28015	28008	28002	27995	27988	27981	27974	27968	27961
330.0	27954	27947	27941	27934	27927	27920	27914	27907	27900	27893
331.0	27886	27880	27873	27866	27859	27853	27846	27839	27832	27826
332.0	27819	27812	27805	27799	27792	27785	27779	27772	27765	27758
333.0	27752	27745	27738	27731	27725	27718	27711	27705	27698	27691
334.0	27684	27678	27671	27664	27658	27651	27644	27638	27631	27624
335.0	27617	27611	27604	27597	27591	27584	27577	27571	27564	27557
336.0	27551	27544	27537	27531	27524	27517	27511	27504	27497	27491
337.0	27484	27477	27471	27464	27457	27451	27444	27437	27431	27424
338.0	27417	27411	27404	27398	27391	27384	27378	27371	27364	27358
339.0	27351	27344	27338	27331	27325	27318	27311	27305	27298	27292
340.0	27285	27278	27272	27265	27258	27252	27245	27239	27232	27225
341.0	27219	27212	27206	27199	27192	27186	27179	27173	27166	27160
342.0	27153	27146	27140	27133	27127	27120	27114	27107	27100	27094
343.0	27087	27081	27074	27068	27061	27054	27048	27041	27035	27028
344.0	27022	27015	27009	27002	26995	26989	26982	26976	26969	26963
345.0	26956	26950	26943	26937	26930	26924	26917	26911	26904	26897
346.0	26891	26884	26878	26871	26865	26858	26852	26845	26839	26832
347.0	26826	26819	26813	26806	26800	26793	26787	26780	26774	26767
348.0	26761	26754	26748	26741	26735	26728	26722	26716	26709	26703
349.0	26696	26690	26683	26677	26670	26664	26657	26651	26644	26638
350.0	26631	26625	26619	26612	26606	26599	26593	26586	26580	26573
351.0	26567	26560	26554	26548	26541	26535	26528	26522	26515	26509
352.0	26503	26496	26490	26483	26477	26470	26464	26458	26451	26445
353.0	26438	26432	26426	26419	26413	26406	26400	26393	26387	26381
354.0	26374	26368	26361	26355	26349	26342	26336	26330	26323	26317
355.0	26310	26304	26298	26291	26285	26278	26272	26266	26259	26253
356.0	26247	26240	26234	26227	26221	26215	26208	26202	26196	26189
357.0	26183	26177	26170	26164	26158	26151	26145	26138	26132	26126
358.0	26119	26113	26107	26100	26094	26088	26081	26075	26069	26062
359.0	26056	26050	26043	26037	26031	26024	26018	26012	26006	25999
360.0	25993	25987	25980	25974	25968	25961	25955	25949	25942	25936
361.0	25930	25924	25917	25911	25905	25898	25892	25886	25880	25873
362.0	25867	25861	25854	25848	25842	25836	25829	25823	25817	25810
363.0	25804	25798	25792	25785	25779	25773	25767	25760	25754	25748
364.0	25742	25735	25729	25723	25716	25710	25704	25698	25692	25685
365.0	25679	25673	25667	25660	25654	25648	25642	25635	25629	25623
366.0	25617	25610	25604	25598	25592	25586	25579	25573	25567	25561
367.0	25554	25548	25542	25536	25530	25523	25517	25511	25505	25499
368.0	25492	25486	25480	25474	25468	25461	25455	25449	25443	25437
369.0	25430	25424	25418	25412	25406	25399	25393	25387	25381	25375
370.0	25369	25362	25356	25350	25344	25338	25332	25325	25319	25313
371.0	25307	25301	25295	25288	25282	25276	25270	25264	25258	25252
372.0	25245	25239	25233	25227	25221	25215	25209	25202	25196	25190
373.0	25184	25178	25172	25166	25159	25153	25147	25141	25135	25129
374.0	25123	25117	25110	25104	25098	25092	25086	25080	25074	25068
375.0	25062	25055	25049	25043	25037	25031	25025	25019	25013	25007
376.0	25001	24994	24988	24982	24976	24970	24964	24958	24952	24946
377.0	24940	24934	24927	24921	24915	24909	24903	24897	24891	24885
378.0	24879	24873	24867	24861	24855	24849	24843	24836	24830	24824
379.0	24818	24812	24806	24800	24794	24788	24782	24776	24770	24764
380.0	24758	24752	24746	24740	24734	24728	24722	24716	24709	24703
381.0	24697	24691	24685	24679	24673	24667	24661	24655	24649	24643
382.0	24637	24631	24625	24619	24613	24607	24601	24595	24589	24583
383.0	24577	24571	24565	24559	24553	24547	24541	24535	24529	24523
384.0	24517	24511	24505	24499	24493	24487	24481	24475	24469	24463
385.0	24457	24451	24445	24439	24433	24427	24421	24415	24409	24403
386.0	24398	24392	24386	24380	24374	24368	24362	24356	24350	24344
387.0	24338	24332	24326	24320	24314	24308	24302	24296	24290	24284
388.0	24278	24273	24267	24261	24255	24249	24243	24237	24231	24225
389.0	24219	24213	24207	24201	24195	24189	24184	24178	24172	24166
390.0	24160	24154	24148	24142	24136	24130	24124	24118	24113	24107
391.0	24101	24095	24089	24083	24077	24071	24065	24059	24054	24048
392.0	24042	24036	24030	24024	24018	24012	24006	24001	23995	23989
393.0	23983	23977	23971	23965	23959	23954	23948	23942	23936	23930
394.0	23924	23918	23912	23907	23901	23895	23889	23883	23877	23871
395.0	23866	23860	23854	23848	23842	23836	23830	23825	23819	23813
396.0	23807	23801	23795	23790	23784	23778	23772	23766	23760	23755
397.0	23749	23743	23737	23731	23725	23720	23714	23708	23702	23696
398.0	23690	23685	23679	23673	23667	23661	23656	23650	23644	23638
399.0	23632	23626	23621	23615	23609	23603	23597	23592	23586	23580
400.0	23574	23568	23563	23557	23551	23545	23539	23534	23528	23522
401.0	23516	23511	23505	23499	23493	23487	23482	23476	23470	23464
402.0	23459	23453	23447	23441	23435	23430	23424	23418	23412	23407
403.0	23401	23395	23389	23384	23378	23372	23366	23361	23355	23349
404.0	23343	23338	23332	23326	23320	23315	23309	23303	23297	23292
405.0	23286	23280	23274	23269	23263	23257	23251	23246	23240	23234
406.0	23229	23223	23217	23211	23206	23200	23194	23188	23183	23177
407.0	23171	23166	23160	23154	23148	23143	23137	23131	23126	23120
408.0	23114	23109	23103	23097	23091	23086	23080	23074	23069	23063
409.0	23057	23052	23046	23040	23034	23029	23023	23017	23012	23006
410.0	23000	22995	22989	22983	22978	22972	22966	22961	22955	22949
411.0	22944	22938	22932	22927	22921	22915	22910	22904	22898	22893
412.0	22887	22881	22876	22870	22864	22859	22853	22847	22842	22836
413.0	22830	22825	22819	22813	22808	22802	22797	22791	22785	22780
414.0	22774	22768	22763	22757	22751	22746	22740	22735	22729	22723
415.0	22718	22712	22706	22701	22695	22690	22684	22678	22673	22667
416.0	22661	22656	22650	22645	22639	22633	22628	22622	22617	22611
417.0	22605	22600	22594	22589	22583	22577	22572	22566	22561	22555
418.0	22549	22544	22538	22533	22527	22521	22516	22510	22505	22499
419.0	22493	22488	22483	22477	22471	22466	22460	22454	22449	22443

TABLE VII - Continued

GEOPOTENTIAL ALTITUDE IN FEET as a function of PRESSURE IN MILLIBARS

P, mb	0.0	0.1	0.2	0.3	0.4	0.5	0.6	0.7	0.8	0.9
420.0	22438	22432	22427	22421	22415	22410	22404	22399	22393	22388
421.0	22382	22376	22371	22365	22360	22354	22349	22343	22338	22332
422.0	22326	22321	22315	22310	22304	22299	22293	22288	22282	22277
423.0	22271	22265	22260	22254	22249	22243	22238	22232	22227	22221
424.0	22216	22210	22205	22199	22194	22188	22182	22177	22171	22166
425.0	22160	22155	22149	22144	22138	22133	22127	22122	22116	22111
426.0	22105	22100	22094	22089	22083	22078	22072	22067	22061	22056
427.0	22050	22045	22039	22034	22028	22023	22017	22012	22006	22001
428.0	21995	21990	21984	21979	21973	21968	21962	21957	21951	21946
429.0	21940	21935	21930	21924	21919	21913	21908	21902	21897	21891
430.0	21886	21880	21875	21869	21864	21858	21853	21848	21842	21837
431.0	21831	21826	21820	21815	21809	21804	21798	21793	21788	21782
432.0	21777	21771	21766	21760	21755	21749	21744	21739	21733	21728
433.0	21722	21717	21711	21706	21700	21695	21690	21684	21679	21673
434.0	21668	21662	21657	21652	21646	21641	21635	21630	21625	21619
435.0	21614	21608	21603	21597	21592	21587	21581	21576	21570	21565
436.0	21560	21554	21549	21543	21538	21533	21527	21522	21516	21511
437.0	21506	21500	21495	21489	21484	21479	21473	21468	21462	21457
438.0	21452	21446	21441	21435	21430	21425	21419	21414	21409	21403
439.0	21398	21392	21387	21382	21376	21371	21366	21360	21355	21349
440.0	21344	21339	21333	21328	21323	21317	21312	21307	21301	21296
441.0	21291	21285	21280	21274	21269	21264	21258	21253	21248	21242
442.0	21237	21232	21226	21221	21216	21210	21205	21200	21194	21189
443.0	21184	21178	21173	21168	21162	21157	21152	21146	21141	21136
444.0	21130	21125	21120	21114	21109	21104	21098	21093	21088	21082
445.0	21077	21072	21066	21061	21056	21050	21045	21040	21035	21029
446.0	21024	21019	21013	21008	21003	20997	20992	20987	20981	20976
447.0	20971	20966	20960	20955	20950	20944	20939	20934	20929	20923
448.0	20918	20913	20907	20902	20897	20892	20886	20881	20876	20870
449.0	20865	20860	20855	20849	20844	20839	20833	20828	20823	20818
450.0	20812	20807	20802	20797	20791	20786	20781	20776	20770	20765
451.0	20760	20754	20749	20744	20739	20733	20728	20723	20718	20712
452.0	20707	20702	20697	20691	20686	20681	20676	20670	20665	20660
453.0	20655	20649	20644	20639	20634	20629	20623	20618	20613	20608
454.0	20602	20597	20592	20587	20581	20576	20571	20566	20561	20555
455.0	20550	20545	20540	20534	20529	20524	20519	20514	20508	20503
456.0	20498	20493	20487	20482	20477	20472	20467	20461	20456	20451
457.0	20446	20441	20435	20430	20425	20420	20415	20409	20404	20399
458.0	20394	20389	20383	20378	20373	20368	20363	20357	20352	20347
459.0	20342	20337	20332	20326	20321	20316	20311	20306	20300	20295
460.0	20290	20285	20280	20275	20269	20264	20259	20254	20249	20244
461.0	20238	20233	20228	20223	20218	20213	20207	20202	20197	20192
462.0	20187	20182	20176	20171	20166	20161	20156	20151	20146	20140
463.0	20135	20130	20125	20120	20115	20109	20104	20099	20094	20089
464.0	20084	20079	20073	20068	20063	20058	20053	20048	20043	20038
465.0	20032	20027	20022	20017	20012	20007	20002	19997	19991	19986
466.0	19981	19976	19971	19966	19961	19956	19950	19945	19940	19935
467.0	19930	19925	19920	19915	19910	19904	19899	19894	19889	19884
468.0	19879	19874	19869	19864	19858	19853	19848	19843	19838	19833
469.0	19828	19823	19818	19813	19807	19802	19797	19792	19787	19782
470.0	19777	19772	19767	19762	19757	19752	19746	19741	19736	19731
471.0	19726	19721	19716	19711	19706	19701	19696	19691	19686	19680
472.0	19675	19670	19665	19660	19655	19650	19645	19640	19635	19630
473.0	19625	19620	19615	19610	19605	19599	19594	19589	19584	19579
474.0	19574	19569	19564	19559	19554	19549	19544	19539	19534	19529
475.0	19524	19519	19514	19509	19504	19498	19493	19488	19483	19478
476.0	19473	19468	19463	19458	19453	19448	19443	19438	19433	19428
477.0	19423	19418	19413	19408	19403	19398	19393	19388	19383	19378
478.0	19373	19368	19363	19358	19353	19348	19343	19338	19333	19328
479.0	19323	19318	19313	19308	19303	19298	19293	19288	19283	19278
480.0	19273	19268	19263	19258	19253	19248	19243	19238	19233	19228
481.0	19223	19218	19213	19208	19203	19198	19193	19188	19183	19178
482.0	19173	19168	19163	19158	19153	19148	19143	19138	19133	19128
483.0	19123	19118	19113	19108	19103	19098	19093	19088	19083	19078
484.0	19073	19068	19063	19058	19053	19048	19043	19038	19033	19029
485.0	19024	19019	19014	19009	19004	18999	18994	18989	18984	18979
486.0	18974	18969	18964	18959	18954	18949	18944	18939	18934	18929
487.0	18925	18920	18915	18910	18905	18900	18895	18890	18885	18880
488.0	18875	18870	18865	18860	18855	18850	18846	18841	18836	18831
489.0	18826	18821	18816	18811	18806	18801	18796	18791	18786	18782
490.0	18777	18772	18767	18762	18757	18752	18747	18742	18737	18732
491.0	18727	18723	18718	18713	18708	18703	18698	18693	18688	18683
492.0	18678	18674	18669	18664	18659	18654	18649	18644	18639	18634
493.0	18629	18625	18620	18615	18610	18605	18600	18595	18590	18585
494.0	18581	18576	18571	18566	18561	18556	18551	18546	18541	18537
495.0	18532	18527	18522	18517	18512	18507	18502	18498	18493	18488
496.0	18483	18478	18473	18468	18464	18459	18454	18449	18444	18439
497.0	18434	18429	18425	18420	18415	18410	18405	18400	18395	18391
498.0	18386	18381	18376	18371	18366	18361	18357	18352	18347	18342
499.0	18337	18332	18328	18323	18318	18313	18308	18303	18298	18294
500.0	18289	18284	18279	18274	18269	18265	18260	18255	18250	18245
501.0	18240	18236	18231	18226	18221	18216	18211	18207	18202	18197
502.0	18192	18187	18183	18178	18173	18168	18163	18158	18154	18149
503.0	18144	18139	18134	18130	18125	18120	18115	18110	18106	18101
504.0	18096	18091	18086	18081	18077	18072	18067	18062	18057	18053
505.0	18048	18043	18038	18033	18029	18024	18019	18014	18009	18005
506.0	18000	17995	17990	17986	17981	17976	17971	17966	17962	17957
507.0	17952	17947	17942	17938	17933	17928	17923	17919	17914	17909
508.0	17904	17899	17895	17890	17885	17880	17876	17871	17866	17861
509.0	17856	17852	17847	17842	17837	17833	17828	17823	17818	17814
510.0	17809	17804	17799	17795	17790	17785	17780	17776	17771	17766
511.0	17761	17756	17752	17747	17742	17737	17733	17728	17723	17718
512.0	17714	17709	17704	17700	17695	17690	17685	17681	17676	17671
513.0	17666	17662	17657	17652	17647	17643	17638	17633	17628	17624
514.0	17619	17614	17610	17605	17600	17595	17591	17586	17581	17576
515.0	17572	17567	17562	17558	17553	17548	17543	17539	17534	17529
516.0	17524	17520	17515	17510	17506	17501	17496	17491	17487	17482
517.0	17477	17473	17468	17463	17459	17454	17449	17444	17440	17435
518.0	17430	17426	17421	17416	17412	17407	17402	17397	17393	17388
519.0	17383	17379	17374	17369	17365	17360	17355	17350	17346	17341

TABLE VII - Continued

GEOPOTENTIAL ALTITUDE IN FEET as a function of PRESSURE IN MILLIBARS

P, mb	0.0	0.1	0.2	0.3	0.4	0.5	0.6	0.7	0.8	0.9
520.0	17336	17332	17327	17322	17318	17313	17308	17304	17299	17294
521.0	17290	17285	17280	17276	17271	17266	17262	17257	17252	17247
522.0	17243	17238	17233	17229	17224	17219	17215	17210	17205	17201
523.0	17196	17191	17187	17182	17177	17173	17168	17163	17159	17154
524.0	17150	17145	17140	17136	17131	17126	17122	17117	17112	17108
525.0	17103	17098	17094	17089	17084	17080	17075	17070	17066	17061
526.0	17056	17052	17047	17043	17038	17033	17029	17024	17019	17015
527.0	17010	17005	17001	16996	16992	16987	16982	16978	16973	16968
528.0	16964	16959	16954	16950	16945	16941	16936	16931	16927	16922
529.0	16917	16913	16908	16904	16899	16894	16890	16885	16881	16876
530.0	16871	16867	16862	16857	16853	16848	16844	16839	16834	16830
531.0	16825	16821	16816	16811	16807	16802	16798	16793	16788	16784
532.0	16779	16775	16770	16765	16761	16756	16752	16747	16742	16738
533.0	16733	16729	16724	16719	16715	16710	16706	16701	16696	16692
534.0	16687	16683	16678	16673	16669	16664	16660	16655	16651	16646
535.0	16641	16637	16632	16628	16623	16618	16614	16609	16605	16600
536.0	16596	16591	16586	16582	16577	16573	16568	16564	16559	16554
537.0	16550	16545	16541	16536	16532	16527	16523	16518	16513	16509
538.0	16504	16500	16495	16491	16486	16481	16477	16472	16468	16463
539.0	16459	16454	16450	16445	16441	16436	16431	16427	16422	16418
540.0	16413	16409	16404	16400	16395	16391	16386	16381	16377	16372
541.0	16368	16363	16359	16354	16350	16345	16341	16336	16332	16327
542.0	16322	16318	16313	16309	16304	16300	16295	16291	16286	16282
543.0	16277	16273	16268	16264	16259	16255	16250	16245	16241	16236
544.0	16232	16227	16223	16218	16214	16209	16205	16200	16196	16191
545.0	16187	16182	16178	16173	16169	16164	16160	16155	16151	16146
546.0	16142	16137	16133	16128	16124	16119	16115	16110	16106	16101
547.0	16097	16092	16088	16083	16079	16074	16070	16065	16061	16056
548.0	16052	16047	16043	16038	16034	16029	16025	16020	16016	16011
549.0	16007	16002	15998	15993	15989	15984	15980	15975	15971	15966
550.0	15962	15957	15953	15949	15944	15940	15935	15931	15926	15922
551.0	15917	15913	15908	15904	15899	15895	15890	15886	15881	15877
552.0	15873	15868	15864	15859	15855	15850	15846	15841	15837	15832
553.0	15828	15823	15819	15815	15810	15806	15801	15797	15792	15788
554.0	15783	15779	15774	15770	15766	15761	15757	15752	15748	15743
555.0	15739	15734	15730	15726	15721	15717	15712	15708	15703	15699
556.0	15694	15690	15686	15681	15677	15672	15668	15663	15659	15654
557.0	15650	15646	15641	15637	15632	15628	15623	15619	15615	15610
558.0	15606	15601	15597	15592	15588	15584	15579	15575	15570	15566
559.0	15562	15557	15553	15548	15544	15539	15535	15531	15526	15522
560.0	15517	15513	15508	15504	15500	15495	15491	15486	15482	15478
561.0	15473	15469	15464	15460	15456	15451	15447	15442	15438	15434
562.0	15429	15425	15420	15416	15412	15407	15403	15398	15394	15390
563.0	15385	15381	15376	15372	15368	15363	15359	15354	15350	15346
564.0	15341	15337	15332	15328	15324	15319	15315	15311	15306	15302
565.0	15297	15293	15289	15284	15280	15275	15271	15267	15262	15258
566.0	15254	15249	15245	15240	15236	15232	15227	15223	15219	15214
567.0	15210	15206	15201	15197	15192	15188	15184	15179	15175	15171
568.0	15166	15162	15157	15153	15149	15144	15140	15136	15131	15127
569.0	15123	15118	15114	15110	15105	15101	15096	15092	15088	15083
570.0	15079	15075	15070	15066	15062	15057	15053	15049	15044	15040
571.0	15036	15031	15027	15023	15018	15014	15010	15005	15001	14996
572.0	14992	14988	14983	14979	14975	14970	14966	14962	14957	14953
573.0	14949	14944	14940	14936	14931	14927	14923	14918	14914	14910
574.0	14905	14901	14897	14893	14888	14884	14880	14875	14871	14867
575.0	14862	14858	14854	14849	14845	14841	14836	14832	14828	14823
576.0	14819	14815	14810	14806	14802	14798	14793	14789	14785	14780
577.0	14776	14772	14767	14763	14759	14754	14750	14746	14742	14737
578.0	14733	14729	14724	14720	14716	14711	14707	14703	14698	14694
579.0	14690	14686	14681	14677	14673	14668	14664	14660	14656	14651
580.0	14647	14643	14638	14634	14630	14626	14621	14617	14613	14608
581.0	14604	14600	14596	14591	14587	14583	14578	14574	14570	14566
582.0	14561	14557	14553	14548	14544	14540	14536	14531	14527	14523
583.0	14519	14514	14510	14506	14501	14497	14493	14489	14484	14480
584.0	14476	14472	14467	14463	14459	14454	14450	14446	14442	14437
585.0	14433	14429	14425	14420	14416	14412	14408	14403	14399	14395
586.0	14391	14386	14382	14378	14374	14369	14365	14361	14357	14352
587.0	14348	14344	14340	14335	14331	14327	14323	14318	14314	14310
588.0	14306	14301	14297	14293	14289	14284	14280	14276	14272	14267
589.0	14263	14259	14255	14251	14246	14242	14238	14234	14229	14225
590.0	14221	14217	14212	14208	14204	14200	14195	14191	14187	14183
591.0	14179	14174	14170	14166	14162	14157	14153	14149	14145	14141
592.0	14136	14132	14128	14124	14119	14115	14111	14107	14103	14098
593.0	14094	14090	14086	14082	14077	14073	14069	14065	14060	14056
594.0	14052	14048	14044	14039	14035	14031	14027	14023	14018	14014
595.0	14010	14006	14002	13997	13993	13989	13985	13981	13976	13972
596.0	13968	13964	13960	13955	13951	13947	13943	13939	13934	13930
597.0	13926	13922	13918	13914	13909	13905	13901	13897	13893	13888
598.0	13884	13880	13876	13872	13867	13863	13859	13855	13851	13847
599.0	13842	13838	13834	13830	13826	13821	13817	13813	13809	13805
600.0	13801	13796	13792	13788	13784	13780	13776	13771	13767	13763
601.0	13759	13755	13751	13746	13742	13738	13734	13730	13726	13721
602.0	13717	13713	13709	13705	13701	13696	13692	13688	13684	13680
603.0	13676	13671	13667	13663	13659	13655	13651	13647	13642	13638
604.0	13634	13630	13626	13622	13617	13613	13609	13605	13601	13597
605.0	13593	13588	13584	13580	13576	13572	13568	13564	13559	13555
606.0	13551	13547	13543	13539	13535	13530	13526	13522	13518	13514
607.0	13510	13506	13501	13497	13493	13489	13485	13481	13477	13473
608.0	13468	13464	13460	13456	13452	13448	13444	13440	13435	13431
609.0	13427	13423	13419	13415	13411	13407	13402	13398	13394	13390
610.0	13386	13382	13378	13374	13369	13365	13361	13357	13353	13349
611.0	13345	13341	13337	13332	13328	13324	13320	13316	13312	13308
612.0	13304	13300	13295	13291	13287	13283	13279	13275	13271	13267
613.0	13263	13259	13254	13250	13246	13242	13238	13234	13230	13226
614.0	13222	13218	13213	13209	13205	13201	13197	13193	13189	13185
615.0	13181	13177	13172	13168	13164	13160	13156	13152	13148	13144
616.0	13140	13136	13132	13128	13123	13119	13115	13111	13107	13103
617.0	13099	13095	13091	13087	13083	13079	13074	13070	13066	13062
618.0	13058	13054	13050	13046	13042	13038	13034	13030	13026	13021
619.0	13017	13013	13009	13005	13001	12997	12993	12989	12985	12981

TABLE VII - Continued

GEOPOTENTIAL ALTITUDE IN FEET as a function of PRESSURE IN MILLIBARS

P, mb	0.0	0.1	0.2	0.3	0.4	0.5	0.6	0.7	0.8	0.9
620.0	12977	12973	12969	12965	12960	12956	12952	12948	12944	12940
621.0	12936	12932	12928	12924	12920	12916	12912	12908	12904	12900
622.0	12896	12891	12887	12883	12879	12875	12871	12867	12863	12859
623.0	12855	12851	12847	12843	12839	12835	12831	12827	12823	12819
624.0	12815	12811	12806	12802	12798	12794	12790	12786	12782	12778
625.0	12774	12770	12766	12762	12758	12754	12750	12746	12742	12738
626.0	12734	12730	12726	12722	12718	12714	12710	12706	12702	12698
627.0	12693	12689	12685	12681	12677	12673	12669	12665	12661	12657
628.0	12653	12649	12645	12641	12637	12633	12629	12625	12621	12617
629.0	12613	12609	12605	12601	12597	12593	12589	12585	12581	12577
630.0	12573	12569	12565	12561	12557	12553	12549	12545	12541	12537
631.0	12533	12529	12525	12521	12517	12513	12509	12505	12501	12497
632.0	12493	12489	12485	12481	12477	12473	12469	12465	12461	12457
633.0	12453	12449	12445	12441	12437	12433	12429	12425	12421	12417
634.0	12413	12409	12405	12401	12397	12393	12389	12385	12381	12377
635.0	12373	12369	12365	12361	12357	12353	12349	12345	12341	12337
636.0	12333	12329	12325	12321	12317	12313	12309	12305	12301	12297
637.0	12293	12289	12285	12281	12277	12273	12269	12265	12261	12257
638.0	12253	12250	12246	12242	12238	12234	12230	12226	12222	12218
639.0	12214	12210	12206	12202	12198	12194	12190	12186	12182	12178
640.0	12174	12170	12166	12162	12158	12154	12150	12146	12142	12139
641.0	12135	12131	12127	12123	12119	12115	12111	12107	12103	12099
642.0	12095	12091	12087	12083	12079	12075	12071	12067	12063	12059
643.0	12056	12052	12048	12044	12040	12036	12032	12028	12024	12020
644.0	12016	12012	12008	12004	12000	11996	11992	11988	11985	11981
645.0	11977	11973	11969	11965	11961	11957	11953	11949	11945	11941
646.0	11937	11933	11929	11926	11922	11918	11914	11910	11906	11902
647.0	11898	11894	11890	11886	11882	11878	11874	11871	11867	11863
648.0	11859	11855	11851	11847	11843	11839	11835	11831	11827	11824
649.0	11820	11816	11812	11808	11804	11800	11796	11792	11788	11784
650.0	11780	11777	11773	11769	11765	11761	11757	11753	11749	11745
651.0	11741	11737	11734	11730	11726	11722	11718	11714	11710	11706
652.0	11702	11698	11694	11691	11687	11683	11679	11675	11671	11667
653.0	11663	11659	11655	11652	11648	11644	11640	11636	11632	11628
654.0	11624	11620	11617	11613	11609	11605	11601	11597	11593	11589
655.0	11585	11582	11578	11574	11570	11566	11562	11558	11554	11550
656.0	11547	11543	11539	11535	11531	11527	11523	11519	11516	11512
657.0	11508	11504	11500	11496	11492	11488	11485	11481	11477	11473
658.0	11469	11465	11461	11457	11454	11450	11446	11442	11438	11434
659.0	11430	11426	11423	11419	11415	11411	11407	11403	11399	11395
660.0	11392	11388	11384	11380	11376	11372	11368	11365	11361	11357
661.0	11353	11349	11345	11341	11338	11334	11330	11326	11322	11318
662.0	11314	11311	11307	11303	11299	11295	11291	11287	11284	11280
663.0	11276	11272	11268	11264	11261	11257	11253	11249	11245	11241
664.0	11237	11234	11230	11226	11222	11218	11214	11211	11207	11203
665.0	11199	11195	11191	11187	11184	11180	11176	11172	11168	11164
666.0	11161	11157	11153	11149	11145	11141	11138	11134	11130	11126
667.0	11122	11118	11115	11111	11107	11103	11099	11095	11092	11088
668.0	11084	11080	11076	11072	11069	11065	11061	11057	11053	11050
669.0	11046	11042	11038	11034	11030	11027	11023	11019	11015	11011
670.0	11008	11004	11000	10996	10992	10988	10985	10981	10977	10973
671.0	10969	10966	10962	10958	10954	10950	10947	10943	10939	10935
672.0	10931	10927	10924	10920	10916	10912	10908	10905	10901	10897
673.0	10893	10889	10886	10882	10878	10874	10870	10867	10863	10859
674.0	10855	10851	10848	10844	10840	10836	10832	10829	10825	10821
675.0	10817	10813	10810	10806	10802	10798	10794	10791	10787	10783
676.0	10779	10776	10772	10768	10764	10760	10757	10753	10749	10745
677.0	10741	10738	10734	10730	10726	10722	10719	10715	10711	10707
678.0	10704	10700	10696	10692	10688	10685	10681	10677	10673	10670
679.0	10666	10662	10658	10654	10651	10647	10643	10639	10636	10632
680.0	10628	10624	10621	10617	10613	10609	10605	10602	10598	10594
681.0	10590	10587	10583	10579	10575	10572	10568	10564	10560	10556
682.0	10553	10549	10545	10541	10538	10534	10530	10526	10523	10519
683.0	10515	10511	10508	10504	10500	10496	10493	10489	10485	10481
684.0	10478	10474	10470	10466	10463	10459	10455	10451	10448	10444
685.0	10440	10436	10433	10429	10425	10421	10418	10414	10410	10406
686.0	10403	10399	10395	10391	10388	10384	10380	10376	10373	10369
687.0	10365	10361	10358	10354	10350	10346	10343	10339	10335	10331
688.0	10328	10324	10320	10317	10313	10309	10305	10302	10298	10294
689.0	10290	10287	10283	10279	10275	10272	10268	10264	10261	10257
690.0	10253	10249	10246	10242	10238	10234	10231	10227	10223	10220
691.0	10216	10212	10208	10205	10201	10197	10193	10190	10186	10182
692.0	10179	10175	10171	10167	10164	10160	10156	10153	10149	10145
693.0	10141	10138	10134	10130	10127	10123	10119	10115	10112	10108
694.0	10104	10101	10097	10093	10089	10086	10082	10078	10075	10071
695.0	10067	10064	10060	10056	10052	10049	10045	10041	10038	10034
696.0	10030	10026	10023	10019	10015	10012	10008	10004	10001	9997
697.0	9993	9990	9986	9982	9978	9975	9971	9967	9964	9960
698.0	9956	9953	9949	9945	9941	9938	9934	9930	9927	9923
699.0	9919	9916	9912	9908	9905	9901	9897	9894	9890	9886
700.0	9882	9879	9875	9871	9868	9864	9860	9857	9853	9849
701.0	9846	9842	9838	9835	9831	9827	9824	9820	9816	9813
702.0	9809	9805	9802	9798	9794	9790	9787	9783	9779	9776
703.0	9772	9768	9765	9761	9757	9754	9750	9746	9743	9739
704.0	9735	9732	9728	9724	9721	9717	9713	9710	9706	9702
705.0	9699	9695	9691	9688	9684	9680	9677	9673	9669	9666
706.0	9662	9659	9655	9651	9648	9644	9640	9637	9633	9629
707.0	9626	9622	9618	9615	9611	9607	9604	9600	9596	9593
708.0	9589	9585	9582	9578	9574	9571	9567	9564	9560	9556
709.0	9553	9549	9545	9542	9538	9534	9531	9527	9523	9520
710.0	9516	9512	9509	9505	9502	9498	9494	9491	9487	9483
711.0	9480	9476	9472	9469	9465	9462	9458	9454	9451	9447
712.0	9443	9440	9436	9432	9429	9425	9422	9418	9414	9411
713.0	9407	9403	9400	9396	9393	9389	9385	9382	9378	9374
714.0	9371	9367	9364	9360	9356	9353	9349	9345	9342	9338
715.0	9335	9331	9327	9324	9320	9316	9313	9309	9306	9302
716.0	9298	9295	9291	9287	9284	9280	9277	9273	9269	9266
717.0	9262	9259	9255	9251	9248	9244	9240	9237	9233	9230
718.0	9226	9222	9219	9215	9212	9208	9204	9201	9197	9194
719.0	9190	9186	9183	9179	9176	9172	9168	9165	9161	9158

TABLE VII- Continued

GEOPOTENTIAL ALTITUDE IN FEET as a function of PRESSURE IN MILLIBARS

P, mb	0.0	0.1	0.2	0.3	0.4	0.5	0.6	0.7	0.8	0.9
720.0	9154	9150	9147	9143	9140	9136	9132	9129	9125	9122
721.0	9118	9114	9111	9107	9104	9100	9096	9093	9089	9086
722.0	9082	9078	9075	9071	9068	9064	9060	9057	9053	9050
723.0	9046	9042	9039	9035	9032	9028	9025	9021	9017	9014
724.0	9010	9007	9003	8999	8996	8992	8989	8985	8982	8978
725.0	8974	8971	8967	8964	8960	8956	8953	8949	8946	8942
726.0	8939	8935	8931	8928	8924	8921	8917	8914	8910	8906
727.0	8903	8899	8896	8892	8889	8885	8881	8878	8874	8871
728.0	8867	8864	8860	8856	8853	8849	8846	8842	8839	8835
729.0	8831	8828	8824	8821	8817	8814	8810	8806	8803	8799
730.0	8796	8792	8789	8785	8782	8778	8774	8771	8767	8764
731.0	8760	8757	8753	8750	8746	8742	8739	8735	8732	8728
732.0	8725	8721	8718	8714	8710	8707	8703	8700	8696	8693
733.0	8689	8686	8682	8678	8675	8671	8668	8664	8661	8657
734.0	8654	8650	8647	8643	8639	8636	8632	8629	8625	8622
735.0	8618	8615	8611	8608	8604	8601	8597	8593	8590	8586
736.0	8583	8579	8576	8572	8569	8565	8562	8558	8555	8551
737.0	8547	8544	8540	8537	8533	8530	8526	8523	8519	8516
738.0	8512	8509	8505	8502	8498	8494	8491	8487	8484	8480
739.0	8477	8473	8470	8466	8463	8459	8456	8452	8449	8445
740.0	8442	8438	8435	8431	8428	8424	8420	8417	8413	8410
741.0	8406	8403	8399	8396	8392	8389	8385	8382	8378	8375
742.0	8371	8368	8364	8361	8357	8354	8350	8347	8343	8340
743.0	8336	8333	8329	8326	8322	8319	8315	8312	8308	8305
744.0	8301	8298	8294	8290	8287	8283	8280	8276	8273	8269
745.0	8266	8262	8259	8255	8252	8248	8245	8241	8238	8234
746.0	8231	8227	8224	8220	8217	8213	8210	8206	8203	8199
747.0	8196	8192	8189	8185	8182	8178	8175	8172	8168	8165
748.0	8161	8158	8154	8151	8147	8144	8140	8137	8133	8130
749.0	8126	8123	8119	8116	8112	8109	8105	8102	8098	8095
750.0	8091	8088	8084	8081	8077	8074	8070	8067	8063	8060
751.0	8056	8053	8049	8046	8043	8039	8036	8032	8029	8025
752.0	8022	8018	8015	8011	8008	8004	8001	7997	7994	7990
753.0	7987	7983	7980	7976	7973	7970	7966	7963	7959	7956
754.0	7952	7949	7945	7942	7938	7935	7931	7928	7924	7921
755.0	7918	7914	7911	7907	7904	7900	7897	7893	7890	7886
756.0	7883	7879	7876	7873	7869	7866	7862	7859	7855	7852
757.0	7848	7845	7841	7838	7834	7831	7828	7824	7821	7817
758.0	7814	7810	7807	7803	7800	7796	7793	7790	7786	7783
759.0	7779	7776	7772	7769	7765	7762	7758	7755	7752	7748
760.0	7745	7741	7738	7734	7731	7727	7724	7721	7717	7714
761.0	7710	7707	7703	7700	7696	7693	7690	7686	7683	7679
762.0	7676	7672	7669	7666	7662	7659	7655	7652	7648	7645
763.0	7641	7638	7635	7631	7628	7624	7621	7617	7614	7611
764.0	7607	7604	7600	7597	7593	7590	7587	7583	7580	7576
765.0	7573	7569	7566	7563	7559	7556	7552	7549	7545	7542
766.0	7539	7535	7532	7528	7525	7521	7518	7515	7511	7508
767.0	7504	7501	7497	7494	7491	7487	7484	7480	7477	7474
768.0	7470	7467	7463	7460	7456	7453	7450	7446	7443	7439
769.0	7436	7433	7429	7426	7422	7419	7415	7412	7409	7405
770.0	7402	7398	7395	7392	7388	7385	7381	7378	7375	7371
771.0	7368	7364	7361	7357	7354	7351	7347	7344	7340	7337
772.0	7334	7330	7327	7323	7320	7317	7313	7310	7306	7303
773.0	7300	7296	7293	7289	7286	7283	7279	7276	7272	7269
774.0	7266	7262	7259	7255	7252	7249	7245	7242	7238	7235
775.0	7232	7228	7225	7222	7218	7215	7211	7208	7205	7201
776.0	7198	7194	7191	7188	7184	7181	7177	7174	7171	7167
777.0	7164	7161	7157	7154	7150	7147	7144	7140	7137	7133
778.0	7130	7127	7123	7120	7117	7113	7110	7106	7103	7100
779.0	7096	7093	7090	7086	7083	7079	7076	7073	7069	7066
780.0	7062	7059	7056	7052	7049	7046	7042	7039	7035	7032
781.0	7029	7025	7022	7019	7015	7012	7009	7005	7002	6998
782.0	6995	6992	6988	6985	6982	6978	6975	6971	6968	6965
783.0	6961	6958	6955	6951	6948	6945	6941	6938	6934	6931
784.0	6928	6924	6921	6918	6914	6911	6908	6904	6901	6898
785.0	6894	6891	6887	6884	6881	6877	6874	6870	6867	6864
786.0	6861	6857	6854	6851	6847	6844	6840	6837	6834	6830
787.0	6827	6824	6820	6817	6814	6810	6807	6804	6800	6797
788.0	6794	6790	6787	6784	6780	6777	6773	6770	6767	6763
789.0	6760	6757	6753	6750	6747	6743	6740	6737	6733	6730
790.0	6727	6723	6720	6717	6713	6710	6707	6703	6700	6697
791.0	6693	6690	6687	6683	6680	6677	6673	6670	6667	6663
792.0	6660	6657	6653	6650	6647	6643	6640	6637	6633	6630
793.0	6627	6623	6620	6617	6613	6610	6607	6603	6600	6597
794.0	6593	6590	6587	6583	6580	6577	6573	6570	6567	6563
795.0	6560	6557	6553	6550	6547	6543	6540	6537	6533	6530
796.0	6527	6524	6520	6517	6514	6510	6507	6504	6500	6497
797.0	6494	6490	6487	6484	6480	6477	6474	6470	6467	6464
798.0	6461	6457	6454	6451	6447	6444	6441	6437	6434	6431
799.0	6427	6424	6421	6417	6414	6411	6408	6404	6401	6398
800.0	6394	6391	6388	6384	6381	6378	6374	6371	6368	6365
801.0	6361	6358	6355	6351	6348	6345	6341	6338	6335	6332
802.0	6328	6325	6322	6318	6315	6312	6308	6305	6302	6299
803.0	6295	6292	6289	6285	6282	6279	6275	6272	6269	6266
804.0	6262	6259	6256	6252	6249	6246	6243	6239	6236	6233
805.0	6229	6226	6223	6220	6216	6213	6210	6206	6203	6200
806.0	6196	6193	6190	6187	6183	6180	6177	6173	6170	6167
807.0	6164	6160	6157	6154	6151	6147	6144	6141	6137	6134
808.0	6131	6128	6124	6121	6118	6114	6111	6108	6105	6101
809.0	6098	6095	6091	6088	6085	6082	6078	6075	6072	6069
810.0	6065	6062	6059	6055	6052	6049	6046	6042	6039	6036
811.0	6033	6029	6026	6023	6019	6016	6013	6010	6006	6003
812.0	6000	5997	5993	5990	5987	5984	5980	5977	5974	5970
813.0	5967	5964	5961	5957	5954	5951	5948	5944	5941	5938
814.0	5935	5931	5928	5925	5922	5918	5915	5912	5908	5905
815.0	5902	5899	5895	5892	5889	5886	5882	5879	5876	5873
816.0	5869	5866	5863	5860	5856	5853	5850	5847	5843	5840
817.0	5837	5834	5830	5827	5824	5821	5817	5814	5811	5808
818.0	5804	5801	5798	5795	5791	5788	5785	5782	5778	5775
819.0	5772	5769	5765	5762	5759	5756	5752	5749	5746	5743

TABLE VII - Continued

GEOPOTENTIAL ALTITUDE IN FEET as a function of PRESSURE IN MILLIBARS

P, mb	0.0	0.1	0.2	0.3	0.4	0.5	0.6	0.7	0.8	0.9
820.0	5740	5736	5733	5730	5727	5723	5720	5717	5714	5710
821.0	5707	5704	5701	5697	5694	5691	5688	5684	5681	5678
822.0	5675	5672	5668	5665	5662	5659	5655	5652	5649	5646
823.0	5642	5639	5636	5633	5629	5626	5623	5620	5617	5613
824.0	5610	5607	5604	5600	5597	5594	5591	5588	5584	5581
825.0	5578	5575	5571	5568	5565	5562	5558	5555	5552	5549
826.0	5546	5542	5539	5536	5533	5529	5526	5523	5520	5517
827.0	5513	5510	5507	5504	5501	5497	5494	5491	5488	5484
828.0	5481	5478	5475	5472	5468	5465	5462	5459	5455	5452
829.0	5449	5446	5443	5439	5436	5433	5430	5427	5423	5420
830.0	5417	5414	5411	5407	5404	5401	5398	5394	5391	5388
831.0	5385	5382	5378	5375	5372	5369	5366	5362	5359	5356
832.0	5353	5350	5346	5343	5340	5337	5334	5330	5327	5324
833.0	5321	5318	5314	5311	5308	5305	5302	5298	5295	5292
834.0	5289	5286	5282	5279	5276	5273	5270	5266	5263	5260
835.0	5257	5254	5250	5247	5244	5241	5238	5234	5231	5228
836.0	5225	5222	5219	5215	5212	5209	5206	5203	5199	5196
837.0	5193	5190	5187	5183	5180	5177	5174	5171	5168	5164
838.0	5161	5158	5155	5152	5148	5145	5142	5139	5136	5133
839.0	5129	5126	5123	5120	5117	5113	5110	5107	5104	5101
840.0	5098	5094	5091	5088	5085	5082	5078	5075	5072	5069
841.0	5066	5063	5059	5056	5053	5050	5047	5044	5040	5037
842.0	5034	5031	5028	5024	5021	5018	5015	5012	5009	5005
843.0	5002	4999	4996	4993	4990	4986	4983	4980	4977	4974
844.0	4971	4967	4964	4961	4958	4955	4952	4948	4945	4942
845.0	4939	4936	4933	4929	4926	4923	4920	4917	4914	4910
846.0	4907	4904	4901	4898	4895	4892	4888	4885	4882	4879
847.0	4876	4873	4869	4866	4863	4860	4857	4854	4850	4847
848.0	4844	4841	4838	4835	4832	4828	4825	4822	4819	4816
849.0	4813	4810	4806	4803	4800	4797	4794	4791	4787	4784
850.0	4781	4778	4775	4772	4769	4765	4762	4759	4756	4753
851.0	4750	4747	4743	4740	4737	4734	4731	4728	4725	4721
852.0	4718	4715	4712	4709	4706	4703	4699	4696	4693	4690
853.0	4687	4684	4681	4677	4674	4671	4668	4665	4662	4659
854.0	4655	4652	4649	4646	4643	4640	4637	4634	4630	4627
855.0	4624	4621	4618	4615	4612	4608	4605	4602	4599	4596
856.0	4593	4590	4587	4583	4580	4577	4574	4571	4568	4565
857.0	4561	4558	4555	4552	4549	4546	4543	4540	4536	4533
858.0	4530	4527	4524	4521	4518	4515	4511	4508	4505	4502
859.0	4499	4496	4493	4490	4487	4483	4480	4477	4474	4471
860.0	4468	4465	4462	4458	4455	4452	4449	4446	4443	4440
861.0	4437	4433	4430	4427	4424	4421	4418	4415	4412	4409
862.0	4405	4402	4399	4396	4393	4390	4387	4384	4381	4377
863.0	4374	4371	4368	4365	4362	4359	4356	4353	4349	4346
864.0	4343	4340	4337	4334	4331	4328	4325	4322	4318	4315
865.0	4312	4309	4306	4303	4300	4297	4294	4290	4287	4284
866.0	4281	4278	4275	4272	4269	4266	4263	4259	4256	4253
867.0	4250	4247	4244	4241	4238	4235	4232	4229	4225	4222
868.0	4219	4216	4213	4210	4207	4204	4201	4198	4194	4191
869.0	4188	4185	4182	4179	4176	4173	4170	4167	4164	4160
870.0	4157	4154	4151	4148	4145	4142	4139	4136	4133	4130
871.0	4126	4123	4120	4117	4114	4111	4108	4105	4102	4099
872.0	4096	4093	4089	4086	4083	4080	4077	4074	4071	4068
873.0	4065	4062	4059	4056	4052	4049	4046	4043	4040	4037
874.0	4034	4031	4028	4025	4022	4019	4016	4012	4009	4006
875.0	4003	4000	3997	3994	3991	3988	3985	3982	3979	3976
876.0	3972	3969	3966	3963	3960	3957	3954	3951	3948	3945
877.0	3942	3939	3936	3933	3930	3926	3923	3920	3917	3914
878.0	3911	3908	3905	3902	3899	3896	3893	3890	3887	3884
879.0	3880	3877	3874	3871	3868	3865	3862	3859	3856	3853
880.0	3850	3847	3844	3841	3838	3835	3831	3828	3825	3822
881.0	3819	3816	3813	3810	3807	3804	3801	3798	3795	3792
882.0	3789	3786	3783	3779	3776	3773	3770	3767	3764	3761
883.0	3758	3755	3752	3749	3746	3743	3740	3737	3734	3731
884.0	3728	3725	3721	3718	3715	3712	3709	3706	3703	3700
885.0	3697	3694	3691	3688	3685	3682	3679	3676	3673	3670
886.0	3667	3664	3661	3658	3654	3651	3648	3645	3642	3639
887.0	3636	3633	3630	3627	3624	3621	3618	3615	3612	3609
888.0	3606	3603	3600	3597	3594	3591	3588	3585	3581	3578
889.0	3575	3572	3569	3566	3563	3560	3557	3554	3551	3548
890.0	3545	3542	3539	3536	3533	3530	3527	3524	3521	3518
891.0	3515	3512	3509	3506	3503	3500	3497	3494	3491	3487
892.0	3484	3481	3478	3475	3472	3469	3466	3463	3460	3457
893.0	3454	3451	3448	3445	3442	3439	3436	3433	3430	3427
894.0	3424	3421	3418	3415	3412	3409	3406	3403	3400	3397
895.0	3394	3391	3388	3385	3382	3379	3376	3373	3370	3367
896.0	3364	3361	3358	3355	3351	3348	3345	3342	3339	3336
897.0	3333	3330	3327	3324	3321	3318	3315	3312	3309	3306
898.0	3303	3300	3297	3294	3291	3288	3285	3282	3279	3276
899.0	3273	3270	3267	3264	3261	3258	3255	3252	3249	3246
900.0	3243	3240	3237	3234	3231	3228	3225	3222	3219	3216
901.0	3213	3210	3207	3204	3201	3198	3195	3192	3189	3186
902.0	3183	3180	3177	3174	3171	3168	3165	3162	3159	3156
903.0	3153	3150	3147	3144	3141	3138	3135	3132	3129	3126
904.0	3123	3120	3117	3114	3111	3108	3105	3102	3099	3096
905.0	3093	3090	3087	3084	3081	3078	3075	3072	3069	3066
906.0	3063	3060	3057	3054	3051	3048	3045	3042	3039	3036
907.0	3033	3030	3027	3024	3021	3018	3015	3012	3009	3006
908.0	3003	3000	2998	2995	2992	2989	2986	2983	2980	2977
909.0	2974	2971	2968	2965	2962	2959	2956	2953	2950	2947
910.0	2944	2941	2938	2935	2932	2929	2926	2923	2920	2917
911.0	2914	2911	2908	2905	2902	2899	2896	2893	2890	2887
912.0	2884	2881	2878	2875	2872	2869	2866	2863	2861	2858
913.0	2855	2852	2849	2846	2843	2840	2837	2834	2831	2828
914.0	2825	2822	2819	2816	2813	2810	2807	2804	2801	2798
915.0	2795	2792	2789	2786	2783	2780	2777	2774	2771	2769
916.0	2766	2763	2760	2757	2754	2751	2748	2745	2742	2739
917.0	2736	2733	2730	2727	2724	2721	2718	2715	2712	2709
918.0	2706	2703	2700	2697	2694	2692	2689	2686	2683	2680
919.0	2677	2674	2671	2668	2665	2662	2659	2656	2653	2650

TABLE VII- Continued

GEOPOTENTIAL ALTITUDE IN FEET as a function of PRESSURE IN MILLIBARS

P, mb	0.0	0.1	0.2	0.3	0.4	0.5	0.6	0.7	0.8	0.9
920.0	2647	2644	2641	2638	2635	2632	2629	2627	2624	2621
921.0	2618	2615	2612	2609	2606	2603	2600	2597	2594	2591
922.0	2588	2585	2582	2579	2576	2573	2571	2568	2565	2562
923.0	2559	2556	2553	2550	2547	2544	2541	2538	2535	2532
924.0	2529	2526	2523	2520	2518	2515	2512	2509	2506	2503
925.0	2500	2497	2494	2491	2488	2485	2482	2479	2476	2473
926.0	2470	2468	2465	2462	2459	2456	2453	2450	2447	2444
927.0	2441	2438	2435	2432	2429	2426	2424	2421	2418	2415
928.0	2412	2409	2406	2403	2400	2397	2394	2391	2388	2385
929.0	2382	2380	2377	2374	2371	2368	2365	2362	2359	2356
930.0	2353	2350	2347	2344	2341	2339	2336	2333	2330	2327
931.0	2324	2321	2318	2315	2312	2309	2306	2303	2301	2298
932.0	2295	2292	2289	2286	2283	2280	2277	2274	2271	2268
933.0	2265	2263	2260	2257	2254	2251	2248	2245	2242	2239
934.0	2236	2233	2230	2228	2225	2222	2219	2216	2213	2210
935.0	2207	2204	2201	2198	2195	2193	2190	2187	2184	2181
936.0	2178	2175	2172	2169	2166	2163	2161	2158	2155	2152
937.0	2149	2146	2143	2140	2137	2134	2131	2129	2126	2123
938.0	2120	2117	2114	2111	2108	2105	2102	2099	2097	2094
939.0	2091	2088	2085	2082	2079	2076	2073	2070	2068	2065
940.0	2062	2059	2056	2053	2050	2047	2044	2041	2039	2036
941.0	2033	2030	2027	2024	2021	2018	2015	2012	2010	2007
942.0	2004	2001	1998	1995	1992	1989	1986	1983	1981	1978
943.0	1975	1972	1969	1966	1963	1960	1957	1955	1952	1949
944.0	1946	1943	1940	1937	1934	1931	1928	1926	1923	1920
945.0	1917	1914	1911	1908	1905	1902	1900	1897	1894	1891
946.0	1888	1885	1882	1879	1876	1874	1871	1868	1865	1862
947.0	1859	1856	1853	1851	1848	1845	1842	1839	1836	1833
948.0	1830	1827	1825	1822	1819	1816	1813	1810	1807	1804
949.0	1802	1799	1796	1793	1790	1787	1784	1781	1779	1776
950.0	1773	1770	1767	1764	1761	1758	1755	1753	1750	1747
951.0	1744	1741	1738	1735	1732	1730	1727	1724	1721	1718
952.0	1715	1712	1710	1707	1704	1701	1698	1695	1692	1689
953.0	1687	1684	1681	1678	1675	1672	1669	1666	1664	1661
954.0	1658	1655	1652	1649	1646	1644	1641	1638	1635	1632
955.0	1629	1626	1623	1621	1618	1615	1612	1609	1606	1603
956.0	1601	1598	1595	1592	1589	1586	1583	1581	1578	1575
957.0	1572	1569	1566	1563	1560	1558	1555	1552	1549	1546
958.0	1543	1540	1538	1535	1532	1529	1526	1523	1520	1518
959.0	1515	1512	1509	1506	1503	1500	1498	1495	1492	1489
960.0	1486	1483	1481	1478	1475	1472	1469	1466	1463	1461
961.0	1458	1455	1452	1449	1446	1443	1441	1438	1435	1432
962.0	1429	1426	1424	1421	1418	1415	1412	1409	1406	1404
963.0	1401	1398	1395	1392	1389	1387	1384	1381	1378	1375
964.0	1372	1369	1367	1364	1361	1358	1355	1352	1350	1347
965.0	1344	1341	1338	1335	1333	1330	1327	1324	1321	1318
966.0	1315	1313	1310	1307	1304	1301	1298	1296	1293	1290
967.0	1287	1284	1281	1279	1276	1273	1270	1267	1264	1262
968.0	1259	1256	1253	1250	1247	1245	1242	1239	1236	1233
969.0	1230	1228	1225	1222	1219	1216	1213	1211	1208	1205
970.0	1202	1199	1196	1194	1191	1188	1185	1182	1179	1177
971.0	1174	1171	1168	1165	1163	1160	1157	1154	1151	1148
972.0	1146	1143	1140	1137	1134	1131	1129	1126	1123	1120
973.0	1117	1115	1112	1109	1106	1103	1100	1098	1095	1092
974.0	1089	1086	1084	1081	1078	1075	1072	1069	1067	1064
975.0	1061	1058	1055	1053	1050	1047	1044	1041	1038	1036
976.0	1033	1030	1027	1024	1022	1019	1016	1013	1010	1007
977.0	1005	1002	999	996	993	991	988	985	982	979
978.0	977	974	971	968	965	962	960	957	954	951
979.0	948	946	943	940	937	934	932	929	926	923
980.0	920	918	915	912	909	906	904	901	898	895
981.0	892	890	887	884	881	878	876	873	870	867
982.0	864	861	859	856	853	850	847	845	842	839
983.0	836	834	831	828	825	822	820	817	814	811
984.0	808	806	803	800	797	794	792	789	786	783
985.0	780	778	775	772	769	766	764	761	758	755
986.0	752	750	747	744	741	738	736	733	730	727
987.0	725	722	719	716	713	711	708	705	702	699
988.0	697	694	691	688	685	683	680	677	674	672
989.0	669	666	663	660	658	655	652	649	647	644
990.0	641	638	635	633	630	627	624	621	619	616
991.0	613	610	608	605	602	599	596	594	591	588
992.0	585	583	580	577	574	571	569	566	563	560
993.0	558	555	552	549	546	544	541	538	535	533
994.0	530	527	524	521	519	516	513	510	508	505
995.0	502	499	497	494	491	488	485	483	480	477
996.0	474	472	469	466	463	461	458	455	452	449
997.0	447	444	441	438	436	433	430	427	425	422
998.0	419	416	414	411	408	405	402	400	397	394
999.0	391	389	386	383	380	378	375	372	369	367
1000.0	364	361	358	356	353	350	347	344	342	339
1001.0	336	333	331	328	325	322	320	317	314	311
1002.0	309	306	303	300	298	295	292	289	287	284
1003.0	281	278	276	273	270	267	265	262	259	256
1004.0	254	251	248	245	243	240	237	234	232	229
1005.0	226	223	221	218	215	212	210	207	204	201
1006.0	199	196	193	190	188	185	182	179	177	174
1007.0	171	168	166	163	160	157	155	152	149	146
1008.0	144	141	138	135	133	130	127	124	122	119
1009.0	116	114	111	108	105	103	100	97	94	92
1010.0	89	86	83	81	78	75	72	70	67	64
1011.0	61	59	56	53	51	48	45	42	40	37
1012.0	34	31	29	26	23	20	18	15	12	10
1013.0	7	4	1	-1	-4	-7	-10	-12	-15	-18
1014.0	-20	-23	-26	-29	-31	-34	-37	-40	-42	-45
1015.0	-48	-50	-53	-56	-59	-61	-64	-67	-70	-72
1016.0	-75	-78	-80	-83	-86	-89	-91	-94	-97	-100
1017.0	-102	-105	-108	-110	-113	-116	-119	-121	-124	-127
1018.0	-129	-132	-135	-138	-140	-143	-146	-149	-151	-154
1019.0	-157	-159	-162	-165	-168	-170	-173	-176	-178	-181

TABLE VII - Continued

GEOPOTENTIAL ALTITUDE IN FEET as a function of PRESSURE IN MILLIBARS

P, mb	0.0	0.1	0.2	0.3	0.4	0.5	0.6	0.7	0.8	0.9
1020.0	-184	-187	-189	-192	-195	-197	-200	-203	-206	-208
1021.0	-211	-214	-216	-219	-222	-225	-227	-230	-233	-235
1022.0	-238	-241	-244	-246	-249	-252	-254	-257	-260	-263
1023.0	-265	-268	-271	-273	-276	-279	-282	-284	-287	-290
1024.0	-292	-295	-298	-300	-303	-306	-309	-311	-314	-317
1025.0	-319	-322	-325	-328	-330	-333	-336	-338	-341	-344
1026.0	-346	-349	-352	-355	-357	-360	-363	-365	-368	-371
1027.0	-373	-376	-379	-382	-384	-387	-390	-392	-395	-398
1028.0	-400	-403	-406	-409	-411	-414	-417	-419	-422	-425
1029.0	-427	-430	-433	-436	-438	-441	-444	-446	-449	-452
1030.0	-454	-457	-460	-463	-465	-468	-471	-473	-476	-479
1031.0	-481	-484	-487	-489	-492	-495	-498	-500	-503	-506
1032.0	-508	-511	-514	-516	-519	-522	-524	-527	-530	-532
1033.0	-535	-538	-541	-543	-546	-549	-551	-554	-557	-559
1034.0	-562	-565	-567	-570	-573	-575	-578	-581	-584	-586
1035.0	-589	-592	-594	-597	-600	-602	-605	-608	-610	-613
1036.0	-616	-618	-621	-624	-626	-629	-632	-635	-637	-640
1037.0	-643	-645	-648	-651	-653	-656	-659	-661	-664	-667
1038.0	-669	-672	-675	-677	-680	-683	-685	-688	-691	-693
1039.0	-696	-699	-701	-704	-707	-710	-712	-715	-718	-720
1040.0	-723	-726	-728	-731	-734	-736	-739	-742	-744	-747
1041.0	-750	-752	-755	-758	-760	-763	-766	-768	-771	-774
1042.0	-776	-779	-782	-784	-787	-790	-792	-795	-798	-800
1043.0	-803	-806	-808	-811	-814	-816	-819	-822	-824	-827
1044.0	-830	-832	-835	-838	-840	-843	-846	-848	-851	-854
1045.0	-856	-859	-862	-864	-867	-870	-872	-875	-878	-880
1046.0	-883	-886	-888	-891	-894	-896	-899	-902	-904	-907
1047.0	-910	-912	-915	-918	-920	-923	-926	-928	-931	-933
1048.0	-936	-939	-941	-944	-947	-949	-952	-955	-957	-960
1049.0	-963	-965	-968	-971	-973	-976	-979	-981	-984	-987
1050.0	-989	-992	-995	-997	-1000	-1003	-1005	-1008	-1010	-1013
1051.0	-1016	-1018	-1021	-1024	-1026	-1029	-1032	-1034	-1037	-1040
1052.0	-1042	-1045	-1048	-1050	-1053	-1056	-1058	-1061	-1063	-1066
1053.0	-1069	-1071	-1074	-1077	-1079	-1082	-1085	-1087	-1090	-1093
1054.0	-1095	-1098	-1101	-1103	-1106	-1108	-1111	-1114	-1116	-1119
1055.0	-1122	-1124	-1127	-1130	-1132	-1135	-1138	-1140	-1143	-1145
1056.0	-1148	-1151	-1153	-1156	-1159	-1161	-1164	-1167	-1169	-1172
1057.0	-1174	-1177	-1180	-1182	-1185	-1188	-1190	-1193	-1196	-1198
1058.0	-1201	-1203	-1206	-1209	-1211	-1214	-1217	-1219	-1222	-1225
1059.0	-1227	-1230	-1232	-1235	-1238	-1240	-1243	-1246	-1248	-1251
1060.0	-1254	-1256	-1259	-1261	-1264	-1267	-1269	-1272	-1275	-1277
1061.0	-1280	-1283	-1285	-1288	-1290	-1293	-1296	-1298	-1301	-1304
1062.0	-1306	-1309	-1311	-1314	-1317	-1319	-1322	-1325	-1327	-1330
1063.0	-1332	-1335	-1338	-1340	-1343	-1346	-1348	-1351	-1353	-1356
1064.0	-1359	-1361	-1364	-1367	-1369	-1372	-1374	-1377	-1380	-1382
1065.0	-1385	-1388	-1390	-1393	-1395	-1398	-1401	-1403	-1406	-1409
1066.0	-1411	-1414	-1416	-1419	-1422	-1424	-1427	-1430	-1432	-1435
1067.0	-1437	-1440	-1443	-1445	-1448	-1450	-1453	-1456	-1458	-1461
1068.0	-1464	-1466	-1469	-1471	-1474	-1477	-1479	-1482	-1485	-1487
1069.0	-1490	-1492	-1495	-1498	-1500	-1503	-1505	-1508	-1511	-1513
1070.0	-1516	-1518	-1521	-1524	-1526	-1529	-1532	-1534	-1537	-1539
1071.0	-1542	-1545	-1547	-1550	-1552	-1555	-1558	-1560	-1563	-1565
1072.0	-1568	-1571	-1573	-1576	-1579	-1581	-1584	-1586	-1589	-1592
1073.0	-1594	-1597	-1599	-1602	-1605	-1607	-1610	-1612	-1615	-1618
1074.0	-1620	-1623	-1625	-1628	-1631	-1633	-1636	-1638	-1641	-1644
1075.0	-1646	-1649	-1651	-1654	-1657	-1659	-1662	-1664	-1667	-1670
1076.0	-1672	-1675	-1678	-1680	-1683	-1685	-1688	-1691	-1693	-1696
1077.0	-1698	-1701	-1704	-1706	-1709	-1711	-1714	-1716	-1719	-1722
1078.0	-1724	-1727	-1729	-1732	-1735	-1737	-1740	-1742	-1745	-1748
1079.0	-1750	-1753	-1755	-1758	-1761	-1763	-1766	-1768	-1771	-1774
1080.0	-1776	-1779	-1781	-1784	-1787	-1789	-1792	-1794	-1797	-1800
1081.0	-1802	-1805	-1807	-1810	-1812	-1815	-1818	-1820	-1823	-1825
1082.0	-1828	-1831	-1833	-1836	-1838	-1841	-1844	-1846	-1849	-1851
1083.0	-1854	-1857	-1859	-1862	-1864	-1867	-1869	-1872	-1875	-1877
1084.0	-1880	-1882	-1885	-1888	-1890	-1893	-1895	-1898	-1900	-1903
1085.0	-1906	-1908	-1911	-1913	-1916	-1919	-1921	-1924	-1926	-1929
1086.0	-1931	-1934	-1937	-1939	-1942	-1944	-1947	-1950	-1952	-1955
1087.0	-1957	-1960	-1962	-1965	-1968	-1970	-1973	-1975	-1978	-1980
1088.0	-1983	-1986	-1988	-1991	-1993	-1996	-1999	-2001	-2004	-2006
1089.0	-2009	-2011	-2014	-2017	-2019	-2022	-2024	-2027	-2029	-2032
1090.0	-2035	-2037	-2040	-2042	-2045	-2047	-2050	-2053	-2055	-2058
1091.0	-2060	-2063	-2065	-2068	-2071	-2073	-2076	-2078	-2081	-2083
1092.0	-2086	-2089	-2091	-2094	-2096	-2099	-2101	-2104	-2107	-2109
1093.0	-2112	-2114	-2117	-2119	-2122	-2125	-2127	-2130	-2132	-2135
1094.0	-2137	-2140	-2143	-2145	-2148	-2150	-2153	-2155	-2158	-2160
1095.0	-2163	-2166	-2168	-2171	-2173	-2176	-2178	-2181	-2184	-2186
1096.0	-2189	-2191	-2194	-2196	-2199	-2202	-2204	-2207	-2209	-2212
1097.0	-2214	-2217	-2219	-2222	-2225	-2227	-2230	-2232	-2235	-2237
1098.0	-2240	-2242	-2245	-2248	-2250	-2253	-2255	-2258	-2260	-2263
1099.0	-2266	-2268	-2271	-2273	-2276	-2278	-2281	-2283	-2286	-2289
1100.0	-2291	-2294	-2296	-2299	-2301	-2304	-2306	-2309	-2312	-2314
1101.0	-2317	-2319	-2322	-2324	-2327	-2329	-2332	-2334	-2337	-2340
1102.0	-2342	-2345	-2347	-2350	-2352	-2355	-2357	-2360	-2363	-2365
1103.0	-2368	-2370	-2373	-2375	-2378	-2380	-2383	-2385	-2388	-2391
1104.0	-2393	-2396	-2398	-2401	-2403	-2406	-2408	-2411	-2414	-2416
1105.0	-2419	-2421	-2424	-2426	-2429	-2431	-2434	-2436	-2439	-2441
1106.0	-2444	-2447	-2449	-2452	-2454	-2457	-2459	-2462	-2464	-2467
1107.0	-2469	-2472	-2475	-2477	-2480	-2482	-2485	-2487	-2490	-2492
1108.0	-2495	-2497	-2500	-2503	-2505	-2508	-2510	-2513	-2515	-2518
1109.0	-2520	-2523	-2525	-2528	-2530	-2533	-2536	-2538	-2541	-2543
1110.0	-2546	-2548	-2551	-2553	-2556	-2558	-2561	-2563	-2566	-2568
1111.0	-2571	-2574	-2576	-2579	-2581	-2584	-2586	-2589	-2591	-2594
1112.0	-2596	-2599	-2601	-2604	-2606	-2609	-2612	-2614	-2617	-2619
1113.0	-2622	-2624	-2627	-2629	-2632	-2634	-2637	-2639	-2642	-2644
1114.0	-2647	-2650	-2652	-2655	-2657	-2660	-2662	-2665	-2667	-2670
1115.0	-2672	-2675	-2677	-2680	-2682	-2685	-2687	-2690	-2692	-2695
1116.0	-2698	-2700	-2703	-2705	-2708	-2710	-2713	-2715	-2718	-2720
1117.0	-2723	-2725	-2728	-2730	-2733	-2735	-2738	-2740	-2743	-2745
1118.0	-2748	-2751	-2753	-2756	-2758	-2761	-2763	-2766	-2768	-2771
1119.0	-2773	-2776	-2778	-2781	-2783	-2786	-2788	-2791	-2793	-2796

TABLE VII- Continued

GEOPOTENTIAL ALTITUDE IN FEET as a function of PRESSURE IN MILLIBARS

P, mb	0.0	0.1	0.2	0.3	0.4	0.5	0.6	0.7	0.8	0.9
1120.0	-2798	-2801	-2803	-2806	-2808	-2811	-2814	-2816	-2819	-2821
1121.0	-2824	-2826	-2829	-2831	-2834	-2836	-2839	-2841	-2844	-2846
1122.0	-2849	-2851	-2854	-2856	-2859	-2861	-2864	-2866	-2869	-2871
1123.0	-2874	-2876	-2879	-2881	-2884	-2886	-2889	-2891	-2894	-2896
1124.0	-2899	-2901	-2904	-2907	-2909	-2912	-2914	-2917	-2919	-2922
1125.0	-2924	-2927	-2929	-2932	-2934	-2937	-2939	-2942	-2944	-2947
1126.0	-2949	-2952	-2954	-2957	-2959	-2962	-2964	-2967	-2969	-2972
1127.0	-2974	-2977	-2979	-2982	-2984	-2987	-2989	-2992	-2994	-2997
1128.0	-2999	-3002	-3004	-3007	-3009	-3012	-3014	-3017	-3019	-3022
1129.0	-3024	-3027	-3029	-3032	-3034	-3037	-3039	-3042	-3044	-3047
1130.0	-3049	-3052	-3054	-3057	-3059	-3062	-3064	-3067	-3069	-3072
1131.0	-3074	-3077	-3079	-3082	-3084	-3087	-3089	-3092	-3094	-3097
1132.0	-3099	-3102	-3104	-3107	-3109	-3112	-3114	-3117	-3119	-3122
1133.0	-3124	-3127	-3129	-3132	-3134	-3137	-3139	-3142	-3144	-3147
1134.0	-3149	-3152	-3154	-3157	-3159	-3162	-3164	-3167	-3169	-3172
1135.0	-3174	-3177	-3179	-3182	-3184	-3187	-3189	-3192	-3194	-3197
1136.0	-3199	-3202	-3204	-3206	-3209	-3211	-3214	-3216	-3219	-3221
1137.0	-3224	-3226	-3229	-3231	-3234	-3236	-3239	-3241	-3244	-3246
1138.0	-3249	-3251	-3254	-3256	-3259	-3261	-3264	-3266	-3269	-3271
1139.0	-3274	-3276	-3279	-3281	-3284	-3286	-3289	-3291	-3293	-3296
1140.0	-3298	-3301	-3303	-3306	-3308	-3311	-3313	-3316	-3318	-3321
1141.0	-3323	-3326	-3328	-3331	-3333	-3336	-3338	-3341	-3343	-3346
1142.0	-3348	-3351	-3353	-3356	-3358	-3360	-3363	-3365	-3368	-3370
1143.0	-3373	-3375	-3378	-3380	-3383	-3385	-3388	-3390	-3393	-3395
1144.0	-3398	-3400	-3403	-3405	-3408	-3410	-3412	-3415	-3417	-3420
1145.0	-3422	-3425	-3427	-3430	-3432	-3435	-3437	-3440	-3442	-3445
1146.0	-3447	-3450	-3452	-3454	-3457	-3459	-3462	-3464	-3467	-3469
1147.0	-3472	-3474	-3477	-3479	-3482	-3484	-3487	-3489	-3492	-3494
1148.0	-3496	-3499	-3501	-3504	-3506	-3509	-3511	-3514	-3516	-3519
1149.0	-3521	-3524	-3526	-3529	-3531	-3533	-3536	-3538	-3541	-3543
1150.0	-3546	-3548	-3551	-3553	-3556	-3558	-3561	-3563	-3566	-3568
1151.0	-3570	-3573	-3575	-3578	-3580	-3583	-3585	-3588	-3590	-3593
1152.0	-3595	-3598	-3600	-3602	-3605	-3607	-3610	-3612	-3615	-3617
1153.0	-3620	-3622	-3625	-3627	-3630	-3632	-3634	-3637	-3639	-3642
1154.0	-3644	-3647	-3649	-3652	-3654	-3657	-3659	-3661	-3664	-3666
1155.0	-3669	-3671	-3674	-3676	-3679	-3681	-3684	-3686	-3688	-3691
1156.0	-3693	-3696	-3698	-3701	-3703	-3706	-3708	-3711	-3713	-3715
1157.0	-3718	-3720	-3723	-3725	-3728	-3730	-3733	-3735	-3738	-3740
1158.0	-3742	-3745	-3747	-3750	-3752	-3755	-3757	-3760	-3762	-3765
1159.0	-3767	-3769	-3772	-3774	-3777	-3779	-3782	-3784	-3787	-3789
1160.0	-3791	-3794	-3796	-3799	-3801	-3804	-3806	-3809	-3811	-3813
1161.0	-3816	-3818	-3821	-3823	-3826	-3828	-3831	-3833	-3835	-3838
1162.0	-3840	-3843	-3845	-3848	-3850	-3853	-3855	-3857	-3860	-3862
1163.0	-3865	-3867	-3870	-3872	-3875	-3877	-3879	-3882	-3884	-3887
1164.0	-3889	-3892	-3894	-3897	-3899	-3901	-3904	-3906	-3909	-3911
1165.0	-3914	-3916	-3919	-3921	-3923	-3926	-3928	-3931	-3933	-3936
1166.0	-3938	-3940	-3943	-3945	-3948	-3950	-3953	-3955	-3958	-3960
1167.0	-3962	-3965	-3967	-3970	-3972	-3975	-3977	-3979	-3982	-3984
1168.0	-3987	-3989	-3992	-3994	-3996	-3999	-4001	-4004	-4006	-4009
1169.0	-4011	-4013	-4016	-4018	-4021	-4023	-4026	-4028	-4031	-4033
1170.0	-4035	-4038	-4040	-4043	-4045	-4048	-4050	-4052	-4055	-4057
1171.0	-4060	-4062	-4065	-4067	-4069	-4072	-4074	-4077	-4079	-4082
1172.0	-4084	-4086	-4089	-4091	-4094	-4096	-4099	-4101	-4103	-4106
1173.0	-4108	-4111	-4113	-4116	-4118	-4120	-4123	-4125	-4128	-4130
1174.0	-4132	-4135	-4137	-4140	-4142	-4145	-4147	-4149	-4152	-4154
1175.0	-4157	-4159	-4162	-4164	-4166	-4169	-4171	-4174	-4176	-4178
1176.0	-4181	-4183	-4186	-4188	-4191	-4193	-4195	-4198	-4200	-4203
1177.0	-4205	-4208	-4210	-4212	-4215	-4217	-4220	-4222	-4224	-4227
1178.0	-4229	-4232	-4234	-4237	-4239	-4241	-4244	-4246	-4249	-4251
1179.0	-4253	-4256	-4258	-4261	-4263	-4266	-4268	-4270	-4273	-4275
1180.0	-4278	-4280	-4282	-4285	-4287	-4290	-4292	-4295	-4297	-4299
1181.0	-4302	-4304	-4307	-4309	-4311	-4314	-4316	-4319	-4321	-4323
1182.0	-4326	-4328	-4331	-4333	-4336	-4338	-4340	-4343	-4345	-4348
1183.0	-4350	-4352	-4355	-4357	-4360	-4362	-4364	-4367	-4369	-4372
1184.0	-4374	-4376	-4379	-4381	-4384	-4386	-4388	-4391	-4393	-4396
1185.0	-4398	-4401	-4403	-4405	-4408	-4410	-4413	-4415	-4417	-4420
1186.0	-4422	-4425	-4427	-4429	-4432	-4434	-4437	-4439	-4441	-4444
1187.0	-4446	-4449	-4451	-4453	-4456	-4458	-4461	-4463	-4465	-4468
1188.0	-4470	-4473	-4475	-4477	-4480	-4482	-4485	-4487	-4489	-4492
1189.0	-4494	-4497	-4499	-4501	-4504	-4506	-4509	-4511	-4513	-4516
1190.0	-4518	-4521	-4523	-4525	-4528	-4530	-4533	-4535	-4537	-4540
1191.0	-4542	-4545	-4547	-4549	-4552	-4554	-4557	-4559	-4561	-4564
1192.0	-4566	-4569	-4571	-4573	-4576	-4578	-4580	-4583	-4585	-4588
1193.0	-4590	-4592	-4595	-4597	-4600	-4602	-4604	-4607	-4609	-4612
1194.0	-4614	-4616	-4619	-4621	-4624	-4626	-4628	-4631	-4633	-4635
1195.0	-4638	-4640	-4643	-4645	-4647	-4650	-4652	-4655	-4657	-4659
1196.0	-4662	-4664	-4667	-4669	-4671	-4674	-4676	-4678	-4681	-4683
1197.0	-4686	-4688	-4690	-4693	-4695	-4698	-4700	-4702	-4705	-4707
1198.0	-4709	-4712	-4714	-4717	-4719	-4721	-4724	-4726	-4729	-4731
1199.0	-4733	-4736	-4738	-4740	-4743	-4745	-4748	-4750	-4752	-4755

TABLE VII- Concluded

GEOPOTENTIAL ALTITUDE IN FEET as a function of PRESSURE IN MILLIBARS

P, mb	0	1	2	3	4	5	6	7	8	9
1200.	-4757	-4781	-4805	-4829	-4852	-4876	-4900	-4923	-4947	-4971
1210.	-4994	-5018	-5042	-5065	-5089	-5113	-5136	-5160	-5183	-5207
1220.	-5230	-5254	-5277	-5301	-5324	-5348	-5371	-5394	-5418	-5441
1230.	-5464	-5488	-5511	-5534	-5558	-5581	-5604	-5627	-5651	-5674
1240.	-5697	-5720	-5743	-5767	-5790	-5813	-5836	-5859	-5882	-5905
1250.	-5928	-5951	-5974	-5997	-6020	-6043	-6066	-6089	-6112	-6135
1260.	-6158	-6181	-6204	-6227	-6249	-6272	-6295	-6318	-6341	-6363
1270.	-6386	-6409	-6432	-6454	-6477	-6500	-6522	-6545	-6568	-6590
1280.	-6613	-6635	-6658	-6681	-6703	-6726	-6748	-6771	-6793	-6816
1290.	-6838	-6861	-6883	-6905	-6928	-6950	-6973	-6995	-7017	-7040
1300.	-7062	-7084	-7107	-7129	-7151	-7173	-7196	-7218	-7240	-7262
1310.	-7285	-7307	-7329	-7351	-7373	-7395	-7417	-7440	-7462	-7484
1320.	-7506	-7528	-7550	-7572	-7594	-7616	-7638	-7660	-7682	-7704
1330.	-7725	-7747	-7769	-7791	-7813	-7835	-7857	-7879	-7900	-7922
1340.	-7944	-7966	-7987	-8009	-8031	-8053	-8074	-8096	-8118	-8139
1350.	-8161	-8183	-8204	-8226	-8248	-8269	-8291	-8312	-8334	-8355
1360.	-8377	-8398	-8420	-8441	-8463	-8484	-8506	-8527	-8549	-8570
1370.	-8591	-8613	-8634	-8656	-8677	-8698	-8720	-8741	-8762	-8783
1380.	-8805	-8826	-8847	-8868	-8890	-8911	-8932	-8953	-8974	-8996
1390.	-9017	-9038	-9059	-9080	-9101	-9122	-9143	-9164	-9186	-9207
1400.	-9228	-9249	-9270	-9291	-9312	-9333	-9354	-9374	-9395	-9416
1410.	-9437	-9458	-9479	-9500	-9521	-9542	-9562	-9583	-9604	-9625
1420.	-9646	-9666	-9687	-9708	-9729	-9749	-9770	-9791	-9811	-9832
1430.	-9853	-9873	-9894	-9915	-9935	-9956	-9977	-9997	-10018	-10038
1440.	-10059	-10079	-10100	-10120	-10141	-10161	-10182	-10202	-10223	-10243
1450.	-10264	-10284	-10305	-10325	-10345	-10366	-10386	-10406	-10427	-10447
1460.	-10467	-10488	-10508	-10528	-10549	-10569	-10589	-10609	-10630	-10650
1470.	-10670	-10690	-10710	-10731	-10751	-10771	-10791	-10811	-10831	-10851
1480.	-10872	-10892	-10912	-10932	-10952	-10972	-10992	-11012	-11032	-11052
1490.	-11072	-11092	-11112	-11132	-11152	-11172	-11192	-11212	-11232	-11251
1500.	-11271	-11291	-11311	-11331	-11351	-11371	-11390	-11410	-11430	-11450
1510.	-11470	-11489	-11509	-11529	-11549	-11568	-11588	-11608	-11627	-11647
1520.	-11667	-11686	-11706	-11726	-11745	-11765	-11785	-11804	-11824	-11843
1530.	-11863	-11882	-11902	-11922	-11941	-11961	-11980	-12000	-12019	-12039
1540.	-12058	-12077	-12097	-12116	-12136	-12155	-12175	-12194	-12213	-12233
1550.	-12252	-12271	-12291	-12310	-12329	-12349	-12368	-12387	-12407	-12426
1560.	-12445	-12464	-12484	-12503	-12522	-12541	-12560	-12580	-12599	-12618
1570.	-12637	-12656	-12675	-12695	-12714	-12733	-12752	-12771	-12790	-12809
1580.	-12828	-12847	-12866	-12885	-12904	-12923	-12942	-12961	-12980	-12999
1590.	-13018	-13037	-13056	-13075	-13094	-13113	-13132	-13151	-13170	-13189
1600.	-13208	-13226	-13245	-13264	-13283	-13302	-13321	-13339	-13358	-13377
1610.	-13396	-13414	-13433	-13452	-13471	-13489	-13508	-13527	-13546	-13564
1620.	-13583	-13602	-13620	-13639	-13658	-13676	-13695	-13713	-13732	-13751
1630.	-13769	-13788	-13806	-13825	-13843	-13862	-13881	-13899	-13918	-13936
1640.	-13955	-13973	-13992	-14010	-14029	-14047	-14065	-14084	-14102	-14121
1650.	-14139	-14157	-14176	-14194	-14213	-14231	-14249	-14268	-14286	-14304
1660.	-14323	-14341	-14359	-14378	-14396	-14414	-14432	-14451	-14469	-14487
1670.	-14505	-14524	-14542	-14560	-14578	-14596	-14614	-14633	-14651	-14669
1680.	-14687	-14705	-14723	-14741	-14760	-14778	-14796	-14814	-14832	-14850
1690.	-14868	-14886	-14904	-14922	-14940	-14958	-14976	-14994	-15012	-15030
1700.	-15048	-15066	-15084	-15102	-15120	-15138	-15156	-15174	-15191	-15209
1710.	-15227	-15245	-15263	-15281	-15299	-15317	-15334	-15352	-15370	-15388
1720.	-15406	-15423	-15441	-15459	-15477	-15494	-15512	-15530	-15548	-15565
1730.	-15583	-15601	-15619	-15636	-15654	-15672	-15689	-15707	-15725	-15742
1740.	-15760	-15777	-15795	-15813	-15830	-15848	-15865	-15883	-15901	-15918
1750.	-15936	-15953	-15971	-15988	-16006	-16023	-16041	-16058	-16076	-16093
1760.	-16111	-16128	-16146	-16163	-16180	-16198	-16215	-16233	-16250	-16268
1770.	-16285	-16302	-16320	-16337	-16354	-16372	-16389	-16406		

Table VIII
Atmospheric Composition Number Density

Altitude		Number density (m^{-3})					
Z (m)	H (m)	N$_2$	O	O$_2$	A	He	H
86000	84852	1.130+ 20	8.600+ 16	3.031+ 19	1.351+ 18	7.582+ 14	I- 00
86500	85339	1.034	9.939	2.772	1.236	6.976	I
87000	85825	9.456+ 19	1.147+ 17	2.535	1.130	6.422	I
87500	86312	8.651	1.320	2.319	1.033	5.915	I
88000	86798	7.915	1.513	2.120	9.437+ 17	5.453	I
88500	87285	7.242	1.724	1.938	8.624	5.031	I
89000	87771	6.626	1.952	1.772	7.880	4.647	I
89500	88257	6.062	2.193	1.619	7.198	4.296	I
90000	88744	5.547+ 19	2.443+ 17	1.479+ 19	6.574+ 17	3.976+ 14	I- 00
90500	89230	5.075	2.699	1.351	6.002	3.685	I
91000	89716	4.643	2.953	1.234	5.478	3.419	I
91500	90202	4.248	3.200	1.126	4.998	3.177	I
92000	90688	3.886	3.434	1.027	4.557	2.956	I
92500	91173	3.553	3.651	9.361+ 18	4.152	2.753	I
93000	91659	3.249	3.846	8.527	3.781	2.568	I
93500	92145	2.970	4.016	7.761	3.441	2.399	I
94000	92630	2.715	4.159	7.060	3.129	2.244	I
94500	93116	2.481	4.275	6.418	2.844	2.103	I
95000	93601	2.268+ 19	4.365+ 17	5.830+ 18	2.583+ 17	1.973+ 14	I- 00
95500	94087	2.072	4.429	5.293	2.345	1.854	I
96000	94572	1.894	4.471	4.801	2.127	1.745	I
96500	95057	1.730	4.493	4.353	1.928	1.645	I
97000	95542	1.581	4.500	3.943	1.746	1.553	I
97500	96027	1.445	4.494	3.570	1.581	1.468	I
98000	96512	1.320	4.476	3.230	1.430	1.390	I
98500	96997	1.206	4.447	2.920	1.292	1.317	I
99000	97482	1.102	4.408	2.639	1.167	1.251	I
99500	97967	1.008	4.358	2.383	1.053	1.190	I
100000	98451	9.210+ 18	4.298+ 17	2.151+ 18	9.501+ 16	1.133+ 14	I- 00
101000	99420	7.740	4.168	1.756	7.735	1.034	I
102000	100389	6.508	4.007	1.430	6.279	9.497+ 13	I
103000	101358	5.475	3.821	1.163	5.082	8.776	I
104000	102326	4.609	3.619	9.434+ 17	4.101	8.160	I
105000	103294	3.883	3.406	7.645	3.299	7.633	I
106000	104261	3.273	3.188	6.189	2.645	7.181	I
107000	105229	2.760	2.968	5.005	2.113	6.789	I
108000	106196	2.327	2.748	4.045	1.681	6.443	I
109000	107162	1.959	2.528	3.263	1.331	6.128	I
110000	108129	1.641+ 18	2.303+ 17	2.621+ 17	1.046+ 16	5.821+ 13	I- 00
111000	109095	1.373	2.083	2.104	8.200+ 15	5.526	I
112000	110061	1.158	1.889	1.706	6.481	5.271	I
113000	111026	9.841+ 17	1.718	1.398	5.169	5.044	I
114000	111992	8.422	1.565	1.156	4.163	4.838	I
115000	112957	7.254	1.428	9.646+ 16	3.386	4.648	I
116000	113921	6.285	1.305	8.120	2.779	4.473	I
117000	114885	5.475	1.194	6.891	2.301	4.310	I
118000	115849	4.794	1.096	5.892	1.920	4.160	I
119000	116813	4.217	1.007	5.072	1.614	4.019	I
120000	117777	3.726+ 17	9.275+ 16	4.395+ 16	1.366+ 15	3.888+ 13	I- 00
121000	118740	3.306	8.562	3.832	1.164	3.766	I
122000	119703	2.947	7.925	3.360	9.979+ 14	3.652	I
123000	120665	2.637	7.354	2.963	8.606	3.547	I
124000	121627	2.368	6.840	2.625	7.460	3.448	I
125000	122589	2.135	6.376	2.336	6.498	3.356	I
126000	123551	1.930	5.956	2.087	5.685	3.270	I
127000	124512	1.750	5.576	1.871	4.994	3.189	I
128000	125473	1.592	5.229	1.683	4.403	3.112	I
129000	126434	1.451	4.914	1.519	3.896	3.040	I
130000	127395	1.326+ 17	4.625+ 16	1.375+ 16	3.458+ 14	2.972+ 13	I- 00
131000	128355	1.215	4.361	1.247	3.078	2.907	I
132000	129315	1.116	4.118	1.134	2.748	2.846	I
133000	130274	1.026	3.894	1.034	2.460	2.787	I
134000	131234	9.460+ 16	3.688	9.444+ 15	2.207	2.732	I
135000	132193	8.735	3.497	8.645	1.985	2.679	I
136000	133151	8.080	3.320	7.927	1.789	2.629	I
137000	134110	7.487	3.156	7.283	1.616	2.581	I
138000	135068	6.947	3.004	6.702	1.463	2.535	I
139000	136026	6.456	2.862	6.177	1.326	2.491	I
140000	136983	6.009+ 16	2.729+ 16	5.702+ 15	1.205+ 14	2.449+ 13	I- 00
141000	137940	5.600	2.605	5.272	1.096	2.408	I
142000	138897	5.225	2.489	4.881	9.989+ 13	2.369	I
143000	139854	4.881	2.380	4.524	9.118	2.332	I
144000	140810	4.565	2.278	4.199	8.335	2.296	I
145000	141766	4.275	2.183	3.903	7.630	2.261	I
146000	142722	4.007	2.092	3.631	6.994	2.228	I
147000	143677	3.760	2.007	3.382	6.420	2.196	I
148000	144632	3.531	1.927	3.153	5.900	2.165	I
149000	145587	3.320	1.852	2.941	5.429	2.135	I

Table VIII
Atmospheric Composition Number Density

Altitude		Number density (m^{-3})					
Z (m)	H (m)	N$_2$	O	O$_2$	A	He	H
150000	146542	3.124+ 16	1.780+ 16	2.750+ 15	5.000+ 13	2.106+ 13	3.767+ 11
151000	147496	2.942	1.712	2.572	4.611	2.078	3.659
152000	148450	2.773	1.648	2.407	4.256	2.051	3.557
153000	149404	2.616	1.587	2.255	3.933	2.024	3.461
154000	150357	2.469	1.530	2.114	3.638	1.999	3.369
155000	151311	2.333	1.475	1.984	3.368	1.974	3.283
156000	152263	2.206	1.423	1.863	3.121	1.950	3.201
157000	153216	2.087	1.373	1.751	2.895	1.927	3.123
158000	154168	1.975	1.326	1.647	2.687	1.905	3.049
159000	155120	1.871	1.281	1.550	2.496	1.883	2.978
160000	156072	1.774+ 16	1.238+ 16	1.460+ 15	2.321+ 13	1.861+ 13	2.911+ 11
161000	157023	1.682	1.197	1.376	2.159	1.841	2.847
162000	157974	1.596	1.158	1.297	2.011	1.820	2.786
163000	158925	1.516	1.120	1.224	1.874	1.801	2.728
164000	159875	1.440	1.085	1.156	1.747	1.782	2.672
165000	160826	1.369	1.050	1.092	1.630	1.763	2.619
166000	161775	1.302	1.018	1.032	1.522	1.745	2.568
167000	162725	1.239	9.863+ 15	9.757+ 14	1.422	1.727	2.520
168000	163674	1.179	9.562	9.232	1.329	1.710	2.473
169000	164623	1.123	9.273	8.739	1.243	1.693	2.429
170000	165572	1.070+ 16	8.996+ 15	8.277+ 14	1.163+ 13	1.676+ 13	2.386+ 11
171000	166521	1.020	8.730	7.843	1.089	1.660	2.345
172000	167469	9.724+ 15	8.474	7.435	1.020	1.644	2.306
173000	168417	9.277	8.228	7.051	9.565+ 12	1.629	2.268
174000	169364	8.853	7.992	6.690	8.970	1.614	2.232
175000	170311	8.452	7.765	6.350	8.417	1.599	2.197
176000	171258	8.072	7.546	6.030	7.901	1.585	2.163
177000	172205	7.712	7.335	5.728	7.420	1.571	2.131
178000	173151	7.371	7.132	5.443	6.971	1.557	2.100
179000	174098	7.047	6.936	5.174	6.553	1.543	2.070
180000	175043	6.740+ 15	6.747+ 15	4.921+ 14	6.162+ 12	1.530+ 13	2.041+ 11
181000	175989	6.448	6.565	4.681	5.797	1.517	2.013
182000	176934	6.170	6.389	4.455	5.456	1.504	1.987
183000	177879	5.907	6.220	4.241	5.136	1.492	1.961
184000	178824	5.656	6.056	4.039	4.838	1.479	1.936
185000	179768	5.417	5.897	3.847	4.558	1.467	1.911
186000	180712	5.190	5.744	3.666	4.296	1.456	1.888
187000	181656	4.974	5.596	3.494	4.050	1.444	1.866
188000	182600	4.768	5.453	3.331	3.820	1.433	1.844
189000	183543	4.572	5.315	3.177	3.604	1.421	1.823
190000	184486	4.385+ 15	5.181+ 15	3.031+ 14	3.401+ 12	1.410+ 13	1.802+ 11
191000	185428	4.207	5.051	2.892	3.211	1.400	1.782
192000	186371	4.037	4.926	2.760	3.033	1.389	1.763
193000	187313	3.875	4.804	2.635	2.865	1.379	1.745
194000	188255	3.720	4.686	2.517	2.707	1.368	1.727
195000	189196	3.572	4.572	2.404	2.558	1.358	1.709
196000	190137	3.430	4.461	2.297	2.419	1.348	1.692
197000	191078	3.295	4.354	2.195	2.288	1.339	1.676
198000	192019	3.166	4.249	2.098	2.164	1.329	1.660
199000	192959	3.043	4.148	2.006	2.047	1.319	1.645
200000	193899	2.925+ 15	4.050+ 15	1.918+ 14	1.938+ 12	1.310+ 13	1.630+ 11
201000	194839	2.812	3.955	1.834	1.834	1.301	1.615
202000	195779	2.704	3.862	1.755	1.737	1.292	1.601
203000	196718	2.601	3.773	1.679	1.645	1.283	1.587
204000	197657	2.502	3.685	1.607	1.558	1.274	1.574
205000	198595	2.407	3.600	1.538	1.477	1.266	1.561
206000	199534	2.316	3.518	1.473	1.399	1.257	1.548
207000	200472	2.229	3.438	1.410	1.327	1.249	1.536
208000	201410	2.146	3.360	1.351	1.258	1.240	1.524
209000	202347	2.066	3.284	1.294	1.193	1.232	1.512
210000	203284	1.989+ 15	3.211+ 15	1.239+ 14	1.131+ 12	1.224+ 13	1.501+ 11
211000	204221	1.915	3.139	1.188	1.073	1.216	1.490
212000	205158	1.845	3.069	1.138	1.019	1.208	1.479
213000	206094	1.777	3.001	1.091	9.666+ 11	1.201	1.468
214000	207030	1.712	2.935	1.046	9.176	1.193	1.458
215000	207966	1.650	2.871	1.003	8.711	1.185	1.448
216000	208902	1.590	2.808	9.617+ 13	8.272	1.178	1.439
217000	209837	1.533	2.747	9.224	7.856	1.171	1.429
218000	210772	1.477	2.688	8.848	7.463	1.163	1.420
219000	211706	1.424	2.630	8.489	7.090	1.156	1.411
220000	212641	1.373+ 15	2.573+ 15	8.145+ 13	6.737+ 11	1.149+ 13	1.402+ 11
221000	213575	1.324	2.518	7.816	6.402	1.142	1.393
222000	214509	1.277	2.465	7.502	6.085	1.135	1.385
223000	215442	1.232	2.412	7.201	5.785	1.128	1.377
224000	216375	1.188	2.361	6.913	5.500	1.122	1.369
225000	217308	1.147	2.312	6.637	5.230	1.115	1.361
226000	218241	1.106	2.263	6.373	4.974	1.108	1.353
227000	219173	1.068	2.216	6.121	4.731	1.102	1.345
228000	220105	1.030	2.170	5.879	4.501	1.095	1.338
229000	221037	9.945+ 14	2.125	5.647	4.282	1.089	1.331

Table VIII
Atmospheric Composition Number Density

Altitude		Number density (m⁻³)					
Z (m)	H (m)	N_2	O	O_2	A	He	H
230000	221969	9.600+ 14	2.081+ 15	5.425+ 13	4.075+ 11	1.083+ 13	1.324+ 11
231000	222900	9.268	2.038	5.212	3.878	1.076	1.317
232000	223831	8.948	1.996	5.009	3.691	1.070	1.310
233000	224762	8.640	1.955	4.813	3.514	1.064	1.304
234000	225692	8.343	1.915	4.626	3.345	1.058	1.297
235000	226622	8.058	1.876	4.446	3.185	1.052	1.291
236000	227552	7.782	1.838	4.274	3.033	1.046	1.285
237000	228481	7.517	1.801	4.109	2.888	1.040	1.279
238000	229411	7.262	1.765	3.951	2.751	1.034	1.273
239000	230340	7.016	1.729	3.799	2.621	1.029	1.267
240000	231268	6.778+ 14	1.695+ 15	3.653+ 13	2.497+ 11	1.023+ 13	1.261+ 11
241000	232197	6.550	1.661	3.513	2.379	1.017	1.256
242000	233125	6.329	1.628	3.379	2.267	1.012	1.250
243000	234053	6.117	1.595	3.251	2.160	1.006	1.245
244000	234980	5.912	1.564	3.127	2.059	1.001	1.240
245000	235908	5.714	1.533	3.008	1.962	9.953+ 12	1.234
246000	236835	5.523	1.503	2.895	1.871	9.899	1.229
247000	237761	5.339	1.473	2.785	1.783	9.846	1.224
248000	238688	5.162	1.444	2.680	1.700	9.794	1.219
249000	239614	4.991	1.416	2.579	1.621	9.741	1.215
250000	240540	4.826+ 14	1.388+ 15	2.482+ 13	1.546+ 11	9.690+ 12	1.210+ 11
251000	241466	4.666	1.361	2.389	1.474	9.638	1.205
252000	242391	4.512	1.335	2.300	1.406	9.587	1.201
253000	243316	4.364	1.309	2.214	1.341	9.537	1.196
254000	244241	4.221	1.284	2.132	1.280	9.487	1.192
255000	245165	4.082	1.259	2.052	1.221	9.438	1.188
256000	246089	3.949	1.235	1.976	1.165	9.389	1.183
257000	247013	3.820	1.211	1.903	1.111	9.340	1.179
258000	247937	3.695	1.188	1.832	1.060	9.292	1.175
259000	248860	3.575	1.165	1.765	1.012	9.244	1.171
260000	249784	3.459+ 14	1.143+ 15	1.700+ 13	9.658+ 10	9.196+ 12	1.167+ 11
261000	250706	3.347	1.121	1.637	9.218	9.149	1.163
262000	251629	3.238	1.100	1.577	8.799	9.103	1.159
263000	252551	3.134	1.079	1.519	8.399	9.056	1.156
264000	253473	3.033	1.059	1.463	8.019	9.010	1.152
265000	254395	2.935	1.039	1.410	7.655	8.965	1.148
266000	255316	2.841	1.019	1.358	7.309	8.920	1.145
267000	256237	2.749	9.998+ 14	1.309	6.979	8.875	1.141
268000	257158	2.661	9.811	1.261	6.665	8.830	1.138
269000	258079	2.576	9.627	1.215	6.365	8.786	1.134
270000	258999	2.494+ 14	9.447+ 14	1.171+ 13	6.078+ 10	8.743+ 12	1.131+ 11
271000	259919	2.414	9.270	1.128	5.805	8.699	1.127
272000	260839	2.337	9.097	1.088	5.545	8.656	1.124
273000	261758	2.263	8.928	1.048	5.297	8.613	1.121
274000	262678	2.191	8.762	1.010	5.060	8.571	1.118
275000	263597	2.121	8.599	9.739+ 12	4.834	8.529	1.115
276000	264515	2.054	8.440	9.388	4.618	8.487	1.112
277000	265434	1.989	8.284	9.050	4.412	8.445	1.109
278000	266352	1.926	8.131	8.725	4.216	8.404	1.106
279000	267269	1.865	7.981	8.412	4.029	8.363	1.103
280000	268187	1.806+ 14	7.834+ 14	8.110+ 12	3.850+ 10	8.322+ 12	1.100+ 11
281000	269104	1.750	7.691	7.820	3.679	8.282	1.097
282000	270021	1.695	7.549	7.540	3.516	8.242	1.094
283000	270938	1.641	7.411	7.271	3.360	8.202	1.091
284000	271854	1.590	7.276	7.011	3.212	8.163	1.088
285000	272771	1.540	7.143	6.761	3.070	8.124	1.086
286000	273686	1.492	7.012	6.521	2.935	8.085	1.083
287000	274602	1.445	6.885	6.289	2.805	8.046	1.080
288000	275517	1.400	6.759	6.065	2.682	8.008	1.078
289000	276432	1.356	6.637	5.850	2.564	7.969	1.075
290000	277347	1.314+ 14	6.516+ 14	5.643+ 12	2.451+ 10	7.931+ 12	1.073+ 11
291000	278262	1.273	6.398	5.443	2.344	7.894	1.070
292000	279176	1.234	6.282	5.251	2.241	7.856	1.067
293000	280090	1.195	6.169	5.065	2.143	7.819	1.065
294000	281004	1.158	6.058	4.886	2.049	7.782	1.063
295000	281917	1.122	5.948	4.714	1.960	7.746	1.060
296000	282830	1.088	5.841	4.548	1.874	7.709	1.058
297000	283743	1.054	5.736	4.388	1.792	7.673	1.055
298000	284656	1.021	5.633	4.234	1.714	7.637	1.053
299000	285568	9.898+ 13	5.532	4.085	1.639	7.602	1.051
300000	286480	9.593+ 13	5.433+ 14	3.942+ 12	1.568+ 10	7.566+ 12	1.049+ 11
302000	288303	9.011	5.241	3.670	1.435	7.496	1.044
304000	290125	8.466	5.055	3.418	1.313	7.427	1.040
306000	291946	7.954	4.877	3.184	1.202	7.358	1.035
308000	293766	7.474	4.705	2.966	1.100	7.290	1.031
310000	295585	7.024	4.540	2.763	1.007	7.224	1.027
312000	297403	6.602	4.380	2.574	9.223+ 9	7.157	1.023
314000	299220	6.206	4.227	2.399	8.447	7.092	1.019
316000	301035	5.834	4.079	2.236	7.737	7.028	1.015
318000	302850	5.485	3.937	2.084	7.087	6.964	1.012

Table VIII
Atmospheric Composition Number Density

Altitude		Number density (m^{-3})					
Z (m)	H (m)	N$_2$	O	O$_2$	A	He	H
320000	304663	5.158+ 13	3.800+ 14	1.942+ 12	6.493+ 9	6.901+ 12	1.008+ 11
322000	306476	4.850	3.668	1.811	5.950	6.839	1.004
324000	308287	4.561	3.541	1.688	5.452	6.777	1.001
326000	310097	4.290	3.418	1.574	4.997	6.717	9.971+ 10
328000	311906	4.035	3.300	1.468	4.580	6.657	9.937
330000	313714	3.796	3.186	1.369	4.199	6.597	9.903
332000	315521	3.571	3.076	1.277	3.850	6.538	9.869
334000	317327	3.360	2.970	1.191	3.530	6.480	9.836
336000	319132	3.162	2.868	1.111	3.237	6.423	9.804
338000	320935	2.975	2.770	1.037	2.969	6.366	9.772
340000	322738	2.800+ 13	2.675+ 14	9.674+ 11	2.723+ 9	6.310+ 12	9.741+ 10
342000	324539	2.635	2.583	9.027	2.498	6.254	9.710
344000	326340	2.480	2.495	8.424	2.292	6.199	9.680
346000	328139	2.335	2.410	7.862	2.103	6.145	9.650
348000	329938	2.198	2.328	7.338	1.929	6.091	9.620
350000	331735	2.069	2.249	6.850	1.771	6.038	9.591
352000	333531	1.948	2.172	6.394	1.625	5.985	9.562
354000	335326	1.834	2.099	5.969	1.491	5.933	9.534
356000	337120	1.727	2.027	5.573	1.369	5.881	9.505
358000	338913	1.627	1.959	5.204	1.257	5.830	9.478
360000	340705	1.532+ 13	1.893+ 14	4.859+ 11	1.154+ 9	5.779+ 12	9.450+ 10
362000	342496	1.443	1.829	4.538	1.059	5.729	9.423
364000	344286	1.359	1.767	4.238	9.728+ 8	5.680	9.397
366000	346074	1.280	1.707	3.958	8.934	5.631	9.370
368000	347862	1.206	1.650	3.697	8.205	5.582	9.344
370000	349648	1.136	1.594	3.454	7.536	5.534	9.318
372000	351434	1.070	1.541	3.226	6.922	5.487	9.293
374000	353218	1.008	1.489	3.014	6.359	5.439	9.268
376000	355002	9.498+ 12	1.243	2.816	5.842	5.393	9.243
378000	356784	8.950	1.391	2.631	5.367	5.347	9.218
380000	358565	8.434+ 12	1.344+ 14	2.459+ 11	4.932+ 8	5.301+ 12	9.193+ 10
382000	360346	7.948	1.300	2.297	4.532	5.256	9.169
384000	362125	7.490	1.256	2.147	4.165	5.211	9.145
386000	363903	7.059	1.214	2.006	3.827	5.167	9.121
388000	365680	6.653	1.174	1.875	3.518	5.123	9.098
390000	367456	6.271	1.135	1.753	3.234	5.079	9.074
392000	369231	5.911	1.097	1.638	2.972	5.036	9.051
394000	371005	5.572	1.061	1.532	2.733	4.993	9.028
396000	372778	5.253	1.025	1.432	2.512	4.951	9.005
398000	374549	4.952	9.913+ 13	1.339	2.310	4.909	8.983
400000	376320	4.669+ 12	9.584+ 13	1.252+ 11	2.124+ 8	4.868+ 12	8.960+ 10
402000	378090	4.402	9.267	1.170	1.953	4.827	8.938
404000	379858	4.151	8.960	1.094	1.796	4.786	8.916
406000	381626	3.914	8.664	1.023	1.652	4.746	8.894
408000	383392	3.691	8.378	9.568+ 10	1.519	4.706	8.872
410000	385158	3.480	8.101	8.948	1.397	4.666	8.851
412000	386922	3.282	7.834	8.369	1.285	4.627	8.829
414000	388686	3.095	7.576	7.827	1.182	4.588	8.808
416000	390448	2.919	7.327	7.321	1.088	4.550	8.787
418000	392210	2.754	7.086	6.848	1.001	4.512	8.766
420000	393970	2.597+ 12	6.853+ 13	6.406+ 10	9.207+ 7	4.474+ 12	8.745+ 10
422000	395729	2.450	6.628	5.993	8.472	4.437	8.725
424000	397487	2.311	6.410	5.606	7.796	4.399	8.704
426000	399245	2.180	6.200	5.245	7.174	4.363	8.684
428000	401001	2.057	5.997	4.907	6.602	4.326	8.663
430000	402756	1.940	5.800	4.592	6.076	4.290	8.643
432000	404510	1.831	5.611	4.297	5.593	4.255	8.623
434000	406263	1.727	5.427	4.020	5.148	4.219	8.603
436000	408015	1.630	5.250	3.762	4.739	4.184	8.583
438000	409766	1.538	5.079	3.521	4.362	4.150	8.564
440000	411516	1.451+ 12	4.913+ 13	3.295+ 10	4.016+ 7	4.115+ 12	8.544+ 10
442000	413265	1.369	4.753	3.084	3.698	4.081	8.525
444000	415013	1.292	4.598	2.887	3.404	4.047	8.505
446000	416760	1.220	4.448	2.702	3.135	4.014	8.486
448000	418505	1.151	4.303	2.529	2.887	3.981	8.467
450000	420250	1.086	4.164	2.368	2.658	3.948	8.448
452000	421994	1.025	4.028	2.216	2.448	3.915	8.429
454000	423737	9.679+ 11	3.898	2.075	2.255	3.883	8.410
456000	425478	9.136	3.771	1.943	2.077	3.851	8.391
458000	427219	8.625	3.649	1.819	1.913	3.819	8.373
460000	428959	8.142+ 11	3.531+ 13	1.703+ 10	1.762+ 7	3.788+ 12	8.354+ 10
462000	430698	7.686	3.416	1.595	1.623	3.757	8.336
464000	432435	7.256	3.306	1.493	1.495	3.726	8.317
466000	434172	6.851	3.199	1.398	1.377	3.695	8.299
468000	435907	6.468	3.096	1.309	1.269	3.665	8.281
470000	437642	6.107	2.996	1.226	1.169	3.635	8.263
472000	439376	5.766	2.899	1.148	1.077	3.605	8.245
474000	441108	5.445	2.806	1.076	9.929+ 6	3.576	8.227
476000	442840	5.142	2.715	1.007	9.149	3.547	8.209
478000	444570	4.855	2.628	9.436+ 9	8.432	3.518	8.191

214

Table VIII
Atmospheric Composition Number Density

Altitude		Number density (m^{-3})					
Z (m)	H (m)	N$_2$	O	O$_2$	A	He	H
480000	446300	4.585+ 11	2.543+ 13	8.839+ 9	7.771+ 6	3.489+ 12	8.173+ 10
482000	448028	4.330	2.461	8.280	7.162	3.461	8.155
484000	449756	4.090	2.382	7.757	6.602	3.432	8.138
486000	451482	3.863	2.306	7.267	6.085	3.404	8.120
488000	453208	3.648	2.232	6.808	5.609	3.377	8.103
490000	454932	3.446	2.160	6.378	5.171	3.349	8.085
492200	456656	3.255	2.091	5.976	4.767	3.322	8.068
494000	458378	3.075	2.024	5.599	4.395	3.295	8.051
496000	460100	2.904	1.959	5.247	4.052	3.268	8.034
498000	461820	2.744	1.896	4.917	3.737	3.242	8.017
500000	463540	2.592+ 11	1.836+ 13	4.607+ 9	3.445+ 6	3.215+ 12	8.000+ 10
505000	467834	2.249	1.693	3.917	2.814	3.151	7.959
510000	472122	1.951	1.561	3.331	2.299	3.087	7.918
515000	476404	1.694	1.440	2.834	1.878	3.026	7.878
520000	480679	1.470	1.328	2.411	1.535	2.965	7.838
525000	484949	1.277	1.225	2.052	1.255	2.906	7.798
530000	489212	1.109	1.130	1.747	1.027	2.848	7.758
535000	493469	9.633+ 10	1.043	1.487	8.400+ 5	2.791	7.719
540000	497719	8.370	9.624+ 12	1.267	6.875	2.735	7.680
545000	501964	7.274	8.883	1.079	5.628	2.681	7.641
550000	506202	6.323+ 10	8.200+ 12	9.196+ 8	4.609+ 5	2.628+ 12	7.602+ 10
555000	510435	5.497	7.570	7.838	3.775	2.576	7.564
560000	514661	4.781	6.989	6.682	3.093	2.525	7.526
565000	518881	4.158	6.454	5.697	2.535	2.475	7.488
570000	523095	3.617	5.960	4.859	2.079	2.426	7.451
575000	527303	3.148	5.505	4.146	1.705	2.379	7.413
580000	531505	2.740	5.085	3.537	1.398	2.332	7.376
585000	535701	2.385	4.698	3.019	1.147	2.286	7.339
590000	539890	2.076	4.341	2.578	9.419+ 4	2.241	7.303
595000	544074	1.808	4.011	2.201	7.733	2.197	7.267
600000	548252	1.575+ 10	3.707+ 12	1.880+ 8	6.351+ 4	2.154+ 12	7.231+ 10
605000	552424	1.372	3.426	1.606	5.217	2.112	7.195
610000	556589	1.196	3.167	1.372	4.287	2.071	7.159
615000	560749	1.042	2.928	1.173	3.524	2.031	7.124
620000	564903	9.085+ 9	2.707	1.003	2.898	1.991	7.089
625000	569051	7.921	2.503	8.573+ 7	2.383	1.953	7.054
630000	573193	6.908	2.315	7.332	1.961	1.915	7.019
635000	577329	6.025	2.141	6.272	1.613	1.878	6.985
640000	581459	5.257	1.981	5.367	1.328	1.842	6.950
645000	585583	4.587	1.832	4.593	1.094	1.806	6.916
650000	589701	4.003+ 9	1.695+ 12	3.932+ 7	9.006+ 3	1.771+ 12	6.883+ 10
655000	593814	3.495	1.569	3.367	7.420	1.737	6.849
660000	597920	3.051	1.452	2.883	6.114	1.704	6.816
665000	602021	2.665	1.344	2.470	5.040	1.671	6.782
670000	606116	2.327	1.244	2.116	4.155	1.639	6.749
675000	610205	2.033	1.151	1.813	3.427	1.608	6.717
680000	614288	1.777	1.066	1.554	2.827	1.577	6.684
685000	618365	1.553	9.870+ 11	1.333	2.333	1.547	6.652
690000	622437	1.357	9.140	1.143	1.926	1.518	6.620
695000	626503	1.187	8.465	9.802+ 6	1.590	1.489	6.588
700000	630563	1.038+ 9	7.840+ 11	8.410+ 6	1.313+ 3	1.461+ 12	6.556+ 10
705000	634617	9.075+ 8	7.263	7.216	1.085	1.433	6.524
710000	638666	7.939	6.728	6.194	8.964+ 2	1.406	6.493
715000	642709	6.946	6.234	5.317	7.409	1.379	6.462
720000	646746	6.078	5.777	4.566	6.126	1.353	6.431
725000	650778	5.320	5.354	3.921	5.066	1.328	6.400
730000	654803	4.658	4.962	3.368	4.191	1.303	6.370
735000	658824	4.078	4.599	2.894	3.467	1.278	6.339
740000	662838	3.572	4.264	2.487	2.870	1.254	6.309
745000	666847	3.129	3.953	2.138	2.376	1.231	6.279
750000	670850	2.741+ 8	3.666+ 11	1.838+ 6	1.967+ 2	1.208+ 12	6.249+ 10
755000	674848	2.402	3.399	1.581	1.630	1.185	6.220
760000	678840	2.105	3.153	1.360	1.350	1.163	6.190
765000	682826	1.845	2.924	1.170	1.119	1.141	6.161
770000	686807	1.618	2.712	1.007	9.276+ 1	1.120	6.132
775000	690782	1.419	2.516	8.664+ 5	7.692	1.099	6.103
780000	694751	1.244	2.335	7.458	6.380	1.079	6.074
785000	698715	1.092	2.166	6.422	5.293	1.059	6.046
790000	702674	9.577+ 7	2.011	5.531	4.392	1.039	6.017
795000	706627	8.404	1.866	4.764	3.646	1.020	5.989
800000	710574	7.377+ 7	1.732+ 11	4.105+ 5	3.027+ 1	1.001+ 12	5.961+ 10
805000	714516	6.476	1.608	3.537	2.514	9.826+ 11	5.933
810000	718452	5.686	1.493	3.049	2.088	9.645	5.905
815000	722383	4.993	1.386	2.628	1.735	9.468	5.878
820000	726309	4.386	1.287	2.267	1.442	9.294	5.851
825000	730229	3.853	1.195	1.955	1.199	9.124	5.823
830000	734143	3.386	1.110	1.686	9.970+ 0	8.957	5.796
835000	738052	2.975	1.031	1.455	8.293	8.793	5.769
840000	741956	2.615	9.580+ 10	1.256	6.900	8.632	5.743
845000	745855	2.300	8.901	1.084	5.742	8.475	5.716

Table VIII
Atmospheric Composition Number Density

Altitude		Number density (m^{-3})					
Z (m)	H (m)	N$_2$	O	O$_2$	A	He	H
850000	749747	2.022+ 7	8.270+ 10	9.358+ 4	4.780+ 0	8.320+ 11	5.690+ 10
855000	753634	1.778	7.685	8.081	3.980	8.169	5.664
860000	757516	1.564	7.142	6.979	3.314	8.021	5.637
865000	761393	1.376	6.638	6.029	2.761	7.875	5.612
870000	765264	1.211	6.171	5.210	2.301	7.733	5.586
875000	769130	1.066	5.737	4.503	1.918	7.593	5.560
880000	772991	9.380+ 6	5.334	3.892	1.599	7.456	5.535
885000	776846	8.258	4.959	3.365	1.333	7.321	5.509
890000	780696	7.271	4.612	2.910	1.112	7.189	5.484
895000	784541	6.404	4.289	2.517	9.277- 1	7.060	5.459
900000	788380	5.641+ 6	3.989+ 10	2.177+ 4	7.742- 1	6.933+ 11	5.434+ 10
905000	792214	4.970	3.711	1.884	6.462	6.809	5.410
910000	796043	4.379	3.452	1.631	5.396	6.687	5.385
915000	799866	3.859	3.212	1.411	4.506	6.567	5.361
920000	803685	3.402	2.989	1.222	3.764	6.450	5.336
925000	807498	2.999	2.781	1.058	3.145	6.335	5.312
930000	811305	2.645	2.588	9.165+ 3	2.629	6.222	5.288
935000	815108	2.332	2.409	7.940	2.197	6.111	5.264
940000	818905	2.057	2.242	6.880	1.837	6.003	5.241
945000	822697	1.815	2.088	5.962	1.537	5.896	5.217
950000	826484	1.602+ 6	1.944+ 10	5.168+ 3	1.286- 1	5.792+ 11	5.194+ 10
955000	830266	1.414	1.810	4.481	1.076	5.689	5.170
960000	834043	1.248	1.685	3.886	9.004- 2	5.589	5.147
965000	837814	1.102	1.569	3.370	7.538	5.490	5.124
970000	841580	9.726+ 5	1.462	2.924	6.312	5.393	5.101
975000	845342	8.590	1.362	2.537	5.287	5.298	5.078
980000	849098	7.587	1.268	2.201	4.430	5.205	5.056
985000	852849	6.703	1.182	1.911	3.712	5.114	5.033
990000	856594	5.922	1.101	1.659	3.111	5.024	5.011
995000	860335	5.234	1.026	1.440	2.609	4.936	4.989
1000000	864071	4.626+ 5	9.562+ 9	1.251+ 3	2.188- 2	4.850+ 11	4.967+ 10

U.S. Standard Atmosphere References

Abel, N., Jaenicke, R., Junge, C., Kanton, H., Prieto, P.R.G., and Seiler, W., 1969: Luftchenusche Studien am Observatorium Izana (Teneriffa). *Meteorologische Rundschau*, 22, Berlin, Germany, pp. 158–167.

Ackerman, M. 1971: Ultraviolet Solar Radiation Related to Mesospheric Process. *Mesospheric Models and Related Experiments*, G. Fiocco, editor, Springer-Verlag, New York, pp. 149–159.

Ackerman, M., Fontanella, J. C., Frimout, D., Girard, A., Louisnard, N., Muller, C., and Nevejans, D., 1973: Infrared Nitrogen Oxide from Infrared Spectra. *Nature Physical Science*, 245, London, England, pp. 205–206.

Ackerman, M. and Muller, C., 1972: Stratospheric Methane from Infrared Spectra. *Proceedings of the Symposium on Sources, Sinks, and Concentrations of Carbon Monoxide and Methane in the Earth's Environment, St. Petersburg, Fla., August 1972*, pp. 12–1—12–11.

Ackerman, M., and Muller, C., 1972: Stratospheric Nitrogen Dioxide from Infrared Absorption Spectra. *Nature*, 240, London, England, pp. 300–301.

Bainbridge, A. E., and Heidt, L. E., 1966: Measurements of Methane in the Troposphere and Lower Stratosphere. *Tellus*, 18, Stockholm, Sweden, pp. 221–225.

Barrett, E. W., Kuhn, C. M., and Shlanta, A., 1972: Recent Measurements of the Injection of Water Vapor and Ozone into the Stratosphere by Thunderstorms. *Abstracts*, 2nd Conference, CIAP, U.S. Department of Transportation, Washington, D.C., pp. 5–7.

Bates, D. R., 1959: Some problems concerning the terrestrial atmosphere above about the 100 km level. *Proceedings of the Royal Society of London*, A253, England, p. 451.

Beaudoin, P. E., Golumb, D., Noel, T. M., Rosenberg, N. W., and Vickery, W. K., 1967: Observations of Mesospheric Winds and Turbulence with Smoke Trails. *Journal of Geophysical Research*, 72, pp. 3729–3733.

Blifford, I. H., 1970: Tropospheric Aerosols. *Journal of Geophysical Research*, 75, pp. 3099–3111.

Blifford, I. H., and Gillette, D. A., 1972: The Influence of Air Origin on the Chemical Composition and Size Distribution of Tropospheric Aerosols. *Atmospheric Environment*, 6, pp. 463–480.

Bolin, B., and Bischof, W., 1970: Variations in the Carbon Dioxide Content of the Atmosphere in the Northern Hemisphere. *Tellus*, 22, Stockholm, Sweden, pp. 431–442.

Brinton, H. C., and Mayr, H. G., 1971: Temporal Variations of Thermospheric Hydrogen Derived from In-Situ Measurements. *Journal of Geophysical Research*, 76, pp. 6198–6201.

Brewer, A. W., 1949: Evidence of World Circulation by Measurement of Helium and Water Vapor Distribution in the Stratosphere. *Quarterly Journal of the Royal Meteorological Society*, 75, London, England, pp. 351–363.

Büchen, M., and Georgii, H. W., 1971 Ein Beitrag zum Atmospharischen Schwefelhaushalt uber dem Atlantik. *Meteor Forshungen Ergevnisse*, B7, pp. 71–77.

Cadle, R. D., 1964: Daytime Atmospheric 0('D). *Discussions of the Faraday Society*, 37, London, England, pp. 66 72

Cadle, R. D., and Powers, J. W., 1966: Some Aspects of Atmospheric Chemical Reactions of Atomic Oxygen. *Tellus*, 18, Stockholm, Sweden, pp. 110–88.

Cadle, R. D., 1972: Composition of the Stratospheric 'Sulfate' Layer. *EOS* (Transactions of the American Geophysical Union), 53, pp. 812–820.

Cadle, R. D., Lazrus, A. L., Pollock, W. H., and Shedlovsky, J. P., 1970: The Chemical Composition of Aerosol Particles in the Tropical Stratosphere. *Proceedings of the Symposium on Tropical Meteorology, American Meteorological Society World Meteorological Organization, University of Hawaii, Honolulu, Hawaii, June 1970*, pp. K IV-1 to K IV-6.

Cavanaugh, L. A., Schadt, C. F., and Robinson, E., 1969: Atmospheric Hydrocarbon and Carbon Monoxide Measurements at Point Barrow, Alaska. *Environmental Science & Technology*, 3, pp. 251–257.

Champion, K. S. W., Marcos, F. A., and McIsaac, J. P., 1970a: Atmospheric density measurements by research satellite OVI-15. *Space Research*, 10, Akademie-Verlag, Berlin, Germany, pp. 450–458.

Champion, K. S. W., Marcos, F. A., and Schweinfurth, R. A., 1970b: Measurements by the low altitude density satellite OVI-16. *Space Research*, 10, Akademie-Verlag, Berlin, Germany, pp. 459–466.

Chapman, S. and Cowling, T. G., 1960: *Mathematical Theory of Non-Uniform Gases*, Cambridge University Press, London, England.

COESA, 1962: *U. S. Standard Atmosphere, 1962*. U.S. Government Printing Office, Washington, D.C., 278 pp.

Colegrove, F. D., Hanson, W. B., and Johnson, F. S., 1965: Eddy diffusion and oxygen transport in the lower thermosphere. *Journal of Geophysical Research*, 70, pp. 4931–4941.

Committee on Extension to the Standard Atmosphere, 1962: *U.S. Standard Atmosphere, 1962*. Government Printing Office, Washington, D.C., 278 pp.

Committee on Extension to the Standard Atmosphere, 1967: *U.S. Standard Atmosphere Supplements, 1966*. Government Printing Office, Washington, D.C. 289 pp.

Craig, R. A., 1965: *The Upper Atmosphere: Meteorology and Physics*. Academic Press, New York, N.Y., 509 pp.

Cumming, C., and Lowe, R. P., 1972: Balloon Borne Spectroscopic Measurement of Stratospheric Methane. *Proceedings of the Symposium on Sources, Sinks and Concentration of Carbon Monoxide and Methane in the Earth's Environment, St. Petersburg, Fla., August 1972*, pp. 13–1—13–11.

Diehl, W. S., 1925: Standard Atmosphere Tables and Data. *NACA Report 218*, U.S. Government Printing Office, Washington, D.C.

Dutsch, H. U., 1966: Two Years of Regular Ozone Soundings Over Boulder, Colorado. *NCAR TN-10*, National Center for Atmospheric Research, Boulder, Colorado, January.

Ehhalt, D. H., 1967: Methane in the Atmosphere. *Journal of the Air Pollution Control Association*, 17, pp. 518–519.

Ehhalt, D. H., and Heidt, L. E., 1972: Vertical Profiles of CH_4 in the Troposphere and Stratosphere. *Proceedings of the Symposium on Sources, Sinks and Concentrations of Carbon Monoxide and Methane in the Earth's Environment, St. Petersburg, Fla., August 1972, American Meteorological Society, Boston, Mass. pp. 11–1—11–11.

Ehhalt, D. H., and Heidt, L. E., 1972: The Concentration of Molecular H₂ and CH₄ in the Stratosphere. Proceedings of the Symposium on Ozone, Arosa, Switzerland, 1972. *Pure and Applied Geophysics*, Basal, Switzerland, in press.

Ehhalt, D. H., Heidt, L. E., and Martell, E. A., 1972: The Concentration of Atmospheric Methane Between 44 and 62 Kilometers Altitude. *Journal of Geophysical Research*, 77, pp. 2193–2196.

Finch, V. C., Trewartha, G. T., Robinson, A. H., and Hammond, E. H., 1957: *Physical Elements of Geography*. McGraw-Hill, New York, N.Y.

Fisher, W. H., Lodge, J. P. Jr., Wartburg, A. F., and Pate, J. B., 1968: Estimation of Some Atmospheric Trace Gases in Antarctica. Environmental Science and Technology, 2, pp. 464–466.

George, J. G., Zimmerman, S. P., and Keneshea, T. J., 1972: The Latitude Variation of Major and Minor Neutral Species in the Upper Atmosphere. *Space Research XII*, S. A. Bowhill et al., editors, Akademie-Verlag, Berlin, Germany, pp. 695–709.

Georgii, H. W., 1963: Oxides of Nitrogen and Ammonia in the Atmosphere. *Journal of Geophysical Research*, 68, pp. 3963–3970.

Georgii, H. W., 1970: Contribution to the Atmospheric Sulfur Budget. *Journal of Geophysical Research*, 75, pp. 2365–2371.

Georgii, H. W., and Vitze, W., 1971: Global and Regional Distribution of Sulfur Components in the Atmosphere. *Idojaras*, Budapest, Hungary, 75, pp. 294–299.

Gillette, D. A., and Blifford, I. H., 1971: Composition of Tropospheric Aerosols as a Function of Altitude. *Journal of the Atmospheric Sciences*, 28, pp. 1199–1210.

Glueckauf, E., 1951: The Composition of Atmospheric Air. *Compendium of Meteorology*, T. F. Malone, editor, American Meteorological Society, Boston, Mass., pp. 3–10.

Glueckauf, E., and Kitt, G. P., 1957: The Hydrogen Content of Atmospheric Air at Ground Level. *Quarterly Journal of the Royal Meteorological Society*, 83, London, England, pp. 522–528.

Goldberg, L., 1951: The Abundance and Vertical Distribution of Methane in the Earth's Atmosphere. *Astrophysical Journal*, 113, pp. 567–582.

Goldberg, L., and Muller, E., 1953: Vertical Distribution of Nitrous Oxide and Methane in the Earth's Atmosphere. *Journal of the Optical Society of America*, 43, pp. 1033–1036.

Goldman, A., Murcray, D. G., Murcray, F. H., Williams, W. J., and Bonomo, F. S., 1970: Identification of the v_3 NO₂ Band in the Solar Spectrum Observed from a Balloon-Borne Spectrometer. *Nature*, 255, London, England, pp. 443–444.

Goldman, A., Murcray, D. G., Murcray, F. H., and Williams, W. J., 1973: Balloon-borne Infrared Measurements of the Vertical Distribution of N₂O in the Atmosphere. *Journal of the Optical Society of America*, 63, pp. 843–846.

Grantham, D. D., and Sissenwine, N., 1970: High Humidity Extremes in the Upper Air. *AFCRL-70-0563*, Air Force Cambridge Research Laboratories, Bedford, Mass., 16 pp.

Gringorten, I. I., Salmela, H. A., Solomon, I., and Sharp, J., 1966: Atmospheric Humidity Atlas—Northern Hemisphere, *Air Force Surveys in Geophysics*, No. 186, AFCRL-66-621, Air Force Cambridge Research Laboratories, Bedford, Mass.

Gutnick, M., 1961: How Dry is the Sky? *Journal of Geophysical Research*, 66, pp. 2867–2871.

Hahn, J., 1972: Improved Gas Chromatographic Method for Field Measurement of Nitrous Oxide in Air and Water Using a 5Å Molecular Sieve Trap. *Analytical Chemistry*, 44, pp. 1889–1892.

Hall, L. A., Chagnon, C. W., and Hinteregger, H. E., 1967: Daytime variations in the composition of the upper atmosphere. *Journal of Geophysical Research*, 72, pp. 3425–3427.

Hall, L. A., Schweizer W., and Hinteregger, H. E., 1965: Improved extreme ultraviolet absorption measurements in the upper atmosphere. *Journal of Geophysical Research*, 70, pp. 105–111.

Hamilton, H. L., Worth, J. J. B., and Ripperton, L. A., 1968: An Atmospheric Physics and Chemistry Study on Pike's Peak in Support of Pulmonary Edema Research. Research Triangle Institute, U.S. Army Research Office, *Contract No. DA-HC19-67-C-0029*, Research Triangle Park, North Carolina, (May 1968).

Harries, J. E., 1973: Measurements of Some Hydrogen-Oxygen-Nitrogen Compounds in the Stratosphere from Concorde 002. *Nature Physical Science*, 241, London, England, pp. 215–218.

Harrison, L. P., 1968: Relation Between Geopotential and Geometric Height. *Smithsonian Meteorological Tables*, Sixth Revised Edition, Fourth Reprint, (List, R. J., editor), Smithsonian Institution, Washington, D.C., p. 217.

Heath, D. F., Mateer, C. L., and Krueger, A. J., 1973: The Nimbus-4 Backscatter Ultraviolet (BUV) Atmospheric Ozone Experiment—Two Years Operation. *PAGEOPH*, 106–108, Barkhauser-Verlag, Basel, Switzerland, pp. 1238–1253.

Hedin, A. E., Hinton, B. B., and Schmitt, G. A., 1973: Role of gas surface interactions in the reduction of OGO-6 neutral gas particle mass spectrometer data. *Journal of Geophysical Research*, 78, pp.

Hedin, A. E., Mayr, H. G., Reber, C. A., Carignan, G. R., Spencer, N. W., 1972: A Global Empirical Model of Thermospheric Composition Based on OGO-6 Mass Spectrometer Measurements, presented at *XV COSPAR Meeting*, United Nations, Geneva, Switzerland.

Hedin, A. E., Mayr, H. G., Reber, C. A., and Spencer, N. W., 1974: Empirical Model of Global Thermospheric Temperature and Composition Based on Data From the OGO-6 Quadrapole Mass Spectrometer. *Journal of Geophysical Research*, 79, pp. 215–225.

Hirschfelder, J. O., Curtiss, C. F., Bird, R. B., 1965: *Molecular Theory of Gases and Liquids*, John Wiley and Sons, N.Y., 1249 pp.

Hering, W. S., and Borden, T. R., 1964: Ozone Observations over North America. *OAR Research Report*, AFCRL-64-30, Vol. 2, Air Force Cambridge Research Laboratories, Bedford, Mass., 280 pp.

Hidy, G. M., and Brock, J. R., 1972: An Assessment of the Global Sources of Tropospheric Aerosols. *Proceedings of the 2nd Clean Air Conference*, Washington, D.C., December 1972.

Hilsenrath, E., Goddard Space Flight Center, NASA, Greenbelt, Md., 1972: private communication.

Hilsenrath, E., Seiden, L., and Goodman, P., 1969: Ozone Measurement in the Mesosphere and Stratosphere by Means of a Rocket Sonde. *Journal of Geophysical Research*, 74, pp. 6873–6880.

Hilsenrath, J., Beckett, C. W., et al. 1955: Tables of Thermal Properties of Gases, *National Bureau of Standards Circular 564*, U.S. Department of Commerce, Washington, D.C.

Hinteregger, H. E., and Hall, L. A. 1969: Thermospheric densities and temperatures from EUV absorption measurements by OSO-III, *Space Research*, 9, Akademie-Verlag, Berlin, Germany, pp. 519–529.

Horvath, J. J., 1972: Neutral Atmospheric Structure Measurements by Pitot-Probe Technique. *05776–1–F*, NASA Contract NAS5–3335, U. of Michigan, Ann Arbor, Mich., pp.

Hudson, R. D., and Mahle, S. H., 1972: Photodissociation Rates of Molecular Oxygen in the Mesosphere and Lower Thermosphere. *Journal of Geophysical Research*, 77, pp. 2902–2914.

International Civil Aviation Organization, 1964: Manual of the ICAO *Standard Atmosphere*. U.S. Government Printing Office, Washington, D.C. pp.

International Standards Organization 1973: Draft International Standard ISO/DIS 253.

Jacchia, L. G., 1971: Revised static models of the thermosphere and exosphere with empirical temperature profiles. *Special Report 332*, Smithsonian Astrophysical Observatory, Cambridge, Mass., pp.

Jacchia, L. G., and Slowey, J. W., 1967: Dirunal, Seasonal, and Latitudinal Variations in the Upper Atmosphere. *Special Report 242*, Smithsonian Astrophysical Observatory, Cambridge, Mass., pp.

Johnson, F. S., Purcell, J. D., Tousey, R., and Watanable, K., 1952: Direct Measurements of the Vertical Distribution of Atmospheric Ozone to 70 Kilometers Altitude. *Journal of Geophysical Research*, 57, pp. 157–177.

Junge, C. E., 1963: *Air Chemistry and Radioactivity*. Academic Press, New York, N.Y.

Junge, C., Seiler, W., and Warneck, P., 1971: The Atmospheric ^{12}CO and ^{14}CO budget. *Journal of Geophysical Research*, 76. pp. 2866–2879.

Kantor, A. J., and Cole, A. E., 1973: Abbreviated Tables of Thermodynamic Properties to 85 km for the U.S. Standard Atmosphere, 1974. *Air Force Surveys in Geophysics*, 278, AFCRL-TR-73-0687, Air Force Cambridge Research Laboratories, Bedford, Mass.

Kantor, A. J., and Grantham, D. D., 1968: A Climatology of Very High Altitude Radar Precipitation Echoes. *AFCRL-68-0630*, Air Force Cambridge Research Laboratories, Bedford, Mass.

Keating, G. M., and Prior, E. J., 1968: The Winter Helium Bulge. *Space Research*, VIII, Mitra, A. P., Jacchia, L. G., Newman, W. S., editors, North-Holland Publishing Co., Amsterdam, the Netherlands, pp. 982–992.

Keeling, C. D., 1960: The Concentration of Isotopic Abundances of Carbon Dioxide in the Atmosphere. *Tellus*, 12, Stockholm, Sweden, pp. 200–203.

Keeling, C. D., Harris, T. B., and Wilkins, E. M., 1968: Concentration of Atmospheric Carbon Dioxide at 500 and 700 Millibars. *Journal of Geophysical Research*, 73, pp. 4511–4528.

Keneshea, T. J., and Zimmerman, S. P., 1970: The Effect of Mixing upon Atomic and Molecular Oxygen in the 70-170 km Region of the Atmosphere. *Journal of the Atmospheric Sciences*, 27, pp. 831–840.

Kockarts, G., and Nicolet, M., 1963: L'Helium et l'Hydrogene Atomique au Cours d'un Minimum d'Activite Solaire. *Annals of Geophysics*, Paris, France, 19, pp. 370–385.

Krueger, A. J., 1975: Rocket Soundings of Ozone; Rococz-Arcas Results (1965–1970), Goddard Space Flight Center, NASA, Greenbelt, Md., in preparation.

Krueger, A. J., and McBride, W. R., 1968: Sounding Rocket-OGO 4 Satellite Ozone Experiment: Rocket Ozonesonde Measurements. *TP4667*, Goddard Space Flight Center, NASA, Greenbelt, Md., December 1968.

Krueger, A. J. and Minzner, R. A., 1976: A Proposed Standard Mid-Latitude Ozone Model, 1975, Goddard Space Flight Center, NASA, Greenbelt, Md., in preparation.

Kuhn, P. M., Lojko, M. S., and Petersen, E. V., 1971: Water Vapor Stratospheric Injection by Thunderstorms. *Science*, 174, pp. 1319–1321.

Lahue, M. D., Axelrod, H. D., and Lodge, J. P., Jr., 1973: Direct Measurement of Atmospheric Nitrous Oxide in a Stored Air Volume Using Thermal Conductivity Gas Chromatography. *Journal of Chromatographic Science*, 11, pp. 585–587.

Lake, L. R., and A. O. Nier, 1973: The loss of atomic oxygen in mass spectrometer ion sources. *Journal of Geophysical Research*, 78, pp. 1645–1653.

Lazrus, A. L., Gandrud, B., and Cadle, R. D., 1972: Nitric Acid Vapor in the Stratosphere. *Journal of Applied Meteorology*, 11, pp. 389–392.

List, R. J., editor, 1968, Acceleration of Gravity, *Smithsonian Meteorological Tables*, Sixth Ed., Smithsonian Institution, Washington, D.C., p. 488.

Lodge, J. P., Jr., and Pate, J. P., 1968: Atmospheric Gases and Particulates in Panama. *Science*, 153, pp. 408–409.

Lodge, J. P., Jr., MacDonald, A. J., Jr., and Vihman, E., 1960: A Study of the Composition of Marine Atmospheres. *Tellus*, Stockholm, Sweden, 12, pp. 184–187.

London, J., 1963: The Distribution of Total Ozone in the Northern Hemisphere. Beitrœge Zur Physik der Atmosphaere, 36, Braunschweig, W. Germany, pp. 254–263.

Machta, L., 1972: Mauna Loa and Global Trends in Air Quality. *Bulletin of the American Meteorological Society*, 53, pp. 402–420.

Mastenbrook, H. J., 1968: Water Vapor Distribution in the Stratosphere and High Troposphere. *Journal of the Atmospheric Sciences*, 25, pp. 299–311.

Mastenbrook, H. J., 1971: The Variability of Water Vapor in the Stratosphere. *Journal of the Atmospheric Sciences*, 28, pp. 1455–1501.

Mastenbrook, H. J., and Purdy, D. R., 1972: Concurrent Measurements of Water Vapor and Ozone over Washington, D.C. During 1969 and 1970. *NRL Report* 7489, U.S. Naval Research Laboratory, Washington, D.C.

Meadows, E. B., and Townsend, Jr., J. W., 1960: IGY rocket measurements of the arctic atmosphere composition above 100 km. *Space Research*, 1, Akademie-Verlag, Berlin, Germany, pp. 175–198.

Mechtly, E. A., 1973: The International System of Units, Physical Constants and Conversion Factors. *NASA SP-7012*, Second Revision, National Aeronautics and Space Administration, Washington, D.C.

Meier, R. R., and Mange, P., 1970: Geocoronal Hydrogen: An Analysis of the Lyman-Alpha Airglow Observed from OGO-4. *Planetary and Space Science*, 18, Oxford, England. pp. 803–821.

Migeotte, M. V., 1948: Spectroscopic Evidence of Methane in the Earth's Atmosphere. *Physical Review*, 73, pp. 519–520.

Minzner, R. A., Reber, C. A., Champion, K. S. W., Moe, O. K., Nies, A. O., Swenson, G. R., Zimmerman, S. P., 1974: Final Report of Task Group II to COESA. *NASA X-911-47-366*, Washington, D.C.

Minzner, R. A., and Ripley, W. S., 1956: The ARDC Model Atmosphere, *AFCRC TN-56-204*, Air Force Cambridge Research Laboratories, Bedford, Mass.

Minzner, R. A., Ripley, W. S. and Condron, T. P., 1958, *U.S. Extension to the ICAO Standard Atmosphere*, Government Printing Office, Washington, D.C.

Moe, K., 1970: The mean molecular mass. *Planetary and Space Science*, 18, Oxford, England, p. 929.

Moe, K., 1973: The density and composition of the lower thermosphere. *Journal of Geophysical Research*, 78, pp. 1633–1644.

Murcray, D. G., Goldman, A., Csoeke-Poeckh, A., Murcray, F. H., Williams, W. J., and Stocker, R. N., 1973: Nitric Acid Distribution in the Stratosphere. *Journal of Geophysical Research*, 78, pp. 7033–7038.

Murcray, D. G., Goldman, A., Murcray, F. H., Williams, W. J., Brooks, J. N., and Barker, D. B., 1972: Vertical Distribution of Minor Atmospheric Constituents as Derived from Air-Borne Measurements of Atmospheric Emission and Absorption Infrared Spectra. Abstracts, 2nd Conference on CIAP, U.S. Department of Transportation, Washington, D.C., pp. 13, 14.

Nagata, T., Tohmatsu, T., and Ogawa, T., 1971: Sounding Rocket Measurement of Atmospheric Ozone Density, 1965-1970. *Space Research*, XI, Akademie-Verlag, Berlin, Germany, pp. 849–855.

Natusch, D. F. S., Klonis, H. B., Axelrod, H. D., Tech, R. J., and Lodge, J. P., Jr., 1972: Sensitive Method for Measurement of Atmospheric Sulfur Dioxide. *Analytical Chemistry*, 44, pp. 2067–2910.

Nicolet, M., 1970: Ozone and Hydrocarbon Reactions. *Annals of Geophysics*, Paris, France, 26, pp. 531–546.

Nier, A. O., 1972: Measurement of thermospheric composition. *Space Research*, 12, Akademie-Verlag, Berlin, Germany, pp. 881–889.

Nier, A. O., Hayden, J. L., French, J. B., and Reid, N. M., 1972: On the determination of thermospheric atomic-oxygen densities with rocket-borne mass spectrometers. *Journal of Geophysical Research*, 77, pp. 1987–1990.

Nier, A. O., Hoffman, J. G., Johnson, C. Y., and Holmes, J. C., 1964: Neutral composition of the atmosphere in the 100- and 200-kilometer range. *Journal of Geophysical Research*, 69, pp. 979–989.

O'Connor, T. C., 1962: Atmospheric Condensation Nuclei and Trace Gases. *Final Report*, Contract No. DA-91-591-EUC-2126, Department of Physics, University College, Galway, Ireland.

Offermann, D., and von Zahn, U., 1971: Atomic Oxygen and carbon dioxide in the lower thermosphere, *Journal of Geophysical Research*, 76, pp. 2520–2522.

Ogawa, T., 1972: University of Tokyo, Japan, private communication.

Panetto, F. A., 1939: Composition of the Upper Atmosphere. Direct Chemical Investigation. *Quarterly Journal of the Royal Meteorological Society*, 65, London, England, p. 304.

Pate, J. B., Lodge, J. P., Jr., Sheesley, D. C., and Wartburg, A. F., 1970: Atmospheric Chemistry of the Tropics, in *Symposium Proceedings on Environment in Amazonia—Part I*, at Manaus, April. Sponsored by Instituto Nacional de Pesquisas de Amazonia and the National Center for Atmospheric Research, Boulder, Colo.

Patterson, T. N. L., 1966: Atomic and Molecular Hydrogen in the Thermosphere. *Planetary and Space Science*, 14, Oxford, England, pp. 417–423.

Philbrick, C. R., Narcisi, R. S., Good, R. E., Hoffman, H. S., Keneshea, T. J., MacLeod, M. H., Zimmerman, S. P., and Reinisch, B. W., 1973: The ALADDIN Experiment, Part II—Composition. *Space Research XIII*, 1, M. J. Rycroft and S. K. Runcorn, Editors, Akademie-Verlag, Berlin, Germany, pp. 441–448.

Pokhunkov, A. A., 1960: The study of the upper atmosphere neutral composition at altitudes above 100 km. *Space Research*, 1, Akademie-Verlag, Berlin, Germany, pp. 101–106.

Quiroz, R. S., 1970: Modification of the atmospheric density field in response to stratospheric warmings. *Proceedings of the Fourth National Conference on Aerospace Meteorology, Las Vegas, Nevada, May 4-7, 1970*, American Meteorological Society, Boston, Mass., pp. 296–305.

Quiroz, R. S., 1974: Estimation of stratospheric-mesospheric density fields from satellite radiance data. *Monthly Weather Review*, 102, pp. 313–318.

Rangarajan, S., 1963: Secondary Source of Water Vapor in the Upper Atmosphere. *Nature*, 3872, London, England, pp. 1099–1101.

Reber, C. A., and Hays, P. B., 1973: Thermospheric Wind Effects on the Distribution of Helium and Argon in the Earth's Upper Atmosphere. Journal of Geophysical Research, 78, pp. 2977–2991.

Reber, C. A., Cooley, J. E., and Harpold, D. N., 1968: Upper Atmosphere Hydrogen and Helium Measurements from the Explorer 32 Satellite. *Space Research*, VIII, Mitra, A. P., Jacchia, L. G., Newman, W. S., editors, North-Holland Publishing Co., Amsterdam, the Netherlands, pp. 993–995.

Reber, C. A., Hedin, A. E., Pelz, D. T., Potter, W. E., and Brace, L. H., 1975: Phase and Amplitude Relationship of Wave Structure Observed in the Lower Thermosphere. Journal of Geophysical Research, (in Press).

Reiter, E. E., Editor, 1974: The Natural Stratosphere of 1974. CIAP, U.S. Department of Transportation, Washington, D.C.

Richard, O. E., and Snelling, H. J., 1971: Working Paper for the Revision of MIL-STD-210A, Climatic Extremes for Military Equipment (1 km to 30 km). *ETAC Report* 5850, U.S. Air Force, Wasnington, D.C., 73 pp.

Ridley, B. A., Schiff, H. I., Shaw, A. W., Megill, L. R., Bates, L., Howlett, C., LeVaux, H., and Ashenfelter, T. E., 1975: Measurement of Nitric Oxide in the Stratosphere between 17.4 and 22.9 km. *Planetary and Space Science*, Oxford, England, (in press).

Riordan, P., 1970: Weather Extremes Around the World. *Technical Report* 70-45-ES, U.S. Army Natick Labs, Natick, Mass., 38 pp.

Ripperton, L. A., Kornreich, L., and Worth, J. J. B., 1970: Nitrogen Dioxide and Nitric Oxide in Non-Urban Air. *Journal of the Air Pollution Control Association*, 20, pp. 589–592.

Ripperton, L. A., Worth, J. J. B., and Kornreich, L., 1968: NO_2 and NO in Non-Urban Air. Paper 68-122, presented to *61st Annual Meeting, Air Pollution Control Association*, June 1968.

Robinson, E., and Robbins, R. C., 1966: Sources, Abundance, and Fate of Gaseous Atmospheric Pollutants. *Project Report* PR-6744, Supplement, Stanford Research Institute, Menlo Park, Calif.

Robinson, E., and Robbins, R. C., 1969: Sources, Abundance, and Fate of Gaseous Atmospheric Pollutants Supplement. *Supplementary Report* on SRI Project PR-6755 for American Petroleum Institute, Stanford Research Institute, Menlo Park, Calif., 77 pp.

Salmela, H. A., and Grantham, D. D., 1972: Diurnal Cycles of High Absolute Humidity at the Earth's Surface. *Report* AFCRL-72-0587, ERP No. 416, Air Force Cambridge Research Laboratories, Bedford, Mass.

Salmela, H. A., and Sissenwine, N., 1970: Estimated Frequency of Cold Temperatures over the Northern Hemisphere. *AFCRL–70–0158*, Air Force Cambridge Research Laboratories, Bedford, Mass, 18 pp.

SCEP: Man's Impact on the Global Environment, 1970: MIT Press, Cambridge, Mass., 318 pp.

Schaefer, E. J., 1973: The dissociation of oxygen measured by a rocket-borne mass spectrometer. *Journal of Geophysical Research*, 68, pp. 1175–1176.

Scholz, T. G., Ehalt, D. H., Heidt, L. E., and Martell, E. A., 1970: Water Vapor, Molecular Hydrogen, Methane, and Tritium Concentrations Near the Stratopause. *Journal of Geophysical Research*, 75, pp. 3049–3054.

Schütz, K., Junge, C., Beck, R., and Albrecht, B., 1970: Studies of Atmospheric N_2O. *Journal of Geophysical Research*, 75, pp. 2230–2246.

Seiler, W., and Junge, C., 1970: Carbon Monoxide in the Atmosphere. *Journal of Geophysical Research*, 75, pp. 2217–2226.

Seiler, W., and Warneck, P., 1972: Decrease of CO Mixing Ratio at the Tropopause. *Journal of Geophysical Research*, 77, pp. 3204–3214.

Shimazaki, T. J., 1967: Dynamic Effects on Atomic and Molecular Oxygen Distribution in the Upper Atmosphere: A Numerical Solution to Equations of Motion and Continuity. *Journal of Atmospheric and Terrestrial Physics*, 29, London, England, pp. 723–741.

Sissenwine, N., and Cormier, R. V., 1972: Synopsis of Background Material for MIL-STD-210B, Climatic Extremes for Military Equipment. *AFCRL draft report* awaiting completion for publication, Air Force Cambridge Research Laboratories, Bedford, Mass.

Sissenwine, N., Grantham, D. D., and Salmela, H. A., 1968a: Midlatitude Humidity to 32 km. *Journal of the Atmospheric Sciences*, 25, pp. 1129–1140.

Sissenwine, N., Grantham, D. D., and Salmela, H. A., 1968b: Humidity Up to the Mesopause. *Report* AFCRL-68-0550, Air Force Cambridge Research Laboratories, Bedford, Mass., 49 pp.

Sissenwine, N., Kantor, A. J., and Grantham, D. D.: How Dry is the Sky? A Decade Later and the SST. *Report* AFCRL-72-0294, Air Force Cambridge Research Laboratories, Bedford, Mass., 22 pp.

Smith, L. G., 1969: Rocket Observations of Ozone above 50 km. *Meeting of Committee on Space Research, Prague, Czechoslovakia*, May, 1969, United Nations, Geneva, Switzerland.

Taeusch, D. R., and Carignan, G. R., 1972: Neutral composition in the thermosphere. *Journal of Geophysical Research*, 77, pp. 4870–4876.

Taylor, B. N., Parker, W. H., and Langenberg, D. N., 1969: Determination of e/h, Using Macroscopic Quantum Phase Coherence in Superconductors: Implications for Quantum Electrodynamics and the Fundamental Physical Constants. *Reviews of Modern Physics*, pp. 375–496.

Theon, J. and Horvath, J., 1973: Private communication.

Theon, J. S., Nordberg, W., and Smith, W. S., 1967: Temperature Measurements in Noctilucent Clouds. *Science*, 157, pp. 419–421.

Theon, J. S., Smith, W. S., Casey, J. F., and Kirkwood, B. R., 1972: The Mean Observed Meteorological Structure and Circulation of the Stratosphere and Mesosphere. *NASA TR R-375*, National Aeronautics and Space Administration, Washington, D.C.

Tinsley, B. A., 1973: The Diurnal Variation of Atomic Hydrogen. *Planetary and Space Science*, 21, Oxford, England, pp. 686–691.

Toth, R. A., Farmer, C. B., Schindler, R. A., Raper, O. F., and Schaper, P. W., 1973: Detection of Nitric Oxide in the Lower Atmosphere. *Nature Physical Science*, 244, London, England,

Toussaint, A., 1919: Etudé des performances d'un avion muni d'un moteur suraliminté *L'Aeronautique*, 1, Paris, France, pp. 188–196.

Tsunogai, S., and Ikeushi, K., 1968: Ammonia in the Atmosphere. *Geochemical Journal*, 2, pp. 1957–1966.

Vidal-Madjar, A., Blamont, J. E., and Phissamay, B., 1973: Solar Lyman Alpha Charges and Related Hydrogen Density Distribution at the Earth's Exobase (1969–1970). *Journal of Geophysical Research*, 78, pp. 1115–1144.

Viebrock, H., 1973: Review of the Atmospheric Carbon Monoxide Distribution. (To be published).

Volman, D. H., 1963: Photochemical Gas Phase Reactions in the Hydrogen Oxygen System. *Advances in Photochemistory*, Vol. 1, Interscience Publishers, New York, N.Y., pp. 43–81.

von Zahn, U., 1970: Neutral air density and composition at 150 km. *Journal of Geophysical Research*, 75, pp. 5517–5527.

Walker, J. C. G., 1965: Analytic representation of upper atmosphere densities based on Jacchia's static diffusion models. *Journal of the Atmospheric Sciences*, 22, pp. 462–463.

Wand, R. H., 1972: Observation of Reversible Heating by Tides in the E Region. *International Union of Radio Science, Spring Meeting, Washington, D.C., April 13-15, 1972*.

Watanabe, K., and Zelikoff, M., 1953: Absorption Coefficients of Water Vapor in the Vacuum Ultraviolet. *Journal of the Optical Society of America*, 43, pp. 753–755.

Williams, W. J., Brooks, N. N., Murcray, D. G., Murcray, F. H., Fried, P. M., and Weinman, J. S., 1972: Distribution of Nitric Acid Vapor in the Stratosphere as Determined From Infrared Atmospheric Emission Data. *Journal of the Atmospheric Sciences*, 29, pp. 1375–1379.

Weeks, L. H., Cuikay, R. S., and Corbin, J. R., 1972: Ozone Measurements in the Mesosphere During the Solar Proton Event of 2 November 1969. *Journal of the Atmospheric Sciences*, 29, pp. 1138–1142.

Weeks, L. H., and Smith, L. G., 1968: A Rocket Measurement of Ozone Near Sunrise. *Planetary and Space Science*, 16, Oxford, England, pp. 1189–1195.

Zimmerman, S. P., and Keneshea, T. J., 1975: The Thermosphere in Motion, submitted for publication, *Journal of Geophysical Research*, 80.

Zimmerman, S. P., and Trowbridge, C. A., 1973: The Measurement of Turbulent Spectra and Diffusion Coefficients in the Altitude Region 95 to 110 km. *Space Research XIII*, Vol. 1, M. J. Rycroft and S. K. Runcorn, editors, Akademie-Verlag, Berlin, Germany, pp. 203–298.

APPENDIX A
Boundary-Value Number Densities of Atmospheric Constituents

The boundary-value neutral number densities of the several constituents defined to comprise the U. S. Standard Atmosphere at 86 km and above were determined using a deductive process based upon several assumptions. The COESA Task Group decided to include as constituents of this model atmosphere only those species which are known to contribute significantly to the total number density in any portion of the atmosphere between 86 and 1000 km, because of either their mixing distribution below the turbopause or their diffusive distribution above this height. Those gases which appear never to contribute more than about 0.5 percent of the total composition at any point within this height region, or which for various reasons do not exhibit predictable behavior, were purposely omitted. Using these guidelines, the following gases were included: molecular nitrogen N_2, molecular oxygen O_2, argon Ar, helium He, and atomic oxygen O. Atomic hydrogen H was included at heights 150 km and above, but was not included in boundary-value considerations at 86 km. The remaining neutral gases which were used in establishing the sea-level value of the mean molecular weight, but which are not used in this model, are listed with the major gases and their respective contribution to the sea-level mean molecular weight in table 25.

The first three of the gases used in this model comprise more than 0.9996 of the air in any unit volume at sea level, as is evident from summing the fractional composition F_i over these three species in table 25. Since the fractional volumes of these major species do not change significantly below the mesopause, which in this model is located at 86 km altitude, the sea-level fractional composition can be assumed to be approximately correct at 86 km. It is believed, however, that photochemical processes lead to small quantities of atomic oxygen in this height region, and a fractional amount of about .00059 by volume, or exactly 8.6×10^{16} atoms per m³, was agreed upon as an acceptable concentration of O for 86 km.

The introduction of the fixed amount of atomic oxygen at this height, and the simultaneous elimination of some minor species made it necessary to adjust the fractional concentrations of each of the four remaining species from their known sea-level values F_i by a common unknown factor ε to the 86-km fractional composition values F', such that

$$F'_i = \varepsilon F_i \qquad \text{(A–1)}$$

The 86-km fractional composition of atomic oxygen is equal to the ratio of $n(O)$ to N, where $n(O)$ is equal to 8.6×10^{16} m⁻³, the adopted atomic-oxygen number density for that height, and N is the unknown total number density at that height. The

TABLE 25.—Sea-level atmospheric composition

Species	Fractional volume F_i	Molecular wt. of species M_i	$F_i \cdot M_i$
N_2	.78084	28.0134	21.87398326
O_2	.209476	31.9988	6.70298063
Ar	.00934	39.948	0.37311432
CO_2	.000314	44.00995	0.01381912
Ne	.00001818	20.183	0.00036693
He	.00000524	4.0026	0.00002097
Kr	.00000114	83.80	0.00009553
Xe	.000000087	131.30	0.00001142
CH_4	.000002	16.04303	0.00003208
H_2	.0000005	2.01594	0.00000101
	$\Sigma F_i = .99999714$		$\Sigma (F_i \cdot M_i) = 28.964425$

sum of the 86-km fractional composition of the remaining four species is

$$\sum_4 F_i' = \epsilon \sum_4 F_i \qquad \text{(A-2)}$$

The sum of the total of the 86-km fractional compositions (i.e., of the five species adopted to comprise the model at this height) must equal unity in accordance with the expression:

$$\epsilon \sum_4 F_i + \frac{n(O)}{N} = 1. \qquad \text{(A-3)}$$

The total number density N *is* expressable in terms of the mean molecular weight M, Avogadro's constant N_A, and ρ the mass density, the value of which is known at 86 km from other considerations. This relationship is

$$N = \frac{N_A \cdot \rho}{M}. \qquad \text{(A-4)}$$

The mean molecular weight at 86 km is the sum of the products $F_i' M_i$ over the five gases comprising the model at this height. For the atomic oxygen this product is

$$F'(O) \cdot M(O) = \frac{n(O) \cdot M(O)}{N} \qquad \text{(A-5)}$$

while the sum of the products of the remaining four gases is expressable as

$$\sum_4 F_i' \cdot M_i = \epsilon \sum_4 F_i \cdot M_i \qquad \text{(A-6)}$$

such that the mean molecular weight M at 86 km is expressed as

$$M = \epsilon \cdot \sum_4 F_i \cdot M_i + \frac{n(O) \cdot M(O)}{N}. \qquad \text{(A-7)}$$

Eliminating M between eq (A-4) and (A-7), and solving for ϵ yields

$$\epsilon = \frac{N_A \cdot \rho - n(O) \cdot M(O)}{N \cdot \sum_4 F_i \cdot M_i}. \qquad \text{(A-8)}$$

The eliminating of ϵ between eq (A-8) and (A-3) leads to the following expression for total number density:

$$N = \frac{\left(\sum_4 F_i\right) \cdot [N_A \cdot \rho - n(O) \cdot M(O)]}{\sum_4 F_i \cdot M_i} + n(O). \qquad \text{(A-9)}$$

From table 25 the value of $\sum_4 F_i$, the sum of F_i for the four species N_2, O_2, Ar, and He is seen to be 0.99966124, while the value of $\sum_4 F_i M_i$ for the same four species is seen to be 28.95009918. The value of $M(O)$ is taken to be one-half of the value of $M(O_2)$, also given in table 25. The value of 8.6×10^{16} m^{-3} was adopted for $n(O)$, as previously stated, and N_A has the standard value 6.022169×10^{26} kmol^{-1}. The value of ρ at 86 km is found to be 6.957880×10^{-6} kg/m^3. These values introduced into eq (A-9) yield a number density of 1.447265×10^{20} m^{-3} at 86 km. This value introduced into eq (A-1) leads to $\epsilon = 0.99974445$, while eq (A-7) then yields $M = 28.952208$ for the molecular weight at 86 km.

For the 86-km height, the values of F_i', the fractional composition of each of the five species comprising the model at that height, are given in table 26 as the product ϵF_i, along with the corresponding products $F_i' M_i$, and the corresponding values of $N \cdot F_i'$ the number densities of the five gas species comprising the model atmosphere at 86-km height.

The value of $\sum_5 F_i'$, the sum of the five values of F_i' listed in table 26, is seen to be 0.999999999, essentially the unit value which it should have. The sum of the five values of $F_i' M_i$ and of the five values of n_i, i.e., $\sum_5 F_i M_i$ and $\sum_5 n_i$, both of which are also given in table 26, show essentially exact agreement with the value of their respective equivalents, M and N, computed independently. Thus the validity of the computation is established.

TABLE 26.—Number densities and molecular weight at 86 km

	$F_i' = \epsilon F_i$	$F_i' \cdot M_i$ (kg/kmol)	$n_i = F_i' \cdot N$ (m^{-3})
N_2	.7806404557	21.86839334	$1.129793736 \times 10^{20}$
O_2	.2094224682	6.701267675	$0.3030898426 \times 10^{20}$
Ar	.00933761315	0.3730189704	$0.0135140022 \times 10^{20}$
He	.00000523866	0.0000209683	$0.0000075817 \times 10^{20}$
O	.00059422421	0.0095072308	0.00086×10^{20}
$\sum_5 F_i' = 1.000000000$		$\sum_5 F_i M_i = 28.9500080$	$\sum_5 n_i = 1.447265163 \times 10^{20}$

APPENDIX B

A Segment of An Ellipse To Express Temperature vs. Height

It is desired to determine the expression for a temperature function for a limited height region, $Z_8 = 91$ to $Z_9 = 110$ km, in the plane defined by Z and T, such that the slope of the function at each of the end points exactly matches a prescribed value. At $Z = Z_8$, where $T = T_8 = 186.8673$ K, the derivative of the function with respect to Z must be zero, to match the slope of the temperature-height profile in the isothermal layer between 86 to 91 km, while at $Z = Z_9$, where $T = T_9 = 240$ K, the derivative of T with respect to Z must be 12K/km to match the slope of a layer of constant temperature-height gradient between 110 and 120 km. A suitably adjusted ellipse will satisfy these conditions.

The general equation of an ellipse in terms of Z and T with center at $Z = 0$ and $T = 0$ is

$$\frac{Z^2}{a^2} + \frac{T^2}{A^2} = 1. \qquad \text{(B–1)}$$

With the center shifted to $Z = Z_c$ and $T = T_c$ the expression becomes

$$\frac{(Z - Z_c)^2}{a^2} + \frac{(T - T_c)^2}{A^2} = 1. \qquad \text{(B–2)}$$

The derivative of eq (B–2) with respect to Z is

$$\frac{2(Z - Z_c)}{a^2} + \frac{2(T - T_c)}{A^2} \cdot \frac{dT}{dZ} = 0. \qquad \text{(B–3)}$$

To meet the condition for $dT/dZ = 0$ at $Z = Z_8$, we evaluate eq (B–3) for those conditions, and find that $Z_c = Z_8$, such that eq (B–2) may be rewritten as

$$\frac{(Z - Z_8)^2}{a^2} + \frac{(T - T_c)^2}{A^2} = 1. \qquad \text{(B–4)}$$

Evaluating eq (B–4), for $Z = Z_8$ and $T = T_8$, leads to

$$A = T_8 - T_c. \qquad \textbf{(B–5)}$$

Substituting Z_c for its equal Z_8 in eq (B–3) and evaluating that expression for $Z = Z_9$, where

$T = T_9$ and where (dT/dZ) has the particular value $L_{K,9}$, and finally solving the resulting expression for $1/a^2$ yields

$$\frac{1}{a^2} = \frac{-(T_9 - T_c) L_{K,9}}{A^2(Z_9 - Z_8)}. \qquad \text{(B–6)}$$

Evaluating eq (B–4) at $Z = Z_9$, where $T = T_9$, and solving for $1/a^2$ yields

$$\frac{1}{a^2} = \frac{A^2 - (T_9 - T_c)^2}{A^2(Z_9 - Z_8)}. \qquad \text{(B–7)}$$

Eliminating $1/a^2$ between eq (B–6) and (B–7), and solving for T_c leads to

$$T_c = \frac{L_{K,9}(Z_9 - Z_8)T_9 + T_8^2 - T_9^2}{L_{K,9}(Z_9 - Z_8) + 2T_8 - 2T_9}. \qquad \text{(B–8)}$$

The elimination of A between eq (B–5) and (B–7) yields

$$a = \frac{(Z_9 - Z_8)(T_8 - T_c)}{[(T_8 - T_c)^2 - (T_9 - T_c)^2]^{1/2}}. \qquad \text{(B–9)}$$

Finally, solving eq (B–4) for T yields the functional expression

$$T(Z) = T_c + A\left[1 - \left(\frac{Z - Z_8}{a}\right)^2\right]^{1/2} \qquad \text{(B–10)}$$

The evaluation of eq (B–5), (B–8), and (B–9), in accordance with $Z_8 = 91$ km, $T_8 = 186.8673$ K, $Z_9 = 110$ km, $T_9 = 240.0$ K, and $L_{K,9} = 12$ K/km, yields the following values for the three constants in eq (B–10):

$$\begin{aligned} T_c &= 263.1905 \text{ K} \\ A &= -76.3232 \text{ K} \\ a &= -19.9429 \text{ km.} \end{aligned}$$

Since it was shown that $Z_c = Z_8$, the ellipse, which meets the required derivative and temperature conditions, has its center at $Z = 91$ km and $T = 263.1905$K, and eq (B–10) represents the function which meets the required conditions.

223

APPENDIX C

The Calculation of A Dynamic Model for The 1976 U.S. Standard Atmosphere

INTRODUCTION

The objective of this appendix is to describe the procedure for the calculation of a dynamic model of the earth's atmosphere between 50 and 150 km, made up of an internally consistent set of diurnally averaged properties of gas concentrations versus altitude. In this height region, one profile exists for each of the four major atmospheric gas species, i.e., nitrogen, molecular and atomic oxygen, and argon, such that each of these concentration profiles meets the following two conditions:

1. the concentration values versus height are the result of a time-dependent, photochemical-transport calculation which incorporates measured chemical-reaction-rate constants, solar radiation fluxes, and turbulent-diffusion coefficients into coupled sets of equations of motion and continuity.
2. the calculated number densities of each of the four species at 150 km fall within particular limits recommended by the COESA Working Group.

The sophisticated and detailed calculation that meets these conditions serves to establish the physical basis for the generation of dynamic models of the earth's atmosphere, and yields height profiles of number-density flux values which are approximated by artificially adjusted functions for the calculation of the 1976 U.S. Standard Atmosphere.

BASIC CONSIDERATIONS

The species considered are O, O_2, O_3, O^1D, $O_2(^1\Delta_g)$, OH, H, HO_2, H_2O, H_2O_2, H_2, Ar, and He. The number densities, from 50 to 150 km are obtained through a semi-implicit, finite-difference solution of a system of mass- and momentum-conservation equations (Shimazaki 1967; Keneshea and Zimmerman 1970). In these calculations, thermal-diffusion factors for the species H, H_2, and He have the values respectively of -0.39, -0.31, and -0.36 (Zimmerman and Keneshea 1975). The numerical approach is essentially that introduced by Shimazaki (1967) but modified at the boundaries and in the volume integrations, following George et al. (1972). Table 27 lists the chemical reactions and the associated rate constants actually used in the generation of the resulting concentration profiles. It should be noted, however, that refined rate-constant measurements made since these calculations were completed indicate the need for a revision of some of the listed values. The current calculations have not been updated with these new rate-constant values, however, since the changes have only a negligible influence on the concentrations of O, O_2, Ar, and He in the altitude region above 80 km. The intensity of the solar radiation flux used in these calculations is 0.65 of that shown in figure 37, which depicts the Ackerman (1971) values of solar radiation flux versus wavelength. The absorption cross sections were taken from various sources. For O_2 and O_3, these cross sections were taken from the compilation of Ackerman (1971) with the exception of those for the Schumann-Runge bands of O_2, for which region the values measured by Hudson and Mahle (1972) were used. The adopted absorption cross sections for water vapor and hydrogen peroxide are those reported by Watanabe and Zelikoff (1953), and by Volman (1963) respectively. The temperature-height profile up to 150 km, and the values of mean molecular weight up to the turbopause are those recommended by the Working Group of COESA. Using these data, the initial species distributions were calculated assuming complete mixing up to the turbopause, and diffusive equilibrium above it.

The total number density was obtained by integrating the hydrostatic equation, where the sea-level values of mass density and of mean molecular weight were taken from the *U.S. Standard Atmosphere, 1962.*

Beginning with these static profiles, the steady-state solution of all species was determined. The time-dependent calculations were then allowed to proceed for 15 solution days using a semi-implicit, finite-difference technique, a variable time step, up to 30 minutes, and a fixed height step of 100 m. This stringent height step was shown to be necessary to restrict the errors generated by species gradients when height steps larger than 100 m were used.

The height-dependent, turbulent-diffusion coefficients used are shown in figure 38, and are based upon observations of turbulence in chemical trails

TABLE 27.—The chemical reactions and associated reaction
rates k_j expressed in the form of the value of rate coefficients A_j, B_j, and C_j where $k_j = A_j \cdot (T/300) \, B_j \times \exp (C_j/T)$

	REACTION				A_j	B_j	C_j
1	O	$+ O$	$+ M \rightarrow O_2$	$+ M$	3.00E–33	–2.9	
2	O	$+ O_2$	$+ M \rightarrow O_3$	$+ M$	5.50E–34	–2.6	
3	O	$+ O_3$	$\rightarrow O_2$	$+ O_2$	1.20E–11		–2.00E + 03
4	H	$+ O_3$	$\rightarrow O_2$	$+ OH$	2.60E–11		
5	OH	$+ O$	$\rightarrow H$	$+ O_2$	5.00E–11		
6	OH	$+ O_3$	$\rightarrow HO_2$	$+ O_2$	4.00E–14		
7	H	$+ O_2$	$+ M \rightarrow HO_2$	$+ M$	7.40E–33		6.10E + 02
8	HO_2	$+ O$	$\rightarrow OH$	$+ O_2$	1.00E–11		
9	HO_2	$+ O_3$	$\rightarrow OH$	$+ O_2 + O_2$	1.00E–17		
10	OH	$+ OH$	$\rightarrow H_2O$	$+ O$	2.00E–12		
11	OH	$+ HO_2$	$\rightarrow H_2O$	$+ O_2$	2.00E–10		
12	H	$+ HO_2$	$\rightarrow H_2$	$+ O_2$	3.00E–12		
13	H	$+ HO_2$	$\rightarrow OH$	$+ OH$	1.00E–11		
14	O	$+ H_2$	$\rightarrow OH$	$+ H$	7.00E–11		–5.10E + 03
15	HO_2	$+ HO_2$	$\rightarrow H_2O_2 + O_2$		3.00E–12		
16	OH	$+ H_2O_2$	$\rightarrow H_2O$	$+ HO_2$	1.70E–11		–9.00E + 02
17	O	$+ H_2O_2$	$\rightarrow OH$	$+ HO_2$	4.00E–15		
18	H	$+ H_2O_2$	$\rightarrow H_2$	$+ HO_2$	3.90E–11		–4.60E + 03
19	O^1D	$+ O_3$	$\rightarrow O_2$	$+ O_2$	3.00E–10		
20	O^1D	$+ O_2$	$\rightarrow O$	$+ O_2$	6.00E–11		
21	O^1D	$+ N_2$	$\rightarrow O$	$+ N_2$	9.00E–11		
22	O^1D	$+ H_2$	$\rightarrow OH$	$+ H$	1.00E–11		
23	O^1D	$+ H_2O$	$\rightarrow OH$	$+ OH$	1.00E–11		
24	$O_2^1 \triangle g + O_3$		$\rightarrow O_2$	$+ O_3$	3.00E–15		
25	$O_2^1 \triangle g + M$		$\rightarrow O_2$	$+ M$	4.40E–19		
26	$O_2^1 \triangle g + H$		$\rightarrow OH$	$+ O$	1.10E–14		
27	$O_2^1 \triangle g$		$\rightarrow O_2$		2.58E–04		
28	O_2	$+ h\nu$	$\rightarrow O$	$+ O$			
29	O_2	$+ h\nu$	$\rightarrow O^1D$	$+ O$			
30	O_3	$+ h\nu$	$\rightarrow O_2$	$+ O$			
31	O_3	$+ h\nu$	$\rightarrow O^1D$	$+ O_2^1 \triangle g$			
32	H_2O	$+ h\nu$	$\rightarrow OH$	$+ H$			
33	H_2O_2	$+ h\nu$	$\rightarrow OH$	$+ OH$			

Note: The units of the two-body reaction rates are
cm^3/s, while those for the three-body reaction rates are
cm^5/s.

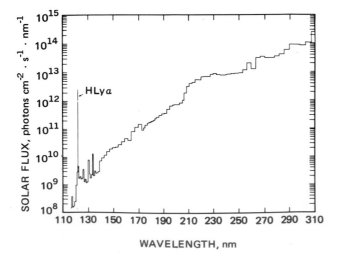

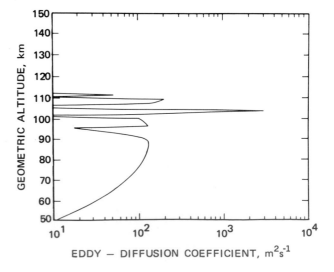

Figure 37. Solar radiation flux as a function of wavelength in the region from 115 to 310 nm (Ackerman)

Figure 38. Eddy-diffusion coefficient as a function of altitude

(Philbrick et al. 1973). These values are derived (Zimmerman and Trowbridge 1973) from the fluctuation dynamics observed in rocket-borne chemical releases, and are valid from about 88 to 112 km. Because of the lack of chemical-tracer wind and turbulence measurements in the altitude region between 50 and 88 km, an exponential fit has been assumed between the reported value of 1×10^5 cm^2/s (Beaudoin et al. 1967) at 50 km, and the values at 88 km.

RESULTS

The time-dependent calculations were continued for the above-mentioned period of time, after which the species concentrations reproduced themselves to within 1 percent over a diurnal cycle, a condition which is called arriving at diurnal reproducibility. The diurnal averages of the concentration of O, O_2, and Ar are then calculated and extrapolated to 250 km by assuming diffusive equilibrium without thermal diffusion above the 150-km boundary. Figure 39, depicting the height profiles of the N_2 concentration and temperature, shows the initial conditions used in these one-dimensional calculations. Figure 40 shows the resulting diurnally averaged height profiles of O, O_2, and Ar, each of which is in good agreement with the 150-km values recommended by the COESA Working Group, and shown as error bars.

Thus, it has been demonstrated that an internally self-consistent model of the density structure of the upper mesosphere and lower thermosphere may be calculated from measured values of solar radiation flux, chemical-reaction-rate constants, and derivatives of measured vertical-turbulent-transport parameters deduced from chemical-trail studies.

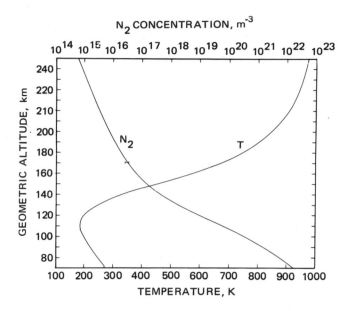

Figure 39. Altitude profile of kinetic temperature and molecular nitrogen concentration

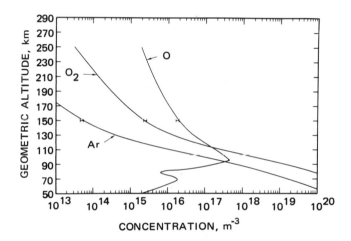

Figure 40. Altitude profiles of diurnally averaged concentrations of O, O_2, and Ar